# HANDBOOK OF ENVIRONMENTAL ANALYSIS

**THIRD EDITION**

*Authored by*

Roy-Keith Smith, PhD
Apichemical Consultants

**Genium Publishing Corporation**
One Genium Plaza., Schenectady, NY 12304-4690   (518) 377-8854

**DISCLAIMER NOTICE:** The information contained herein was prepared with reasonable care and is based on the most reliable information available to the Author. Genium Publishing Corp. and the Author make no warranty, express or implied, of the merchantability, fitness, accuracy or completeness of this information. It is the reader's responsibility to determine the suitability of this book and its updates for the reader's particular purposes. Genium Publishing Corp. and the Author assume no responsibility as to the suitability of this information or for any consequences of its use.

# FOREWORD

Environmental analysis is the fundamental technology of the whole environmental industry. It is a combination of traditional and modern chemistry techniques and civil engineering materials characterizations, mixed together with a hefty dose of legalistic regulatory jargon. The majority of the users of the information produced by environmental laboratories, and for that matter the majority of the people performing the analyses, have little or no formal training in chemistry. The writers of analytical methods in both the EPA and the *Standard Methods* manuals have sought to simplify the procedures to the greatest extent possible and present each method as a recipe, which, if followed exactly, will produce an acceptable answer. This results in situations where seemingly anomalous results cannot be explained because an in-depth chemical understanding of the test procedure is lacking.

While teaching environmental chemistry as a course to civil engineering students, I found that the most profitable approach was to present the chemical and biological background information as an adjunct to understanding the individual analytical procedures. I have always felt that a fundamental understanding of how the procedure worked led to better performance of the test by the technician. Unfortunately, the explanations for many of the tests used in environmental analysis are difficult to find, being scattered in many texts. This text is a collection of all the explanations for all the questions I have asked while working as an environmental analyst.

Another reason for writing this handbook is to gather together in one convenient place the miscellaneous facts and figures necessary in performing environmental analysis. Having this handbook nearby will be appreciated by those who, like me, keep misplacing the tables for Langelier's index and the $t$-statistic, and can't remember the COD value for KHP.

Finally, this handbook was written as a general guide to what information is important in environmental analysis and where to find it. Every year the environmental business changes with new programs, new regulations, and new methods. It's a daunting task for the newcomer to assimilate enough information to get up to speed and function, let alone appear literate.

## What's New in this Third Edition

I have frequently characterized the environmental industry as "often frustrating, but never boring." Superimposed on the normal ebb and flow of the scientific advancements and method approvals/recissions that have been made in environmental analysis, there was the federal government shutdown during the Fall of 1995 and the Winter of 1996. Some of the shutdown programs, such as the CLP, did not restart to the previous level after the government resumed operations, and the ramifications within the industry were enormous. Laboratories that had grown prosperous on government contracts overnight faced lay-offs and major restructurings. There was suddenly an oversupply of laboratory capacity and a reduction in the number of samples to analyze. In the scramble for the remaining work, some laboratories, both big and small, slashed prices to get any work in the lab. Instead of technical competence and quality/defensibility of results being the reason to choose a lab, competition has resulted in shopping for labs on the basis of low price. A knee-jerk response privatization bill was introduced into Congress to prevent any government laboratory from performing analysis for any parameter that could be determined in a commercial lab.

In the meantime, the EPA has made many changes to cut its overhead. There have been shifts of personnel from headquarters offices to the Regional offices. The approval and development of water analytical methods has been moved to the Office of Science and Technology within the Office of Water in Washington. The EPA has made a major reduction in the amount of analytical research it performs in its own labs, and simultaneously has made progress in the streamlining of the methods approval process for private organizations that do perform research. The WP Performance Evaluation studies have been cut from two concentrations for each analyte to a single concentration, and then completely merged with the DMR annual QA Study Program to further reduce the number of samples being distributed. EPA has announced the intention to divorce itself from the costs of the PE sample programs and have labs pay for the samples. All of these events have resulted in chaos in the laboratory business.

But life goes on, and the environmental analytical business continues to evolve. Many of the references used in this and preceding editions have been from the "soft" literature, *i.e.* non-peer reviewed publications and conference abstracts. Information presented in the soft literature is quite valuable, although it needs to be examined closely and sometimes taken with a liberal dose of salt. [Which is not to say that all published articles in the peer-reviewed literature are completely reliable. Just this last year an article appeared where the authors spent a lot of wasted space trying to justify what was in reality laboratory contamination, not methylene chloride and bis(2-ethylhexyl)phthalate in their samples.] Although some environmental scientists will take the time to shepherd a publication through the review process and pay the page charges for placement of the paper in a formal journal, for the most part the potential authors of informative articles, for one reason or another, cannot make the effort, and thus look for the easiest and quickest way to get the information out to fellow professionals. In this industry particularly, time is money. This attitude is also reflected in the conferences and scientific gatherings that occur each year. Although the ACS, PittCon, WEF, and AWWA conferences attract many attendees, the best information available to the environmental professional is presented in two annual EPA sponsored meetings: the Office of Water "Annual Conference on Analysis of Pollutants in the Environment," held in Norfolk VA in May, and the Office of Solid Waste "Waste Testing and Quality Assurance" conference in Washington, D.C in July.

I belatedly need to acknowledge the continued support of Robert G. Owens, Jr., President and Chief Chemist, and G. Wyn Jones, Marketing Director of Analytical Services, Inc. in the preparation of this work. Joe Romano and Jim Krol of Waters, Inc. deserve special acknowledgement for involving me with the development of methods for environmental applications of capillary ion electrophoresis. My wife, Michelle, and my children, Tayor Frost and Jennifer Lindsey, continue to provide the impetus to work on this publication. Finally, the staff at Genium, and particularly my editor, Erik Roy, are thanked for their many contributions and advice.

Roy-Keith Smith, PhD
February, 1997

# Table of Contents

**Section 1    Introduction to Environmental Analysis**                                1

    I.    Applicable Federal and State Regulations                                1

         A.   Title 40, CFR: Protection of Environment                        1

         B.   Government Regulations Administered by EPA                       2

   II.   Analytical Methodologies                                               34

  III.   Sampling Procedures                                                   80

         A.   Safety of Collector                                            80

         B.   Record Keeping                                                 80

         C.   Sample Security                                               83

         D.   Obtaining a Representative Sample                              83

         E.   Sample Containers                                             84

         F.   Preservatives                                                 84

         G.   Holding Times                                                 85

  IV.   Quality Assurance and Quality Control                                110

         A.   Calibration                                                  112

         B.   Data Quality Objectives                                       130

         C.   Reporting Units and Common Conversions                        139

         D.   Volumetric Measurements                                       140

         E.   Significant Figures                                           142

         F.   Record Keeping and File Management                            143

         G.   Quality Control Procedures for Sampling                       153

         H.   Quality Control Procedures for Sample Preparation             153

         I.   Quality Control Procedures during Analysis                    160

         J.   Control Charts                                                161

         K.   Performance Evaluation (PE) samples                           167

         L.   Evaluation of Laboratory Data                                 175


**Section 2    Physical, Biological and General Chemical Parameters**                   177

    I.   Physical Parameters                                                   177

         A.   Solids                                                        177

         B.   Moisture                                                      180

         C.   Temperature                                                   182

         D.   Turbidity                                                     184

**Section 2    Physical, Biological and General Chemical Parameters,** *continued*

|   |   | E.   | Conductivity | 185 |
|---|---|---|---|---|
|   | II. | | Biological Parameters | 186 |
|   |   | A. | Fecal Coliform | 186 |
|   |   | B. | MPN Tube Tests | 186 |
|   |   | C. | Membrane Filter Test | 189 |
|   |   | D. | Presence-absence Coliform Test | 190 |
|   |   | E. | Colilert™ Chromogenic Substrate Coliform Test | 190 |
|   |   | F. | Toxicity Testing | 191 |
|   | III. | | Chemical Parameters | 194 |
|   |   | A. | pH | 194 |
|   |   | B. | Alkalinity | 199 |
|   |   | C. | Hardness | 200 |
|   |   | D. | Langelier's Index | 201 |
|   |   | E. | Dissolved Oxygen | 202 |
|   |   | F. | Biochemical Oxygen Demand (BOD) | 203 |
|   |   | G. | Chemical Oxygen Demand (COD) | 205 |
|   |   | H. | Metals | 206 |
|   |   | I. | Mercury by Cold Vapor | 221 |
|   |   | J. | Residual Chlorine | 222 |
|   |   | K. | Total Organic Carbon (TOC) | 230 |
|   |   | L. | Total Organic Halide (TOX) | 231 |
|   |   | M. | Surfactants | 232 |
|   |   | N. | Oil and Grease | 234 |
|   |   | O. | Total Phenols | 235 |
|   |   | P. | Cyanide | 237 |
|   |   | Q. | Sulfide | 240 |
|   |   | R. | Nitrogen | 241 |
|   |   | S. | Ammonia | 241 |
|   |   | T. | Nitrite | 242 |
|   |   | U. | Nitrate | 243 |
|   |   | V. | Total (Kjeldahl) | 244 |
|   |   | W. | Phosphorous | 244 |
|   |   | X. | Fluoride | 247 |
|   |   | Y. | Chloride | 250 |
|   |   | Z. | Ion Chromatography | 251 |
|   |   | AA. | Ion Selective Electrodes | 252 |
|   | IV. | | Application to Solids and Other Matrices | 254 |

| | | |
|---|---|---|
| **Section 3.** | **Organic Parameters** | **261** |
| I. | Volatiles | 268 |
| | A. Instrumentation | 269 |
| | B. Methods | 283 |
| II. | Semivolatiles | 283 |
| | A. Instrumentation | 283 |
| | B. Methods 500, 600, and 1600 Series | 285 |
| | C. Extraction Techniques | 318 |
| | D. Other Extraction Techniques | 320 |
| | E. Clean-up | 321 |
| | F. Methods 8000 Series | 324 |
| III. | Miscellaneous Organic Information | 343 |
| | A. Mass Spectrometer Tuning | 343 |
| | B. Freons | 344 |
| | C. Dyes and Pigments | 348 |
| | D. Hydrocarbon Solvents and Fuels | 361 |
| | E. Explosives and Chemical Warfare Residues | 372 |
| | F. Plasticizers, Anti-oxidants and Other Additives | 378 |
| | G. Endocrine Disruptors | 381 |
| **Section 4.** | **Hazardous Waste and Remediation Analysis** | **383** |
| I. | Hazardous Waste Characterization | 383 |
| | A. Ignitability Characteristic | 383 |
| | B. Corrosivity Characteristic | 384 |
| | C. Reactivity Characteristic | 385 |
| | D. Toxicity Characteristic | 386 |
| | E. TCLP | 386 |
| II. | Groundwater Monitoring | 389 |
| III. | Underground Storage Tanks | 393 |
| IV. | EPA Contract Laboratory Program | 397 |
| V. | Other Government Contract Agencies | 407 |
| VI. | Mixed Waste | 420 |
| | A. Units of Radiation Measure | 421 |
| | B. Acute Radiation Dosage Results | 422 |
| | C. Radiation Quality Factors | 422 |
| VII. | Field Analytical Methods | 426 |
| | A. Immunoassay Kits | 431 |
| | B. Qualitative Screening Tests | 433 |

**Section 5.    Air Pollution and Monitoring**                              **437**

    I.   Sampling                                                        437
          A.   Filter Cassette                                         437
          B.   Annular Denuder                                         438
          C.   Impinger                                                439
          D.   Adsorbent Trap                                          439
          E.   Grab Sample                                             440
          F.   Bulk Sample                                             440
          G.   Cascade Impactor                                        440
          H.   Colorimetric Indicator Tubes                            441
          I.   Stack Testing                                           441
   II.   Reporting Results                                           442
  III.   Specific Methodologies                                      443
          A.   Carbon Oxides                                           443
          B.   Organic Analytes                                        444
          C.   Inorganic Analytes                                      448
   IV.   EPA Methods                                                 454

**Appendices**

      A.  List of Analytes
      B.  Common Acronyms
      C.  Specialized Laboratory Glassware
      D.  References
      E.  Vendors
      F.  Regulatory Contact Directory
      G.  Alphabetical Elements List
      H.  Periodic Chart
      I.   40 CFR 136.3
      J.  Glossary
      K.  Index

# Illustrations

| Figure No. | Illustration Titles | Page No. |
|---|---|---|

**Section 1  Introduction to Environmental Analysis**

| | | |
|---|---|---|
| 1-1. | Offices within EPA that generate and specify methods | 34 |
| 1-2. | Example of a final analytical report | 82 |
| 1-3. | Example of a page header to establish document control. | 112 |
| 1-4. | Generalized point-to-point calibration curve | 113 |
| 1-5. | Non-linear point-to-point calibration curve for sulfate analysis in Table 1-41 | 114 |
| 1-6. | Linear regression calculation | 115 |
| 1-7. | Linear regression calibration curve for sulfate analysis in Table 1-41. | 117 |
| 1-8. | Sulfate second degree polynomial regression calibration. | 118 |
| 1-9. | Sulfate third degree polynomial regression calibration. | 118 |
| 1-10. | Plot of RF vs. concentration (ng/uL) for data in Table 1-42. | 121 |
| 1-11. | Plot of initial calibration RF vs. concentration (ng/uL) for bis(2-chloroisopropyl) ether along with average RF and allowed daily RF variations by method 625 | 122 |
| 1-12. | Plot of RF vs. As/Ais for manual calibration. | 123 |
| 1-13. | Linear regression performed on the data in Figure 1-12. | 124 |
| 1-14. | Second degree polynomial regression performed on the data in Figure 1-12 | 125 |
| 1-15. | Third degree polynomial regression performed on the diethyl phthalate data from Table 1-42. | 126 |
| 1-16. | Third degree polynomial regression performed on the bis(2-chloroisopropyl) ether data from Table 1-41 | 126 |
| 1-17. | Multi-component target analytes (PCBs) | 128 |
| 1-18. | Graph of MSA example. | 129 |
| 1-19. | Accuracy and precision. | 131 |
| 1-20. | Instrument detection limit problem. | 134 |
| 1-21. | Intersection of IDL with calibration curve. | 135 |
| 1-22. | Distribution of instrument noise levels. | 135 |
| 1-23. | Distribution of results around a true value. | 138 |
| 1-24. | False negative determinations at the MDL. | 138 |
| 1-25. | Multiplication of two numbers using an old fashioned slide rule. | 142 |
| 1-26. | Chain of custody form. | 144 |
| 1-27. | Work assignment for TSS. | 145 |
| 1-28. | Example of a bench worksheet. | 146 |
| 1-29. | Analytical balance daily calibration logbook. | 148 |
| 1-30. | Sample report worksheet. | 151 |
| 1-31. | Standard preparation log. | 152 |
| 1-32. | Batch matrix spike results for BNA analysis. | 154 |
| 1-33. | Batch surrogate recovery form. | 155 |
| 1-34. | I chart of average recovery for trichlorobenzene. | 162 |
| 1-35. | I chart for RPD for trichlorobenzene. | 162 |
| 1-36. | X-bar chart for recovery of trichlorobenzene. | 163 |
| 1-37. | R chart for recovery of trichlorobenzene. | 164 |
| 1-38. | X-bar chart for recovery of trichlorobenzene with daily moving limits | 165 |
| 1-39. | Example of WP sample reporting form. | 169 |
| 1-40. | Example of the DMR QA Study 16 result reporting form. | 173 |

| Figure No. | Illustration Titles, *continued* | Page No. |
|---|---|---|

**Section 2   Physical, Biological and General Chemical Parameters**

| | | |
|---|---|---|
| 2-1. | Size of common objects. | 180 |
| 2-2. | Temperature monitoring log. | 183 |
| 2-3. | Schematic of a nephelometer for measuring turbidity | 184 |
| 2-4. | Formazin polymer formation. | 184 |
| 2-5. | Fermentation of lactose by coliforms. | 186 |
| 2-6. | Chemistry of the Colilert P-A test. | 191 |
| 2-7. | Generalized log dose-response curve. | 193 |
| 2-8. | Single pole pH electrode. | 194 |
| 2-9. | Combination pH electrode. | 195 |
| 2-10. | pH plotted against potential for a pH electrode. | 195 |
| 2-11. | Chemistry of the common indicator methyl orange | 198 |
| 2-12. | Chemistry of the common indicator phenolphthalein. | 198 |
| 2-13. | Equilibrium chemistry of carbon dioxide in water. | 199 |
| 2-14. | pH dependence of the mole fraction of carbonate, bicarbonate and carbon dioxide. | 199 |
| 2-15. | Reagents used in hardness titration. | 201 |
| 2-16. | Chemistry of the Winkler DO method. | 203 |
| 2-17. | Chemistry of oxidation of KHP and glucose-glutamic acid. | 204 |
| 2-18. | Chemistry of COD reaction and titration. | 205 |
| 2-19. | Reaction of KHP in the COD procedure. | 206 |
| 2-20. | Structures of potassium hydrogen phthalate (KHP) and ferroin indicator. | 206 |
| 2-21. | Microwave digestion vessel. | 208 |
| 2-22. | Ionophore (MBTBT) and chromoionophore (ETH 5315) used in an optode for silver ion detection. | 217 |
| 2-23. | Reactions of organic materials with chlorine to produce pollutants. | 223 |
| 2-24. | Production of MX by reaction of chlorine with 3,5-dihydroxybenzaldehyde. | 223 |
| 2-25. | Neutralization of residual chlorine with ascorbic acid. | 224 |
| 2-26. | Reactions of chlorine with ammonia. | 224 |
| 2-27. | Breakpoint chlorination curve. | 225 |
| 2-28. | Chemistry of thiosulfate solutions. | 226 |
| 2-29. | Chemistry of DPD-FAS chlorine determination. | 228 |
| 2-30. | FACTS chemistry. | 228 |
| 2-31. | Orthotolidine reaction with chlorine. | 229 |
| 2-32. | Reaction of leuco crystal violet with chlorine. | 229 |
| 2-33. | Methyl orange determination of residual chlorine. | 230 |
| 2-34. | Structure of methylene blue. | 232 |
| 2-35. | 4-AAP reaction for analysis of total phenols. | 236 |
| 2-36. | Standardization of phenol solutions | 236 |
| 2-37. | Chlorination chemistry of cyanide. | 237 |
| 2-38. | Electrolytic decomposition of cyanide. | 238 |
| 2-39. | Structure of dimethylaminobenzalrhodanine. | 238 |
| 2-40. | Chemistry of pyridine-barbituric acid cyanide determination. | 239 |
| 2-41. | Structure of pyralozone used in colorimetric cyanide determination. | 239 |
| 2-42. | Chemistry of methylene blue formation as a sulfide assay. | 241 |
| 2-43. | Phenate method for ammonia determination. | 242 |
| 2-44. | Chemistry of nitrite colorimetric analysis. | 243 |

**Figure
No.**             **Illustration Titles,** *continued*           **Page
No.**

**Section 2   Physical, Biological and General Chemical Parameters,** *continued*

2-45.   Coupling site with other nitrite colorimetric reagents to form azo dyes ........................... 243

2-46.   Structure of ATP, an organic phosphate .................................................. 246

2-47.   Formation of phosphomolybdate from phosphate .................................. 246

2-48.   Bleaching reaction of fluoride on zirconium-SPADNS reagent ..................... 248

2-49.   SPADNS fluoride calibration curve ........................................................ 249

2-50.   Structure of alizarin fluorine blue .......................................................... 249

2-51.   Chemistry of the diphenyl carbazone indication of the mercuric nitrate titration
       end-point ................................................................................................ 250

**Section 3.   Organic Parameters**

3-1.   Energy spectrum ........................................................................................ 262

3-2.   Molecular bond motions .......................................................................... 263

3-3.   Diagram of a gas chromatograph. ............................................................ 268

3-4.   Diagram of a purge and trap for GC. ....................................................... 269

3-5.   Diagram of dual column GC. .................................................................... 285

3-6.   Derivatization of biphenyls to decachlorobiphenyl ................................. 288

3-7.   Generation of diazomethane from Diazald®. .......................................... 289

3-8.   Diazald® microgenerator for diazomethane ............................................ 290

3-9.   Generation of diazomethane from 1-methyl-3-nitro-1-nitrosoguanidine. ... 290

3-10.   Post-column derivatization of glyphosate ............................................... 293

3-11.   Derivatization of endothall. ..................................................................... 294

3-12.   Diquat and paraquat. ................................................................................ 294

3-13.   Dichlorophen and hexachlorophene ....................................................... 297

3-14.   Structure of decafluorotriphenylphosphine (DFTPP). ........................... 306

3-15.   Tailing factor calculation. ........................................................................ 307

3-16.   Cyanazine ................................................................................................. 309

3-17.   Colorimetric determination of $CS_2$ in Method 630 ............................... 309

3-18.   Hydrolysis of benomyl to carbendazim in Method 631 ......................... 310

3-19.   Structure of thiabendazole. ...................................................................... 312

3-20.   Hydrolysis reaction of dazomet. ............................................................. 317

3-21.   Phase diagram for supercritical carbon dioxide ...................................... 320

3-22.   4-way valve configuration used for manual GPC ..................................... 323

3-23.   Derivatization reaction of acrylamide ..................................................... 324

3-24.   Derivatization reaction of phenols. ......................................................... 324

3-25.   Breakdown equations for monitoring column conditions ....................... 326

3-26.   PCBs 1016, 1242 and 1248 ..................................................................... 328

3-27.   PCBs 1221, 1232 and 1242 ..................................................................... 329

3-28.   PCBs 1248, 1254 and 1260 ..................................................................... 330

3-29.   Reaction of formaldehyde with 2,4-DNP ............................................... 341

3-30.   Post-column derivatization/fluorescence detection of N-methyl carbamates ......... 342

3-31.   Gas chromatogram of diesel fuel bracketed by the surrogates n-nonane and
       n-pentacosane ......................................................................................... 366

3-32.   Kerosene by GC-FID ............................................................................... 367

3-33.   Mineral Spirits by GC-FID ...................................................................... 368

3-34.   Charcoal lighter fluid by GC-FID ........................................................... 369

3-35.   SAE 30 weight oil by GC-FID ................................................................ 370

| **Figure No.** | **Illustration Titles, *continued*** | **Page No.** |
|---|---|---|

**Section 3. Organic Parameters**

| 3-36. | Louisiana crude oil by GC-FID. | 371 |
| 3-37. | Breakdown products from common military chemical agents. | 377 |
| 3-38. | Alkaline/alcohol decontamination products from common military nerve agents. | 377 |

**Section 4. Hazardous Waste and Remediation Analysis**

| 4-1. | Relationship of temperature to pKw and pH for constant strength alkaline solution. | 385 |
| 4-2. | Flowchart of TCLP | 388 |
| 4-3. | Interaction of enzyme, substrate, antibody and PCB target analyte | 432 |

**Section 5. Air Pollution and Monitoring**

| 5-1. | Diagram of an air sampling filter cassette | 438 |
| 5-2. | Diagram of an annular denuder. | 438 |
| 5-3. | Diagram of a hi-flow semivolatiles sampler. | 440 |
| 5-4. | Diagram of a cascade impactor. | 441 |
| 5-5. | Simplified sampling train for stack testing. | 442 |
| 5-6. | Relationship between ppm and mg/m³ for reporting air results | 442 |
| 5-7. | Equation for the evaporation rate. | 443 |
| 5-8. | Diagram of a non-dispersive IR instrument for measuring carbon monoxide | 444 |
| 5-9. | Reaction of chromotropic acid with formaldehyde | 446 |
| 5-10. | Reaction of DNPH with aldehydes | 446 |
| 5-11. | Structure of MBTH | 446 |
| 5-12. | Reaction of aldehydes with dansylhydrazine. | 447 |
| 5-13. | Reaction of aldehydes with bisulfite. | 447 |
| 5-14. | Structure of 4-hexyl-resorcinol | 448 |
| 5-15. | Proposed first step for the bleaching reaction of methyl orange with chlorine. | 448 |
| 5-16. | Chemiluminescent detection of sulfur compounds. | 449 |
| 5-17. | Determination of mercaptans. | 449 |
| 5-18. | Formation of methylene blue from sulfide | 449 |
| 5-19. | Iodometric determination of sulfide. | 449 |
| 5-20. | Impinger collection of sulfur dioxide | 450 |
| 5-21. | Reaction of formaldehyde-bisulfite with p-rosaniline | 450 |
| 5-22. | Oxidation of sulfur dioxide with peroxide to sulfate. | 450 |
| 5-23. | Structure of methylthymol blue | 451 |
| 5-24. | Structure of thorin. | 451 |
| 5-25. | Structure of barium chloranilate. | 451 |
| 5-26. | Chemiluminescent reaction of nitric oxide with ozone | 452 |
| 5-27. | Luminol reaction with nitrogen dioxide. | 453 |

# Tables

| Table No. | Table Titles | Page No. |
|---|---|---|
| **Section 1** | **Introduction to Environmental Analysis** | |
| 1-1. | Contents of Title 40, Code of Federal Regulations | 2 |
| 1-2. | Primary Drinking Water Monitoring requirements | 4 |
| 1-3. | Secondary Drinking Water Monitoring requirements | 7 |
| 1-4. | Toxic Pollutant list from 40 CFR 401.15. | 9 |
| 1-5. | Priority Pollutant lists and required reportable detection limits for monitoring | 11 |
| 1-6. | Industries with 40 CFR wastewater effluent guidelines. | 14 |
| 1-7. | Subpart groups for the OCPSF industry. | 16 |
| 1-8. | Toxic Pollutant Effluent Guideline Example, Subpart J 40 CFR 414.101, Organic Chemicals, Plastics and Synthetic Fibers, 9 July, 1993. | 16 |
| 1-9. | Contents of analytical methods for the National Sewage Sludge Survey | 18 |
| 1-10. | Test procedures in 40 CFR for data supporting TSCA submissions | 21 |
| 1-11. | Hazardous organic air pollutants | 24 |
| 1-12. | Hazardous Air Pollutants under Title III CAAA. | 26 |
| 1-13. | Standards of performance for new stationary sources listed in 40 CFR 60, 1 July, 1993 | 31 |
| 1-14. | EPA 100-400 series methods. | 35 |
| 1-15. | EPA 500 series methods. | 40 |
| 1-16. | EPA 600 series methods. | 42 |
| 1-17. | EPA 1600 series methods | 44 |
| 1-18. | EPA 900 series methods. | 45 |
| 1-19. | EPA 1000 series methods for compliance monitoring | 46 |
| 1-20. | General numbering scheme of Test Methods for Evaluating Solid Wastes Physical/Chemical Methods (SW-846, 3rd Edition, Revision I July, 1992 and Revisions II and IIa, September, 1994) | 47 |
| 1-21. | Contents of SW-846 including the proposed Update III to the Third Edition. | 47 |
| 1-22. | General method numbering of *NIOSH Manual of Analytical Methods* 4th Edition. | 53 |
| 1-23. | Method contents of *NIOSH Manual of Analytical Methods* 4th Edition. | 53 |
| 1-24. | EPA CLP methods and documents. PB numbers are NTIS document identifiers | 60 |
| 1-25. | USGS methods. | 62 |
| 1-26. | Method contents of *Standard Methods* 19th Edition | 67 |
| 1-27. | Method contents of *Air Sampling* 3th Edition. | 77 |
| 1-28. | Drinking water holding time, preservation and sample container requirements from *Manual for the Certification of Laboratories Analyzing Drinking Water - Criteria and Procedures Quality Assurance* Third Edition, Change 2 EPA-814B-92-002, September 1992 | 87 |
| 1-29. | Holding times, containers and preservatives for wastewater samples. From 40 CFR 136, II, as amended 31 Jan 1994, 59 FR 4504 | 90 |
| 1-30. | Preservation, holding times and sample containers for aqueous matrices, Table 2-21 from Chapter 2, SW-846, Third Edition, Revision 1, July, 1992 | 95 |
| 1-31. | Sample containers, preservatives and holding times for hazardous waste samples analyzed by SW-846 methods | 97 |
| 1-32. | Sampling and preservation procedures for groundwater detection monitoring, Table 11-1, Chapter 11, page 7, SW-846, Third Edition, Revision 0, September, 1986. | 99 |
| 1-33. | Sample container, preservation and holding time requirements in CLP-SOW | 100 |

| Table No. | Table Titles, *continued* | Page No. |
|---|---|---|

**Section 1    Introduction to Environmental Analysis, *continued***

| | | |
|---|---|---|
| 1-34. | USACE sample containers, preservatives and holding times, low concentration samples | 101 |
| 1-35. | USACE sample containers, preservatives and holding times, medium and high concentration samples | 102 |
| 1-36. | AFCEE requirements for containers, preservation techniques, sample volumes and holding times | 104 |
| 1-37. | Holding times, preservatives, containers and minimum sample size for HAZWRAP | 107 |
| 1-38. | Contents for a Quality Assurance Project Plan in compliance with 40 CFR 30.503 | 111 |
| 1-39. | Generalized contents for a Quality Assurance Manual | 111 |
| 1-40. | General calibration example | 112 |
| 1-41. | Calibration of sulfate analysis by EPA method 375.4 using spectrophotometric analysis at 420 nm | 114 |
| 1-42. | Raw areas and RFs of compounds and associated internal standards vs. concentration (ng/uL) | 120 |
| 1-43. | Example of MSA data | 129 |
| 1-44. | Data quality levels | 130 |
| 1-45. | Oil and grease batch data for DQO calculation | 133 |
| 1-46. | One-tailed t-statistic at 99% confidence level for a variety of repetitions | 137 |
| 1-47. | MDL example for total suspended solids in mg/L | 137 |
| 1-48. | SI prefixes | 139 |
| 1-49. | Common environmental reporting units. | 140 |
| 1-50. | Commonly encountered conversions and definitions | 140 |
| 1-51. | Class A tolerances for volumetric measuring devices | 141 |
| 1-52. | Density of reagent water at different temperatures | 141 |
| 1-53. | Tolerances (in mg) of various ASTM and NIST classes of standard weights | 149 |
| 1-54. | Phthalates and other contaminants found in common laboratory items. Amounts are in ng/uL injected into the GC-MS from 1.0 mL final volume of extract. | 157 |
| 1-55. | Preparation of 1 L of synthetic seawater | 159 |
| 1-56. | Synthetic freshwater recipe amounts in mg/L | 159 |
| 1-57. | Western Electric rules for evaluating control charts | 165 |
| 1-58. | WP Analytes in WP035 | 167 |
| 1-59. | WS Analytes in WS038 | 170 |
| 1-60. | DMR QA Study 16 (1996) Chemical Analytes | 172 |
| 1-61. | WS QA study acceptance criteria based on true value (40 CFR 141) | 174 |

**Section 2    Physical, Biological and General Chemical Parameters**

| | | |
|---|---|---|
| 2-1. | Standard sieve sizes. | 178 |
| 2-2. | Formulations of common culture media for coliforms | 187 |
| 2-3. | MPN values for drinking water | 188 |
| 2-4. | MPN/100 mL for five tube, three dilution series (10, 1.0, 0.1 mL) | 188 |
| 2-5. | Media formulations for fecal coliforms | 190 |
| 2-6. | Presence-absence media formulation | 190 |
| 2-7. | EPA toxicity testing procedural manuals | 194 |
| 2-8. | Temperature dependent pH variation of a neutral water solution | 196 |
| 2-9. | Reference electrode voltage variation with temperature due to increased solubility of silver chloride | 196 |

| Table No. | Table Titles, *continued* | Page No. |
|---|---|---|

**Section 2    Physical, Biological and General Chemical Parameters, *continued***

| | | |
|---|---|---|
| 2-10. | Common laboratory buffer systems and their $pK_a$ | 197 |
| 2-11. | Primary standards for pH calibration | 198 |
| 2-12. | Langelier's Index values for A | 201 |
| 2-13. | Langelier's Index values for B | 202 |
| 2-14. | KHP used as a 300 mg/L solution as standard for a number of tests | 206 |
| 2-15. | Vapor pressure of pure water at a variety of temperatures | 209 |
| 2-16. | Metals that can be digested by microwave techniques | 210 |
| 2-17. | Method numbers for FLAA (Direct Aspiration) metals procedures | 211 |
| 2-18. | Method numbers for GFAA metals procedures | 212 |
| 2-19. | Generic ICP interference correction factors | 214 |
| 2-20. | Examples of polyatomic interferences found in ICP-MS | 215 |
| 2-21. | Contents of *Manual for the Determination of Metals in Environmental Samples.* Methods marked with an * are in the Supplement. | 219 |
| 2-22. | Metals methods and associated guidance for the clean metals program | 221 |
| 2-23. | Commonly encountered chelation agents | 234 |
| 2-24. | Forms and names of mono-phosphates | 245 |
| 2-25. | Forms, names, and structures of inorganic phosporus | 245 |
| 2-26. | Absorbance data obtained from SPADNS procedure with 3.5 mg/L fluoride standard set at zero absorbance | 248 |
| 2-27. | Target analytes of anion chromatography | 251 |
| 2-28. | Ideal ISE slope values for common ions at 25 °C | 253 |
| 2-29. | Commonly available ISE | 253 |
| 2-30. | Overview of analytical methods for soil samples. | 254 |

**Section 3.    Organic Parameters**

| | | |
|---|---|---|
| 3-1. | Correlation of photon wavelength to energy content | 263 |
| 3-2. | Representative IR frequencies | 264 |
| 3-3. | Commonly used detectors for gas chromatography | 265 |
| 3-4. | Target analytes and MDLs for Method 501 | 270 |
| 3-5. | Target analytes and MDLs for Method 502.1 | 270 |
| 3-6. | Target analytes and MDLs for Method 502.2 | 271 |
| 3-7. | Target analytes and MDLs for Method 503.1 | 272 |
| 3-8. | Daily BFB MS tuning criteria for Method 524.1 | 273 |
| 3-9. | Target analytes and MDLs for Method 524.1 | 273 |
| 3-10. | Target analytes and MDLs for Method 524.2 | 274 |
| 3-11. | Version 4.0 of 524.2 adds the following analytes | 274 |
| 3-12. | Target analytes and MDLs for Method 601 | 275 |
| 3-13. | Target analytes and MDLs for Method 602 | 276 |
| 3-14. | Internal standards and surrogates for Method 624 | 276 |
| 3-15. | Daily MS tuning requirements for BFB for Method 624 | 276 |
| 3-16. | Target analytes, MDLs, precision and accuracy (20 ug/L spike) for Method 624 | 277 |
| 3-17. | Target analytes and MDLs for Method 1624 | 278 |
| 3-18. | Daily BFB MS tuning requirements for Method 1624 | 278 |
| 3-19. | Target analytes and MDLs for Method 8015 | 279 |
| 3-20. | Daily MS BFB tuning requirements. | 279 |
| 3-21. | Daily SPCC criteria for Method 8240 | 280 |

| Table No. | Table Titles, *continued* | Page No. |
|---|---|---|

**Section 3. Organic Parameters,** *continued*

| Table No. | Table Titles | Page No. |
|---|---|---|
| 3-22. | Target analytes and MDLs for Method 8240 | 280 |
| 3-23. | Daily CCC criteria for Method 8240 | 280 |
| 3-24. | Surrogates and internal standards for Method 8240 | 281 |
| 3-25. | Matrix spike compounds for Method 8240 | 281 |
| 3-26. | Daily MS BFB tuning requirements for Method 8260 | 281 |
| 3-27. | Daily SPCC requirements for Method 8260 | 281 |
| 3-28. | Daily CCC requirements for Method 8260 | 282 |
| 3-29. | Surrogates and internal standards for Method 8260 | 282 |
| 3-30. | Matrix spike compounds for Method 8260 | 282 |
| 3-31. | Target analytes and MDLs for Method 8260 | 282 |
| 3-32. | Other VOA related procedures listed in SW-846 | 283 |
| 3-33. | Target analytes and MDLs for Method 505 | 285 |
| 3-34. | Target analytes and MDLs for Method 506 | 286 |
| 3-35. | Target analytes and MDLs for Method 507 | 286 |
| 3-36. | Target analytes and MDLs for Method 508 | 287 |
| 3-37. | Target analytes and MDLs for Method 515 | 291 |
| 3-38. | Target analytes and MDLs for Method 525 | 292 |
| 3-39. | Daily MS DFTPP tune requirements for Method 525 | 292 |
| 3-40. | Target analytes and MDLs for Method 531.1 | 293 |
| 3-41. | Target analytes and MDLs for Method 550 | 295 |
| 3-42. | Target analytes and MDLs for Method 551 | 295 |
| 3-43. | Target analytes and MDLs for Method 552 | 296 |
| 3-44. | Target analytes and MDLs for Method 604 | 297 |
| 3-45. | Target analytes and MDLs for Method 606 | 298 |
| 3-46. | Target analytes and MDLs for Method 607 | 298 |
| 3-47. | Target analytes, MDLs, precision and accuracy for Method 608 | 299 |
| 3-48. | Target analytes and MDLs for Method 608.1 | 299 |
| 3-49. | Target analytes and MDLs for Method 608.2 | 300 |
| 3-50. | Target analytes and MDLs for Method 609 | 300 |
| 3-51. | Target analytes and MDLs for Method 610 | 301 |
| 3-52. | Target analytes and MDLs for Method 611 | 301 |
| 3-53. | Target analytes and MDLs for Method 612 | 301 |
| 3-54. | Target analytes and MDLs for Methods 614 and 614.1 | 302 |
| 3-55. | Target analytes and MDLs for Method 615 | 303 |
| 3-56. | Target analytes and MDLs for Method 616 | 303 |
| 3-57. | Target analytes and MDLs for Method 617 | 303 |
| 3-58. | Target analytes and MDLs for Method 618 | 304 |
| 3-59. | Target analytes and MDLs for Method 619 | 304 |
| 3-60. | Target analytes and MDLs for Method 622 | 305 |
| 3-61. | Target analytes and MDLs for Method 622.1 | 305 |
| 3-62. | Daily MS tune criteria for DFTPP | 306 |
| 3-63. | Base/neutral extractable target analytes and MDLs for Method 625 | 307 |
| 3-64. | Acid extractable target analytes and MDLs for Method 625 | 308 |
| 3-65. | Suggested internal and surrogate standards for Method 625 | 308 |
| 3-66. | Target analytes and MDLs for Method 627 | 308 |
| 3-67. | Target analytes and MDLs for Methods 630 and 630.1 | 309 |

| Table No. | Table Titles, *continued* | Page No. |
|---|---|---|
| **Section 3.** | **Organic Parameters,** *continued* | |
| 3-68. | Target analytes and MDLs for Method 632 | 310 |
| 3-69. | Target analytes and MDLs for Method 632.1 | 311 |
| 3-70. | Target analytes and MDLs for Methods 633 and 633.1 | 311 |
| 3-71. | Target analytes and MDLs for Method 634 | 311 |
| 3-72. | Target analytes and MDLs for Method 645 | 312 |
| 3-73. | Target analytes and MDLs for Method 646 | 313 |
| 3-74. | Daily MS tune criteria for DFTPP | 313 |
| 3-75. | Target analytes and MDLs for Method 1656 | 314 |
| 3-76. | Target analytes and MDLs for Method 1657 | 316 |
| 3-77. | Target analytes and MDLs for Method 1658 | 317 |
| 3-78. | Target analytes and MDLs for Method 1660 | 317 |
| 3-79. | Target analytes and MDLs for Method 8040 | 325 |
| 3-80. | Target analytes and MDLs for Method 8061 | 325 |
| 3-81. | Target analytes and MDLs for Method 8081 | 326 |
| 3-82. | Target analytes and MDLs for Method 8121 | 331 |
| 3-83. | Target analytes and MDLs for Method 8151 | 331 |
| 3-84. | SPCC for Method 8250 | 332 |
| 3-85. | Daily MS DFTPP tune criteria for Method 8250 | 332 |
| 3-86. | Calibration check compounds (CCC) for Method 8250 | 333 |
| 3-87. | Internal standards and surrogates for Method 8250 | 333 |
| 3-88. | Matrix spike compounds for Method 8250 | 333 |
| 3-89. | Target analytes and MDLs for Method 8250 | 333 |
| 3-90. | Daily MS DFTPP tune criteria for Method 8270 | 335 |
| 3-91. | SPCC for Method 8270 | 335 |
| 3-92. | Calibration check compounds (CCC) for Method 8270 | 335 |
| 3-93. | Internal standards and surrogates for Method 8270 | 336 |
| 3-94. | Matrix spike compounds for Method 8270 | 336 |
| 3-95. | Target analytes and EQLs for Method 8270 | 336 |
| 3-96. | Target analytes and % recovery for Method 8275 | 338 |
| 3-97. | Internal standards of Method 8290 | 339 |
| 3-98. | Surrogate and alternate standards of Method 8290 | 339 |
| 3-99. | Target analytes and minimum calibration levels of Method 8290 | 340 |
| 3-100. | Acceptance ranges for molecular ion ratios | 340 |
| 3-101. | Target analytes and MDLs for Method 8318 | 342 |
| 3-102. | MS tune criteria using PEG 400 for Method 8321 | 343 |
| 3-103. | PFTBA target tune for DFTPP | 343 |
| 3-104. | Ideal results for PFTBA with peak widths of 0.50 | 344 |
| 3-105. | Freons | 345 |
| 3-106. | Some common and cross-named dyes within the C.I. | 348 |
| 3-107. | Functional groups found in dyes and representative examples | 349 |
| 3-108. | Classes of dyes that present potential environmental/health hazards | 349 |
| 3-109. | Structures of common dyes and pigments | 351 |
| 3-110. | Common industrial hydrocarbon solvents and fuels encountered in GC analysis | 361 |
| 3-111. | Common additives in hydrocarbon fuels | 363 |
| 3-112. | Boiling points of common hydrocarbon standards | 372 |
| 3-113. | Common military explosives and residues | 373 |

| Table No. | Table Titles, *continued* | Page No. |
|---|---|---|

**Section 3. Organic Parameters,** *continued*

| | | |
|---|---|---|
| 3-114. | Target analytes of Method 8330 | 375 |
| 3-115. | Chemical warfare agent residues | 377 |
| 3-116. | Holding times, preservatives and sample containers for chemical warfare residue samples | 378 |
| 3-117. | Plasticizers, anti-oxidants, flame retardants and other additives | 379 |
| 3-118. | Some endocrine disruptors | 381 |

**Section 4. Hazardous Waste and Remediation Analysis**

| | | |
|---|---|---|
| 4-1. | Substances listed under TCLP toxicity characteristic | 386 |
| 4-2. | Analytical methods required under TCLP | 388 |
| 4-3. | Appendix I target analytes for landfill leachate monitoring | 390 |
| 4-4. | Analyte groups in 40 CFR Part 258, Appendix II | 390 |
| 4-5. | Semivolatile organic target analytes from Appendix II by Method 8270 | 391 |
| 4-6. | Volatile organic target analytes from Appendix II by Method 8260 | 392 |
| 4-7. | Organochlorine pesticide target analytes from Appendix II by Method 8080 | 393 |
| 4-8. | Metal elements target analytes from Appendix II by Method 6010. | 393 |
| 4-9. | Chlorinated acid herbicide target analytes from Appendix II by Method 8150 | 393 |
| 4-10. | Miscellaneous target analytes from Appendix II | 393 |
| 4-11. | Analytical methods required for UST characterizations from a random selection of state srograms | 394 |
| 4-12. | CLP inorganic target analyte list (TAL) for metals | 398 |
| 4-13. | CLP forms included as deliverables with each sample for metals | 399 |
| 4-14. | CLP VOA target compound list (TCL) | 400 |
| 4-15. | CLP forms included as deliverables with each sample for VOA | 401 |
| 4-16. | CLP target analyte list (TCL) for semivolatile organic compounds | 401 |
| 4-17. | CLP forms included as deliverables with each sample for semivolatile organic compounds | 402 |
| 4-18. | CLP pesticide/aroclor target compound List (TCL) | 403 |
| 4-19. | CLP forms included as deliverables with each sample for pesticide/aroclor | 404 |
| 4-20. | Laboratory flags for organic data. | 405 |
| 4-21. | Data reviewer flags for organic data. | 405 |
| 4-22. | Laboratory flags for inorganic data. | 406 |
| 4-23. | Data reviewer flags for inorganic data. | 406 |
| 4-24. | USACE VOA target compound list (TCL) | 408 |
| 4-25. | USACE BNA semi-volatile target compound list (TCL) | 408 |
| 4-26. | USACE pesticide/PCB target compound list (TCL) | 409 |
| 4-27. | Target analyte list (TAL) for metals under USACE | 409 |
| 4-28. | HAZWRAP Level C deliverables | 411 |
| 4-29. | AFCEE inorganic target analyte list | 413 |
| 4-30. | AFCEE organic target compound list | 414 |
| 4-31. | Characteristics of radioactivity | 421 |
| 4-32. | Quality factors for radiation types | 422 |
| 4-33. | Uranium decay series | 423 |
| 4-34. | DOE methods | 424 |
| 4-35. | Contents of EPA Field Methods Compendium (Draft), OERR-9285.2-11, February, 1994 | 427 |

| Table No. | Table Titles, *continued* | Page No. |
|---|---|---|
| **Section 5.** | **Air Pollution and Monitoring** | |
| 5-1. | Coating materials used on annular denuders | 438 |
| 5-2. | Trapping solutions used in impingers | 439 |
| 5-3. | Nitrogen oxides | 452 |
| 5-4. | Amphibole asbestos | 454 |
| 5-5. | EPA Air Program Methods found in 40 CFR | 454 |
| 5-6. | Methods for compliance with burning hazardous wastes in boilers and industrial furnaces (BIF) regulations | 460 |
| 5-7. | Compendium of Methods for the determination of toxic organic compounds in ambient air | 460 |
| 5-8. | Compendium of Methods for the determination of inorganic compounds in ambient air | 461 |
| 5-9. | Quality assurance handbook for air pollution measurement systems | 461 |
| 5-10. | Compendium of Methods for the determination of air pollutants in indoor air | 462 |
| 5-11. | CLP Draft Statement of Work for air analysis at CERCLA sites | 462 |

# Introduction to Environmental Analysis

No plant manager wakes up in the morning and on the spur of the moment decides to go down to the plant wastewater outfall, take a sample of the effluent and send it off to an environmental laboratory for testing. The testing is expensive and adds directly to the cost of manufacturing products without creating any additional value in the product. The only reason that the plant manager takes the sample is because he is directed to do so by a federal or state government regulation. The environmental industry is a regulated industry in the sense that it exists solely because it services government requirements for monitoring, remediation and pollution prevention. Persons in the industry who refuse to recognize this fundamental motivating force and fail to keep themselves informed of changes in the regulations are deluding themselves and will eventually run into the reality of what it means to be ignorant of government directives.

## I. APPLICABLE FEDERAL AND STATE REGULATIONS

### A. Title 40, Code of Federal Regulations: Protection of Environment

Titles in the Code of Federal Regulations (CFR) are compilations of laws enacted by the Congress of the USA and signed into effect by the President. They are the ultimate authority (other than the Supreme Court) of Federal regulations. Many commercial (and municipal) laboratories miss this point. It is against the Federal law of the land not to follow explicitly the methods listed in the CFR. Every laboratory should have a copy of 40 CFR on hand and a competent legal firm, which specializes in environmental issues, under retainer to interpret the laws. New editions of 40 CFR are published annually, and the most recent edition should be in the lab's collection of reference materials. 40 CFR is available on-line from the Government Printing Office, See Appendix F of this book for the address.

**Table 1–1. Contents of Title 40, Code of Federal Regulations**

| Chapter I - Environmental Protection Agency (Parts 1-799) | |
|---|---|
| **Subchapters and Parts** | **Title** |
| Subchapter A - Parts 1-29 | General |
| Subchapter B - Parts 30-46 | Grants and other Federal Assistance |
| Subchapter C - Parts 50-87 | Air Programs |
| Subchapter D - Parts 104-149 | Water Programs |
| Subchapter E - Parts 152-180 | Pesticide Programs |
| Subchapter F - Parts 190-192 | Radiation Protection Programs |
| Subchapter G - Parts 201-211 | Noise Abatement Programs |
| Subchapter H - Parts 220-233 | Ocean Dumping |
| Subchapter I - Parts 240-280 | Solid Wastes |
| Subchapter J - Parts 300-370 | Superfund, Emergency Planning and Community Right-to-Know Programs |
| Subchapter N - Parts 401-471 | Effluent Guidelines and Standards |
| Subchapter Q - Parts 600-610 | Energy Policy |
| Subchapter R - Parts 702-799 | Toxic Substances Control Act |
| Chapter V - Council on Environmental Quality (Parts 1500-1599) | |

# B. Government Regulations Administered By EPA

## 1. RCRA – Resource Conservation and Recovery Act

The original Federal Act was the Solid Waste Disposal Act of 1965. With the creation of the EPA, expanded legislative frameworks were needed to enable the EPA to perform its mission. Passage of RCRA in 1976 gave EPA the authority to oversee waste disposal and hazardous waste management. Integral to the law is the definition of what is a hazardous waste. The identification of a waste as hazardous relies on either the results of specific analytical tests or its being on a list of recognized hazardous wastes. The analytical methods are compiled in SW-846. Important subtitles to RCRA are:

**a. Subtitle C. Hazardous Waste Management** - Introduces the "cradle-to-grave" concept of hazardous waste accounting. The originator or manufacturer of the hazardous waste is the cradle, and the treatment, storage and disposal facility (TSD) is the grave. The law requires traceability through the *Uniform Hazardous Waste Manifest* of the waste as it moves from the originator to the transporter to the TSD, with the federal or state EPA serving in the oversight role. Subtitle C also defines and regulates the construction, operation, and closure of hazardous waste TSD's. As far as environmental analysis is concerned this subtitle specifies the responsibility of the waste originator to characterize the waste, and the groundwater and other analytical monitoring responsibilities of the TSD. The Hazardous Substance List (HSL) analytes are located in 40 CFR Part 261, Appendix VIII. The groundwater monitoring target analytes are located in 40 CFR Part 264, Appendix IX and make-up the so-called Appendix IX analyses.

**b. Subtitle D. Solid Waste Management** - This is the subtitle that regulates your local municipal landfill. It details the construction, operation, maintenance, monitoring, and closure of municipal landfills. The newest version of this regulation establishes two sets of extensive monitoring lists, 40 CFR 258, Appendix I and Appendix II, in addition to construction specifications for impermeable liners and leacheate collection and treatment systems with all facilities required to come into full compliance by 1996.

   **c. Subtitle E. Underground Storage Tanks** - These are defined as storage tanks with at least 10% of the volume underground. There are 1.5 million existing in the US. Over 15% are estimated to be leaking and spreading their contents into the soil and groundwater. Petroleum tanks make up the bulk of leaking storage tanks, although they may not be the most significant as illustrated by recent videos from remote-controlled cameras in the radioactive waste storage tanks at the Hanford, Washington and Savannah River, South Carolina atomic energy plants. Under the Leaking Underground Storage Tank (LUST) program, individual states with general environmental responsibility, establish the proper methods of analysis and require some sort of laboratory certification. The most common analytical requests under this program are for benzene, toluene, ethyl benzene and xylene (BTEX), and total petroleum hydrocarbons (TPH), both from soil matrix. A variety of methods are in use to determine these groups.

## 2. CERCLA – Comprehensive Environmental Response, Compensation and Liability Act (Superfund)

The EPA is given two powers under this legislation, passed in 1980. The first is the authority to take any necessary short-term or emergency steps to cope with hazardous situations that affect health. A representative situation could be an explosion and fire that results in contamination of the environment, the food chain, and drinking water supplies. The second power is the ability to enter into long-term (greater than six months) projects to clean-up hazardous sites that are listed on the National Priority List (NPL). The EPA further has the authority to investigate the origins of waste found in hazardous sites and force the generators and other responsible parties to pay for the remediation (clean-up). Analytical support for investigations and remediations under CERCLA is provided through the Contract Laboratory Program (CLP), with the detailed methods contained in the contract Statements of Work, which are updated almost annually.

## 3. Drinking Water and Wastewater

These two programs cover all aspects of drinking water and wastewater under the below two legislations. Laboratory performance is monitored by issuance of two sets of bi-annual check (performance evaluation, PE) samples by EPA-Cincinnati. The PE samples are the WP (water pollution) and the WS (water supply) series. Both programs are administered by the individual states. States with primacy offer a range of laboratory certifications for submitting sample results in support of required periodic monitoring. They may range from simple certification of a lab for only microbiology (fecal coliform), to complete certification of micro, chemistry, and toxicology testing. The WS and WP PE samples are used by many states as an indicator of laboratory performance in regard to certification.

## a. SDWA - Safe Drinking Water Act

Last amended in 1996, this Act gives the EPA the ability to regulate drinking water quality. This is done through two tiers of analytes. The first is the National Primary Drinking Water Standards. These compounds directly affect human health, and all drinking water systems are required to reduce their presence to below the Maximum Contaminant Levels (MCL), set for each compound by the federal government. Any Primary Contaminant that assays above the MCL in a drinking water system sets off an escalating chain of regulatory actions. The National Sanitation Foundation *International* requires method detection limits to be lower than 1/5 of the MCL for tested parameters in its drinking water laboratory accreditation program. Florida requires MDLs to be no greater than 1/10 of the MCL for each Primary Contaminant. The second tier of analytes consists of the National Secondary Drinking Water Standards. They include materials that affect the taste, odor, color and other non-health related qualities of water and collectively serve as a suggested list for states to act upon. The same material may appear on both lists but generally at different action levels, for example, copper and fluoride. Almost all states have accepted primacy for administration of the Act.

The scheduled introduction (Phases I, II, & V) of 25 new drinking water analytes every 3 years by EPA was abolished by the Safe Drinking Water Act of 1996. New analytes are now added as needed by EPA according to risk based criteria. The required analytes along with proper sampling procedures and approved analytical methodologies are found in 40 CFR 141 (National Primary Drinking Water Standards), 40 CFR 143 (National Secondary Drinking Water Standards), and the Manual for Certification of Laboratories Analyzing Drinking Water. These analytes are listed in Tables 1-2 and 1-3.

### Table 1-2. Primary Drinking Water Monitoring Requirements[1]

| Contaminant | MCL mg/L | MDL mg/L[2] | Method[3] |
|---|---|---|---|
| **Inorganics** | | | |
| Antimony | 0.006 | .0008-.003 | EPA 200.8, 200.9, SM 3113B |
| Arsenic | 0.05 | | EPA 200.7A, 200.8, 200.9, SM 3120B, 3113B, 3114B |
| Asbestos | 7 mf/L[4] | .01 | EPA[5] 100.1, 100.2 |
| Barium | 2 | .001-.1 | EPA 200.7, 208.1, 200.8, SM 3120B, 3111D, 3113B |
| Beryllium | 0.004 | .00002-.0003 | EPA 200.7, 200.9, SM 3120B, 3113B |
| Cadmium | 0.005 | .0001-.001 | EPA 200.7, 200.8, 200.9, SM 3113B |
| Chromium | 0.1 | .001-.007 | EPA 200.7, 200.8. 200.9, SM 3120B, 3113B |
| Copper[6] | 1.3 | .001-.05 | EPA 200.7, 200.8, 200.9, SM 3120B, 3113B, 3111B |
| Cyanide | 0.2 | .005-.02 | EPA 335.4, SM 4500-CN C, E, F, & G |
| Fluoride | 4 | | SM 4500-F B, C, D, & E, 4110B |

Continued on next page.

---

[1]  Approved methods are from the CFR, 1 July, 1996
[2]  MDL will vary with the particular method.
[3]  EPA: Environmental Protection Agency; *SM: Standard Methods for the Examination of Water and Wastewater*, 18th Edition, 1992.
[4]  Million fibers per liter exceeding 10 um in length.
[5]  Analytical method for the determination of asbestos fibers in water, EPA 600/4-83-0433, Jan 1983 NTIS PB83-260471; Determination of asbestos structure over 10 um in length in drinking water, EPA 600/R-94-134, NTIS PB94-201902
[6]  Found in the Lead and Copper Rule, 40 CFR 141.89.

## Table 1-2. Primary Drinking Water Monitoring Requirements[7], *continued*

| Contaminant | MCL mg/L | MDL mg/L[8] | Method[9] |
|---|---|---|---|
| **Inorganics, *continued*** | | | |
| Lead[10] | 0.015 | .001 | EPA 200.8, 200.9, SM 3113B |
| Mercury | 0.002 | .0002 | EPA 245.1, 245.2, 200.8, SM 3112B |
| Nickel | 0.1 | .0006-.005 | EPA 200.7, 200.8, 200.9, SM 3120B, 3113B, 3111B |
| Nitrate-N | 10 | .01-1 | EPA 300.0A, 353.2, SM 4110B, 4500-NO3 D & F |
| Nitrite-N | 1 | .004-.05 | EPA 300.0A, 353.2, SM 4110B, 4500-NO2 B, 4500-NO3 E & F |
| Selenium | 0.05 | .002 | EPA 200.8, 200.9, SM 3114B, 3113B |
| Sodium | 20 | | EPA 200.7, SM 3113B |
| Thallium | 0.002 | .0007-.001 | EPA 200.8, 200.9 |
| **Synthetic organic compounds (SOC)** | | | |
| Adipates (Di[ethylhexyl]adipate) | 0.4 | .0006 | EPA 506, 525.2 |
| Alachlor | 0.002 | .0002 | EPA 505, 507, 525.2, 508.1 |
| Atrazine | 0.003 | .0001 | EPA 505, 507, 525.2, 508.1 |
| Carbofuran | 0.04 | .0009 | EPA 531.1, SM 6610 |
| Chlordane | 0.002 | .0002 | EPA 505, 508, 525.2, 508.1 |
| Dalapon | 0.2 | .001 | EPA 515.1, 552.1 |
| Dibromochloropropane (DBCP) | 0.0002 | .00002 | EPA 504.1, 551 |
| 2,4-D | 0.07 | .0001 | EPA 515.2, 515.1, 555 |
| Dinoseb | 0.007 | .0002 | EPA 515.1, 515.2, 555 |
| Diquat | 0.02 | .0004 | EPA 549.1 |
| Endothall | 0.1 | .009 | EPA 548.1 |
| Endrin | 0.002 | .00001 | EPA 505, 508, 525.2, 508.1 |
| Ethylene dibromide (EDB) | 0.00005 | .00001 | EPA 504.1, 551 |
| Glyphosate | 0.7 | .006 | EPA 547, SM 6651 |
| Heptachlor | 0.0004 | .00004 | EPA 505, 508, 525.2, 508.1 |
| Hepatchlor epoxide | 0.0002 | .00002 | EPA 505, 508, 525.2, 508.1 |
| Hexachlorobenzene | 0.001 | .0001 | EPA 505, 508, 525.2. 508.1 |
| Hexachlorocyclopentadiene | 0.05 | .0001 | EPA 505, 525.2, 508.1, 508 |
| Lindane | 0.0002 | .00002 | EPA 505, 508, 525.2, 508.1 |
| Methoxychlor | 0.04 | .0001 | EPA 505, 508, 525.2, 508.1 |
| Oxamyl (Vydate) | 0.2 | .002 | EPA 531.1, SM 6610 |

Continued on next page.

---

[7]  Approved methods are from the CFR, 1 July, 1996
[8]  MDL will vary with the particular method.
[9]  EPA: Environmental Protection Agency; *SM: Standard Methods for the Examination of Water and Wastewater*, 18th Edition, 1992.
[10]  See footnote 5.

## Table 1-2. Primary Drinking Water Monitoring Requirements[11], *continued*

| Contaminant | MCL mg/L | MDL mg/L[12] | Method[13] |
|---|---|---|---|
| **Synthetic organic compounds (SOC),** *continued* | | | |
| (PAHs) Benzo[a]pyrene | 0.0002 | .00002 | EPA 525.2, 550, 550.1 |
| Pentachlorophenol | 0.001 | .00004 | EPA 515.2, 525.2, 555, 515.1 |
| Phthalates (di[ethylhexyl]phthalate) | 0.006 | .0006 | EPA 506, 525.2 |
| Picloram | 0.5 | .0001 | EPA 515.1, 515.2, 555 |
| Polychlorinated biphenyls (PCB) | 0.0005 | .0001 | EPA 508A, 505, 508 |
| Simazine | 0.004 | .00007 | EPA 505, 507, 525.2, 508.1 |
| Toxaphene | 0.003 | .001 | EPA 505, 508, 525.2 |
| 2,3,7,8-TCDD (Dioxin) | $3 \times 10^{-8}$ | $5 \times 10^{-9}$ | EPA 1613 |
| 2,4,5-TP (Silvex) | 0.05 | .0002 | EPA 515.1, 515.2, 555 |
| Total Trihalomethanes[14] | 0.10 | .0005 | EPA 502.2, 524.2, 551 |
| **Volatile organic compounds (VOC)[15]** | | | |
| Benzene | 0.005 | .0005 | EPA 502.2, 524.2 |
| Carbon tetrachloride | 0.005 | .0005 | EPA 502.2, 524.2, 551 |
| Chlorobenzene | 0.1 | .0005 | EPA 502.2, 524.2 |
| p-Dichlorobenzene | 0.075 | .0005 | EPA 502.2, 524.2 |
| o-Dichlorobenzene | 0.6 | .0005 | EPA 502.2, 524.2 |
| 1,2-Dichloroethane | 0.005 | .0005 | EPA 502.2, 524.2 |
| 1,1-Dichloroethylene | 0.007 | .0005 | EPA 502.2, 524.2 |
| c-1,2-Dichloroethylene | 0.07 | .0005 | EPA 502.2, 524.2 |
| t-1,2-Dichloroethylene | 0.1 | .0005 | EPA 502.2, 524.2 |
| Dichloromethane | 0.005 | .0005 | EPA 502.2, 524.2 |
| 1,2-Dichloropropane | 0.005 | .0005 | EPA 502.2, 524.2 |
| Ethylbenzene | 0.7 | .0005 | EPA 502.2, 524.2 |
| Styrene | 0.1 | .0005 | EPA 502.2, 524.2 |
| Tetrachloroethylene | 0.005 | .0005 | EPA 502.2, 524.2, 551 |
| Toluene | 1 | .0005 | EPA 502.2, 524.2 |
| 1,2,4-Trichlorobenzene | 0.07 | .0005 | EPA 502.2, 524.2 |
| 1,1,1-Trichloroethane | 0.2 | .0005 | EPA 502.2, 524.2, 551 |
| 1,1,2-Trichloroethane | 0.005 | .0005 | EPA 502.2, 524.2 |
| Trichloroethylene | 0.005 | .0005 | EPA 502.2, 524.2, 551 |
| Vinyl chloride | 0.002 | .0005 | EPA 502.2, 524.2 |
| Total xylene | 10 | .0005 | EPA 502.2, 524.2 |
| **Microbiological** | | | |
| Total coliform | Zero | Zero | MPN, MF, P-A, MMO-MUG |
| Fecal coliform | Zero | Zero | MPN, MF, MMO-MUG |
| Legionella | Zero | Zero | SM$_{18}$ 9260J |

Continued on next page.

[11] Approved methods are from the CFR, 1 July, 1996
[12] MDL will vary with the particular method.
[13] EPA: Environmental Protection Agency; *SM: Standard Methods for the Examination of Water and Wastewater*, 18th Edition, 1992.
[14] These methods are also included as Parts I and II of 40 CFR 141.30, Appendix C.
[15] The required detection limits for the VOCs are found in 40 CFR 141.24.

**Table 1-2.  Primary Drinking Water Monitoring Requirements,** *continued*

| Contaminant | MCL mg/L | MDL mg/L | Method |
|---|---|---|---|
| **Microbiological,** *continued* | | | |
| Giardia lamblia | Zero | Zero | $SM_{18}$ 9711B |
| Heterotrophic Bacteria | - | - | HPC |
| Viruses | Zero | Zero | $SM_{18}$ 9510 |
| **Radiological** [16] | | | |
| Gross alpha | 15 pCi/L | 3 pCi/L | EPA 900, $SM_{18}$ 7110 |
| Gross beta | 4 millirem/yr[17] | 4 pCi/L | EPA 900.0, $SM_{18}$ 7110 |
| Radium 226 + Radium 228 | 5 pCi/L | 1 pCi/L | EPA 903.0, $SM_{18}$ 7500-Ra |
| Tritium | 20,000 pCi/L | 1000 pCi/L | EPA 906.0, $SM_{18}$ 7500-$^{3}$H |
| Strontium 90 | 8 pCi/L | 2 pCi/L | EPA 905.0, $SM_{18}$ 7500-Sr |
| Strontium 89 | 4 millirem/yr[17] | 10 pCi/L | EPA 905.0, $SM_{18}$ 7500-Sr |
| Iodine 131 | 4 millirem/yr[17] | 1 pCi/L | EPA 902.0, $SM_{18}$ 7500-I |
| Cesium 134 | 4 millirem/yr[17] | 10 pCi/L | EPA 901.0, $SM_{18}$ 7500-Cs |

**Table 1-3.  Secondary Drinking Water Monitoring Requirements**

| Contaminant | Level mg/L | Method[18] |
|---|---|---|
| Aluminum | 0.05 to 0.2 | EPA 200.7, 200.8, 202.1, 202.2, 200.9 |
| Chloride | 250 | $SM_{14}$ 408C |
| Color | 15 color units | EPA 110.2 |
| Copper | 1.0 | EPA 200.7, 200.8, 200.9, 220.1, 220.2 |
| Corrosivity | Noncorrosive | $SM_{14}$ 203 |
| Fluoride | 2.0 | EPA 340.1, 340.2, 340.3 |
| Foaming agents | 0.5 | EPA 425.1 |
| Iron | 0.3 | EPA 200.7, 236.1, 236.2 |
| Manganese | 0.05 | EPA 200.7, 243.1, 243.2 |
| Odor | 3 TON | EPA 140.1 |
| pH | 6.5-8.5 | EPA 150.1 |
| Silver | 0.1 | EPA 200.7, 200.8, 200.9, 272.1, 272.2 |
| Sulfate | 250 | EPA 375.4 |
| Total dissolved solids (TDS) | 500 | EPA 160.1 |
| Zinc | 5 | EPA 200.7, 289.1 |

---

[16]  EPA methods are found in *Prescribed Procedures for Measurement of Radioactivity in Drinking Water*, EPA-600/4-80-032, USEPA EMSL Cincinnati, OH.  Other radiological methods were approved for use by EPA on 5 March, 1997 in *Federal Register* 62(43):10167-10174.

[17]  The 4 millirem/year exposure MCL is based upon consumption of 2 L/day of water.

[18]  EPA: Environmental Protection Agency; *SM: Standard Methods for the Examination of Water and Wastewater*, 18th Edition, 1992.

## b. CWA – Clean Water Act

Last amended in 1987, the Act provides for grants to POTW (publicly owned treatment works) to build and upgrade treatment facilities, and establishes a permitting system NPDES (National Pollutant Discharge Elimination System), for discharge of water to natural water bodies by industry and municipalities. Over two thirds of the states have accepted primary responsibility for administration of the Act. The Act also mandates the EPA to collect data about environmental pollutants and make decisions about treatment based on water quality goals and best available technology (BAT). The following precepts are established in the Act and its amendments:

1. No one has the right to pollute the navigable waters of the United States.
2. Permits shall limit the composition of a discharge and the concentrations of pollutants in it.
3. Some permit conditions require the best controls technology can produce, regardless of the receiving water's ability to purify itself naturally.
4. Any limits or control higher than the minimum federal requirements must be based on receiving water quality.

Wastewater effluents are monitored through the NPDES, quite probably the number one money maker for commercial analytical laboratories. Each industry and wastewater treatment facility (Publicly Owned Treatment Works, POTW) that directly discharges into a receiving stream or river has either a Federal or State NPDES permit. Industries that discharge in a municipality to a sewer system are permitted through the wastewater treatment plant at the end of the sewer system, and the POTW holds the Federal or State permit. For industries not specifically listed in the CFR, the federal and state EPAs set allowable limits for contaminant levels in wastewaters discharged by the particular plant, based on submitted analysis of the wastewaters generated by the commercial operation. A permit is given to the industrial location allowing release of certain maximum limits of target parameters based on either the limits in 40 CFR Subchapter N or on historical records and local environmental concerns, and specifying regular analysis for target analytes in the waste stream to back-up the allowable limits. Often a time-frame for collection and analysis of wastewater samples is specified, which may or may not coincide with actual releases of contaminants. The approved methods of analysis along with approved sampling containers, preservatives, and holding times are found in 40 CFR 136.3 (the most current version, 1 July, 1996, is reproduced in Appendix I of this book). Consult the most recent edition for specific approved methods as these do change over time. Three classes of pollutants are recognized.

1) Conventional Pollutants: BOD, COD, pH, total suspended solids, bacteria, oil & grease, and fecal coliforms.
2) Non-conventional Pollutants: nitrogen, phosphorous, ammonia and other pollutants that may endanger water quality. Not listed as toxic pollutants, most are what are considered nutrients.
3) Toxic Pollutants: The so-called 129 priority pollutants are listed in Table 1-4.

The origin of the toxic pollutant list is a Committee Report from the House Committee of Public Works and Transportation, which was adopted into the CWA by specific reference in section 301(a)(1) of the Act. The list is transcribed in 40 CFR 401.15 and is reproduced in Table 1-4. Quality control check samples (DMR, discharge monitoring report) are issued to facilities holding Federal or State NPDES permits for analysis by the contracted laboratories on an annual basis to back-up the analytical results submitted by the plant.

**Table 1-4.  Toxic Pollutant list from 40 CFR 401.15**

| Analyte |
|---|
| 1.   Acenaphthene |
| 2.   Acrolein |
| 3.   Acrylonitrile |
| 4.   Aldrin/Dieldrin |
| 5.   Antimony and compounds |
| 6.   Arsenic and compounds |
| 7.   Asbestos |
| 8.   Benzene |
| 9.   Benzidine |
| 10.  Beryllium and compounds |
| 11.  Cadmium and compounds |
| 12.  Carbon tetrachloride |
| 13.  Chlordane (technical mixture and metabolites) |
| 14.  Chlorinated benzenes (other than dichlorobenzenes) |
| 15.  Chlorinated ethanes (including 1,2-dichloroethane, 1,1,1-trichloroethane and hexachloroethane) |
| 16.  Chloroalkyl ethers (chloroethyl and mixed ethers) |
| 17.  Chlorinated naphthalene |
| 18.  Chlorinated phenols (other than those listed elsewhere; includes trichlorophenols and chlorinated cresols) |
| 19.  Chloroform |
| 20.  2-Chlorophenol |
| 21.  Chromium and compounds |
| 22.  Copper and compounds |
| 23.  Cyanides |
| 24.  DDT and metabolites |
| 25.  Dichlorobenzenes (1,2-, 1,3-, and 1,4-dichlorobenzenes) |
| 26.  Dichlorobenzidine |
| 27.  Dichloroethylenes (1,1- and 1,2-dichloroethylene) |
| 28.  2,4-Dichlorophenol |
| 29.  Dichloropropane and dichloropropene |
| 30.  2,4-Dimethylphenol |
| 31.  Dinitrotoluene |
| 32.  Diphenylhydrazine |
| 33.  Endosulfan and metabolites |
| 34.  Endrin and metabolites |
| 35.  Ethylbenzene |
| 36.  Fluoranthene |
| 37.  Haloethers (other than those listed elsewhere; includes chlorophenylphenyl ethers, bromophenyl-phenyl ether, bis(dichloroisopropyl) ether, bis(chloroethoxy) methane and polychlorinated diphenyl ethers |

Continued on next page.

**Table 1-4. Toxic Pollutant list from 40 CFR 401.15,** *continued*

| Analyte |
|---|
| 38. Halomethanes (other than those listed elsewhere; includes methylene chloride, methyl chloride, methyl bromide, bromoform, dichlorobromomethane, trichlorofluoromethane and dichlorodifluoromethane) |
| 39. Heptachlor and metabolites |
| 40. Hexachlorobutadiene |
| 41. Hexachlorocyclohexane |
| 42. Hexachlorocyclopentadiene |
| 43. Isophorone |
| 44. Lead and compounds |
| 45. Mercury and compounds |
| 46. Naphthalene |
| 47. Nickel and compounds |
| 48. Nitrobenzene |
| 49. Nitrophenols (includes 2,4-dinitrophenol, dinitrocresol) |
| 51. Pentachlorophenol |
| 52. Phenol |
| 53. Phthalate esters |
| 54. Polychlorinated biphenyls (PCBs) chrysenes, dibenzoanthracenes and indenopyrenes) |
| 56. Selenium and compounds |
| 57. Silver and compounds |
| 58. 2,3,7,8-Tetrachlorodibenzo-*p*-dioxin (TCDD) |
| 59. Tetrachloroethylene |
| 60. Thallium and compounds |
| 61. Toluene |
| 62. Toxaphene |
| 63. Trichloroethylene |
| 64. Vinyl chloride |
| 65. Zinc and compounds |

A number of states have accepted primacy from EPA for administration of NPDES permits. In general the state is required to establish permit limits that would be at least as stringent as those of the federal government. States often establish priority pollutant lists based on the EPA lists and add required analysis detection limits as a structure within which monitoring must be conducted by the reporting facility. As Table 1-5 indicates, there can be considerable variation between states in their priority pollutant lists. A study was conducted by the General Accounting Office in 1995 in response to a specific request by Senator Max Baucus for information concerning State differences in permitting, the causes of the differences and how EPA was overseeing the program. Although the study limited itself to examination of the permitting of five metals (cadmium, copper, lead, mercury and zinc) in municipal wastetater treatment facilities, the results were interesting. In general it was found that "in some states, the permitting authorities consistently established numeric limits on the discharges, while in other states, the authorities consistently required monitoring. In some states no controls were imposed. In addition, the numeric discharge limits for specific pollutants differed from state to state and even within the same state for facilities of similar capacity."[19]  What is allowable in one state can and often is specifically prohibited in another state.

In March, 1994, EPA issued a draft memorandum that set forth guidelines for establishment of effluent limits below analytical detection limits that are achievable using current technology.  Some states have jumped on this program and have issued modified permit limits to affected industries.  Other states have taken a wait-and-see attitude.

**Table 1-5.    Priority Pollutant lists and required reportable detection limits for monitoring**

| Parameter | GA[20] DL ug/L | SC[21] DL ug/L | NC[22] DL ug/L |
|---|---|---|---|
| Acrolein | 50 | - | 100 |
| Acrylonitrile | 50 | - | 100 |
| Benzene | 2 | 2 | 5 |
| Bromodichloromethane | 10 | 2 | 5 |
| Bromoform | 10 | 2 | 5 |
| Bromomethane | 10 | 2 | 10 |
| Carbon tetrachloride | 2 | 2 | 5 |
| Chlorobenzene | 10 | 2 | 6 |
| Chloroethane | 5 | 2 | 10 |
| 2-Chloroethylvinyl ether | 10 | 2 | 10 |
| Chloroform | 2 | 2 | 5 |
| Chloromethane | 10 | 2 | 10 |
| Dibromochloromethane | 10 | 2 | 5 |
| 1,1-Dichloroethane | 2 | 2 | 5 |
| 1,2-Dichloroethane | 2 | 2 | 5 |
| 1,1-Dichloroethylene | 2 | 2 | 5 |
| trans-1,2-Dichloroethylene | 2 | 2 | 5 |
| 1,2-Dichloropropane | 2 | 2 | 6 |
| cis-1,3-Dichloropropene | 2 | 2 | 5 |
| trans-1,3-Dichloropropene | 2 | 2 | 5 |
| Ethylbenzene | 2 | 2 | 8 |
| Methylene chloride | 10 | 2 | 5 |
| 1,1,2,2-Tetrachloroethane | 2 | 2 | 7 |
| Tetrachloroethylene | 2 | 2 | 5 |
| Toluene | 2 | 2 | 6 |
| 1,1,1-Trichloroethane | 2 | 2 | 5 |
| 1,1,2-Trichloroethane | 2 | 2 | 5 |
| Trichloroethylene | 2 | 2 | 5 |
| Trichlorofluoromethane | - | 2 | 10 |
| Vinyl chloride | 10 | 2 | 10 |
| 4-Chloro-3-methylphenol | 10 | 10 | 10 |
| 2-Chlorophenol | 10 | 10 | 10 |
| 2,4-Dichlorophenol | 10 | 10 | 10 |

Continued on next page.

---

[19]  United States General Accounting Office, January, 1996.  Water pollution:  Differences among the states in issuing permits limiting the discharge of pollutants.  GAO/RCED-96-42.

[20]  GA EPD 13 January, 1994.

[21]  SC DEHC January, 1994.

[22]  NC DEHNR June, 1990.

**Table 1-5.** **Priority Pollutant lists and required reportable detection limits for monitoring,** *continued*

| Parameter | GA[23] DL ug/L | SC[24] DL ug/L | NC[25] DL ug/L |
|---|---|---|---|
| 2,4-Dimethylphenol | 10 | 10 | 10 |
| 2,4-Dinitrophenol | 50 | - | 50 |
| 2-Methyl-4,6-dinitrophenol | 50 | 10 | 50 |
| 2-Nitrophenol | 50 | 10 | 10 |
| 4-Nitrophenol | 50 | 10 | 50 |
| Pentachlorophenol | 20 | 10 | 50 |
| Phenol | 10 | 10 | 10 |
| 2,4,6-Trichlorophenol | 10 | 10 | 10 |
| Acenaphthene | 10 | 10 | 10 |
| Acenaphthylene | 10 | 10 | 10 |
| Anthracene | 10 | 10 | 10 |
| Benzidine | 80 | - | 50 |
| Benzo(a)anthracene | 10 | 10 | 10 |
| Benzo(a)pyrene | 10 | 10 | 10 |
| Benzo(b)fluoranthene | 10 | 10 | 10 |
| Benzo(ghi)perylene | 10 | 10 | 10 |
| Benzo(k)fluoranthene | 10 | 10 | 10 |
| Bis(2-chloroethoxy)methane | 10 | 10 | 10 |
| Bis(2-chloroethyl)ether | 10 | 10 | 10 |
| Bis(2-chloroisopropyl)ether | 10 | 10 | 10 |
| Bis(2-ethylhexyl)phthalate | 10 | 10 | 10 |
| 4-Bromophenylphenyl ether | 10 | 10 | 10 |
| Benzylbutylphthalate | 10 | 10 | 10 |
| 2-Chloronaphthalene | 10 | 10 | 10 |
| 4-Chlorophenylphenyl ether | 10 | 10 | 10 |
| Chrysene | 10 | 10 | 10 |
| Dibenzo(ah)anthracene | 10 | 10 | 10 |
| 1,2-Dichlorobenzene | 10 | 10 | 10 |
| 1,3-Dichlorobenzene | 10 | 10 | 10 |
| 1,4-Dichlorobenzene | 10 | 10 | 10 |
| 3,3'-Dichlorobenzidine | 20 | 10 | 20 |
| Diethylphthalate | 10 | 10 | 10 |
| Dimethylphthalate | 10 | 10 | 10 |
| Di-n-butylphthalate | 10 | 10 | 10 |
| 2,4-Dinitrotoluene | 20 | 10 | 10 |
| 2,6-Dinitrotoluene | 20 | 10 | 10 |
| Di-n-octylphthalate | 10 | 10 | 10 |
| 1,2-Diphenylhydrazine | 10 | - | 10 |
| Fluoranthene | 10 | 10 | 10 |
| Fluorene | 10 | 10 | 10 |
| Hexachlorobenzene | 10 | 10 | 10 |
| Hexachlorobutadiene | 10 | 10 | 10 |
| Hexachlorocyclopentadiene | 10 | 10 | 10 |

Continued on next page.

---

[23] GA EPD 13 January, 1994.
[24] SC DEHC January, 1994.
[25] NC DEHNR June, 1990.

**Table 1-5.** **Priority Pollutant lists and required reportable detection limits for monitoring,** *continued*

| Parameter | GA[26] DL ug/L | SC[27] DL ug/L | NC[28] DL ug/L |
|---|---|---|---|
| Hexachloroethane | 2 | 10 | 10 |
| Indeno(123-cd)pyrene | 10 | 10 | 10 |
| Isophorone | 10 | 10 | 10 |
| Naphthalene | 10 | 10 | 10 |
| Nitrobenzene | 10 | 10 | 10 |
| N-nitrosodimethylamine | 10 | 10 | 10 |
| N-nitrosodi-n-propylamine | 10 | 10 | 10 |
| N-nitrosodiphenylamine | 10 | 10 | 10 |
| Phenanthrene | 10 | 10 | 10 |
| Pyrene | 10 | 10 | 10 |
| 1,2,4-Trichlorobenzene | 10 | 10 | 10 |
| Aldrin | 0.1 | 0.05 | 0.05 |
| α-BHC | 0.1 | 0.05 | 0.05 |
| β-BHC | 0.1 | 0.05 | 0.05 |
| δ-BHC | 0.1 | 0.05 | 0.1 |
| γ-BHC (Lindane) | 0.1 | 0.05 | 0.05 |
| Chlordane | 0.5 | 0.05 | 0.2 |
| 4,4'-DDD | 0.2 | 0.05 | 0.1 |
| 4,4'-DDE | 0.2 | 0.05 | 0.1 |
| 4,4'-DDT | 0.2 | 0.05 | 0.1 |
| Dieldrin | 0.1 | 0.05 | 0.02 |
| Endosulfan I | 0.5 | 0.05 | 0.1 |
| Endosulfan II | 0.5 | 0.05 | 0.1 |
| Endosulfan sulfate | 0.5 | 0.05 | 0.7 |
| Endrin | 0.2 | 0.05 | 0.06 |
| Endrin aldehyde | 0.2 | 0.05 | 0.2 |
| Heptachlor | 0.1 | 0.05 | 0.05 |
| Heptachlor epoxide | 0.1 | 0.05 | 0.8 |
| Methoxychlor | 0.3 | 0.05 | 0.5 |
| Mirex | - | - | 0.2 |
| Toxaphene | 2 | 0.05 | 2.4 |
| PCB 1016 | 1 | 0.5 | 0.5 |
| PCB 1221 | 1 | 0.5 | 0.5 |
| PCB 1232 | 1 | 0.5 | 0.5 |
| PCB 1242 | 1 | 0.5 | 0.5 |
| PCB 1248 | 1 | 0.5 | 0.5 |
| PCB 1254 | 1 | 0.5 | 1.0 |
| PCB 1260 | 1 | 0.5 | 1.0 |
| Demeton | - | 0.1 | 2.5 |
| Parathion (ethyl) | - | 0.1 | 0.6 |
| 2,4-D | 5 | 0.05 | 12 |
| Silvex | 10 | 0.025 | 2 |
| 2,4,5-T | - | 0.025 | 2 |

Continued on next page.

---

[26] GA EPD 13 January, 1994.
[27] SC DEHC January, 1994.
[28] NC DEHNR June, 1990.

**Table 1-5. Priority Pollutant lists and required reportable detection limits for monitoring,** *continued*

| Parameter | GA[29] DL ug/L | SC[30] DL ug/L | NC[31] DL ug/L |
|---|---|---|---|
| Aluminum | - | 50 | 50 |
| Antimony | 50 | 50 | 50 |
| Arsenic | 30 | 5 | 10 |
| Barium | - | 50 | 500 |
| Beryllium | 10 | 3 | 25 |
| Cadmium | 10 | 10 | 2 |
| Total Chromium | 10 | 10 | 5 |
| Hexavalent Chromium | 10 | - | - |
| Copper | 20 | 10 | 2 |
| Lead | 25 | 50 | 10 |
| Mercury | 0.5 | 0.2 | 0.2 |
| Nickel | 20 | 20 | 10 |
| Selenium | 40 | 5 | 5 |
| Silver | 10 | 30 | 5 |
| Thallium | 50 | 500 | - |
| Zinc | 20 | 10 | 10 |
| Chloride | - | 1000 | 1000 |
| Cyanide | 25 | 10 | 20 |
| Fluoride | - | 100 | 100 |

Subchapter N, 40 CFR, also lists many specific types of industries that have effluent guidelines set by EPA. The list of affected industries is presented in Table 1-6 along with an indication of the class of pollutants specified.

**Table 1-6. Industries with 40 CFR wastewater effluent guidelines**

| Part | Industry Category | Pollutant Type |
|---|---|---|
| 405 | Dairy products processing | Conventional |
| 406 | Grain mills | Conventional |
| 407 | Canned and preserved fruits and vegetables processing | Conventional |
| 408 | Canned and preserved seafood processing | Conventional |
| 409 | Sugar processing | Conventional |
| 410 | Textile mills | Conventional and toxic |
| 411 | Cement manufacturing | Conventional |
| 412 | Feedlots | Conventional |
| 413 | Electroplating | Conventional and toxic |
| 414 | Organic chemicals, plastics and synthetic fibers | Conventional and toxic |
| 415 | Inorganic chemicals manufacturing | Conventional and toxic |
| 417 | Soap and detergent manufacturing | Conventional and surfactants |
| 418 | Fertilizer manufacturing | Conventional and non-conventional |

Continued on next page.

---

[29] GA EPD 13 January, 1994.
[30] SC DEHC January, 1994.
[31] NC DEHNR June, 1990.

**Table 1-6.   Industries with 40 CFR wastewater effluent guidelines,** *continued*

| Part | Industry Category | Pollutant Type |
|------|-------------------|----------------|
| 419 | Petroleum refining | Conventional, non-conventional and toxic |
| 420 | Iron and steel manufacturing | Conventional, non-conventional and toxic |
| 421 | Nonferrous metal manufacturing | Conventional and toxic |
| 422 | Phosphate manufacturing | Conventional and non-conventional |
| 423 | Steam electric power generating | Conventional and toxic |
| 424 | Ferroalloy manufacturing | Conventional and toxic |
| 425 | Leather tanning and finishing | Conventional and toxic |
| 426 | Glass manufacturing | Conventional and toxic |
| 427 | Asbestos manufacturing | Conventional and toxic |
| 428 | Rubber manufacturing | Conventional and toxic |
| 429 | Timber products processing | Conventional and toxic |
| 430 | Pulp, paper and paperboard | Conventional and toxic |
| 431 | The builder's paper and board mills | Conventional and toxic |
| 432 | Meat products | Conventional and toxic |
| 433 | Metal finishing | Conventional and toxic |
| 434 | Coal mining | Conventional and toxic |
| 435 | Oil and gas extraction | Conventional and toxic |
| 436 | Mineral mining and processing | Conventional and toxic |
| 439 | Pharmaceutical manufacturing | Conventional and toxic |
| 440 | Ore mining and dressing | Conventional and toxic |
| 443 | Paving and roof materials (tars and asphalt) | Conventional and toxic |
| 446 | Paint formulating | Conventional and toxic |
| 447 | Ink formulating | Conventional and toxic |
| 454 | Gum and wood chemicals manufacturing | Conventional and toxic |
| 455 | Pesticide chemicals | Conventional and toxic |
| 457 | Explosives manufacturing | Conventional and toxic |
| 458 | Carbon black manufacturing | Conventional and toxic |
| 459 | Photographic | Conventional and toxic |
| 460 | Hospitals | Conventional and toxic |
| 461 | Battery manufacturing | Conventional and toxic |
| 463 | Plastics molding and forming | Conventional and toxic |
| 464 | Metal molding and casting | Conventional and toxic |
| 465 | Coil coating | Conventional and toxic |
| 466 | Porcelain enameling | Conventional and toxic |
| 467 | Aluminum forming | Conventional and toxic |
| 468 | Copper forming | Conventional and toxic |
| 469 | Electrical and electrical components | Conventional and toxic |
| 471 | Nonferrous metals forming and metal powders | Conventional and toxic |

The broad industrial categories are further broken down into Subpart groups. An example is the Organic Chemicals, Plastics and Synthetic Fibers (OCPSF) industry as indicated in Table 1-7. An example of a specific guideline is presented for the direct discharge point sources that do not use end-of-pipe biological treatment under the OCPSF category (Subpart J), Table 1-8.

**Table 1-7. Subpart groups for the OCPSF industry**

| Subpart | Industry |
|---|---|
| B | Rayon fibers |
| C | Other fibers |
| D | Thermoplastic resins |
| E | Thermosetting resins |
| F | Commodity organic chemicals |
| G | Bulk organic chemicals |
| H | Specialty organic chemicals |
| I | Direct discharge point sources that use end-of-pipe biological treatment |
| J | Direct discharge point sources that do not use end-of-pipe biological treatment |
| K | Indirect discharge point source |

**Table 1-8. Toxic Pollutant Effluent Guideline Example, Subpart J 40 CFR 414.101, Organic Chemicals, Plastics and Synthetic Fibers[32], 9 July 1993**

| Effluent Characteristic | Maximum for any one day | Maximum for monthly average |
|---|---|---|
| Acenaphthene | 47 | 19 |
| Acenaphthylene | 47 | 19 |
| Acrylonitrile | 232 | 94 |
| Anthracene | 47 | 19 |
| Benzene | 134 | 57 |
| Benzo(a)anthracene | 47 | 19 |
| Benzo(b)fluoranthene | 48 | 20 |
| Benzo(k)fluoranthene | 47 | 19 |
| Benzo(a)pyrene | 48 | 20 |
| Bis(2-ethylhexyl)phthalate | 258 | 95 |
| Carbon tetrachloride | 380 | 142 |
| Chlorobenzene | 380 | 142 |
| Chloroethane | 295 | 110 |
| Chloroform | 325 | 111 |
| Chrysene | 47 | 19 |
| Di-n-butylphthalate | 43 | 20 |
| 1,2-Dichlorobenzene | 794 | 196 |
| 1,3-Dichlorobenzene | 380 | 142 |
| 1,4-Dichlorobenzene | 380 | 142 |
| 1,1-Dichloroethane | 59 | 22 |
| 1,2-Dichloroethane | 574 | 180 |
| 1,1-Dichloroethylene | 60 | 22 |
| 1,2-*trans*-Dichloroethylene | 66 | 25 |
| 1,2-Dichloropropane | 794 | 196 |
| 1,3-Dichloropropylene | 794 | 196 |
| Diethylphthalate | 113 | 46 |

Continued on next page.

---

[32] All units are micrograms per liter except pH.

**Table 1-8.** **Toxic Pollutant Effluent Guideline Example, Subpart J 40 CFR 414.101, Organic Chemicals, Plastics and Synthetic Fibers**[33], **9 July 1993,** *continued*

| Effluent Characteristic | Maximum for any one day | Maximum for monthly average |
|---|---|---|
| 2,4-Dimethylphenol | 47 | 19 |
| Dimethylphthalate | 47 | 19 |
| 4,6-Dinitro-o-cresol | 277 | 78 |
| 2,4-Dinitrophenol | 4291 | 1207 |
| Ethylbenzene | 380 | 142 |
| Fluoranthene | 54 | 22 |
| Fluorene | 47 | 19 |
| Hexachlorobenzene | 794 | 196 |
| Hexachlorobutadiene | 380 | 142 |
| Hexachloroethane | 794 | 196 |
| Methyl chloride | 295 | 110 |
| Methylene chloride | 170 | 36 |
| Naphthalene | 47 | 19 |
| Nitrobenzene | 6402 | 2237 |
| 2-Nitrophenol | 231 | 65 |
| 4-Nitrophenol | 576 | 162 |
| Phenanthrene | 47 | 19 |
| Phenol | 47 | 19 |
| Pyrene | 48 | 20 |
| Tetrachloroethylene | 164 | 52 |
| Toluene | 74 | 28 |
| Total chromium | 2770 | 1110 |
| Total copper | 3380 | 1450 |
| Total cyanide | 1200 | 420 |
| Total lead | 690 | 320 |
| Total nickel | 3980 | 1690 |
| Total zinc | 2610 | 1050 |
| 1,2,4-Trichlorobenzene | 794 | 196 |
| 1,1,1-Trichloroethane | 59 | 22 |
| 1,1,2-Tichloroethane | 127 | 32 |
| Trichloroethylene | 69 | 26 |
| Vinyl chloride | 172 | 97 |

Another permitting program is the stormwater run-off. Target analytes under this program are listed in 40 CFR 122, Appendix D. EPA estimates that 30% of the pollution entering the nation's water systems comes from run-off from agriculture, large industry, and landfills (so called non-point sources).

An example of a program that falls under two sets of regulations is the Standards for the Use or Disposal of Sewage Sludge, 40 CFR 503. The regulation provides for incineration, land application, surface disposal and pathogen and vector attraction reduction, and is authorized jointly under the CWA and RCRA. The analytical requirements are for trace metals analysis on the chemistry side plus a variety of microbiological procedures.

---

[33] All units are micrograms per liter except pH.

The metals are tested by SW-846 methods. The biological analyses required include fecal coliform and *Salmonella* sp. bacteria, enteric viruses, and helminth ova. Although the fecal coliform assays are simple extensions of procedures routinely performed in environmental laboratories, the other three tests are laborious and expensive. To assist laboratories and treatment facilities in coming into compliance with these regulations, EPA has published "Environmental Regulations and Technology Control of Pathogens and Vector Attraction in Sewage Sludge" (EPA/625/R-92/013, December, 1992), commonly called the "White House Manual" due to the picture on the front cover. Prior to the promulgation of the 503 regulations EPA conducted the National Sewage Sludge Survey. The contents of the manual of analytical methods[34], which was a part of the survey, are listed in the Table. An additional relevant-methods manual is POTW *Sludge Sampling and Analysis Guidance Document*, USEPA Office of Water, August, 1989.

**Table 1-9. Contents of Analytical Methods for the National Sewage Sludge Survey**

| Method | Title |
|--------|-------|
| 1624C | Volatile organic compounds by isotopic dilution GCMS |
| 1625C | Semivolatile organic compounds by isotopic dilution GCMS |
| 1618 | Organo-halide pesticides, organo-phosphorous pesticides and phenoxy-acid herbicides by wide bore capillary column gas chromatography with selective detectors |
| 1613 | Tetra- through octa- chlorinated dioxines and furans by isotope dilution HRGC/HRMS |
| 1620 | Metals by inductively coupled plasma atomic emission spectroscopy and atomic absorption spectrometry |
| 160.3 | Residue, total, gravimetric, dried at 103-105 °C |
| 335.2 | Cyanide, total titrimetric, spectrophotometric |
| 340.2 | Fluoride potentiometric, ion selective electrode |
| 351.3 | Nitrogen, Kjeldahl, total, colorimetric; titrimetric; potentiometric |
| 353.2 | Nitrogen, nitrate-nitrite, colorimetric, automated cadmium reduction |
| 365.2 | Phosphorous, all forms, colorimetric, ascorbic acid single reagent |

Industries that discharge their wastewater into a sanitary sewer system that is collected for treatment at a POTW, may be subject to permitting under the Industrial Pretreatment program. If it is accepted that there are variations and inconsistencies among the states in NPDES permits, then it should be expected that an even greater degree of chaos reigns in industrial pretreatment permits. EPA has published a large number of documents related to pretreatment permits, and compliance monitoring[35]. If a municipality implements a pretreatment program, complete with periodic duplicate sampling and analysis to verify industrial self-monitoring compliance, this places an extra burden on the municipal lab. On the one hand the lab is a generator of self-monitoring compliance data to the regulatory agency that issued the POTW NPDES permit, while on the other hand, the lab is also the enforcement lab for the municipality's pretreatment program. Although it might be expected that placing a municipal lab in a position of preparing legally defensible data to be used in enforcement actions would serve to increase the lab's performance and adherence to approved method protocols,

---

[34] *Analytical Methods for the National Sewage Sludge Survey*, EPA Office of Water (WH-585), September, 1990.

[35] EPA, 1994. Industrial user inspection and sampling manual for POTW's. EPA 831-B-94-001, April, 1994

this has not always been the case. The lack of legally suitable data for enforcement actions is the soft spot in most pretreatment programs.

The development of the regulatory structure enabling enforcement of the provisions of the Clean Water Act has concentrated upon a permiting and compliance monitoring system for specific contaminants known to be pollutants that have a history of degrading the environment. Whole effluent toxicity (WET) has been used with increasing frequency to monitor effluents, but it still is limited to the examination of the specific effects on one particular organism. However, the chemical cleanliness of the receiving water is but one measure of man's impact upon the environment. Within the EPA and a few of the states a move has been made toward examination of the overall biological effect of effluents on nature. These examinations have led to the concept of "biocriteria" that serve to measure the greater overall picture of biological quality. Since biological quality is a relative term, and biocriteria is formulated as a quantitative measure, the evaluation is performed on the receiving water body and a closely related environ that is minimally affected by man-derived influences. The identified variables of biological quality are:

- Water quality - Temperature, turbidity, chemical pollutants
- Habitat structure - Substrate type, water depth and velocity, physical complexity of the habitat
- Flow regime - Water volume and temporal distribution of flows
- Energy source - Type, amount and seasonal variability of food resources
- Biotic interactions - Competition, predation, disease, parasitism and mutalism of organisms.

Insofar as assessment of the biological quality of the water is concerned, four areas of analysis have been identified[36]:

- Community structure - Species richness, relative abundances and extent to which one or a few species dominates
- Taxonomic composition - Identification of the resident species
- Individual organism condition - Health evaluation of individuals of the resident species
- Biological processes - Rates of biological activities/interactions among the resident species.

Five groups of organisms are recognized as important participants in the biological system. *Periphyton* are the algae and bacterial inhabitants of the water. *Macrophytes* are the larger plants in the system. *Macroinvertebrates* consist of the visible crustaceans, molluscs, insects, nematodes and other non-vertebrate inhabitants. *Fish* and *wildlife* (mammals, birds, reptiles and amphibians) are the vertebrate groups. Sampling methods for inventory and census are fairly well established.

## 4. FIFRA – Federal Insecticide, Fungicide, and Rodenticide Act

Administered by EPA, this regulation requires the EPA to oversee the manufacture and use of "-icides" in the US. Most commercial environmental laboratories have little to no contact with the provisions detailed under this legislation. Various facets of the act:

---

[36] Biological Criteria: Technical Guidance for Streams and Small Rivers, May 1996. USEPA Office of Water 822-B-96-001.

- Authorize the EPA to collect risk assessment data on the manufacture, use and disposal of the substances;
- Require submission from the manufacturer of extensive health and environmental fate data resulting from the use of the compounds;
- Require analytical methodologies to be submitted for the analysis of residues in air, soil, and water, resulting from the normal use or possible misuse of the substances; and,
- Specify labeling and warning requirements for sale of the product.

Under FIFRA EPA wrote the Good Laboratory Practice Standards (40 CFR 160) as a means of ensuring comparable quality data on all contracted laboratory studies, generating data about the biological effects on non-target organisms of proposed materials to be registered as pesticides. These standards have been defacto generalized to the whole of the environmental analysis industry and should be consulted as a guide to how the laboratory should organize and conduct business.

## 5. FDCA – Food, Drug, and Cosmetic Act

Administered by the Food and Drug Administration (FDA), this act governs all chemicals labeled as, or considered to be, foods, food additives, vitamins, drugs (both over-the-counter and prescription) and cosmetics. By legislative fiat these substances and mixtures are effectively removed from EPA oversight. However the wastes and by-products generated from the manufacture of these substances are controlled by EPA.

## 6. TSCA – Toxic Substances Control Act

Begining in 1976 with the enactment of TSCA, the EPA is given the authority to gather basic information on the toxicity and hazardous nature of individual chemicals. The heart of the TSCA is the list of compounds already examined by the EPA. New compounds are defined as any compound not on the list. The EPA requires chemical producers to supply information dealing with risk assesment of proposed products 90 days before proposed manufacture or import. Proposed products are defined as either new chemicals or new uses for listed chemicals. Small volume chemicals used for research and development are exempted, as are specific groups of chemicals and substances such as drugs, cosmetics, food, food additives, pesticides, tobacco products, radioactive and nuclear substances, and firearms. These latter groups are controlled under other legislation.

The information required for a new or existing compound under TSCA includes data from chemical fate testing (40 CFR 796), environmental effects testing (40 CFR 797) and health effects testing (40 CFR 798). The appropriate CFR parts have detailed direc-tions for the testing procedures, listed in Table 1-10. As is apparent from examination of the procedures in the Table, this legislation has very little to do with the normal workload of environmental analytical laboratories. In general, very specialized laboratories provide the test results.

Laboratories performing TSCA studies are required to comply with Good Laboratory Practice Standards (40 CFR 792). These Standards are somewhat similar to those discussed under FIFRA (above), however in the specifics they are exactly applicable only to TSCA mandated studies

### Table 1-10. Test Procedures in 40 CFR for data supporting TSCA submissions

| Part | Title |
|------|-------|
| **Provisional Test Guidelines** | |
| 795.45 | Inherent biogradability: Modified SCAS test for chemical substances that are water insoluble or water insoluble and volatile |
| 795.54 | Anaerobic microbiological transformation rate data for chemicals in the subsurface environment |
| 795.70 | Indirect photolysis screening test: Sunlight photolysis in waters containing dissolved humic substances |
| 795.120 | Gammarid acute toxicity test |
| 795.223 | Pharmacokinetic test |
| 795.225 | Dermal pharmocokinetics of DGBE and DGBA |
| 795.228 | Oral/dermal pharmacokinetics |
| 795.230 | Oral and inhalation pharmacokinetic test |
| 795.231 | Pharmacokinetics of isopropanal |
| 795.232 | Inhalation and dermal pharmacokinetics of commercial hexane |
| 795.235 | Toxicokinetic test |
| 795.250 | Developmental neurotoxicity screen |
| 795.260 | Subchronic oral toxicity test |
| 795.285 | Morphologic transformation of cells in culture |
| **Chemical Fate Testing Guidelines** | |
| 796.1050 | Absorption in aqueous solution: Ultraviolet/visible spectra |
| 796.1220 | Boiling point/boiling range |
| 796.1370 | Dissociation constants in water |
| 796.1520 | Particle size distribution/fiber length and diameter distributions |
| 796.1550 | Partition coefficient (n-octanol/water) |
| 796.1570 | Partition coefficient (n-octanol/water) - Estimation by liquid chromatography |
| 796.1720 | Octanol/water partition coefficient, generator column method |
| 796.1840 | Water solubility |
| 796.1860 | Water solubility (generator column method) |
| 796.1950 | Vapor pressure |
| 796.2700 | Soil thin layer chromatography |
| 796.2750 | Sediment and soil adsorption isotherm |
| 796.3100 | Aerobic aquatic biodegradation |
| 796.3140 | Anaerobic biodegradability of organic chemicals |
| 796.3180 | Ready biodegradability: Modified AFNOR test |
| 796.3200 | Ready biodegradability: Closed bottle test |
| 796.3220 | Ready biodegradability: Modified MITI test (I) |
| 796.3240 | Ready biodegradability: Modified OECD screening test |
| 796.3260 | Ready biodegradability: Modified Sturm test |
| 796.3300 | Simulation test - aerobic sewage treatment: Coupled units test |
| 796.3340 | Inherent biodegradability: Modified SCAS test |
| 796.3360 | Inherent biodegradability: Modified Zahn-Wellens test |
| 796.3400 | Inherent biodegradability in soil |

Continued on next page.

**Table 1-10.** **Test Procedures in 40 CFR for data supporting TSCA submissions,** *continued*

| Part | Title |
|------|-------|
| **Chemical Fate Testing Guidelines, continued** | |
| 796.3480 | Complex formation ability in water |
| 796.3500 | Hydrolysis as a function of pH at 25 °C |
| 796.3700 | Photolysis in aqueous solution in sunlight |
| 796.3780 | Laboratory determination of the direct photolysis reaction quantum yield in aqueous solution and sunlight photolysis |
| 796.3800 | Gas phase absorption spectra and photolysis |
| **Environmental Effects Testing Guidelines** | |
| 797.1050 | Algal acute toxicity test |
| 797.1060 | Freshwater algae acute toxicity test |
| 797.1075 | Freshwater and marine algae acute toxicity test |
| 797.1160 | Lemna acute toxicity test |
| 797.1300 | Daphnid acute toxicity test |
| 797.1330 | Daphnid chronic toxicity test |
| 797.1350 | Daphnid chronic toxicity test |
| 797.1400 | Fish acute toxicity test |
| 797.1440 | Fish acute toxicity test |
| 797.1520 | Fish bioconcentration test |
| 797.1560 | Fish bioconcentration test |
| 797.1600 | Fish early life state toxicity test |
| 797.1800 | Oyster acute toxicity test |
| 797.1830 | Oyster bioconcentration test |
| 797.1930 | Mysid shrimp acute toxicity test |
| 797.1950 | Mysid shrimp chronic toxicity test |
| 797.1970 | Penaeid shrimp acute toxicity test |
| 797.2050 | Avian dietary toxicity test |
| 797.2130 | Bobwhite reproduction test |
| 797.2150 | Mallard reproduction test |
| 797.2175 | Avian acute oral toxicity test |
| 797.2750 | Seed germination/root elongation toxicity test |
| 797.2800 | Early seedling growth toxicity test |
| 797.2850 | Plant uptake and translocation test |
| **Health Effects Testing Guidelines** | |
| 798.1100 | Acute dermal toxicity |
| 798.1150 | Acute inhalation toxicity |
| 798.1175 | Acute oral toxicity |
| 798.2250 | Dermal toxicity |
| 798.2450 | Inhalation toxicity |
| 798.2650 | Oral toxicity |
| 798.2675 | Oral toxicity with satellite reproduction and fertility study |
| 798.3260 | Chronic toxicity |
| 798.3300 | Oncogenicity |
| 798.3320 | Combined chronic toxicity/oncogenicity |

Continued on next page.

**Table 1-10.**  **Test Procedures in 40 CFR for data supporting TSCA submissions,** *continued*

| Part | Title |
|---|---|
| **Health Effects Testing Guidelines,** *continued* | |
| 798.4100 | Dermal sensitization |
| 798.4350 | Inhalation developmental toxicity study |
| 798.4420 | Preliminary developmental toxicity |
| 798.4470 | Primary dermal irritation |
| 798.4500 | Primary eye irritation |
| 798.4700 | Reproduction and fertility effects |
| 798.4900 | Developmental toxicity study |
| 798.5100 | Escheria coli WP2 and WP2 urvA reverse mutation assays |
| 798.5140 | Gene mutations in aspergillus nidulans |
| 798.5195 | Mouse biochemical specific locus test |
| 798.5200 | Mouse visible specific locus test |
| 798.5250 | Gene mutation in neurospora crassa |
| 798.5265 | The salmonella typhimurium reverse mutation assay |
| 798.5275 | Sex-linked recessive lethal test in drosophila melanogaster |
| 798.5300 | Detection of gene mutations in somatic cells in culture |
| 798.5375 | In vitro mammalian cytogenetics |
| 798.5385 | In vivo mammalian bone marrow cytogenetics tests: Chromosomal analysis |
| 798.5395 | In vivo mammalian bone marrow cytogenetics tests: Micronucleus assay |
| 798.5450 | Rodent dominent lethal assay |
| 798.5460 | Rodent heritable translocation assays |
| 798.5500 | Differential growth inhibition of repair proficient and repair deficient bacteria: Bacterial DNA damage or repair tests |
| 798.5550 | Unscheduled DNA synthesis in mammalian cells in culture |
| 798.5575 | Mitotic gene conversion in Saccharomyces cervisitiae |
| 798.5900 | In vitro sister chromatid exchange assay |
| 798.5915 | In vivo sister chromatid exchange assay |
| 798.5955 | Heritable translocation test in drosophila melanogaster |
| 798.6050 | Functional observational battery |
| 798.6200 | Motor activity |
| 798.6400 | Neuropathology |
| 798.6450 | NTE neurotox assay |
| 798.6500 | Schedule-controlled operant behavior |
| 798.6540 | Acute delayed neurotoxicity of organophosphorous substances |
| 798.6560 | Subchronic delayed neurotoxicity of organophosphorous substances |
| 798.7100 | Metabolism |

## 7. SARA – Superfund Amendments and Reauthorization Act

Passed in 1986, SARA extends the lifetime of the legislation begun in CERCLA and gives EPA the authority to remediate a site if no responsible parties can be found to pay.

## 8. CAA - Clean Air Act

The Clean Air Act Amendments of 1990 empowered EPA to regulate a variety of hazardous air pollutants (HAP).  Under this authority EPA has established the National Emission Standards for Hazardous Air Pollutants (NESHAP).  These compounds can be grouped into volatiles (vp > 0.1 mm Hg, BP <300 °C), semivolatiles (vp $10^{-1}$ to $10^{-7}$ mm Hg, BP 300-600 °C) and particulates (vp <$10^{-7}$, BP >600 °C). Organic materials are listed in 40 CFR 63.106, Table 2 as Hazardous Organic National Emission Standards for Hazardous Air Pollutants (HON) (Table 1-11).

### Table 1-11. Hazardous organic air pollutants[37]

| Compound | CAS |
|----------|-----|
| Acetaldehyde | 75-07-0 |
| Acetamide | 60-35-5 |
| Acetonitrile | 75-05-8 |
| Acetophenone | 98-86-2 |
| Acrolein | 107-02-8 |
| Acrylamide | 79-06-1 |
| Acrylic acid | 79-10-7 |
| Acrylonitrile | 107-13-1 |
| Allyl chloride | 107-05-1 |
| Aniline | 62-53-3 |
| o-Anisidine | 90-04-0 |
| Benzene | 71-43-2 |
| Benzotrichloride | 98-07-7 |
| Benzyl chloride | 100-44-7 |
| Biphenyl | 92-52-4 |
| Bis(chloromethyl)ether | 542-88-1 |
| Bromoform | 75-25-2 |
| 1,3-Butadiene | 106-99-0 |
| Caprolactam | 105-60-2 |
| Carbon disulfide | 75-15-0 |
| Carbon tetrachloride | 56-23-5 |
| Chloroacetic acid | 79-11-8 |
| 2-Chloroacetophenone | 532-27-4 |
| Chlorobenzene | 108-90-7 |
| Chloroform | 67-66-3 |
| Chloroprene | 126-99-8 |
| Cresols and cresylic acids | 1319-77-3 |
| o-Cresol and o-Cresylic acid | 95-48-7 |
| m-Cresol and m-Cresylic acid | 108-39-4 |
| p-Cresol and p-Cresylic acid | 106-44-5 |
| Cumene | 98-82-8 |
| 1,4-Dichlorobenzene | 106-46-7 |
| 3,3'-Dichlorobenzidine | 91-94-1 |
| Dichloroethylether | 111-44-4 |
| 1,3-Dichloropropene | 542-75-6 |
| Diethanolamine | 11-142-2 |
| N,N-dimethylaniline | 121-69-7 |
| Diethyl sulfate | 64-67-5 |
| 3,3'-Dimethylbenzidine | 119-93-7 |
| Dimethylformamide | 68-12-2 |
| 1,1-Dimethylhydrazine | 57-14-7 |

Continued on next page.

37  Federal Register, Vol. 57. No. 252. Thursday, December 31. 1992. p. 62690.

**Table 1-11. Hazardous organic air pollutants,** *continued*

| Compound | CAS |
|---|---|
| Dimethyl phthalate | 131-11-3 |
| Dimethyl sulfate | 77-78-1 |
| 2,4-Dinitrophenol | 51-28-5 |
| 2,4-Dinitrotoluene | 121-14-2 |
| 1,4-Dioxane | 123-91-1 |
| 1,2-Diphenylhydrazine | 122-66-7 |
| Epichlorohydrin | 106-89-8 |
| Ethyl acrylate | 140-88-5 |
| Ethylbenzene | 100-41-4 |
| Ethylchloride | 75-00-3 |
| Ethylene dibromide | 106-93-4 |
| Ethylene dichloride | 107-06-2 |
| Ethylene glycol | 107-21-1 |
| Ethylene oxide | 75-21-8 |
| Ethylidene dichloride | 75-34-3 |
| Formaldehyde | 50-00-0 |
| Glycol ethers[38] | - |
| Hexachlorobenzene | 118-74-1 |
| Hexachlorobutadiene | 87-68-3 |
| Hexachloroethane | 67-72-1 |
| Hexane | 100-54-3 |
| Hydroquinone | 123-31-9 |
| Isophorone | 78-59-1 |
| Maleic anhydride | 108-31-6 |
| Methanol | 67-56-1 |
| Methyl bromide | 74-83-9 |
| Methyl chloride | 74-87-3 |
| Methyl chloroform | 71-55-6 |
| Methyl ethyl ketone | 78-93-3 |
| Methyl hydrazine | 60-34-4 |
| Methyl isobutyl ketone | 108-10-1 |
| Methyl isocyanate | 624-83-9 |
| Methyl methacrylate | 80-62-6 |
| Methyl tert-butyl ether | 1634-04-4 |
| Methylene chloride | 75-09-2 |
| Methylene diphenyl diisocyanate | 101-68-8 |
| 4,4'-Methylene dianiline | 101-77-9 |
| Naphthalene | 91-20-3 |
| Nitrobenzene | 98-95-3 |
| 4-Nitrophenol | 100-02-7 |
| 2-Nitropropane | 79-46-9 |
| Phenol | 108-95-2 |
| p-Phenylenediamine | 106-50-3 |
| Phosgene | 75-44-5 |

Continued on next page.

[38] Includes mono- and di-ethers of ethylene glycol, diethylene glycol, and triethylene glycol R-$(OCH_2CH_2)_n$-OR', where n=1,2, or 3, R = alkyl or aryl groups and R'=R, H or groups, which, when removed, yield glycol ethers with the structure R-$(OCH_2CH_2)_n$-OH. Polymers are excluded from the glycol ether category.

**Table 1-11. Hazardous organic air pollutants,** *continued*

| Compound | CAS |
|---|---|
| Phthalic anhydride | 85-44-9 |
| Polycyclic organic matter[39] | - |
| Propiolactone | 57-57-8 |
| Propionaldehyde | 123-38-6 |
| Propylene dichloride | 78-87-5 |
| Propylene oxide | 75-56-9 |
| Quinone | 106-51-4 |
| Styrene | 100-42-5 |
| 1,1,2,2-Tetrachloroethane | 79-34-5 |
| Tetrachloroethylene | 127-18-4 |
| Toluene | 108-88-3 |
| 2,4-Toluene diamine | 95-80-7 |
| 2,4-Toluene disocyanate | 584-84-9 |
| o-Toluidine | 95-53-4 |
| 1,2,4-Trichlorobenzene | 120-82-1 |
| 1,1,2-Trichloroethane | 79-00-5 |
| Trichloroethene | 79-01-6 |
| 2,4,5-Trichlorophenol | 95-95-4 |
| Triethylamine | 121-44-8 |
| 2,2,4-Trimethylpentane | 540-84-1 |
| Vinyl acetate | 108-05-4 |
| Vinyl chloride | 75-01-4 |
| Vinylidene chloride | 75-35-4 |
| Xylenes | 1330-20-7 |
| o-Xylene | 95-47-6 |
| m-Xylene | 108-38-3 |
| p-Xylene | 106-42-3 |

**Table 1-12. Hazardous Air Pollutants under Title III CAAA**

| Compound | CAS |
|---|---|
| Acetaldehyde | 75-07-0 |
| Acetamide | 60-35-5 |
| Acetonitrile | 75-05-8 |
| Acetophenone | 98-86-2 |
| 2-Acetylaminofluorene | 53-96-3 |
| Acrolein | 107-02-8 |
| Acrylamide | 79-06-1 |
| Acrylic acid | 79-10-7 |
| Acrylonitrile | 107-13-1 |
| Allyl chloride | 107-05-1 |
| 4-Aminobiphenyl | 92-67-1 |
| Aniline | 62-53-3 |
| o-Anisidine | 90-04-0 |
| Asbestos | 1332-21-4 |
| Benzene | 71-43-2 |
| Benzidine | 92-87-5 |

Continued on next page.

---

[39] Includes organic compounds with more than one benzene ring, and that have a boiling point greater than or equal to 100 °C.

**Table 1-12. Hazardous Air Pollutants under Title III CAAA,** *continued*

| Compound | CAS |
|---|---|
| Benzotrichloride | 98-07-7 |
| Benzyl chloride | 100-44-7 |
| Biphenyl | 92-52-4 |
| Bis(2-ethylhexyl) phthalate | 117-81-7 |
| Bis(chloromethyl)ether | 542-88-1 |
| Bromoform | 75-25-2 |
| 1,3-Butadiene | 106-99-0 |
| Calcium cyanamide | 156-62-7 |
| Caprolactam | 105-60-2 |
| Captan | 133-06-2 |
| Carbaryl | 63-25-2 |
| Carbon disulfide | 75-15-0 |
| Carbon tetrachloride | 56-23-5 |
| Carbonyl sulfide | 463-58-1 |
| Catechol | 120-80-9 |
| Chloramben | 133-90-4 |
| Chlordane | 57-74-9 |
| Chlorine | 7782-50-5 |
| Chloroacetic acid | 79-11-8 |
| 2-Chloroacetophenone | 532-27-4 |
| Chlorobenzene | 108-90-7 |
| Chlorobenzilate | 510-15-6 |
| Chloroform | 67-66-3 |
| Chloromethyl methyl ether | 107-30-2 |
| Chloroprene | 126-99-8 |
| Cresols/cresylic acids | 1319-77-3 |
| *o*-Cresol | 95-48-7 |
| *m*-Cresol | 108-39-4 |
| *p*-Cresol | 106-44-5 |
| Cumene | 98-82-8 |
| 2,4-D, salts and esters | 94-75-7 |
| DDE | 3547-04-4 |
| Diazomethane | 334-88-3 |
| Dibenzofurans | 132-64-9 |
| 1,2-Dibromo-3-chloropropane | 96-12-8 |
| Dibutylphthalate | 84-74-2 |
| 1,4-Dichlorobenzene | 106-46-7 |
| 3,3'-Dichlorobenzidine | 91-94-1 |
| Dichloroethylether | 111-44-4 |
| 1,3-Dichloropropene | 542-75-6 |
| Dichlorvos | 62-73-7 |
| Diethanolamine | 111-42-2 |
| N,N-dimethylaniline | 121-69-7 |
| Diethyl sulfate | 64-67-5 |
| 3,3'-Dimethoxybenzidine | 119-90-4 |
| Dimethyl aminoazobenzene | 60-11-7 |
| 3,3'-Dimethyl benzidine | 119-93-7 |
| Dimethyl carbamoyl chloride | 79-44-7 |

Continued on next page.

**Table 1-12. Hazardous Air Pollutants under Title III CAAA,** *continued*

| Compound | CAS |
|---|---|
| Dimethylformamide | 68-12-2 |
| 1,1-Dimethylhydrazine | 57-14-7 |
| Dimethyl phthalate | 131-11-3 |
| Dimethyl sulfate | 77-78-1 |
| 4,6-Dinitrophenol and salts | 534-52-1 |
| 2,4-Dinitrophenol | 51-28-5 |
| 2,4-Dinitrotoluene | 121-14-2 |
| 1,4-Dioxane | 123-91-1 |
| 1,2-Diphenylhydrazine | 122-66-7 |
| Epichlorohydrin | 106-89-8 |
| 1,2-Epoxybutane | 106-88-7 |
| Ethyl acrylate | 140-88-5 |
| Ethylbenzene | 100-41-4 |
| Ethyl carbamate | 51-79-6 |
| Ethylchloride | 75-00-3 |
| Ethylene dibromide | 106-93-4 |
| Ethylene dichloride | 107-06-2 |
| Ethylene glycol | 107-21-1 |
| Ethylene imine | 151-56-4 |
| Ethylene oxide | 75-21-8 |
| Ethylene thiourea | 96-45-7 |
| Ethylidene dichloride | 75-34-3 |
| Formaldehyde | 50-00-0 |
| Heptachlor | 76-44-8 |
| Hexachlorobenzene | 118-74-1 |
| Hexachlorobutadiene | 87-68-3 |
| Hexachlorocyclopentadiene | 77-47-4 |
| Hexachloroethane | 67-72-1 |
| Hexamethylene-1,6-diisocyanate | 822-06-0 |
| Hexamethylphosphoramide | 680-31-9 |
| Hexane | 100-54-3 |
| Hydrazine | 302-01-2 |
| Hydrochloric acid | 7647-01-0 |
| Hydrofluoric acid | 7664-39-3 |
| Hydroquinone | 123-31-9 |
| Isophorone | 78-59-1 |
| Lindane | 58-89-9 |
| Maleic anhydride | 108-31-6 |
| Methanol | 67-56-1 |
| Methoxychlor | 72-43-5 |
| Methyl bromide | 74-83-9 |
| Methyl chloride | 74-87-3 |
| Methyl chloroform | 71-55-6 |
| Methyl ethyl ketone | 78-93-3 |
| Methyl hydrazine | 60-34-4 |
| Methyl iodide | 74-88-4 |
| Methyl isobutyl ketone (hexone) | 108-10-1 |
| Methyl isocyanate | 624-83-9 |

Continued on next page.

**Table 1-12. Hazardous Air Pollutants under Title III CAAA,** *continued*

| Compound | CAS |
|---|---|
| Methyl methacrylate | 80-62-6 |
| Methyl tert-butyl ether | 1634-04-4 |
| 4,4'-Methylene bis(2-chloroaniline) | 101-14-4 |
| Methylene chloride | 75-09-2 |
| Methylene diphenyl diisocyanate | 101-68-8 |
| 4,4'-Methylene dianiline | 101-77-9 |
| Naphthalene | 91-20-3 |
| Nitrobenzene | 98-95-3 |
| 4-Nitrobiphenyl | 92-93-3 |
| 4-Nitrophenol | 100-02-7 |
| 2-Nitropropane | 79-46-9 |
| N-Nitroso-N-methylurea | 684-93-5 |
| N-Nitrosodimethylamine | 62-75-9 |
| N-Nitrosomorpholine | 59-89-2 |
| Parathion | 56-38-2 |
| Pentachloronitrobenzene | 82-68-8 |
| Pentachlorophenol | 87-86-5 |
| Phenol | 108-95-2 |
| *p*-Phenylenediamine | 106-50-3 |
| Phosgene | 75-44-5 |
| Phosphine | 7803-51-2 |
| Phosphorous | 7723-14-0 |
| Phthalic anhydride | 85-44-9 |
| PCB | 1336-36-3 |
| 1,3-Propane sultone | 1120-71-4 |
| Propiolactone | 57-57-8 |
| Propionaldehyde | 123-38-6 |
| Propoxur | 114-26-1 |
| Propylene dichloride | 78-87-5 |
| Propylene oxide | 75-56-9 |
| 1,2-Propylenimine | 75-55-8 |
| Quinoline | 91-22-5 |
| Quinone | 106-51-4 |
| Styrene | 100-42-5 |
| Styrene oxide | 96-09-3 |
| 2,3,7,8-Tetrachlorodibenzo-p-dioxin | 1746-01-6 |
| 1,1,2,2-tetrachloroethane | 79-34-5 |
| Tetrachloroethylene | 127-18-4 |
| Titanium tetrachloride | 7550-45-0 |
| Toluene | 108-88-3 |
| 2,4-Toluene diamine | 95-80-7 |
| 2,4-Toluene diisocyanate | 584-84-9 |
| *o*-Toluidine | 95-53-4 |
| Toxaphene | 8001-35-2 |
| 1,2,4-Trichlorobenzene | 120-82-1 |

Continued on next page.

**Table 1-12. Hazardous Air Pollutants under Title III CAAA,** *continued*

| Compound | CAS |
|---|---|
| 1,1,2-Trichloroethane | 79-00-5 |
| Trichloroethene | 79-01-6 |
| 2,4,5-Trichlorophenol | 95-95-4 |
| 2,4,6-Trichlorophenol | 88-06-2 |
| Triethylamine | 121-44-8 |
| Trifluralin | 1582-09-8 |
| 2,2,4-Trimethylpentane | 540-84-1 |
| Vinyl acetate | 108-05-4 |
| Vinyl bromide | 593-60-2 |
| Vinyl chloride | 75-01-4 |
| Vinylidene chloride | 75-35-4 |
| Xylenes | 1330-20-7 |
| *o*-Xylene | 95-47-6 |
| *m*-Xylene | 108-38-3 |
| *p*-Xylene | 106-42-3 |
| Antimony compounds | - |
| Arsenic compounds | - |
| Beryllium compounds | - |
| Cadmium compounds | - |
| Chromium compounds | - |
| Cobalt compounds | - |
| Coke oven emissions | - |
| Cyanide compounds | - |
| Glycol ethers[40] | - |
| Lead compounds | - |
| Manganese compounds | - |
| Mercury compounds | - |
| Fine mineral fibers | - |
| Nickel compounds | - |
| Polycyclic organic matter[41] | - |
| Radionuclides | - |
| Selenium compounds | - |

A number of different techniques have been developed by EPA for analysis of the compounds and substances on the HAP list. These have been reviewed by Winberry in two articles[42]. These are also presented in a publication, *Instant EPA's Air Toxics*, from Instant Reference Sources, Inc., Austin, Texas. The applicable methods encompass sampling and analysis in the 00xx series methods in SW-846, the draft Air CLP-SOW, 40 CFR parts 60 and 61 and the TO-1 to -14 manual. Although a number of analytical procedures are available, as far as the list of HAP target compounds is concerned the

---

[40]  Includes mono- and di-ethers of ethylene glycol, diethylene glycol, and triethylene glycol R-$(OCH_2CH_2)_n$-OR', where n=1,2, or 3, R = alkyl or aryl groups and R'=R, H or groups, which, when removed, yield glycol ethers with the structure R-$(OCH_2CH_2)_n$-OH. Polymers are excluded from the glycol ether category.

[41]  Includes organic compounds with more than one benzene ring, and which have a boiling point greater than or equal to 100 °C.

[42]  Winberry, W.T. Jr. *Sampling and Analysis Under Title III. Part I.* "Environmental Lab," June/July 1993. pp. 46-58; *Part II: Source Test Methodology.* "Environmental Lab," August/September, 1993. pp. 52-67.

analysis technology lags behind the regulations. With respect to the HAP list, 19% of the target analytes have validated methods, 24% have partially validated methods, 32% have possibly applicable methods and a full 25% of the compounds have no reliable analytical technique. Multi-analyte methods are the preferred techniques, and for the majority of the HAP, Method 29 for the metals, Method 18 for the volatile organics, and Method 0010/8270 (SW-846) are the most efficient techniques.

The CAA also requires EPA to establish permits for maximum amounts of emissions by industries, similar to the NPDES program for wastewater effluent. For many specific type industries, the EPA has defined air emission standards. These are listed in 40 CFR 60 and consist, in general, of an applicability statement, definitions, required standards, monitoring requirements, approved test methods and procedures, and reporting and recordkeeping requirements. Most of the approved methods of analysis are found in 40 CFR 60, Appendix A. Table 1-13 lists industries for which air emission standards exist.

**Table 1-13. Standards of performance for new stationary sources listed in 40 CFR 60, 1 July, 1993**

| Subpart | Title |
|---------|-------|
| Ca | Emissions guidelines and compliance times for municipal waste combustors |
| Cb | Emissions guidelines and compliance times for sulfuric acid production units |
| D | Standards of performance for fossil-fuel fired steam generators for which construction is commenced after August 17, 1971 |
| Da | Standards of performance for electric utility steam generating units for which construction is commenced after September 18, 1978 |
| Db | Standards of performance for industrial-commercial-institutional steam generating units |
| Dc | Standards of performance for small industrial-commercial-institutional steam generating units |
| E | Standards of performance for incinerators |
| Ea | Standards of performance for municipal waste combustors |
| F | Standards of performance for portland cement plants |
| G | Standards of performance for nitric acid plants |
| H | Standards of performance for sulfuric acid plants |
| I | Standards of performance for asphalt concrete plants |
| J | Standards of performance for petroleum refineries |
| K | Standards of performance for storage vessels for petroleum liquids for which construction, reconstruction, or modification commenced after June 11, 1973 and prior to May 18, 1978 |
| Ka | Standards of performance for storage vessels for petroleum liquids for which construction, reconstruction, or modification commenced after May 18, 1978 and prior to July 23, 1984 |
| Kb | Standards of performance for volatile organic liquid storage vessels (including petroleum liquid storage vessels) for which construction, reconstruction or modification commenced after July 23, 1984 |
| L | Standards of performance for secondary lead smelters |
| M | Standards of performance for secondary brass and bronze production plants |
| N | Standards of performance for primary emissions from basic oxygen process furnaces for which construction is commenced after June 11, 1973 |

Continued on next page.

**Table 1-13.  Standards of performance for new stationary sources listed in 40 CFR 60, 1 July, 1993,** *continued*

| Subpart | Title |
|---------|-------|
| Na | Standards of performance for secondary emissions from basic oxygen process steelmaking facilities for which construction is commenced after January 20, 1983 |
| O | Standards of performance for sewage treatment plants |
| P | Standards of performance for primary copper smelters |
| Q | Standards of performance for primary zinc smelters |
| R | Standards of performance for primary lead smelters |
| S | Standards of performance for primary aluminum reduction plants |
| T | Standards of performance for the phosphate fertilizer industry: wet-process phosphoric acid plants |
| U | Standards of performance for the phosphate fertilizer industry: superphosphoric acid plants |
| V | Standards of performance for the phosphate fertilizer industry: diammonium phosphate plants |
| W | Standards of performance for the phosphate fertilizer industry: triple superphosphate plants |
| X | Standards of performance for the phosphate fertilizer industry: granular triple superphosphate storage facilities |
| Y | Standards of performance for coal preparation plants |
| Z | Standards of performance for ferroalloy production facilities |
| AA | Standards of performance for steel plants: electric arc furnaces constructed after October 21, 1974 and on or before August 17, 1983 |
| AAa | Standards of performance for steel plants: electric arc furnaces and argon-oxygen decarburization vessels constructed after August 7, 1983 |
| BB | Standards of performance for kraft pulp mills |
| CC | Standards of performance for glass manufacturing plants |
| D D | Standards of performance for grain elevators |
| E E | Standards of performance for surface coating of metal furniture |
| GG | Standards of performance for stationary gas turbines |
| H H | Standards of performance for lime manufacturing plants |
| KK | Standards of performance for lead-acid battery manufacturing plants |
| LL | Standards of performance for metallic mineral processing plants |
| M M | Standards of performance for automobile and light-duty truck surface coating operations |
| N N | Standards of performance for phosphate rock plants |
| PP | Standards of performance for ammonium sulfate manufacture |
| QQ | Standards of performance for the graphic arts industry: publication rotogravure printing |
| RR | Standards of performance for pressure sensitive tape and label surface coating operations |
| SS | Standards of performance for industrial surface coating: large applications |
| TT | Standards of performance for metal coil surface coating |
| UU | Standards of performance for asphalt processing and asphalt roofing manufacture |
| VV | Standards of performance for equipment leaks of VOC in the synthetic organic chemicals manufacturing industry |
| W W | Standards of performance for the beverage can surface coating industry |
| XX | Standards of performance for bulk gasoline terminals |

Continued on next page.

**Table 1-13.** **Standards of performance for new stationary sources listed in 40 CFR 60, 1 July, 1993,** *continued*

| Subpart | Title |
|---------|-------|
| AAA | Standards of performance for new residential wood heaters |
| BBB | Standards of performance for the rubber tire manufacturing industry |
| DDD | Standards of performance for volatile organic compound (VOC) emissions from the polymer manufacturing industry |
| FFF | Standards of performance for flexible vinyl and urethane coating and printing |
| GGG | Standards of performance for equipment leaks of VOC in petroleum refineries |
| HHH | Standards of performance for synthetic fiber production facilities |
| III | Standards of performance for volatile organic compound (VOC) emissions from the synthetic organic chemical manufacturing industry (SOCMI) air oxidation unit processes |
| JJJ | Standards of performance for petroleum dry cleaners |
| KKK | Standards of performance for equipment leaks of VOC from on-shore natural gas processing plants |
| LLL | Standards of performance for onshore natural gas processing: $SO_2$ emissions |
| NNN | Standards of performance for volatile organic compound (VOC) emissions from synthetic organic chemical manufacturing industry (SOCMI) distillation operations |
| OOO | Standards of performance for nonmetallic mineral processing plants |
| PPP | Standards of performance for wool fiberglass insulation manufacturing plants |
| QQQ | Standards of performance for VOC emissions from petroleum refinery wastewater systems |
| SSS | Standards of performance for magnetic tape coating facilities |
| TTT | Standards of performance for industrial surface coating: surface coating of plastic parts for business machines |
| UUU | Standards of performance for calciners and dryers in mineral industries |
| VVV | Standards of performance for polymeric coating of supporting substrates facilities |

The number of industries with standards is growing rapidly and the most recent edition of 40 CFR Part 60 should be consulted. The EPA Air Website at http://ttnwww.rtpnc.epa.gov contains a listing of all the promulgated and proposed industry standards.

For example, Subpart V, Standards of performance for the phosphate fertilizer industry: diammonium phosphate plants, specifies that fluoride emissions to the air will not exceed 30 g/metric ton of equivalent phosphorus pentoxide feed. The Standard then specifies that this shall be verified by installation and use of a continuous monitoring device for mass flow of phosphorus bearing feed material to the system, installation and use of a monitoring device that constantly records the pressure drop across the scrubbing system, and, finally, use of either methods 13A or 13B to measure fluoride concentration and flow rate of effluent gas from each emission point. An equation is presented that uses these measurements to arrive at the g/metric ton Standard.

## II. ANALYTICAL METHODOLOGIES

There are many different analytical methods circulating through the environmental industry. Many are published by the EPA. The offices within EPA that are responsible for generating or requiring the use of specific analytical methods are shown in Figure 1-1.

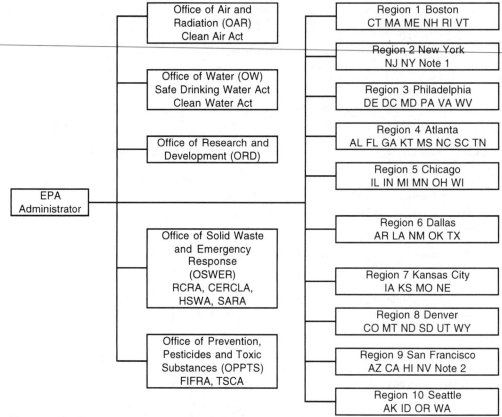

Note 1. Also Puerto Rico and Virgin Islands
Note 2. Also American Samoa, Guam and Trust territories of the Pacific

**Figure 1-1. Offices within EPA that generate and specify methods.**

There are also officially recognized compilations of methods that are published by the commercial side of the industry. The regulations discussed above often specify approved methods of analysis as a part of the regulation. Following is a list of published methods that are available and should be present in an environmental lab.

### Federal Methods

Methods Series 1-29
Air monitoring methods 40 CFR 60 Appendix A (see Table 5-4 at end of Section 5)

Methods 101-115
Air monitoring methods 40 CFR 61 Appendix B (see Table 5-4 at end of Section 5)

Methods Series 110.0-430.2

*Methods for Chemical Analysis of Water and Wastes* 1983 (EPA-600/4-79/020 PB84-128677) and *Methods for the determination of inorganic substances in environmental samples* 1993 (EPA 600/R-93/100), *Methods for the determination of chemical substances in marine and estuarine environmental samples* (EPA/600/R-92/121), November 1992, *Methods for the Determination of Metals in Environmental Samples*, 1991 (EPA 600/4-91/010), and *Methods for the Determination of Metals in Environmental Samples* Supplement I, 1994 (EPA-600/R-94/111)

| 100's | Physical Properties |
| 200's | Metals |
| 300's | Inorganic, Non-metallics |
| 400's | Organics |

**Table 1-14. EPA 100-400 series methods**

| Method[43] | Title/Description |
|---|---|
| 100.1 (f) | Asbestos fibers by TEM |
| 100.2 (g) | Asbestos fiber size by TEM |
| 110.1 (a) | ADMI colorimetric olor |
| 110.2 (a) | Platinum-cobalt colorimetric color |
| 110.3 (a) | Spectrophotometric color |
| 120.1 (a) | Specific conductance |
| 130.1 (a) | EDTA automated hardness |
| 130.2 (a) | EDTA titration hardness |
| 140.1 (a) | Odor |
| 150.1 (a) | pH, electometric |
| 150.2 (a) | pH electrometric continuous monitoring |
| 160.1 (a) | Filterable residue (TDS) |
| 160.2 (a) | Non-filterable residue (TSS) |
| 160.3 (a) | Total residue (TS) |
| 160.4 (a) | Volatile residue (VS) |
| 160.5 (a) | Settleable matter |
| 170.1 (a) | Temperature |
| 180.1 (b) | Nephelometric turbidity |
| 200.1 (d) | Determination of acid-soluble metals |
| 200.2 (e) | Sample preparation procedure for spectrochemical determination of total recoverable elements |
| 200.3 (d) | Sample preparation procedure for spectrochemical determination of total recoverable elements in biological tissues |

Continued on next page.

---

[43]   (a) *Methods for Chemical Analysis of Water and Wastes* 1983 (EPA-600/4-79/020 PB84-128677); (b) *Methods for the determination of inorganic substances in environmental samples* 1993 (EPA 600/R-93/100); (c) *Methods for the determination of chemical substances in marine and estuarine environmental samples* (EPA/600/R-92/121), November 1992; (d) *Methods for the Determination of Metals in Environmental Samples*, 1991 (EPA 600/4-91/010); (e) *Methods for the Determination of Metals in Environmental Samples* Supplement I, 1994 (EPA-600/R-94/111); (f) *Analytical method for the determination of asbestos fibers in water*, September, 1983 NTIS PB83-260471; (g) *Determination of asbestos structure over 10 um in length in drinking water*, June 1994, EPA 600/R-94-134, NTIS PB94-201902.

## Table 1-14. EPA 100-400 series methods, *continued*

| Method[44] | Title/Description |
|---|---|
| 200.7 (e) | Determination of metals and trace elements in water and wastes by ICP-AES |
| 200.8 (e) | Determination of trace elements in water and wastes ICP-MS |
| 200.9 (e) | Determination of trace elements by stabilized temperature GFAA |
| 200.10 (c)(d) | Determination of trace elements in marine waters by on-line chelation preconcentration and ICP-MS |
| 200.11 (d) | Determination of metals in fish tissue by ICP-AES |
| 200.12 (c) | Determination of trace elements in marine waters by STGFAA |
| 200.13 (c) | Determination of trace elements in marine waters by off-line chelation pre-concentration with GFAA |
| 200.15 (e) | Determination of metals and trace elements in water by ultrasonic nebulization ICP-AES |
| 202.1 (a) | Aluminum FLAA |
| 202.2 (a) | Aluminum GFAA |
| 204.1 (a) | Antimony FLAA |
| 204.2 (a) | Antimony GFAA |
| 206.2 (a) | Arsenic GFAA |
| 206.3 (a) | Arsenic hydride AA |
| 206.4 (a) | Arsenic SDDC Spectrophotometric |
| 206.5 (a) | Arsenic digestion method for hydride and SDDC |
| 208.1 (a) | Barium FLAA |
| 208.2 (a) | Barium GFAA |
| 210.1 (a) | Beryllium FLA |
| 210.2 (a) | Beryllium GFAA |
| 212.3 (a) | Boron, Curcumin colorimetric |
| 213.1 (a) | Cadmium FLAA |
| 213.2 (a) | Cadmium GFAA |
| 215.1 (a) | Calcium FLAA |
| 215.2 (a) | Calcium EDTA titrimetric |
| 218.1 (a) | Chromium FLAA |
| 218.2 (a) | Chromium GFAA |
| 218.3 (a) | Chromium chelation-extraction |
| 218.4 (a) | Hexavalent chromium chelation-extraction |
| 218.5 (a) | Hexavalent chromium dissolved |
| 218.6 (e) | Determination of dissolved hexavalent chromium in drinking water, groundwater, and industrial wastewater effluents by ion chromatography |
| 219.1 (a) | Cobalt FLAA |
| 219.2 (a) | Cobalt GFAA |

Continued on next page.

---

[44]  (a) *Methods for Chemical Analysis of Water and Wastes* 1983 (EPA-600/4-79/020 PB84-128677); (b) *Methods for the determination of inorganic substances in environmental samples* 1993 (EPA 600/R-93/100); (c) *Methods for the determination of chemical substances in marine and estuarine environmental samples* (EPA/600/R-92/121), November 1992; (d) *Methods for the Determination of Metals in Environmental Samples*, 1991 (EPA 600/4-91/010); (e) *Methods for the Determination of Metals in Environmental Samples* Supplement I, 1994 (EPA-600/R-94/111); (f) *Analytical method for the determination of asbestos fibers in water*, September, 1983 NTIS PB83-260471; (g) *Determination of asbestos structure over 10 um in length in drinking water*, June 1994, EPA 600/R-94-134, NTIS PB94-201902.

**Table 1-14. EPA 100-400 series methods,** *continued*

| Method[45] | Title/Description |
|---|---|
| 220.1 (a) | Copper FLAA |
| 220.2 (a) | Copper GFAA |
| 231.1 (a) | Gold FLAA |
| 231.2 (a) | Gold GFAA |
| 235.1 (a) | Iridium FLAA |
| 235.2 (a) | Iridium GFAA |
| 236.1 (a) | Iron FLAA |
| 236.2 (a) | Iron GFAA |
| 239.1 (a) | Lead FLAA |
| 239.2 (a) | Lead GFAA |
| 242.1 (a) | Magnesium FLAA |
| 243.1 (a) | Manganese FLAA |
| 243.2 (a) | Manganese GFAA |
| 245.1 (e) | Determination of mercury in water by manual CVAA |
| 245.2 (a) | Mercury by automated CVAA |
| 245.3 (d) | Determination of inorganic mercury (II) and selected organomercurials in drinking and ground water by HPLC with electrochemical detection |
| 245.5 (d) | Determination of mercury in sediment by CVAA |
| 245.6 (d) | Determination of mercury in tissues by CVAA |
| 246.1 (a) | Molybdenum FLAA |
| 246.2 (a) | Molybdenum GFAA |
| 249.1 (a) | Nickel FLAA |
| 249.2 (a) | Nickel GFAA |
| 252.1 (a) | Osmium FLAA |
| 252.2 (a) | Osmium GFAA |
| 253.1 (a) | Palladium FLAA |
| 253.2 (a) | Palladium GFAA |
| 255.1 (a) | Platinum FLAA |
| 255.2 (a) | Platinmum GFAA |
| 258.1 (a) | Potassium FLAA |
| 264.1 (a) | Rhenium FLAA |
| 264.2 (a) | Rhenium GFAA |
| 265.1 (a) | Rhodium FLAA |
| 265.2 (a) | Rhodium GFAA |
| 267.1 (a) | Ruthenium FLAA |
| 267.2 (a) | Ruthenium GFAA |

Continued on next page.

[45] (a) *Methods for Chemical Analysis of Water and Wastes* 1983 (EPA-600/4-79/020 PB84-128677); (b) *Methods for the determination of inorganic substances in environmental samples* 1993 (EPA 600/R-93/100); (c) *Methods for the determination of chemical substances in marine and estuarine environmental samples* (EPA/600/R-92/121), November 1992; (d) *Methods for the Determination of Metals in Environmental Samples*, 1991 (EPA 600/4-91/010); (e) *Methods for the Determination of Metals in Environmental Samples* Supplement I, 1994 (EPA-600/R-94/111); (f) *Analytical method for the determination of asbestos fibers in water*, September, 1983 NTIS PB83-260471; (g) *Determination of asbestos structure over 10 um in length in drinking water*, June 1994, EPA 600/R-94-134, NTIS PB94-201902.

**Table 1-14. EPA 100-400 series methods,** *continued*

| Method[46] | Title/Description |
|---|---|
| 270.2 (a) | Selenium GFAA |
| 270.3 (a) | Selenium hydride |
| 272.1 (a) | Silver FLAA |
| 272.2 (a) | Silver GFAA |
| 273.1 (a) | Sodium FLAA |
| 273.2 (a) | Sodium GFAA |
| 279.1 (a) | Thallium FLAA |
| 279.2 (a) | Thallium GFAA |
| 282.1 (a) | Tin FLAA |
| 282.2 (a) | Tin GFAA |
| 283.1 (a) | Titanium FLAA |
| 283.2 (a) | Titanium GFAA |
| 286.1 (a) | Vanadium FLAA |
| 286.2 (a) | Vanadium GFAA |
| 289.1 (a) | Zinc FLAA |
| 289.2 (a) | Zinc GFAA |
| 300.0 (b) | Ion chromatography of anions |
| 305.1 (a) | Acidity |
| 310.1 (a) | Alkalinity titrimetric |
| 310.2 (a) | Alkalinity automated colorimetric |
| 320.1 (a) | Bromide titrimetric |
| 325.1 (a) | Chloride automated ferricyanide I |
| 325.2 (a) | Chloride automated ferrocyanide II |
| 325.3 (a) | Chloride mercuric nitrate titration |
| 330.1 (a) | Chlorine amperometric titration |
| 330.2 (a) | Chlorine back-iodometric titration |
| 330.3 (a) | Chlorine iodometric titration |
| 330.4 (a) | Chlorine DPD-FAS titration |
| 330.5 (a) | Chlorine DPD colorimetric |
| 335.1 (a) | Cyanide amenable to chlorination |
| 335.2 (a) | Total cyanide, titrimetric spectrophotometric |
| 335.3 (a) | Total cyanide automated UV colorimetric |
| 335.4 (b) | Total cyanide semi-automated colorimetry |
| 340.1 (a) | Fluoride SPADNS |
| 340.2 (a) | Fluoride ion selective electrode |
| 340.3 (a) | Fluoride automated complexone |

Continued on next page.

---

[46] (a) *Methods for Chemical Analysis of Water and Wastes* 1983 (EPA-600/4-79/020 PB84-128677); (b) *Methods for the determination of inorganic substances in environmental samples* 1993 (EPA 600/R-93/100); (c) *Methods for the determination of chemical substances in marine and estuarine environmental samples* (EPA/600/R-92/121), November 1992; (d) *Methods for the Determination of Metals in Environmental Samples*, 1991 (EPA 600/4-91/010); (e) *Methods for the Determination of Metals in Environmental Samples* Supplement I, 1994 (EPA-600/R-94/111); (f) *Analytical method for the determination of asbestos fibers in water*, September, 1983 NTIS PB83-260471; (g) *Determination of asbestos structure over 10 um in length in drinking water*, June 1994, EPA 600/R-94-134, NTIS PB94-201902.

## Table 1-14. EPA 100-400 series methods, *continued*

| Method[47] | Title/Description |
|---|---|
| 345.1 (a) | Iodine titration |
| 350.1 (b) | Ammonia semi-automated colorimetry |
| 350.2 (a) | Ammonia distillation with titration, colorimetric or electrode |
| 350.3 (a) | Ammonia electrode |
| 351.1 (b) | TKN semi-automated phenate |
| 351.2 (a) | TKN Block digester AAII colorimetric |
| 351.3 (a) | TKN colorimetric, titrimetric, potentiometric |
| 351.4 (a) | TKN ion selective electrode |
| 352.1 (a) | Nitrate brucine sulfate |
| 353.1 (a) | Nitrate-nitrite automated hydrazine reduction |
| 353.2 (b) | Nitrate-nitrite automated cadmium reduction colorimetry |
| 353.3 (a) | Nitrate-nitrite manual cadmium reduction colorimetry |
| 353.4 (c) | Nitrate-nitrite in estuarine and coastal waters by automated colorimetric analysis |
| 354.1 (a) | Nitrite colorimetric |
| 360.1 (a) | Oxygen membrane electrode |
| 360.2 (a) | Oxygen modified Winkler titration |
| 365.1 (b) | Phosphorus automated ascorbic acid |
| 365.2 (a) | Phosphorus ascorbic acid single reagent |
| 365.3 (a) | Phosphorus ascorbic acid two reagent |
| 365.4 (a) | Phosphorus automated block digester AAII colorimetric |
| 365.5 (c) | Orthophospate in estuarine and coastal waters by automated colorimetry |
| 370.1 (a) | Silica colorimetric |
| 375.1 (a) | Sulfate automated chloranilate colorimetric |
| 375.2 (b) | Sulfate automated methyl thymol blue |
| 374.3 (a) | Sulfate gravimetric |
| 375.4 (a) | Sulfate turbidimetric |
| 376.1 (a) | Sulfide iodine titrimetric |
| 376.2 (a) | Sulfide methylene blue colorimetric |
| 377.1 (a) | Sulfite titrimetric |
| 405.1 (a) | Biochemical oxygen demand (BOD) |
| 410.1 (a) | Chemical oxygen demand (COD) mid-level titrimetric |
| 410.2 (a) | COD low level titrimetric |
| 410.3 (a) | COD high level titrimetric |
| 410.4 (a) | COD automated or manual colorimetry |
| 413.1 (a) | Oil and grease gravimetric |
| 413.2 (a) | Oil and grease infrared |

Continued on next page.

---

[47]   (a) *Methods for Chemical Analysis of Water and Wastes* 1983 (EPA-600/4-79/020 PB84-128677); (b) *Methods for the determination of inorganic substances in environmental samples* 1993 (EPA 600/R-93/100); (c) *Methods for the determination of chemical substances in marine and estuarine environmental samples* (EPA/600/R-92/121), November 1992; (d) *Methods for the Determination of Metals in Environmental Samples,* 1991 (EPA 600/4-91/010); (e) *Methods for the Determination of Metals in Environmental Samples* Supplement I, 1994 (EPA-600/R-94/111); (f) *Analytical method for the determination of asbestos fibers in water*, September, 1983 NTIS PB83-260471; (g) *Determination of asbestos structure over 10 um in length in drinking water*, June 1994, EPA 600/R-94-134, NTIS PB94-201902.

**Table 1-14. EPA 100-400 series methods,** *continued*

| Method[48] | Title/Description |
|---|---|
| 415.1 (a) | Total organic carbon (TOC) combustion or oxidation |
| 415.2 (a) | TOC UV-persulfate oxidation |
| 418.1 (a) | Total petroleum hydrocarbons extraction infrared |
| 420.1 (a) | Total phenolics manual 4-AAP |
| 420.2 (a) | Total phenolics automated 4-AAP |
| 420.3 (a) | Total phenolics MBTH colorimetric |
| 420.4 (b) | Total phenolics semi-automated colorimetry |
| 425.1 (a) | MBAS surfactants |
| 430.1 (a) | NTA manual zinc-zincon |
| 430.2 (a) | NTA automated zinc-zincon |
| 440.0 (c) | Carbon and nitrogen in estuarine/coastal sediments using elemental analysis |
| 445.0 (c) | Chlorophyll $\partial$ and Pheophytin $\partial$ in marine and freshwater phytoplankton by fluorescence |

Methods Series 500-555

*Methods for the Determination of Organic Compounds in Drinking Water* (EPA-600/4-88/039) 1988, Supplement I (EPA 600/4-90/020) 1990, Supplement II (EPA 600/R-92/129) 1992, and Supplement III (EPA 600/R-95/131) 1995.

**Table 1-15. EPA 500 series methods**

| Method[49] | Revision | Title |
|---|---|---|
| 502.1 (a) | 2.0 | Volatile organic compounds in water by purge and trap GC |
| 502.2 (d) | 2.1 | Volatile organic compounds in water by purge and trap capillary column gas chromatography with photoionization and electrolytic conductivity detectors in series |
| 503.1 (a) | 2.0 | Volatile aromatic and unsaturated organic compounds in water by purge and trap GC |
| 504 (a) | 2.0 | 1,2-dibromoethane (EDB) and 1,2-dibromo-3-chloropropane (DBCP) in water by microextraction and GC |
| 504.1 (d) | 1.1 | 1,2-dibromoethane (EDB), 1,2-dibromo-3-chloropropane (DBCP) and 1,2,3-trichloropropane (123TCP) in water by microextraction and gas chromatography |

Continued on next page.

---

[48]  (a) *Methods for Chemical Analysis of Water and Wastes* 1983 (EPA-600/4-79/020 PB84-128677); (b) *Methods for the determination of inorganic substances in environmental samples* 1993 (EPA 600/R-93/100); (c) *Methods for the determination of chemical substances in marine and estuarine environmental samples* (EPA/600/R-92/121), November 1992; (d) *Methods for the Determination of Metals in Environmental Samples,* 1991 (EPA 600/4-91/010); (e) *Methods for the Determination of Metals in Environmental Samples* Supplement I, 1994 (EPA-600/R-94/111); (f) *Analytical method for the determination of asbestos fibers in water,* September, 1983 NTIS PB83-260471; (g) *Determination of asbestos structure over 10 um in length in drinking water,* June 1994, EPA 600/R-94-134, NTIS PB94-201902.

[49]  (a) *Methods for the Determination of Organic Compounds in Drinking Water* (EPA-600/4-88/039) 1988; (b) Supplement I (EPA 600/4-90/020) 1990; (c) Supplement II (EPA 600/R-92/129) 1992; and (d) Supplement III (EPA 600/R-95/131) 1995.

**Table 1-15. EPA 500 series methods,** *continued*

| Method[50] | Revision | Title |
|---|---|---|
| 505 (d) | 2.1 | Analysis of organohalide pesticides and commercial polychlorinated biphenyl (PCB) products in water by microextraction and gas chromatography |
| 506 (d) | 1.1 | Determination of phthalate and adipate esters in drinking water by liquid-liquid extraction or liquid-solid extraction and gas chromatography with photoionization detection |
| 507 (d) | 2.1 | Determination of nitrogen- and phosphorus-containing pesticides in water by gas chromatography with a nitrogen-phosphorus detector |
| 508 (d) | 3.1 | Determination of chlorinated pesticides in water by gas chromatography with an electron capture detector |
| 508.1 (d) | 2.0 | Determination of chlorinated pesticides, herbicides, and organohalides by liquid-solid extraction and electron capture gas chromatography |
| 508A (a) | 1.0 | Screening for polychlorinated biphenyls by perchlorination and GC |
| 509 (d) | 1.1 | Determination of ethylene thiourea (ETU) in water using gas chromatography with a nitrogen-phosphorus detector |
| 513 (b) | 1 | Determination of 2,3,7,8-tetrachloro-dibenzo-p-dioxin in drinking water by liquid-liquid extraction and GC with high resolution MS |
| 515.1 (d) | 4.1 | Determination of chlorinated acids in water by gas chromatography with an electron capture detector |
| 515.2 (d) | 1.1 | Determination of chlorinated acids in water using liquid-solid extraction and gas chromatography with an electron capture detector |
| 524.2 (d) | 4.1 | Measurement of purgeable organic compounds in water by capillary column gas chromatography/mass spectrometry |
| 525.2 (d) | 2.0 | Determination of organic compounds in drinking water by liquid-solid extraction and capillary column gas chromatography/mass spectrometry |
| 531.1 (d) | 3.1 | Measurement of N-methylcarbamoyloximes and N-methylcarbamates in water by direct aqueous injection HPLC with post column derivatization |
| 547 (b) | 1 | Determination of glyphosate in drinking water by direct aqueous injection HPLC, post-column derivatization and fluorescence detection |
| 548 (b) | 1 | Determination of endothall in drinking water by aqueous derivatization, liquid-solid extraction and GC with ECD |
| 548.1 (c) | 1.0 | Determination of endothall in drinking water by ion exchange extraction, acidic methanol methylation and GC/MS |
| 549 (b) | 1 | Determination of diquat and paraquat in drinking water by liquid-solid extraction and HPLC with ultraviolet detection |
| 549.1 (c) | 1.0 | Determination of diquat and paraquat in drinking water by liquid-solid extraction and HPLC with ultraviolet detector |
| 550 (b) | 1 | Determination of polycyclic aromatic hydrocarbons in drinking water by liquid-liquid extraction and HPLC with coupled ultraviolet and fluorescence detection |
| 550.1 (b) | 1 | Determination of polycyclic aromatic hydrocarbons in drinking water by liquid-liquid extraction and HPLC with coupled ultraviolet and fluorescence detection |

Continued on next page.

[50] (a) *Methods for the Determination of Organic Compounds in Drinking Water* (EPA-600/4-88/039) 1988; (b) Supplement I (EPA 600/4-90/020) 1990; (c) Supplement II (EPA 600/R-92/129) 1992; and (d) Supplement III (EPA 600/R-95/131) 1995.

**Table 1-15. EPA 500 series methods,** *continued*

| Method[51] | Revision | Title |
|---|---|---|
| 551 (b) | 1 | Determination of chlorination disinfection byproducts and chlorinated solvents in drinking water by liquid-liquid extraction and GC with ECD |
| 551.1 (d) | 1.0 | Determination of chlorination disinfection byproducts, chlorinated solvents and halogenated pesticides/herbicides in drinking water by liquid-liquid extraction and GC with ECD |
| 552 (b) | 1 | Determination of haloacetic acids in drinking water by liquid-liquid extraction, derivatization and GC with ECD |
| 552.2 (d) | 1.0 | Determination of haloacetic acids and dalapon in drinking water by liquid-liquid extraction and GC with ECD |
| 553 (c) | 1.1 | Determination of benzidines and nitrogen-containing pesticides in water by liquid-liquid extraction or liquid-solid extraction and reversed phase high performance liquid chromatography/particle beam/mass specrometry |
| 554 (c) | 1.0 | Determination of carbonyl compounds in drinking water by DNPH derivatization and high performance liquid chromatography |
| 555 (c) | 1.0 | Determination of chlorinated acids in water by high performance liquid chromatography with a photodiode array ultraviolet detector |

Methods Series 600's (developed by EMSL Cincinnati) and 1600's (developed by ORD/OST)

*Guidelines Establishing Test Procedures for the Analysis of Pollutants (in Water)* (40 CFR - Part 136, Appendix A), *Methods for the Determination of Nonconventional Pesticides in Municipal and Industrial Wastewater* (EPA 821 RR-92-002) 1992, *Analytical Methods for the Determination of Pollutants in Pulp and Paper Industry Wastewater*, EPA 821-R-93-017 (PB94-107059), October 1993; *Analytical Methods for the Determination of Pollutants in Pharmaceutical Manufacturing Industry Wastewater* (EPA-821-94-001) February, 1995.

**Table 1-16. EPA 600 series methods**

| Method[52] | Title/Description |
|---|---|
| 601 (a) | Purgeable halocarbons by purge and trap GC-ELCD |
| 602 (a) | Purgeable aromatics by purge and trap GC-PID |
| 603 (a) | Acrolein and Acrylonitrile by purge and trap GC-FID |
| 604 (a) | Phenold by GC-FID |
| 604.1 (b) | Hexachlorophene and dichlorophen by HPLC |
| 605 (a) | Benzidines by HPLC |
| 606 (a) | Phthalate esters by GC-ECD |
| 607 (a) | Nitrosamines by GC-NPD |
| 608 (a) | Organochlorine pesticides by GC-ECD |

Continued on next page.

---

[51] (a) *Methods for the Determination of Organic Compounds in Drinking Water* (EPA-600/4-88/039) 1988; (b) Supplement I (EPA 600/4-90/020) 1990; (c) Supplement II (EPA 600/R-92/129) 1992; and (d) Supplement III (EPA 600/R-95/131) 1995.

[52] (a) 40 CFR 136, Appendix A; (b) *Methods for the Determination of Nonconventional Pesticides in Municipal and Industrial Wastewater* (EPA 821 RR-92-002) 1992; (c) *Analytical Methods for the Determination of Pollutants in Pulp and Paper Industry Wastewater*, EPA 821-R-93-017 (PB94-107059), October, 1993; (d) *Analytical Methods for the Determination of Pollutants in Pharmaceutical Manufacturing Industry Wastewater* (EPA-821-94-001) February, 1995.

## Table 1-16. EPA 600 series methods, *continued*

| Method[53] | Title/Description |
|---|---|
| 608.1 (b) | Organochlorine pesticides by GC |
| 608.2 (b) | Certain organochlorine pesticides and PCBs by GC |
| 609 (a) | Nitroaromatics and isophorone by GC-FID and GC-ECD |
| 610 (a) | Polynuclear aromatic hydrocarbons by GC or HPLC |
| 611 (a) | Haloethers by GC-ECD or ELCD |
| 612 (a) | Chlorinated hydrocarbons by GC-ECD |
| 613 (b) | 2,3,7,8-TCDD by HRGC-HRMS Revision B, 1994 EPA 821-B-94-005 |
| 614 (b) | Organophosphorus pesticides by GC-NPD or FPD |
| 614.1 (b) | Organophosphorus pesticides by GC-NPD |
| 615 (b) | Chlorinated herbicides by GC-ECD |
| 616 (b) | Certain carbon-, hydrogen- and oxygen containing pesticides by GC-FID |
| 617 (b) | Organochlorine pesticides and PCBs by GC-ECD |
| 618 (b) | Volatile pesticides by GC-ECD |
| 619 (b) | Triazine pesticides by GC-NPD |
| 620 (b) | Diphenylamine by GC-AFD (Alkali flame detector) |
| 622 (b) | Organophosphorus pesticides by GC-NPD or FPD |
| 622.1 (b) | Thiophosphate pesticides by GC-AFD |
| 624 (a) | Purgeables by purge and trap GC/MS |
| 625 (a) | Base/neutrals and acids by GC/MS |
| 627 (b) | Dinitroaniline pesticides by GC-ECD |
| 629 (b) | Cyanazine by HPLC |
| 630 (b) | Dithiocarbamate pesticides by carbon disulfide colorimetry |
| 630.1 (b) | Dithiocarbamate pesticides by detection of carbon disulfide by GC-sulfur mode ELCD |
| 631 (b) | Benomyl and Carbendazim by HPLC |
| 632 (b) | Carbamate and urea pesticides by HPLC-UV |
| 632.1 (b) | Carbamate and amide pesticides by HPLC-UV |
| 633 (b) | Organonitrogen pesticides by GC-NPD |
| 633.1 (b) | Neutral nitrogen-containing pesticides by GC-AFD |
| 634 (b) | Thiocarbate pesticides by GC-AFD |
| 635 (b) | Rotenone by HPLC |
| 636 (b) | Bensulfide by HPLC |
| 637 (b) | MBTS and TCMTB by HPLC |
| 638 (b) | Oryzalin by HPLC |
| 639 (b) | Bendiocarb by HPLC |
| 640 (b) | Mercaptobenzothiazole by HPLC |
| 641 (b) | Thiabendazole by HPLC-fluorescence detection |
| 642 (b) | Biphenyl and *o*-phenylphenol by HPLC-UV |
| 643 (b) | Bentazon by HPLC |
| 644 (b) | Pichloram by HPLC |

Continued on next page.

---

[53] (a) 40 CFR 136, Appendix A; (b) *Methods for the Determination of Nonconventional Pesticides in Municipal and Industrial Wastewater* (EPA 821 RR-92-002) 1992; (c) *Analytical Methods for the Determination of Pollutants in Pulp and Paper Industry Wastewater*, EPA 821-R-93-017 (PB94-107059), October, 1993; (d) *Analytical Methods for the Determination of Pollutants in Pharmaceutical Manufacturing Industry Wastewater* (EPA-821-94-001) February, 1995.

**Table 1-16. EPA 600 series methods,** *continued*

| Method[54] | Title/Description |
|---|---|
| 645 (b) | Certain amine pesticides and lethane by GC-NPD |
| 646 (b) | Dinitro aromatic pesticides by GC-ECD |
| EV-024/EV-025 (b) | Total tin and organotin in wastewater |

**Table 1-17. EPA 1600 series methods**

| Method[55] | Title/Description |
|---|---|
| 1613 rev. B | Tetra- through octa-chlorinated dioxins and furans by isotope dilution HRGC/HRMS, EPA 821-B-94-005, October 1994 |
| 1618 (e) | Organohalide pesticides, organophosphorus pesticides and phenoxyacid herbicides by wide bore capillary GC with selective detectors |
| 1620 (e) | Metals by ICP-AES and AA spectrometry |
| 1624 (a) | Volatile organic compounds by isotope dilution GC/MS |
| 1624C (e) | Volatile organic compounds by isotope dilution GC/MS |
| 1625 (a) | Semivolatile organic compounds by isotope dilution GC/MS |
| 1625C (e) | Semivolatile organic compounds by isotope dilution GC/MS |
| 1631 | Mercury in water by oxidation, purge and trap, and cold vapor atomic fluorescence spectrometry EPA 821-R-95-027, April 1995 |
| 1632 | Determination of inorganic arsenic in water by hydride generation flame atomic absorption EPA 821-R-95-028 April 1995 |
| 1636 | Determination of hexavalent chromium by ion chromatography EPA 821-R-95-029 April 1995 |
| 1637 | Determination of trace elements in ambient waters by chelation preconcentration with graphite furnace atomic absorption EPA 821-R-95-030, April 1995 |
| 1638 | Determination of trace elements in ambient waters by inductively coupled plasma-mass spectrometry EPA 821-R-95-031, April 1995 |
| 1639 | Determination of trace elements in ambient waters by stabilized temperature graphite furnace atomic absorption EPA 821-R-95-032 April 1995 |
| 1640 | Determination of trace elements in ambient waters by on-line chelation preconcentration and inductively coupled plasma-mass spectrometry EPA 821-R-95-033, April 1995 |
| 1650 (c) | Absorbable organic halides by adsorption and coulometric titration |
| 1651 rev A (f) | Total oil and diesel oil in drilling muds and drill cuttings by retort, gavimetry, and GC/FID |
| 1653 (c) | Chlorinated phenolics in wastewater by *in situ* acetylation and GC-MS |

Continued on next page.

---

54   (a) 40 CFR 136, Appendix A; (b) *Methods for the Determination of Nonconventional Pesticides in Municipal and Industrial Wastewater* (EPA 821 RR-92-002) 1992; (c) *Analytical Methods for the Determination of Pollutants in Pulp and Paper Industry Wastewater*, EPA 821-R-93-017 (PB94-107059), October, 1993; (d) *Analytical Methods for the Determination of Pollutants in Pharmaceutical Manufacturing Industry Wastewater* (EPA-821-94-001) February, 1995.

55   (a) 40 CFR 136, Appendix A; (b) *Methods for the Determination of Nonconventional Pesticides in Municipal and Industrial Wastewater* (EPA 821 RR-92-002) 1992; (c) *Analytical Methods for the Determination of Pollutants in Pulp and Paper Industry Wastewater*, EPA 821-R-93-017 (PB94-107059), October, 1993; (d) *Analytical Methods for the Determination of Pollutants in Pharmaceutical Manufacturing Industry Wastewater* (EPA-821-94-001) February, 1995; (e) *Analytical Methods for the National Sewage Sludge Survey*, Office of Water WH-585, September, 1990; (f) *Methods for the determination of diesel, mineral, and crude oils in offshore oil and gas industry discharges*, December, 1992, EPA 821-R-92-008, PB 93-166932.

**Table 1-17. EPA 1600 series methods,** *continued*

| Method[56] | Title/Description |
|---|---|
| 1654 rev A (f) | PAH content of oil by HPLC/UV |
| 1656 (b) | Organohalide pesticides by GC |
| 1657 (b) | Organophosphorus pesticides by GC-FPD |
| 1658 (b) | Phenoxy-acid herbicides by GC-ECD |
| 1659 (b) | Dazomet by GC-NPD |
| 1660 (b) | Pyrethrins and pyrethroids by HPLC-UV |
| 1661 (b) | Bromoxynil by HPLC-UV |
| 1662 (f) | Total extractable material in drilling mud by SDS extraction and gravimetry |
| 1663 (f) | Differentiation of diesel and crude oil by GC/FID |
| 1664 | *N*-hexane extractable material (HEM) and silica gel treated *n*-hexane extractable material (SGT-HEM) by extraction and gravimetry (oil and grease and total petroleum hydrocarbons) EPA-821-B-94-004b, April 1995 |
| 1665 (d) | Semi-volatile organic compounds specific to the pharmaceutical manufacturing industry by isotope dilution GC/MS |
| 1666 (d) | Volatile organic compounds specific to the pharmaceutical manufacturing industry by isotope dilution GC/MS |
| 1667 (d) | Formaldehyde, isobutyraldehyde, and furfural by derivatization and high-pressure liquid chromatography |
| 1669 | Sampling ambient water for determination of trace metals at EPA water quality criteria levels and Quality Control Supplement for Determination of Trace Metals at EPA Water Quality Criteria Levels using EPA Metals Methods. EPA 821-R-95-034, April 1995 |
| 1671 (d) | Volatile organic compounds specific to the pharmaceutical manufacturing industry by GC/FID |
| 1673 (d) | Poly(ethylene glycol)-600 by derivatization and high-pressure liquid chromatography |

Methods Series 900's
*Prescribed Procedures for Measurement of Radioactivity in Drinking Water*
(EPA-600/4-80-032) 1980.

**Table 1-18. EPA 900 series methods**

| Method | Title/Description |
|---|---|
| 900.0 | Gross alpha and gross beta radioactivity |
| 900.1 | Gross radium alpha screening procedure |
| 901.0 | Radioactive cesium |
| 901.1 | Gamma emitting radionuclides |
| 902.0 | Radioactive iodine |
| 903.0 | Alpha-emitting radium isotopes |

Continued on next page.

---

[56] (a) 40 CFR 136, Appendix A; (b) *Methods for the Determination of Nonconventional Pesticides in Municipal and Industrial Wastewater* (EPA 821 RR-92-002) 1992; (c) *Analytical Methods for the Determination of Pollutants in Pulp and Paper Industry Wastewater*, EPA 821-R-93-017 (PB94-107059), October, 1993; (d) *Analytical Methods for the Determination of Pollutants in Pharmaceutical Manufacturing Industry Wastewater* (EPA-821-94-001) February, 1995; (e) *Analytical Methods for the National Sewage Sludge Survey*, Office of Water WH-585, September, 1990; (f) *Methods for the Determination of Diesel, Mineral, and Crude Oils in Offshore Oil and Gas Industry Discharges*, December, 1992, EPA 821-R-92-008, PB 93-166932.

**Table 1-18. EPA 900 series methods,** *continued*

| Method | Title/Description |
|--------|-------------------|
| 903.1 | Radium-226 Radon emanation technique |
| 904.0 | Radium-228 |
| 905.0 | Radioactive strontium |
| 906.0 | Tritium |
| 907.0 | Actinide elements |
| 908.0 | Uranium - Radiochemical method |
| 908.1 | Uranium - Fluorometric method |

Methods Series 1000's

A set of microbiological and toxicity procedures used for compliance monitoring under the Clean Water Act. Reference documents include those listed in the footnotes to Table 1-19.

**Table 1-19. EPA 1000 series methods for compliance monitoring**

| Method[57] | Title |
|------------|-------|
| 1000.0 (a) | Fathead minnow, *Pimephales promelas*, larval survival and growth test method |
| 1001.0 (a) | Fathead minnow, *Pimephales promelas*, embryo-larval survival and teratogenicity test method |
| 1002.0 (a) | Daphnid, *Ceriodaphnia dubia*, survival and reproduction test method |
| 1003.0 (a) | Green alga, *Selenastrum Capricornutum*, growth test method |
| 1004.0 (b) | Sheepshead minnow, *Cyprinodon variegatus*, larval survival and growth test method |
| 1005.0 (b) | Sheepshead minnow, *Cyprinodon variegatus*, embryo-larval survival and teratogenicity test method |
| 1006.0 (b) | Inland silverside, *Menidia beryllina*, larval survival and growth method |
| 1007.0 (b) | Mysid, *Mysidopsis bahia*, survival, growth and fecundity test method |
| 1008.0 (b) | Sea urchin, *Arbacia punctulata*, fertilization test method |
| 1009.0 (b) | Red macroalga, *Champia parvula*, reproduction test method |
| 1103.1 (c) | Test method for *Escherichia coli* in water by the membrane filter procedure |
| 1106.1 (c) | Test method for *Enterococci* in water by the membrane filter procedure |

Methods Series 0000-9999

*Test Methods for Evaluating Solid Wastes Physical/Chemical Methods,* or as it is commonly called, SW-846, is the testing manual for RCRA. The third edition was proposed in 1986, with draft updates published in 1987, and 1990. Promulgation of the third edition did not occur until July, 1993. In the same final notice, the 1987 and 1990 draft updates were scrapped by the Office of Solid Waste in favor of promulgating a completely new Update 1, dated July 1992. On 13 February, 1995, EPA announced in the *Federal Register*, the promulgation of Updates II and IIa, with the date of September, 1994 on the pages. A draft copy of Update III was released to subscribers in

---

[57] (a) *Short-term Methods for Estimating the Chronic Toxicity of Effluents and Receiving Water to Freshwater Organisms*, Third Edition, July, 1994. EPA-600-4-91-002; (b) *Short-term Methods for Estimating the Chronic Toxicity of Effluents and Receiving Water to Marine and Estuarine Organisms*, Second Edition, July, 1994 EPA-600-4-91-003; (c) *Test methods for Eschericia coli and Enterococci in Water by the Membrane Filter Procedure*, EPA 600/4-85-076 1985, NTIS PB86-158052.

mid-1995, however, as of January, 1997, it has not been promulgated. Update III represents a major change in analysis conducted under the Solid Waste program as some methods are proposed to be deleted from SW-846.

The layout of SW-846 is by Chapters, such as Chapter 3 for metals, Chapter 4 for Organics, *etc.* With few exceptions the methods are modular, with one method number relating to the sample preparation, another method number relating to sample clean-up, and a final method describing the determinative (instrument) operating procedures. In addition there are general methods that describe in broad strokes techniques to be used in all methods. For example Method 3500 is where a complete description of organic surrogates will be found, and Method 8000 discusses the calibration options and variations for organic determinative methods. Table 1-20 presents the general numbering scheme of SW-846, while Table 1-21 presents a detailed list of the contents by Method number.

**Table 1-20.  General numbering scheme of** *Test Methods for Evaluating Solid Wastes Physical/Chemical Methods* **(SW-846, 3rd Edition, Revision I July, 1992 and Revisions II and IIa, September, 1994)**

| Method | Title |
|---|---|
| 0000's | Air Sampling Methods |
| 1000's | Determination of Hazardous Characteristics |
| 2000's | (Unused) |
| 3000's | Sample Preparation Methods |
| 3000's | Sample Preparation for Metals Analysis |
| 3500's | Sample Extraction for Organic Analysis |
| 3600's | Sample Cleanup for Organic Analysis |
| 3800's | Volatile Organic Screening Methods |
| 4000's | Field Screening Methods |
| 5000's | Volatile and Miscellaneous Sample Preparation Methods |
| 6000's | Multi-metal Instrumental Determinations |
| 7000's | Single-metal Instrumental Determinations |
| 8000's | Determination of Organic Analytes |
| 8000-8100's | GC |
| 8200's | GC-MS |
| 8300's | HPLC |
| 8400's | GC-FTIR |
| 9000's | Miscellaneous Test Methods |
| 9000-9200's | Miscellaneous Analytes |
| 9300's | Radioisotopes |

**Table 1-21.  Contents of SW-846 including the proposed Update III to the Third Edition**

| | |
|---|---|
| 0010 | Modified method 5 sampling train |
| 0011 | Sampling for formaldehyde emissions from stationary sources |
| 0020 | Source assessment sampling system (SASS) |
| 0023A | Sampling method for dioxins and furans from stationary sources |
| 0030 | Volatile organic sampling train (VOST) |

Continued on next page.

### Table 1-21. Contents of SW-846 including the proposed Update III to the Third Edition, *continued*

| | |
|---|---|
| 0031 | Sampling method for volatile organic compounds (SMVOC) |
| 0040 | Sampling of principal organic hazardous constituents from combustion sources using Tedlar bags |
| 0050 | Isokenetic HCl/Cl$_2$ emission sampling train |
| 0051 | Midget impinger HCl/Cl$_2$ emission sampling train |
| 0060 | Determination of metals in stack emissions |
| 0061 | Determination of hexavalent chromium emissions from stationary sources |
| 0100 | Sampling for formaldehyde and other carbonyl compounds in indoor air |
| 1010 | Pensky-Martins closed cup method for determining ignitability |
| 1020A | Setaflash closed cup method for determining ignitability |
| 1030 | Ignitability of solids |
| 1110 | Corrosivity toward steel |
| 1120 | Dermal corrosion |
| 1310A | Extraction procedure (EP) toxicity test method and structural integrity test |
| 1311 | Toxic characteristic leaching procedure |
| 1312 | Synthetic precipitation leaching procedure |
| 1320 | Multiple extraction procedure |
| 1330A | Extraction procedure for oily wastes |
| 3005A | Acid digestion of waters for total recoverable or dissolved metals by FLAA or ICP |
| 3010A | Acid digestion of aqueous samples and extracts for total metals for analysis by FLAA or ICP |
| 3015 | Microwave assisted acid digestion of aqueous samples and extracts |
| 3020A | Acid digestion of aqueous samples and extracts for total metals for analysis by GFAA |
| 3031 | Acid digestion of oils for metals analysis by FLAA or ICP |
| 3040A | Dissolution procedure for oils, greases or waxes |
| 3050B | Acid digestion of sediments, sludges, or soils |
| 3051 | Microwave assisted acid digestion of sediments, sludges, soils and oils |
| 3052 | Microwave assisted acid digestion of siliceous and organically based matrices |
| 3060A | Alkaline digestion for hexavalent chromium |
| 3500B | Organic extraction and sample preparation |
| 3510C | Separatory funnel liquid-liquid extraction |
| 3520C | Continuous liquid-liquid extraction |
| 3535 | Solid phase extraction (SPE) |
| 3540C | Soxhlet extraction |
| 3541 | Automated soxhlet extraction |
| 3542 | Extraction of semivolatile analytes collected using modified method 5 (Method 0010) sampling train |
| 3545 | Accelerated solvent extraction (ASE) |
| 3550B | Ultrasonic extraction |
| 3560 | Supercritical fluid extraction of total recoverable petroleum hydrocarbons (TRPH) |
| 3561 | Supercritical fluid extraction of polynuclear aromatic hydrocarbons |
| 3580A | Waste dilution |
| 3585 | Waste dilution for volatile organics |
| 3600C | Cleanup |
| 3610B | Alumina cleanup |
| 3611B | Alumina column cleanup and separation of petroleum wastes |

Continued on next page.

**Table 1-21. Contents of SW-846 including the proposed Update III to the Third Edition,** *continued*

| | |
|---|---|
| 3620B | Florisil cleanup |
| 3630C | Silica gel cleanup |
| 3640A | Gel-permeation cleanup |
| 3650B | Acid-base partition cleanup |
| 3660B | Sulfur cleanup |
| 3665A | Sulfuric acid/permanganate cleanup |
| 3810 | Headspace |
| 3820 | Hexadecane extraction and screening of purgeable organics |
| 4000 | Immunoassay |
| 4010A | Screening for pentachlorophenol by immunoassay |
| 4015 | Screening for 2,4-D by immunoassay |
| 4020 | Screening for PCBs by immunoassay |
| 4030 | Soil screening for petroleum hydrocarbons by immunoassay |
| 4035 | Soil screening for PAH by immunoassay |
| 4040 | Soil screening for toxaphene by immunoassay |
| 4041 | Soil screening for chlordane by immunoassay |
| 4042 | Soil screening for DDT by immunoassay |
| 4050 | TNT explosives in water and soils by immunoassay |
| 4051 | RDX in soil and water by immunoassay |
| 5000 | Sample preparation for volatile organic compounds |
| 5021 | Volatile organic compounds in soils and other solid matrices using equilibrium headspace |
| 5030B | Purge and trap for aqueous samples |
| 5031 | Volatile, nonpurgeable, water-soluble compounds by azeotropic distillation |
| 5032 | Volatile organic compounds by vacuum distillation |
| 5035 | Closed system purge and trap and extraction for volatile organics in soil and waste samples |
| 5041A | Analysis for desorption of sorbent cartridges from volatile organic sampling train (VOST): capillary GC/MS technique |
| 5050 | Bomb preparation method for solid waste |
| 6010B | ICP-AES |
| 6020 | ICP-MS |
| 7000A | AA Methods |
| 7020 | Aluminum FLAA |
| 7040 | Antimony FLAA |
| 7041 | Antimony GFAA |
| 7060A | Arsenic GFAA |
| 7061A | Arsenic Hydride AA |
| 7062 | Antimony and Arsenic (Borohydride reduction AA) |
| 7063 | Arsenic by anodic stripping voltammetry (ASV) |
| 7080A | Barium FLAA |
| 7081 | Barium GFAA |
| 7090 | Beryllium FLAA |
| 7091 | Beryllium GFAA |
| 7130 | Cadmium FLAA |
| 7131A | Cadmium GFAA |

Continued on next page.

### Table 1-21. Contents of SW-846 including the proposed Update III to the Third Edition, *continued*

| | |
|------|---|
| 7140 | Calcium FLAA |
| 7190 | Chromium FLAA |
| 7191 | Chromium GFAA |
| 7195 | Chromium, hexavalent (Coprecipitation) |
| 7196A | Chromium, hexavalent (Colorimetric) |
| 7197 | Chromium, hexavalent (Chelation/extraction) |
| 7198 | Chromium, hexavalent (Differential pulse polarography) |
| 7199 | Determination of hexavalent chromium in drinking water, groundwater and industrial wastewater effluents by ion chromatography |
| 7200 | Cobalt FLAA |
| 7201 | Cobalt GFAA |
| 7210 | Copper FLAA |
| 7211 | Copper GFAA |
| 7380 | Iron FLAA |
| 7381 | Iron GFAA |
| 7420 | Lead FLAA |
| 7421 | Lead GFAA |
| 7430 | Lithium FLAA |
| 7450 | Magnesium FLAA |
| 7460 | Manganese FLAA |
| 7461 | Manganese GFAA |
| 7470A | Mercury in liquid waste CVAA |
| 7471A | Mercury in solid or semi-solid waste CVAA |
| 7472 | Mercury in aqueous samples and extracts by anodic stripping voltammetry (ASV) |
| 7480 | Molybdenum FLAA |
| 7481 | Molybdenum GFAA |
| 7520 | Nickel FLAA |
| 7521 | Nickel GFAA |
| 7550 | Osmium FLAA |
| 7580 | White phosphorus by solvent extraction and gas chromatography |
| 7610 | Potassium FLAA |
| 7740 | Selenium GFAA |
| 7741A | Selenium Hydride AA |
| 7742 | Selenium Borohydride reduction AA |
| 7760A | Silver FLAA |
| 7761 | Silver GFAA |
| 7770 | Sodium FLAA |
| 7780 | Strontium FLAA |
| 7840 | Thallium FLAA |
| 7841 | Thallium GFAA |
| 7870 | Tin FLAA |
| 7910 | Vanadium FLAA |
| 7911 | Vanadium GFAA |
| 7950 | Zinc FLAA |
| 7951 | Zinc GFAA |
| 8000B | Determinative chromatographic separations |

Continued on next page.

**Table 1-21. Contents of SW-846 including the proposed Update III to the Third Edition,** *continued*

| | |
|---|---|
| 8011 | EDB and DBCP by microextraction and GC |
| 8015B | Nonhalogenated organics using GC/FID |
| 8021B | Halogenated volatiles by GC using PID and ECD in series; capillary column technique |
| 8031 | Acrylonitrile by GC |
| 8032A | Acrylamide by GC |
| 8033 | Acetonitrile by GC-NPD |
| 8041 | Phenols by GC: capillary column technique |
| 8061A | Phthalate esters by capillary GC-ECD |
| 8070A | Nitrosamines by GC |
| 8081A | Organochlorine pesticides by capillary column GC |
| 8082 | PCB by capillary GC |
| 8091 | Nitroaromatics and cyclic ketones: capillary column technique |
| 8100 | Polynuclear aromatic hydrocarbons |
| 8111 | Haloethers: capillary column technique |
| 8121 | Chlorinated hydrocarbons by GC: capillary column technique |
| 8131 | Aniline and selected derivatives by GC: capillary column technique |
| 8141A | Organophosphorus compounds by GC: capillary column technique |
| 8151A | Chlorinated herbicides by GC using methylation or pentafluorobenzylation derivatization |
| 8260B | Volatile organic compounds by GC/MS |
| 8270C | Semivolatile organic compounds by GC/MS |
| 8275A | Semivolatile organic compounds (PAH and PCB) in soils/sludges and solid wastes using TE/GC/MS |
| 8280A | Dioxins and furans by HRGC/LRMS |
| 8290 | Dioxins and furans by HRGC/HRMS |
| 8310 | Polynuclear aromatic hydrocarbons |
| 8315A | Determination of carbonyl compounds by HPLC |
| 8316 | Acrylamide, acrylonitrile and acrolein by HPLC |
| 8321A | Solvent extractable non-volatile compounds by HPLC/TS/MS or UV |
| 8325 | Solvent extractable non-volatile compounds by HPLC/PB/MS |
| 8330 | Nitroaromatics and nitramines by HPLC |
| 8331 | Tetrazene by HPLC |
| 8332 | Nitroglycerine by HPLC |
| 8410 | GC/FTIR for semivolatile organics |
| 8430 | Analysis of bis(2-chloroethyl)ether hydrolysis products by direct aqueous injection GC/FTIR |
| 8440 | TRPH by IR |
| 8515 | Colorimetric screening method for TNT in soil |
| 8520 | Continuous measurement of formaldehyde in ambient air |
| 9010A | Total and amenable cyanide (colorimetric manual) |
| 9012A | Total and amenable cyanide (colorimetric automated UV) |
| 9013 | Cyanide extraction procedure for solids and oils |
| 9020B | Total organic halides (TOX) |
| 9021 | Purgeable organic halides |
| 9022 | TOX by neutron activation analysis |
| 9023 | Extractable organic halides (EOX) in solids |
| 9030A | Acid-soluble and acid-insoluble sulfides |

Continued on next page.

**Table 1-21.  Contents of SW-846 including the proposed Update III to the Third Edition,** *continued*

| | |
|---|---|
| 9031 | Extractable sulfides |
| 9035 | Sulfate (colorimetric, automated chloranilate) |
| 9036 | Sulfate (colorimetric, automated methylthymol blue) |
| 9038 | Sulfate (turbidimetric) |
| 9040B | pH electrometric measurement |
| 9041A | pH paper method |
| 9045C | Soil and waste pH |
| 9050A | Specific conductance |
| 9056 | Determination of inorganic anions by ion chromatography |
| 9057 | Determination of chloride from HCl/Cl$_2$ emissions sampling train (Methods 0050 and 0051) by anion chromatography |
| 9060 | Total organic carbon (TOC) |
| 9065 | Phenolics (spectrophotometric 4AAP manual) |
| 9066 | Phenolics (colorimetric, automated 4AAP) |
| 9067 | Phenolics (spectrophotometric, MBTH) |
| 9070 | Total recoverable oil & grease |
| 9071A | Oil & grease extraction method for sludge and sediment samples |
| 9075 | Test method for total chlorine in new and used petroleum products by XRF |
| 9076 | Test method for total chlorine in new and used petroleum products by oxidative combustion and microcoulometry |
| 9077 | Test methods for total chlorine in new and used petroleum products (field test kit methods) |
| 9078 | Screening test method for PCB in soil |
| 9079 | Screening test method for PCB in transformer oil |
| 9080 | Cation exchange capacity of soils (ammonium acetate) |
| 9081 | Cation exchange capacity of soils (sodium acetate) |
| 9090A | Compatibility test for wastes and membrane liners |
| 9095A | Paint filter liquids test |
| 9096 | Liquid release test |
| 9100 | Saturated hydraulic conductivity, saturated leachate conductivity and intrinsic permeability |
| 9131 | Total coliform MPN |
| 9132 | Total coliform MF |
| 9210 | Nitrate ISE |
| 9211 | Bromide ISE |
| 9212 | Chloride ISE |
| 9213 | Cyanide ISE |
| 9214 | Fluoride ISE |
| 9215 | Sulfide ISE |
| 9250 | Chloride (automated ferricyanide AAI) |
| 9251 | Chloride (automated ferricyanide AAII) |
| 9253 | Chloride (titrimetric, silver nitrate) |
| 9310 | Gross alpha and gross beta |
| 9315 | Alpha-emitting radium isotopes |
| 9320 | Radium-228 |

Methods TO1-TO14
  *Compendium of Methods for the Determination of Toxic Organic Compounds in Ambient Air* (PB90-127374) (see Table 5-6 at end of Section 5)

Methods IP1A-IP10B
  *Compendium of Methods for the Determination of Air Pollutants in Indoor Air* (PB90-200288) (see Table 5-7 at end of Section 5)

*DOE Methods for Evaluating Environmental and Waste Management Samples* (DOE/EM-0089T, from NTIS) (see Table 4-35 in Section 4)

*NIOSH Manual of Analytical Methods*, 3rd Edition, 1988 and 4th Edition, 1995. Volumes 1-2 cover air analysis. The 4th Edition is available as a disk for operation in *Windows* on a PC. The method numbers are assigned in the NIOSH methods by sampling technique. The general categories are listed in Table 1-22. The following Table lists the contents of the 4th Edition.

**Table 1-22. General method numbering of *NIOSH Manual of Analytical Methods* 4th Edition**

| Method | Sampling Technique |
|---|---|
| 0001-0899 | General air samples |
| 0900-0999 | Bioaerosols |
| 1000-1999 | Organic gases on charcoal |
| 2000-3499 | Organic gases on other solid supports |
| 3500-3999 | Organic gases on other samplers |
| 4000-4999 | Organic gases on diffusive samplers |
| 5000-5999 | Organic aerosols |
| 6000-6999 | Inorganic gases |
| 7000-7999 | Inorganic aerosols |
| 8000-8999 | Biological samples |
| 9000-9999 | Bulk samples |

**Table 1-23. Method contents of *NIOSH Manual of Analytical Methods* 4th Edition**

| Method | Title/Description |
|---|---|
| 2538 | Acetaldehyde by GC |
| 3507 | Acetaldehyde by HPLC |
| 1603 | Acetic acid |
| 3506 | Acetic anhydride |
| 2506 | Acetone cyanohydrin |
| 1606 | Acetonitrile |
| 7903 | Acids, inorganic |
| 2501 | Acrolein |
| 1604 | Acrylonitrile |
| 1400 | Alcohols I (tert-butyl, isopropyl and ethyl alcohols) |

Continued on next page.

**Table 1-23. Method contents of *NIOSH Manual of Analytical Methods* 4th Edition,** *continued*

| 1401 | Alcohols II (*n*-butyl, *s*-butyl, isobutyl and *n*-propyl alcohols) |
|------|--------------------------------------------------------------------|
| 1402 | Alcohols III (allyl, isoamyl, cyclohexyl, and diacetone alcohols, methyl isobutyl carbinaol) |
| 1403 | Alcohols IV (2-butoxyethyl, 2-ethoxyethyl and 2-methoxyethyl alcohols) |
| 2539 | Aldehydes, screening |
| 5502 | Aldrin and lindane |
| 7401 | Alkaline dusts |
| 1000 | Allyl chloride |
| 2545 | Allyl glycidyl ether |
| 7013 | Aluminum |
| 2010 | Aliphatic amines |
| 2002 | Aromatic amines |
| 2007 | Aminoethanol compounds I |
| 3509 | Aminoethanol compounds II |
| 6015 | Ammonia |
| 2514 | Anisidine |
| 7900 | Arsenic (hydride AA) |
| 5022 | Arsenic, organo- |
| 7901 | Arsenic trioxide |
| 6001 | Arsine |
| 9002 | Asbestos |
| 9000 | Asbestos, chrysotile by XRD |
| 7400 | Asbestos and other fibers |
| 7402 | Asbestos fibers by TEM |
| 5031 | Aspartame |
| 5019 | Azelaic acid |
| 7056 | Barium, soluble compounds |
| 3700 | Benzene |
| 5509 | Benzidine and 3,3'-dichlorobenzidine |
| 8306 | Benzidine in urine |
| 5009 | Benzoyl peroxide |
| 7102 | Beryllium |
| 7506 | Boron carbide |
| 5010 | Bromoxynil and bromoxynil octanoate |
| 1024 | 1,3-Butadiene |
| 2012 | *n*-Butylamine |
| 1616 | *n*-Butyl glycidyl ether |
| 7048 | Cadmium |
| 7020 | Calcium |
| 5006 | Carbaryl |
| 5000 | Carbon black |
| 6603 | Carbon dioxide |
| 1600 | Carbon disulfide |

Continued on next page.

**Table 1-23. Method contents of** *NIOSH Manual of Analytical Methods* **4th Edition,** *continued*

| | |
|------|---------------------------------------------|
| 5510 | Chlordane |
| 5039 | Chlorinated camphene (toxaphene) |
| 5025 | Chlorinated diphenyl oxide |
| 5014 | Chlorinated terphenyl |
| 6011 | Chlorine and bromine |
| 2015 | Chloroacetaldehyde |
| 2008 | Chloroacetic acid |
| 2014 | *p*-Chlorophenol |
| 1002 | *b*-Chloroprene |
| 7024 | Chromium by FAAS |
| 7600 | Chromium, hexavalent by Vis |
| 7604 | Chromium, hexavalent by IC |
| 7027 | Cobalt |
| 7029 | Copper dust and fume |
| 2546 | Cresols and phenol |
| 3516 | Crotonaldehyde |
| 7904 | Cyanides by ISE |
| 5030 | Cyanuric acid |
| 2523 | 1,3-Cyclopentadiene |
| 5001 | 2,4-D and 2,4,5-T |
| 5514 | Demeton |
| 2515 | Diazomethane |
| 6006 | Diborane |
| 5017 | Dibutylphosphate |
| 5020 | Dibutyl and Bis(2-ethylhexyl) phthalates |
| 1018 | Freons |
| 1004 | Dichloroethylether |
| 2516 | Dichlorofluoromethane |
| 1601 | 1,1-Dichloro-1-nitroethane |
| 1012 | Difluorodibromomethane |
| 2004 | Dimethylacetamide and dimethylformamide |
| 3515 | 1,1-Dimethylhydrazine |
| 2524 | Dimethyl sulfate |
| 1602 | Dioxane |
| 2530 | Diphenyl |
| 5013 | Dyes |
| 8005 | Elements (metals) in blood or tissue |
| 7300 | Elements (metals) by ICP |
| 5519 | Endrin |
| 1010 | Epichlorohydrin |
| 5012 | EPN |
| 1450 | Esters I |

Continued on next page.

**Table 1-23. Method contents of *NIOSH Manual of Analytical Methods* 4th Edition,** *continued*

| | |
|---|---|
| 1457 | Ethyl acetate |
| 1011 | Ethyl bromide |
| 2519 | Ethyl chloride |
| 1610 | Ethyl ether |
| 1452 | Ethyl formate |
| 2513 | Ethylene chlorohydrin |
| 2540 | Ethylene diamine, diethylene triamine and triethylene tetraamine |
| 1008 | Ethylene dibromide |
| 1614 | Ethylene oxide |
| 3702 | Ethylene oxide (portable GC) |
| 5011 | Ethylene thiourea |
| 3514 | Ethylenimine |
| 8308 | Fluorides in urine |
| 7906 | Fluorides by IC |
| 7902 | Fluorides by ISE |
| 1006 | Fluorotrichloromethane |
| 2541 | Formaldehyde (2-hydroxymethyl-piperidine) by GC |
| 3500 | Formaldehyde (chromotropic acid) |
| 5700 | Formaldehyde on dust |
| 2011 | Formic acid by IC |
| 2529 | Furfural |
| 2505 | Furfuryl alcohol |
| 2532 | Glutaraldehyde by HPLC |
| 1608 | Glycidol |
| 2543 | Hexachlorobutadiene |
| 2518 | Hexachloro-1,3-cyclopentadiene |
| 8300 | Hippuric acid in urine (Vis) |
| 8301 | Hippuric and methyl hippuric acid in urine (HPLC) |
| 3503 | Hydrazine |
| 1500 | Hydrocarbons BP 36-126 °C |
| 1501 | Hydrocarbons, aromatic |
| 1003 | Hydrocarbons, halogenated |
| 6010 | Hydrogen cyanide |
| 6013 | Hydrogen sulfide by IC |
| 5004 | Hydroquinone |
| 6005 | Iodine |
| 5521 | Isocyanates |
| 2508 | Isophorone |
| 1454 | Isopropyl acetate |
| 1618 | Isopropyl ether |
| 1620 | Isopropyl glycidyl ether |
| 5508 | Kepone |

Continued on next page.

**Table 1-23. Method contents of** *NIOSH Manual of Analytical Methods* **4th Edition,** *continued*

| | |
|---|---|
| 1300 | Ketones I |
| 1301 | Ketones II |
| 8003 | Lead in blood and urine |
| 9100 | Lead in surface wipe samples |
| 7082 | Lead by FAAS |
| 7105 | Lead by HGAAS |
| 7505 | Lead sulfide |
| 3512 | Maleic anhydride |
| 8302 | MBOCA in urine |
| 2542 | Mercaptans |
| 6009 | Mercury |
| 8310 | Metals in urine (ICP) |
| 2000 | Methanol |
| 1458 | Methyl acetate |
| 1459 | Methyl acrylate |
| 1611 | Methylal |
| 1451 | Methyl cellosolve acetate |
| 1001 | Methyl chloride |
| 1404 | Methylcyclohexanol |
| 2521 | Methylcyclohexanone |
| 1005 | Methylene chloride |
| 5029 | 4,4'-Methylenedianiline (MDA) |
| 2500 | Methyl ethyl ketone |
| 8002 | Methyl ethyl ketone, ethanol and toluene in blood |
| 3508 | Methyl ethyl ketone peroxide |
| 1014 | Methyl iodide |
| 2537 | Methyl methacrylate |
| 1615 | Methyl *t*-butyl ether |
| 3511 | Monomethylaniline |
| 3510 | Monomethylhydrazine |
| 1550 | Naphthas |
| 5518 | Naphthylamines |
| 6007 | Nickel carbonyl |
| 2544 | Nicotine |
| 6014 | Nitric oxide and nitrogen dioxide |
| 5033 | *p*-Nitroaniline |
| 2005 | Nitrobenzenes |
| 2526 | Nitroethane |
| 2507 | Nitroglycerin/EGDN |
| 2527 | Nitromethane |
| 2528 | 2-Nitropropane |
| 2522 | Nitrosamines |

Continued on next page.

**Table 1-23.** **Method contents of** *NIOSH Manual of Analytical Methods* **4th Edition,** *continued*

| | |
|---|---|
| 6600 | Nitrous oxide |
| 2510 | 1-Octanethiol |
| 5026 | Oil mist - mineral |
| 5600 | Organophosphorus pesticides |
| 5504 | Organotin compounds |
| 6601 | Oxygen |
| 5003 | Paraquat |
| 0600 | Particulates, respirable |
| 0500 | Particulates, total |
| 2517 | Pentachloroethane |
| 5512 | Pentachlorophenol |
| 8001 | Pentachlorophenol in blood |
| 8303 | Pentachlorophenol in urine |
| 5032 | Pentamidine isothionate |
| 8305 | Phenol and *p*-cresol in urine |
| 1617 | Phenyl ether |
| 2013 | Phenyl ether-diphenyl mix |
| 1619 | Phenyl glycidyl ether |
| 3518 | Phenylhydrazine |
| 6002 | Phosphine |
| 7905 | Phosphorus |
| 6402 | Phosphorus trichloride |
| 5517 | Polychlorobenzenes |
| 5503 | Polychlorobiphenyls |
| 8004 | Polychlorobiphenyls in serum |
| 5506 | Polynuclear aromatic hydrocarbons (HPLC) |
| 5515 | Polynuclear aromatic hydrocarbons (GC) |
| 1013 | Propylene dichloride |
| 1612 | Propylene oxide |
| 5008 | Pyrethrum |
| 1613 | Pyridine |
| 5027 | Ribavirin |
| 5007 | Rotenone |
| 7501 | Silica, amorphous |
| 7603 | Silica in coal mine dust by IR |
| 7500 | Silica, crystalline respirable by XRD |
| 7601 | Silica, crystalline by Vis |
| 7602 | Silica, crystalline by IR |
| 6008 | Stilbine |
| 5016 | Strychnine |
| 6004 | Sulfur dioxide |
| 6602 | Sulfur hexafluoride |

Continued on next page.

**Table 1-23. Method contents of *NIOSH Manual of Analytical Methods* 4th Edition, *continued***

| 6012 | Sulfuryl fluoride |
|------|-------------------|
| 5035 | Super absorbent polymer |
| 5021 | *o*-Terphenyl |
| 2003 | 1,1,2,2-Tetrabromoethane |
| 1016 | Tetrachlorodifluoroethane |
| 1019 | 1,1,2,2-Tetrachloroethane |
| 2533 | Tetraethyl lead |
| 2504 | Tetraethyl pyrophosphate (TEPP) |
| 1609 | Tetrahydrofuran |
| 2534 | Tetramethyl lead |
| 3505 | Tetramethyl thiourea |
| 3513 | Tetranitromethane |
| 5005 | Thiram |
| 4000 | Toluene |
| 5516 | 2,4- and 2,6-Toluenediamine |
| 2535 | Toluene, 2,4-diisocyanate |
| 5034 | Tributylphosphate |
| 1022 | Trichloroethylene |
| 3701 | Trichloroethylene (portable GC) |
| 1020 | 1,1,2-Trichlorotrifluoroethane |
| 1017 | Trifluorobromomethane |
| 5036 | Trimellitic anhydride |
| 5018 | 2,4,7-Trinitrofluoren-9-one |
| 5037 | Triorthocresol phosphate |
| 5038 | Triphenyl phosphate |
| 7074 | Tungsten |
| 1551 | Turpentine |
| 2536 | Valeraldehyde |
| 7504 | Vanadium oxides |
| 1453 | Vinyl acetate |
| 1009 | Vinyl bromide |
| 1007 | Vinyl chloride |
| 1015 | Vinylidene chloride |
| 5002 | Warfarin |
| 7030 | Zinc |
| 7502 | Zinc oxide |

40 CFR Part 50, Appendix A-J and 40 CFR 52 Appendix D,
 Air Methods for Lead, Ozone, particulates, NO$_x$, etc. (see Table 5-4 at end of Section 5)

40 CFR 80, Appendix A and B
 Phosphorous and lead in gasoline (see Table 5-4 at end of Section 5)

EPA Contract Laboratory Protocol Statement of Work for Organics, Dioxins and Inorganics. Updated for every contract period. A SOW for air analysis exists.

**Table 1-24. EPA CLP methods and documents. PB numbers are NTIS document identifiers**

| SOW | Title/Description |
|---|---|
| 7/88 | Laboratory Data Validation Functional Guidelines for Evaluating Inorganics Analyses 7/88 PB95-963525 |
| 7/88 | USEPA CLP SOW for Inorganics Analysis, multi-media, multi-concentration PB95-963516 |
| 2/88 | Laboratory Data Validation Functional Guidelines for Evaluating Organics Analyses 2/88 PB95-963526 |
| 2/88 | USEPA CLP SOW for Organics Analysis, multi-media, multi-concentration 2/88 PB95-963512 |
| 1989 | USEPA CLP SOW for Organics Analysis, multi-media, high-concentration PB95-963507 |
| IHC01.3 | USEPA CLP SOW for Inorganic Analysis, multi-media high-concentration PB95-963504 |
| ILM01.0 | USEPA CLP SOW for Inorganics Analysis, multi-media, multi-concentration PB95-963515 |
| 10/91 | Superfund Analytical Methods for Low Concentration Water for Inorganics Analysis 10/91 PB95-963517 |
| OLM01.1 | USEPA CLP SOW for Organics Analysis, multi-media, multi-concentration and revisions 8/91 PB95-963508 |
| OLC01.0 | Superfund Analytical Methods for Low Concentration Water for Organics Analysis 6/91 PB95-963505 |
|  | USEPA CLP National Functional Guidelines for Organic Data Review, multi-media, multi-concentration (OLM01.0) and Low concentration water (OLC01.0) 6/91 PB95-963519 |
| ILM02.1 | USEPA CLP SOW for Inorganics Analysis, multi-media, multi-concentration 9/91 PB95963514 |
| ILM03.0 | USEPA CLP SOW for Inorganics Analysis, multi-media, multi-concentration 12/94 PB95-963506 |
|  | USEPA CLP National Functional Guidelines for Inorganic Data Review 2/94 PB94-963502 |
| ILMO4.0 | USEPA CLP SOW for Inorganics Analysis, multi-media 7/95 PB95-963545 |
| OLM03.1 | USEPA CLP SOW for Organic Analysis 8/94 PB95-963503 |
|  | USEPA CLP National Functional Guidelines for Organic Data Review 2/94 PB94-963501 |
| ILC03.1 | Superfund Analytical Methods for Low Concentration Water for Inorganics Analysis, March, 1996 PB96-963504 |
| VCAAO 1.0 | USEPA Volatile Organics of Ambient Air in Canisters 12/91 PB95-963524 |
| DFLM01.0 | USEPA CLP SOW for Analysis of Polychlorinated Dibenzo-P-Dioxins (PCDD) and Polychlorinated Dibenzofurans (PCDF), multi-media, multi-concentration 9/91 PB95-963520 |
|  | USEPA CLP SOW for Rapid Turnaround Dioxin Analysis, multi-media 11/92 PB95-963518 |
|  | USEPA CLP draft SOW for Quick Turnaround Analysis 8/94 PB95-963523 |
|  | USEPA CLP National Functional Guidelines for Quick Turnaround Method Data Review 7/94 PB95-963535 |
| IAIR01.2 | USEPA CLP SOW for Analysis of Ambient Air 7/91 PB95-963537 |

EPA has also incorporated by reference into Title 40 CFR many methods from ASTM (American Society for Testing and Materials), ASME (American Society of Mechanical Engineers) and other groups.

## USGS Methods

The United States Geological Survey (USGS) has published a large number of methods in the *Techniques of Water Resource Investigations* (TWI). Book 5 of TWI addresses laboratory analysis. Book 5 is actually divided into 7 separately bound chapters. Many of these methods are approved for use in analysis of wastewater compliance monitoring samples.

1) TWI 5-A1 Methods for the determination of inorganic substances in water and fluvial sediments (3rd edition 1989)

2) TWI 5-A2 Determination of minor elements in water by emission spectroscopy (1971)

3) TWI 5-A3 Methods for the determination of organic substances in water and fluvial sediments (revised 1987)

4) TWI 5-A4 Methods for the collection and analysis of aquatic biological and microbiological samples (revised 1989)

5) TWI 5-A5 Determination of radioactive substances in water and fluvial sediments (1977)

6) TWI 5-A6 Quality assurance practices for the chemical and biological analysis of water and fluvial sediments (1982)

7) TWI 5-C1 Laboratory theory and practice for sediment analysis (1969)

The USGS methods are identified by a letter followed by a four-digit number and then a year designator to indicate the revision date. The letters are (P) physical characteristic, (I) inorganic substance, (O) organic substance, (B) biological method, (R) radioactive determination, (S) sediment characteristic, and (E) emission spectrographic method. The first digit of the four-digit code for the organic and inorganic methods indicates the type of determination:

0 Sample preparation

1 Manual method for dissolved parameters

2 Automated method for dissolved parameters

3 Manual method for analyzing water-suspended sediment mixtures

4 Automated method for analyzing water-suspended sediment mixtures

5 Manual method for analyzing bottom material

6 Automated method for analyzing bottom material

7 Method for determining suspended parameters

9 Method for fish and other materials.

The last three digits of the four-digit code identify the parameter. For instance barium by direct atomic absorption spectrometry (FLAA) has the parameter code 084. A method identified as I-7084-85 is a FLAA barium method performed on suspended material, last updated in 1985.

## Table 1-25. USGS Methods

| Method code | Title/Description |
|---|---|
| Inorganic (I) | |
| 020 | Acidity by electrometric titration |
| 030 | Alkalinity by electrometric titration |
| 051 | Aluminum by FLAA |
| 052 | Aluminum by chelation-extraction FLAA |
| 054 | Aluminum by d-c plasma AES |
| 055 | Antimony by hydride FLAA |
| 057 | Anions by ion chromatography |
| 058 | Anions by ion-exchange chromatography |
| 060 | Arsenic by silver diethyldithiocarbamate colorimetric |
| 062 | Arsenic by hydride FLAA |
| 084 | Barium by FLAA |
| 095 | Beryllium by FLAA |
| 110 | Boron colorimetric dianthrimide |
| 112 | Boron colorimetric curcumin |
| 114 | Boron by d-c plasma AES |
| 115 | Boron colorimetric azomethine H |
| 125 | Bromide titrimetric hypochlorite oxidation |
| 128 | Bromide ion-chromatography electrochemical detection |
| 129 | Bromide by fluorescein colorimetric |
| 135 | Cadmium by FLAA |
| 136 | Cadmium by chelation-extraction FLAA |
| 137 | Cadmium by GFAA |
| 152 | Calcium by FLAA |
| 153 | Calcium by EPA FLAA |
| 160 | Carbon dioxide calculation |
| 183 | Chloride, Mohr titration |
| 184 | Chloride titrimetric mercurimetric |
| 187 | Chloride ferric thiocyanate colorimetric |
| 230 | Hexavalent chromium diphenylcarbazide colorimetric |
| 232 | Hexavalent chromium chelation-extraction FLAA |
| 235 | Chromium GFAA |
| 236 | Chromium FLAA |
| 238 | Chromium chelation-extraction FLAA |
| 239 | Cobalt FLAA |
| 240 | Cobalt chelation-extraction FLAA |
| 241 | Cobalt GFAA |
| 250 | Color, visual comparison Pt-Co |
| 270 | Copper FLAA |
| 271 | Copper chelation-extraction FLAA |
| 272 | Copper GFAA |
| 300 | Cyanide pyridine-pyrazolone colorimetric |

Continued on next page.

**Table 1-25. USGS Methods,** *continued*

| Method code | Title/Description |
|---|---|
| | **Inorganic (I)** |
| 302 | Cyanide barbituric acid colorimetric |
| 312 | Density, gravimetric |
| 325 | Fluoride zirconium-eriochrome cyanine R colorimetric |
| 327 | Fluoride ISE |
| 338 | Hardness complexometric titration |
| 340 | Hardness calculation |
| 344 | Hardness, non-carbonate calculation |
| 370 | Iodide bromine oxidation titration |
| 371 | Iodide ceric-arsenious oxidation colorimetric |
| 381 | Iron FLAA |
| 399 | Lead FLAA |
| 400 | Lead chelation-extraction FLAA |
| 401 | Lead GFAA |
| 425 | Lithium FLAA |
| 447 | Magnesium FLAA |
| 448 | Magnesium EPA FLAA |
| 454 | Manganese FLAA |
| 455 | Manganese GFAA |
| 456 | Manganese chelation-extraction FLAA |
| 462 | Mercury CVAA |
| 472 | Metals by ICP-AES |
| 473 | Metals total-in-sediment by lithium fusion and FLAA |
| 474 | Metals total-in-sediment by acid digestion FLAA |
| 475 | Metals total-in-sediment by hydride FLAA |
| 490 | Molybdenum chelation-extraction FLAA |
| 499 | Nickel FLAA |
| 500 | Nickel chelation-extraction FLAA |
| 501 | Nickel GFAA |
| 520 | Ammonia distillation nesslerization |
| 521 | Ammonia salicylate-hypochlorite colorimetric (automated discrete) |
| 522 | Ammonia salicylate-hypochlorite colorimetric (separated flow) |
| 523 | Ammonia indophenol colorimetric |
| 524 | Ammonia ISE |
| 539 | Nitrite colorimetric automated |
| 540 | Nitrite colorimetric |
| 543 | Nitrate + Nitrite hydrazine reduction |
| 545 | Nitrate + Nitrite cadmium reduction-diazotization |
| 550 | Ammonia + organic nitrogen nesslerization |
| 552 | Ammonia + organic nitrogen salicylate-hypochlorite colorimetric |
| 553 | Ammonia + organic nitrogen titration |
| 554 | Total nitrogen digestion distillation |

Continued on next page.

**Table 1-25. USGS Methods,** *continued*

| Method code | Title/Description |
|---|---|
| | **Inorganic (I)** |
| 558 | Ammonia + organic nitrogen salicylate-hypochlorite colorimetric |
| 561 | COD colorimetric |
| 562 | COD titration |
| 586 | pH electrode |
| 598 | Orthophosphate colorimetric automated |
| 599 | Phosphorus phosphomolybdate automated colorimetric |
| 600 | Phosphorus phosphomolybdate colorimetric |
| 601 | Orthophosphate colorimetric |
| 602 | Phosphate digestion colorimetric |
| 630 | Potassium FLAA |
| 631 | Potassium EPA FLAA |
| 667 | Selenium hydride AA |
| 700 | Silica molybdate colorimetric |
| 702 | Silica FLAA |
| 720 | Silver chelation-extraction FLAA |
| 735 | Sodium FLAA |
| 736 | Sodium EPA FLAA |
| 738 | Sodium adsorption ratio calculation |
| 740 | Sodium percent calculation |
| 749 | Solids at 105 °C |
| 750 | Solids at 180 °C |
| 751 | Solids, calculation |
| 752 | Solids non-volatile at ignition |
| 753 | Solids volatile at ignition |
| 765 | Solids suspended at 105 °C |
| 766 | Solids non-volatile suspended at ignition |
| 767 | Solids volatile suspended at ignition |
| 780 | Specific conductance electrometric |
| 800 | Strontium FLAA |
| 820 | Sulfate thorin titration |
| 822 | Sulfate methylthymol blue colorimetric |
| 823 | Sulfate turbidometric |
| 840 | Sulfide iodometric titration |
| 851 | Tin hydride AA |
| 860 | Turbidity |
| 866 | Thallium GFAA |
| 880 | Vanadium catalytic oxidation colorimetric |
| 900 | Zinc FLAA |
| 901 | Zinc GFAA |
| | **Organics (O)** |
| 100 | Organic carbon wet oxidation |

Continued on next page.

**Table 1-25. USGS Methods,** *continued*

| Method code | Title/Description |
|---|---|
| **Organics (O),** *continued* ||
| 101 | Total carbon dry weight induction furnace |
| 102 | Inorganic carbon modified Van Slyke |
| 103 | Organic carbon fractionation |
| 104 | Organochlorine and organophosphorus pesticides GC |
| 105 | Chlorophenoxy acids GC |
| 106 | Triazines GC |
| 107 | Carbamate pesticides HPLC |
| 108 | Oil & Grease extraction-gravimetric |
| 109 | Light fuel oils GC |
| 110 | Phenols colorimetric |
| 111 | MBAS surfactants |
| 112 | TNT, RDX and picric acid HPLC |
| 113 | PAH HPLC |
| 114 | Ethylene and propane GC |
| 115 | Purgeable organic compounds GC/MS |
| 117 | Acid extractable compounds GC/MS |
| 118 | Base/neutral extractable compounds GC/MS |
| **Biological (B)** ||
| 0001 | Standard plate count membrane filter |
| 0025 | Total coliform MF immediate incubation |
| 0030 | Total coliform MF delayed incubation |
| 0035 | Total coliform MPN |
| 0040 | Total coliform MPN presumptive on-site |
| 0045 | Total coliform MPN confirmation |
| 0050 | Fecal coliform MF immediate incubation |
| 0051 | Fecal coliform MPN presumptive |
| 0055 | Fecal streptococcal MF immediate incubation |
| 0060 | Fecal streptococcal MF confirmation |
| 0065 | Fecal streptococcal MPN presumptive and confirmation |
| 0420 | Nitrifying bacteria MPN |
| 0430 | Denitrifying and nitrate-reducing bacteria MPN |
| 0400 | Sulfate-reducing bacteria MPN |
| 0005 | Total bacteria epifluorescence |
| 0100 | Salmonella and shigella |
| 0105 | Pseudomonas aeruginosa |
| 1505 | Phytoplankton counting cell |
| 1520 | Phytoplankton inverted microscope |
| 1580 | Planktonic diatoms permanent slide |
| 2501 | Zooplankton counting cell |
| 2520 | Zooplankton gravimetric biomass |
| 3401 | Seston glass-fiber filter |

Continued on next page.

**Table 1-25. USGS Methods,** *continued*

| Method code | Title/Description |
|---|---|
| **Biological (B),** *continued* | |
| 3501 | Periphyton Sedgwick-Rafter |
| 3520 | Periphyton gravimetric biomass |
| 3540 | Periphytic diatoms permanent slide |
| 3545 | Periphytic diatoms inverted microscope |
| 4501 | Macrophytes Floral survey |
| 4520 | Macrophytes distribution and abundance |
| 5001 | Benthic invertebrates faunal survey |
| 5020 | Benthic invertebrates numerical assessment |
| 5040 | Benthic invertebrate distribution and abundance |
| 5050 | Benthic invertebrate drift |
| 5200 | Chironomidae larvae permanent slide |
| 5220 | Identification of immature simuliidae |
| 5240 | Aquatic acari slide |
| 6001 | Aquatic vertebrates faunal survey |
| 6020 | Aquatic vertebrates life history |
| 6040 | Investigation of aquatic vertebrate kills |
| 6501 | Phytoplankton chlorophyll spectroscopy |
| 6520 | Phytoplankton chlorophyll TLC |
| 6530 | Phytoplankton chlorophyll HPLC |
| 6540 | Phytoplankton chlorophyll TLC fluorometry |
| 6560 | Phytoplankton biomass/chlorophyll ratio |
| 6601 | Periphyton chlorophyll spectroscopy |
| 6620 | Periphyton chlorophyll TLC spectrometry |
| 6630 | Periphyton chlorophyll HPLC |
| 6640 | Periphyton chlorophyll TLC fluorometry |
| 6660 | Periphyton biomass/chlorophyll ratio |
| 6700 | Adenosine triphosphate |
| 8001 | Phytoplankton productivity oxygen light- and dark-bottle |
| 8020 | Phytoplankton productivity carbon-14 light- and dark-bottle |
| 8040 | Periphyton productivity oxygen light- and dark-bottle |
| 8120 | Stream productivity and community metabolism Diel oxygen-curve |
| 8100 | Stratified water productivity and community metabolism Diel oxygen-curve |
| 8502 | Algal growth potential |

### State Methods

Many states have methods that are approved for use in that state under a variety of monitoring programs. An example of this involves the petroleum LUST program. Total Petroleum Hydrocarbons (TPH) are tested by either gas chromatography (the California method), IR spectroscopy (EPA method 9073 or 418.1), or gravimetry (EPA method 413.1 modified). Other variations exist such as the Wisconsin methods for Gasoline Range Organics (GRO) and Diesel Range Organics (DRO). See the petroleum hydrocarbon discussion in Section 3.

## Commercial Private Sources of Methods

*Standard Methods for the Examination of Water and Wastewater* (*APHA, AWWA, WEF*, 18th Edition, 1992 and 19th Edition, 1995) (abbreviated in this book as $SM_{18}$ or $SM_{19}$).

**Table 1-26. Method contents of *Standard Methods* 19th Edition**

| Method | Title/Description |
|--------|-------------------|
| **Physical and Aggregate Properties** ||
| 2120 | Color |
| B | Visual comparison method |
| C | Spectrophotometric method |
| D | Tristimulus filter method |
| E | ADMI method |
| 2130 | Turbidity |
| 2150 | Odor |
| 2160 | Taste |
| 2170 | Flavor profile analysis |
| 2310 | Acidity |
| 2320 | Alkalinity |
| 2330 | Calcium carbonate saturation |
| 2340 | Hardness |
| B | Calculation |
| C | Titration |
| 2350 | Oxidant demand/requirement |
| B | Chlorine demand |
| C | Chlorine dioxide demand |
| D | Ozone demand - batch |
| E | Ozone demand - semibatch |
| 2510 | Conductivity |
| 2520 | Salinity |
| B | Electrical conductivity method |
| C | Density method |
| 2530 | Floatables |
| B | Particulate floatables |
| C | Floatable oil and grease |
| 2540 | Solids |
| B | Total solids (TS) |
| C | Total dissolved solids (TDS) |
| D | Total suspended solids (TSS) |
| E | Fixed and volatile solids |
| F | Settleable solids |
| G | Total, fixed and volatile solids in solid and semisolid samples |

Continued on next page.

**Table 1-26. Method contents of *Standard Methods* 19th Edition,** *continued*

| Method | Title/Description |
|--------|-------------------|
| **Physical and Aggregate Properties** | |
| 2550 | Temperature |
| 2560 | Particulate counting and size |
| B | Electrical sensing zone method |
| C | Light-blockage methods |
| D | Light-scattering methods |
| 2570 | Asbestos |
| 2580 | Oxidation-reduction potential |
| 2710 | Tests on sludges |
| B | Oxygen consumption rate |
| C | Settled sludge volume |
| D | Sludge volume index |
| E | Zone settling rate |
| F | Specific gravity |
| G | Capillary-suction factor |
| H | Time-to-filter |
| 2720 | Anaerobic sludge digester gas analysis |
| B | Volumetric method |
| C | Gas chromatographic method |
| 2810 | Dissolved gas supersaturation |
| **Metals** | |
| 3030 | Preliminary treatment |
| B | Filtration for dissolved and suspended metals |
| C | Treatment for acid extractable metals |
| D | Digestion for metals |
| E | Nitric acid digestion |
| F | Nitric acid-Hydrochloric acid digestion |
| G | Nitric acid-Sulfuric acid digestion |
| H | Nitric acid-Perchloric acid digestion |
| I | Nitric acid-Perchloric acid-Hydrofluoric acid digestion |
| J | Dry ashing |
| K | Microwave-assisted digestion |
| 3110 | Metals by atomic absorption spectrometry |
| 3111 | Metals by flame atomic absorption |
| B | Direct air-acetylene flame |
| C | Extraction/air-acetylene flame |
| D | Direct nitrous oxide-acetylene flame |
| E | Extraction/nitrous oxide-acetylene flame |
| 3112 | Metals by cold vapor atomic absorption spectrometry |

Continued on next page.

**Table 1-26. Method contents of *Standard Methods* 19th Edition,** *continued*

| Method | Title/Description |
|--------|-------------------|
| Metals, *continued* | |
| 3113 | Metals by electrothermal atomic absorption spectrometry |
| 3114 | Arsenic and selenium by hydride generation atomic absorption spectrometry |
| B | Manual hydride generation |
| C | Continuous hydride generation |
| 3120 | Metals by plasma emission spectrometry |
| 3130 | Metals by anodic stripping voltammetry |
| **Inorganic Nonmetallic Constituents** | |
| 4110 | Determination of anions by ion chromatography |
| 4500-B | Boron |
| B | Curcumin method |
| C | Carmine method |
| D | ICP |
| 4500-Br⁻ | Bromine |
| B | Phenol red colorimetric |
| C | Ion Chromatography |
| 4500-$CO_2$ | Carbon dioxide |
| B | Nomographic determination |
| C | Titration for free carbon dioxide |
| D | Carbon dioxide by calculation |
| 4500-CN⁻ | Cyanide |
| B | Preliminary treatment |
| C | Total cyanide after distillation |
| D | Titrimetric method |
| E | Colorimetric method |
| F | Cyanide-selective electrode |
| G | Cyanides amenable to chlorination with distillation |
| H | Cyanides amenable to chlorination without distillation |
| I | Weak acid dissociable cyanide |
| J | Cyanogen chloride |
| K | Spot test for sample screening |
| L | Cyanates |
| M | Thiocyanate |
| 4500-Cl | Chlorine (Residual) |
| B | Iodometric I |
| C | Iodometric II |
| D | Amperometric titration |
| E | Low-level amperometric titration |

Continued on next page.

**Table 1-26. Method contents of *Standard Methods* 19th Edition, *continued***

| Method | Title/Description |
|---|---|
| | **Inorganic Nonmetallic Constituents, *continued*** |
| F | DPD Ferrous titrimetric |
| G | DPD colorimetric |
| H | Syringaldazine (FACTS) method |
| I | Iodometric Electrode technique |
| $4500\text{-}Cl^-$ | Chloride |
| B | Argentometric method |
| C | Mercuric nitrate method |
| D | Potentiometric method |
| E | Automated ferrocyanide method |
| F | Ion chromatography |
| $4500\text{-}ClO_2$ | Chlorine dioxide |
| B | Iodometric method |
| C | Amperometric method I |
| D | DPD method |
| E | Amperometric method II |
| $4500\text{-}F^-$ | Fluoride |
| B | Preliminary distillation |
| C | Ion selective electrode |
| D | SPADNS |
| E | Complexone method |
| F | Ion chromatography |
| $4500\text{-}H^+$ | pH |
| $4500\text{-}I$ | Iodine |
| B | Leuco crystal violet |
| C | Amperometric titration |
| $4500\text{-}N$ | Nitrogen |
| $4500\text{-}NH_3$ | Nitrogen (ammonia) |
| B | Preliminary distillation |
| C | Titrimetric method |
| D | Ammonia selective electrode |
| E | Ammonia selective electrode with known addition |
| F | Phenate method |
| G | Automated phenate |
| $4500\text{-}NO_2^-$ | Nitrogen (nitrite) |
| B | Colorimetric method |
| C | Ion chromatography |
| $4500\text{-}NO_3^-$ | Nitrogen (nitrate) |

Continued on next page.

**Table 1-26. Method contents of *Standard Methods* 19th Edition, *continued***

| Method | Title/Description |
|---|---|
| | **Inorganic Nonmetallic Constituents, *continued*** |
| B | UV spectrophotometric screening |
| C | Ion chromatography |
| D | Nitrate electrode |
| E | Cadmium reduction |
| F | Automated cadmium reduction |
| G | Titanous chloride reduction |
| H | Automated hydrazine reduction |
| 4500-N$_{org}$ | Nitrogen (organic) |
| B | Macro-Kjeldahl |
| C | Semimicro-Kjeldahl |
| D | Persulfate |
| 4500-O | Oxygen (dissolved) |
| B | Iodometric method |
| C | Azide modification |
| D | Permanganate modification |
| E | Alum flocculation modification |
| F | Copper sulfate-sulfamic acid flocculation modification |
| G | Membrane electrode |
| 4500-O$_3$ | Ozone (residual) |
| 4500-P | Phosphorus |
| B | Sample preparation |
| C | Vanadomolybdophosphoric acid colorimetric method |
| D | Stannous chloride method |
| E | Ascorbic acid method |
| F | Automated ascorbic acid reduction method |
| 4500-Si | Silicon |
| B | AA method |
| C | Gravimetric method |
| D | Molybdosilicate method |
| E | Heteropoly blue method |
| F | Automated method for molybdate reactive silica |
| G | ICP |
| 4500-S$^{2-}$ | Sulfide |
| B | Separation of soluble and insoluble sulfides |
| C | Sample pretreatment to remove interferences |
| D | Methylene blue method |
| E | Gas dialysis automated methylene blue |
| F | Iodometric method |

Continued on next page.

**Table 1-26. Method contents of** *Standard Methods* **19th Edition,** *continued*

| Method | Title/Description |
|---|---|
| **Inorganic Nonmetallic Constituents,** *continued* ||
| G | Ion selective electrode method |
| H | Calculation of un-ionized hydrogen sulfide |
| 4500-SO$_3$$^{2-}$ | Sulfite |
| B | Iodometric method |
| C | Phenanthroline method |
| 4500-SO$_4$$^{2-}$ | Sulfate |
| B | Ion chromatographic method |
| C | Gravimetric method with ignition |
| D | Gravimetric method with drying |
| E | Turbidimetric method |
| F | Automated methylthymol blue |
| **Aggregate Organic Constituents** ||
| 5210 | Biochemical oxygen demand (BOD) |
| B | 5-day BOD |
| C | Ultimate BOD |
| D | Respirometric method |
| 5220 | Chemical oxygen demand (COD) |
| B | Open reflux method |
| C | Closed reflux, titrimetric |
| D | Closed reflux, colorimetric |
| 5310 | Total organic carbon (TOC) |
| B | Combustion-Infrared |
| C | Persulfate-Ultraviolet oxidation |
| D | Wet oxidation |
| 5320 | Dissolved organic halogen |
| B | Adsorption-pyrolysis titrimetric method |
| 5510 | Aquatic humic substances |
| B | Diethylaminoethyl (DEAE) method |
| C | XAD method |
| 5520 | Oil and grease |
| B | Partition-gravimetric method |
| C | Partition-infrared method |
| D | Soxhlet extraction method |
| E | Extraction method for sludge samples |
| F | Hydrocarbons |
| 5530 | Phenols |
| B | Cleanup procedures |
| C | Chloroform extraction method |

Continued on next page.

**Table 1-26.** Method contents of *Standard Methods* 19th Edition, *continued*

| Method | Title/Description |
|---|---|
| Aggregate Organic Constituents, *continued* | |
| D | Direct photometric method |
| 5540 | Surfactants |
| B | Surfactant separation by sublation |
| C | Anionic surfactants as MBAS |
| D | Nonionic surfactants as CTAS |
| 5550 | Tannin and lignin |
| 5560 | Organic and volatile acids |
| B | Chromatographic separation method for organic acids |
| C | Distillation method |
| 5710 | Formation of trihalomethanes and other disinfection by-products |
| B | Trihalomethane formation potential |
| C | Simulated distribution system trihalomethanes (SDS-THM) |
| D | Formation of other disinfection by-products (DBPs) |
| 5910 | UV-absorbing organic constituents |
| Individual Organic Compounds | |
| 6040 | Constituent concentration by gas extraction |
| B | Closed loop stripping, GC/MS analysis |
| C | Purge and trap technique |
| 6210 | Volatile organic compounds |
| B | Purge and trap packed column GC/MS method I |
| C | Purge and trap packed column GC/MS method II |
| D | Purge and trap capillary column GC/MS method |
| 6211 | Methane |
| B | Combustible gas indicator method |
| C | Volumetric method |
| 6220 | Volatile aromatic organic compounds |
| B | Purge and trap GC method I |
| C | Purge and trap GC method II |
| D | Purge and trap GC/MS method |
| E | Liquid-liquid extraction GC/MS method |
| 6230 | Volatile halocarbons |
| B | Purge and trap packed column GC method I |
| C | Purge and trap packed column GC method II |
| D | Purge and trap capillary column GC method |
| E | Purge and trap GC/MS method |
| 6231 | 1,2-Dibromoethane (EB) and 1,2-dibromo-3-chloropropane (DBCP) |
| B | Liquid-liquid extraction GC method |
| C | Purge and trap GC/MS method |

Continued on next page.

**Table 1-26. Method contents of** *Standard Methods* **19th Edition,** *continued*

| Method | Title/Description |
|---|---|
| **Individual Organic Compounds,** *continued* | |
| D | Purge and trap GC method |
| 6232 | Trihalomethanes and chlorinated organic solvents |
| B | Liquid-liquid extraction GC method |
| C | Purge and trap GC/MS method |
| D | Purge and trap GC method |
| 6251 | Disinfection by-products: haloacetic acids and trichlorophenol |
| B | Micro liquid-liquid extraction GC method |
| 6252 | Disinfection by-products: aldehydes |
| B | PFBHA liquid-liquid extraction GC method |
| 6410 | Extractable base/neutrals and acids |
| B | Liquid-liquid extraction GC/MS method |
| 6420 | Phenols |
| B | Liquid-liquid extraction GC method |
| C | Liquid-liquid extraction GC/MS method |
| 6431 | Polychlorinated biphenyls (PCBs) |
| B | Liquid-liquid extraction GC method |
| C | Liquid-liquid extraction GC/MS method |
| 6440 | Polynuclear aromatic hydrocarbons |
| B | Liquid-liquid extraction chromatographic method |
| C | Liquid-liquid extraction GC/MS method |
| 6610 | Carbamate pesticides |
| B | HPLC method |
| 6630 | Organochlorine pesticides |
| B | Liquid-liquid extraction GC method I |
| Appendix | Lauric acid standardization of magnesia-silica gel columns |
| C | Liquid-liquid extraction GC method II |
| D | Liquid-liquid extraction GC/MS method |
| 6640 | Acidic herbicide compounds |
| B | Micro liquid-liquid extraction GC method |
| 6651 | Glyphosate herbicide |
| **Radioactivity** | |
| 7110 | Gross alpha and gross beta radioactivity |
| B | Evaporation method for gross alpha |
| C | Coprecipitation method for gross alpha radioactivity in drinking water |
| 7120 | Gamma-emitting radionuclides |
| 7500-Cs | Cesium |
| B | Precipitation method |
| 7500-I | Radioactive iodine |

Continued on next page.

**Table 1-26.** Method contents of *Standard Methods* 19th Edition, *continued*

| Method | Title/Description |
|---|---|
| \multicolumn{2}{c}{**Radioactivity,** *continued*} ||
| B | Precipitation method |
| C | Ion-exchange method |
| D | Distillation method |
| 7500-Ra | Radium |
| B | Precipitation method |
| C | Emanation method |
| D | Sequential precipitation method |
| 7500-Sr | Strontium |
| B | Precipitation method |
| 7500-$^3$H | Tritium |
| B | Liquid scintillation spectrometric method |
| 7500-U | Uranium |
| B | Radiochemical method |
| C | Isotopic method |
| \multicolumn{2}{c}{**Toxicity**} ||
| 8030 | Mutagenesis |
| 8050 | Bacterial bioluminescence |
| 8110 | Algae |
| 8111 | Biostimulation |
| 8112 | Phytoplankton |
| 8211 | Duckweed |
| 8220 | Aquatic rooted plants |
| 8510 | Annelids |
| 8610 | Mollusks |
| 8710 | Microcrustaceans |
| 8711 | Daphnia |
| 8720 | Macrocrustaceans |
| 8750 | Aquatic insects |
| 8910 | Fish |
| \multicolumn{2}{c}{**Microbiological Examination**} ||
| 9211 | Rapid detection methods |
| B | Seven hour fecal coliform |
| D | Coliphage detection |
| 9212 | Stressed organisms |
| 9215 | Heterotrophic plate count |
| B | Pour plate method |
| C | Spread plate method |
| D | Membrane filter method |

Continued on next page.

**Table 1-26. Method contents of** *Standard Methods* **19th Edition,** *continued*

| Method | Title/Description |
|--------|------------------|
| **Microbiological Examination,** *continued* ||
| 9216 | Direct total microbial count |
| 9217 | Assimilable organic carbon |
| 9221 | Multiple tube fermentation technique for members of the coliform group |
| 9222 | Membrane filter technique for members of the coliform group |
| 9223 | Chromogenic substrate coliform test |
| 9225 | Differentiation of the coliform bacteria |
| 9230 | Fecal streptococcus and enterococcus groups |
| 9240 | Iron and sulfur bacteria |
| B | Iron bacteria |
| C | Sulfur bacteria |
| 9250 | Detection of actinomycetes |
| 9260 | Detection of pathogenic bacteria |
| 9510 | Detection of enteric viruses |
| 9610 | Detection of fungi |
| 9711 | Pathogenic protozoa |
| **Biological Examination** ||
| 10200 | Plankton |
| 10300 | Periphyton |
| 10400 | Macrophyton |
| 10500 | Benthic macroinvertebrates |
| 10550 | Nematological examination |
| 10600 | Fish |
| 10900 | Identification of aquatic organisms |

*DOE Methods for Evaluating Environmental and Waste Management Samples*, 1997 edition. Initially prepared under contract to DOE by employees of Battelle Northwest, now completely a private effort and available through Battelle Press, 1-800-451-3543. A listing of the methods is included in Section 4

ASTM Standards: *Water and Environmental Technology* (Updated yearly)

Volumes 11.01 and 11.02, Water

Volume 11.03, Atmospheric Analysis, Occupational Health and Safety

Volume 11.04, Pesticides, Resource Recovery, Hazardous Substances, Waste Disposal and Biological Effects.

Methods of soil characterization and analysis: *Methods of Soil Analysis*, Part 1: Physical and Mineralogical Methods Second Edition, 1986, and *Methods of Soil Analysis*, Part 2: Chemical and Microbiological Properties Second Edition, 1982, both from American Society of Agronomy, Inc., Soil Science Society of America, Inc, 677 South Segoe Rd, Madison, WI 53711; *Soil Sampling and Methods of Analysis*, 1993, Canadian Society of

Soil Science, 907-151 Slater St., Ottawa, Ontario K1P5H4 Canada, Lewis Publishers, Boca Raton FL.  See Table at the end of Section 2.

*Methods of Air Sampling and Analysis* (3rd Edition, 1990, Lodge, MASA), Lewis Publishers Boca Raton, FL.

**Table 1-27.  Method contents of *Air Sampling* 3th Edition**

| Method | Title/Description |
|---|---|
| **Ambient Air Methods** ||
| 101 | Determination of C1 through C5 atmospheric hydrocarbons |
| 102 | Separation and determination of PAH and benzo(a)pyrene |
| 102A | Extraction and cleanup procedures for PAH in atmospheric particulate matter |
| 102B | Separation and microanalysis of airborne particulate matter for benzo(a)pyrene using TLC and spectrofluorimetry |
| 102C | Measurement of benzo(a)pyrene and benzo(k)fluoranthene by spectrofluorimetry |
| 102D | Measurement of PAH using HPLC with fluorescence detection |
| 108 | Continuous determination of total hydrocarbons (FID) |
| 109 | Flame ionization detector |
| 114 | Determination of acrolein (colorimetric) |
| 116 | Determination of formaldehyde (colorimetric) |
| 117 | Determination of formaldehyde (MBTH colorimetric) |
| 118 | Determination of mercaptans |
| 121 | Determination of phenols (GC) |
| 122 | Determination of C1-C5 aldehydes by HPLC |
| 128 | Continuous determination of CO (Nondispersive infrared) |
| 133 | Determination of $O_2$, $N_2$, CO, $CO_2$, and $CH_4$ (GC) |
| 134 | Constant pressure volumetric analysis for $O_2$, $N_2$, CO and $CO_2$ |
| 135 | Determination of volatile organic compounds in surface coatings |
| 201 | Chloride content |
| 202 | Free chlorine (Methyl orange) |
| 203 | Fluoride in atmosphere and plant tissues (manual) |
| 204 | Fluoride in atmosphere and plant tissues (semi-automated) |
| 205 | Fluoride in plant tissues (potentiometric) |
| 206 | Particulate and gaseous fluorides (Sodium bicarbonate coated glass tube and filter) |
| 207 | Particulate and gaseous fluorides (double paper tape) |
| 301 | Antimony |
| 302 | Arsenic |
| 303A | Preparation of environmental samples for trace metal analysis |
| 317 | Mercury by collection on Ag wool and AAS |
| 319 | Molybdenum by AAS |

Continued on next page.

**Table 1-27. Method contents of *Air Sampling* 3th Edition, *continued***

| Method | Title/Description |
|---|---|
| | **Ambient Air Methods, *continued*** |
| 401 | Ammonia (indophenol method) |
| 404 | Nitrate (brucine method) |
| 405 | Nitric oxide |
| 406 | Nitrogen dioxide (Greiss-Saltzman reaction) |
| 407 | Total nitrogen oxides as nitrate (phenoldisulfonic acid method) |
| 408 | Nitrogen dioxide (24H average) |
| 411 | Oxidizing substances |
| 413 | Ozone by gas phase chemiluminescence |
| 415 | Nitric acid |
| 416 | Continuous monitoring of nitric oxide and nitrogen dioxide |
| 417 | Continuous monitoring of ozone |
| 501 | High volume measurement of size classified particulates |
| 502 | Measurement of dustfall |
| 503 | Continuous tape sampling of coefficient of haze |
| 507 | Nephelometer measurement of scattering coefficient and fine particles |
| 601 | Gross alpha |
| 602 | Gross beta |
| 603 | Iodine-131 |
| 606 | Radon-222 |
| 609A | Tritium in water vapor |
| 609B | Total tritium |
| 701 | Hydrogen sulfide |
| 704A | Sulfur dioxide (tetrachloromercurate/pararosaniline) |
| 704B | Sulfur dioxide (formaldehyde/pararosaniline) |
| 704C | Sulfur dioxide (hydrogen peroxide method) |
| 707 | Continuous sulfur dioxide measurement (amperometric) |
| 708 | Mercaptans |
| 709 | Sulfur containing gases (continuous with FPD) |
| 709A | Sulfur containing gases (GC-FPD) |
| 709B | Sulfur containing gases (total with FPD) |
| 711 | Gaseous sulfuric acid and sulfur dioxide in stack gases |
| 713 | Semi-continuous particulate sulfur, sulfuric acid and ammonium sulfates |
| 714 | Sulfur dioxide emissions in stack gases by pulsed fluorescence |
| 720A | Suppressed anion chromatography |
| 720B | Nonsuppressed anion chromatography |
| 720C | Flow injection determination of aqueous sulfate (MTB method) |
| 720D | Barium sulfate turbidimetry |
| 720E | Barium perchlorate microtitration |

Continued on next page.

**Table 1-27. Method contents of** *Air Sampling* **3th Edition,** *continued*

| Method | Title/Description |
|--------|-------------------|
| **Ambient Air Methods,** *continued* | |
| 720F | Barium chloranilate spectrophotometry |
| 730 | Particulate sulfur by X-ray fluorescence |
| **Workplace Air and Biological Samples** | |
| 801 | Ammonia in air |
| 804 | As, Se, and Sb in urine and air by hydride generation AAS |
| 805 | Chloride in air |
| 806 | Free chlorine in air |
| 807 | Chromic acid mist in air |
| 808 | Cyanide in air |
| 809 | Flouride and hydrogen fluoride in air |
| 810 | Particulate and gaseous fluorides in air |
| 811 | Fluoride in urine |
| 812 | Hydrogen sulfide in air |
| 815 | Mercury in urine |
| 818 | Nitrogen dioxide in air |
| 819 | Ozone in air |
| 821 | Phosgene in air |
| 822 | AAS method for trace metals in air |
| 822A | Preparation of tissue samples for analysis of trace metals |
| 822B | X-ray fluorescence for multielement analysis of particulate and biological materials |
| 824 | Sulfates in air |
| 825 | Acrolein in air |
| 826 | Acrolein in air |
| 827 | Aromatic amines in air |
| 828 | Bis-2-chloromethyl ether |
| 829 | Chloromethyl methyl ether and bis-2-chloromethyl ether in air |
| 830 | 3,3'-Dichloro-4,4'-diaminodiphenylmethane in air |
| 831 | p,p'-Diphenylmethane diisocyanate |
| 832 | Nitroglycerine and ethylene glycol dinitrate in air |
| 833 | N-Nitrosodimethylamine in air |
| 834 | Organic solvent vapors |
| 835 | EPN, malathion and parathion in air |
| 836 | Total particulate PAH (ultrasonic extraction method) |
| 837 | 2,4-Toluenediisocyanate in air |

## III. SAMPLING PROCEDURES

Over 50% of all errors in environmental analysis result from incorrect sampling. Five factors control sampling. They are:

1) The safety of the person performing the sampling,
2) Obtaining a representative sample of whatever is being tested,
3) Preventing contamination of the sample,
4) Providing legal documentation of the sampling event, and finally,
5) Protecting the sample from chemical, physical or biological change prior to analysis.

All these factors are discussed in detail in the EPA Region IV *Standard Operating Procedure and Quality Assurance Manual* (February, 1991). Other good sources for information about sampling are *Standard Operating Procedures for Laboratory Operations and Sample Collection Activities* by the Florida Department of Environmental Regulation Quality Assurance Section, 2600 Blair Stone Road, Tallahassee, FL 32399-2400 (publication DER QA-001/92) and two books by Larry Keith *Environmental Sampling and Analysis, A Practical Guide* (1991, Lewis Publishers) and *Principles of Environmental Sampling* (1988, American Chemical Society, a second edition has been published). Also helpful is a database from Instant Reference Resources, 7605 Rockpoint Dr., Austin, TX, 78731, *Instant Gloves + CPC Database.* ASTM has published in book form a collection of 81 ASTM procedures related to sampling, *ASTM Standards on Environmental Sampling* (1995, ASTM, 1916 Race St., Philadelphia PA 19103). EPA published a two volume desk reference guide, *Subsurface Characterization and Monitoring Techniques*, (EPA 625/R-93/003 a and b) that includes a substantial amount of information of sampling soil and groundwater sources.

## A. Safety of Collector

Environmental samples must always be considered to be hazardous to the health of the person performing the sampling. The samples can have toxic, corrosive, explosive, and flammable properties. The minimum protection consists of eye protection, latex or other types of gloves, steel-capped workboots, and normal clothing. Other specialized protection could include respirators and oxygen breathing apparatus for sampling from manholes, enclosed areas, and chemical waste drums. Special protective clothing such as overalls and Tyvek® (Trade mark of Dupont U.K. Ltd.) polyethylene suits may be required. Mixed waste (radioactive) samples present their own particular hazards, and the appropriate DOE (Department of Energy) guidelines should be consulted.

## B. Record Keeping

Environmental sampling always has the potential of leading to legal court challenges. As a result, each sampling event must be legally defensible. Adequate documentation and records must be obtained prior to, during, and after the field operations. Satisfactory site description could be augmented with field pictures by the sampling technicians. A field log book that is bound with waterproof resin-coated pages must be maintained and must fully document everything performed by the field technicians during the sampling event. Other information in the log book includes time and date of the sampling event, names of persons performing the sampling, lot numbers of the pre-cleaned sample containers used, duration and flow rates of sampling equipment, results of field tests performed, lists of samples obtained, preservatives used, QC measures or samples obtained, weather and site conditions, etc. All entries are made in waterproof ink. Corrections are lined through with a single line, and the person making the correction dates and initials it. Some sort of laboratory analysis request form should be used for sampling and invoicing records.

The most important part of the required legal documentation is the chain of custody. It is a form that lists a description of the sample, who collected it in what container, and where and when the sample was collected. The form has room for the signatures and times/dates when the sample was passed from person to person as it made its way to the laboratory. Other information on the chain of custody could include the requested test parameters, preservatives used, comments on the condition of the sample when it arrived in the laboratory, verification of correct preservation by the lab, contact persons for information about the sample and possibly notes about particular characteristics of the sample that may be of interest to the laboratory.

Sample labeling is very important. Since many samples are sent to the laboratory in ice chests containing a slurry of ice and water, each sample container must be properly labeled. This may consist of a tag or waterproof gummed label, written in waterproof ink and containing the name of the collector, date, time, exact location of sampling, preservatives added, analysis desired, sample number, and other information such as weather, temperature, water level, flow rate, pump rate, and downdraw (wells). Each sample container in the ice chest must have a corresponding entry in the chain of custody, and the information on the sample label must agree with the chain of custody entry.

A record of the sample receipt in the laboratory is maintained in the laboratory log book. The entries may be very detailed, particularly in the situations where the receipts book is maintained in a central computerized Laboratory Information Management System (LIMS), however the minimum information contained must consist of time and date of sampling, time and date of receipt, field and laboratory sample number, client information and desired analysis.

Detailed records must be maintained of the work performed upon the sample in the laboratory. A discussion of appropriate records supporting these procedures is included in the next section. One record that must be generated and maintained in the laboratory that directly affects field operations is the performance of blank analysis upon sample container lots. A laboratory will purchase many cases of pre-cleaned sample containers from the same vendor's lot number. A random selection of the containers is filled with analyte-free water, then the water is analyzed for the parameters for which the sample containers are intended. The blank tests must give BDL results for all the intended parameters, or the lot is not suitable for sampling. These records must be maintained by the lab to verify the suitablility of the sample containers.

The final report of analysis should contain a summary of the field operations that collected the sample. Problems with the sample resulting from the sampling procedures that result in unacceptable deviations from the required procedure must be indicated on the final report as qualified data. A flag is placed by the parameter result, and a footnote is attached to that page of the final result, beginning with the statement that the data is unsuitable for regulatory reporting due to a reason. Figure 1-2 has an example.

# ANALYTICAL SERVICES, INC.

ENVIRONMENTAL MONITORING & LABORATORY ANALYSIS
110 TECHNOLOGY PARKWAY • NORCROSS, GEORGIA 30092
(770) 743-4200 • FAX (770) 734-4201

## *LABORATORY REPORT*

Springfield Power Plant                                    December 12, 1992
PO Box 1234
1st St.
Springfield, Ohio

Attention:              Mr. Homer Simpson              Report No. 9999-1

Sample:    Water, grab, 435Z, 10-18-92, Time, received 10-25-92

### *RESULTS*

|  | Result | Detection Limit |
|---|---|---|
| Total Lead (Pb) (mg/L) (EPA 239.2) | 1.41* | 0.005 |
| Total Copper (Cu) (mg/L) (EPA 220.2) | 0.12* | 0.002 |

Respectfully submitted,

By:

* Result Not Suitable for Regulatory Reporting:  Sample Received Incorrectly Preserved, Not Acidified.

**Figure 1–2.  Example of a final analytical report.**

## C. Sample Security

Another aspect of producing legally defensible data is establishing and documenting sample security. Most people would not consider tampering with samples to be a serious problem in real life, and it probably is not. However, within the legal system, sample tampering must always be considered a possibility, and active steps must be taken to eliminate it. The chain of custody is the primary document of sample security, and it records the length of time that each person who came in contact with the sample was responsible for the sample's security. The security is defined as either the sample being in the physical possession of the person, in the unimpeded eyesight of the person, or in a locked container that provided restricted access to the sample by the responsible person.

Sample security can be further verified by placing a sample seal across the opening of the sample container. A sample seal is a strip of adhesive plastic or waterproofed paper that contains many small cuts so that after application to the sample container, the seal will tear upon attempted removal. The seal is labeled with the initials of the person applying it and the time and date. The condition of the sample seals are noted in writing by each person receiving custody of the sample on the chain of custody.

Sample security also involves restricted storage, which can consist of locked refrigerators or storage cabinets with limited access, locked sample rooms with limited access, locked buildings with controlled access, or in the most extreme case, locked sample access that is controlled by a dedicated clerk or guard. An internal chain of custody is maintained in any of these cases. A recent innovation to the written internal chain of custody is to let the LIMS maintain the records and to inform the LIMS of sample movement through use of bar code readers, where each sample container has a unique bar code, and each analyst has a unique password to activate the reading function. Restricted storage includes not only the sample itself but any digestates or extracts made from the sample.

## D. Obtaining a Representative Sample

The best sample is the whole item itself, either a lake, stream, landfill, hazardous waste dump, field, or whatever. Due to laboratory size restraints, analyzing a whole lake is not feasible, thus a small portion of the water from the lake is taken for analysis and the result extrapolated back to represent the whole of the lake. From this point of view, no sample is truly representative of the system as a whole. Over time a number of sampling schemes have been developed that attempt to represent the whole.

A single sampling event is called a grab sample. Many analytes such as oil & grease, petroleum hydrocarbons, dissolved oxygen, total coliform, fecal coliform, and volatile organics can only be sampled as grabs. A grab sample is limited to the single time (less than a period of 15 minutes) and location of the sample. Representation of the whole sampling area requires the obtaining of many grab samples over a period of time, analysis of each sample and then averaging of the results.

The concept of multiple sampling as a means of obtaining an overall picture of a test site has been formalized into a series of variables. These variables of multiple sampling are based upon obtaining a standard size sample per unit time, per unit flow, or per unit distance from one sampling point to the next. The time domain is where a sample is obtained at regular time intervals, generally at one sampling location. The flow domain is when a sample is obtained from a stationary sampling location after every set amount of flow, such as every 1000 gallons. The areal domain can be either vertical or horizontal, but both are based upon obtaining a sample at a set distance frequency through a sampling site. Sequential samples are samples obtained under a particular domain that are maintained and analyzed as separate samples. Composite samples are samples obtained under a variety of domains that are mixed together to form an average sample, then subsamples of the well-mixed composite are analyzed for the parameters of interest. The most common situation is under either time- or flow- domain. Both sequential and composite samples are assisted in the flow- or time- domain through the use of automated samplers designed to refrigerate the samples as they are obtained. An areal composite sample is obtained from samples taken over an area under the same conditions, then mixed to form a composite. An example is taking grab samples from a number of points around the shore of a lake, then compositing the samples to obtain an average of the lake. A vertical composite sample is obtained from samples taken from a variety of depths at one or several sampling points. The most complete sampling scheme is the integrated sample, which uses a variety of different methods of sampling together to form an overall picture of the site.

## E. Sample Containers

Sample containers are normally borosilicate glass or high density polyethylene (HDPE). Sample containers must be clean and proven free of target analytes. Some directions for cleaning containers are given in Appendix E. Similar instructions are provided in guidance[58] published under the Superfund program. Containers can also be purchased as pre-cleaned and then checked by the laboratory, as described above, to insure that the container is not adding or subtracting analytes to the sample. The idea is to avoid situations such as a sample taken in a metal solvent can with requested parameter tests for iron, chromium, zinc and tin. Containers must be of an appropriate size to obtain enough sample for performing the analysis and the associated QC procedures such as duplicates and matrix spikes.

- Some samples must be collected in several containers as only one analysis is performed per container.
- Samples for volatile organic analysis must be obtained in duplicate (or better triplicate) in glass with a Teflon® (Trademark of Dupont) faced silicone cap liner and no headspace.
- Non-volatile organics are normally obtained in glass with a Teflon-lined cap.
- Microbiological samples must be obtained in sterile containers.
- Metals are normally collected in HDPE containers as glass can exchange out metal ions. Mercury in elemental form will pass through the walls of an HDPE container and should be collected in glass.

## F. Preservatives

Preservatives are used to maintain the chemical integrity of the sample. Most solid samples have only cooling as a preservative. Water samples are subject to a variety of specific preservation techniques, depending on the target analytes. Preservatives can consist of chemical additives such as acids or bases added to control pH, ascorbic acid or thiosulfate added to reduce the effect of residual chlorine and other oxidizers, etc. A

---

[58] *Specifications and Guidance for Contaminant-free Sample Containers.* USEPA Office of Solid Waste and Emergency Response. December, 1992. (EPA 540/R-93/051, PB93-963316).

common preservative is storage temperature, normally 4 °C, however, metals may precipitate out of solution on cooling, such solutions should be kept at room temperature. The cool temperature of 4 °C is obtained by storing the samples in an ice chest of either metal or polyethylene construction with a slurry of ice and water used to maintain the proper temperature. The use of reusable cold packs is not currently accepted. Preservation may also include the storing of the samples in the dark or in amber bottles. See Tables 1-28 through 1-37.

Preservation always has a quantitative measure of success associated with it. For example, when the indicated preservation technique is to cool the sample, a desired temperature is included, such as, "Cool 4 °C". The existence of the quantitative aspect of preservation means that the pH, removal of residual chlorine, or temperature of the sample should be checked in the field and definitely in the laboratory. At the same time concern over possible contamination of the sample resulting from dipping a probe or a test strip into the sample suggests that a slight modification in how samples are obtained may be in order. The suggested modification is to take at least two identical samples for each analytical parameter, then use one of the samples to determine the preservation requirements. If it is found that say 1.2 mL of nitric acid are required to lower the sample pH to <2, then addition of the same amount of acid to the other container of sample will achieve the correct preservation, without contaminating the sample to be sent to the laboratory.

Preservation techniques in conjunction with holding times have come under scrutiny, particularly the preservation of volatiles. References to these research efforts are in holding time discussion following.

## G. Holding Times

The holding time before analysis is of critical practical and regulatory importance. Analytes will degrade and be lost from the sample over time, even when correctly preserved and stored. All analytes have required holding times, from immediate analysis for dissolved oxygen, to 6 hours for coliform determination, and up to 6 months for heavy metals. The holding time clock starts with the moment of sampling and ends with the beginning of the analysis procedure. Holding times are not (except in the CLP) measured as the lapsed time from receipt of the sample in the laboratory to the beginning of the analysis. Holding times are often required parts of submitted QA reports on data submitted in support of regulatory requirements. The assorted regulations commonly conflict in terms of sample containers, holding times and preservation, thus it is necessary to consult the appropriate regulation reference to discover the compliance requirements. The most frequently used charts are reproduced in Tables 1-28 through 1-37.

Holding times were the subject of a symposium during a July 1994 EPA conference in Washington, D.C. Holding times were originally conceived with the idea of providing guidelines for performing analyses within a sensible timeframe to minimize sample degradation. Now holding times have taken on a legal life of their own, often with no connection to scientific reality. The inconsistency of the regulatory interpretation of holding times was most succinctly made by John Gumper from DataChem in Utah. He described the phenomenon of how a sample with a holding time of 7 days prior to extraction, is acceptable if extraction is begun 6 days, 23 hours, 59 minutes and 59 seconds after the moment of sampling, but magically turns to garbage one second later if not in a separatory funnel. Not particularly obvious at the moment of occurrence in the laboratory, this transition is most easily observed 5 years later in a courtroom.

A number of studies of suitable preservation and holding times have recently been performed and reported for mercury[59], volatile organic compounds[60] and explosives residues[61]. As to be expected the instructions included in many regulatory methods are found in some cases appropriate while in others they are simply wrong.

[59]   Hamlin, S.N. Preservation of Samples for Dissolved Mercury, 1989. *Water Resources Bulletin*, 25(2):255-262.

[60]   Turriff, D., C. Reitmeyer, L. Jacobs and N. Melberg. *Comparison of Alternatives for Sampling & Storage of VOCs in Soil*; Hewitt, A. *Determining Volatile Organic Compound Concentration Stability in Soil*. Eleventh Annual Waste Testing and Quality Assurance Symposium, July 22-26, 1995. Washington, D.C.; Liikala, T.L., K.B. Olsen, S.S. Teel, and D.C. Lanigan. 1996. "Volatile Organic compounds: Comparison of Two Sample Collection and Preservation Methods." *Environ. Sci. Technol.* 30(12). pp. 3441-3447; Hewett, A. D. 1997. "Chemical Preservation of Volatile Organic Compounds in Soil." *Environ. Sci. Technol.* 31(1). pp. 67-70.

[61]   Jenkins, T., and P.G. Thorne, *Evaluation of the New Clean Solid Phases for Extraction of Nitroaromatics and Nitramines from Water*. Eleventh Annual Waste Testing and Quality Assurance Symposium. July 22-26, 1995. Washington, D.C.

**Table 1-28.** **Drinking water holding time, preservation and sample container requirements from** *Manual for the Certification of Laboratories Analyzing Drinking Water - Criteria and Procedures Quality Assurance* **Third Edition, Change 2 EPA-814B-92-002, September 1992**

| Parameter | Sample Volume & Container[62] | Preservation | Max. Holding Time |
|---|---|---|---|
| **Bacterial Tests** | | | |
| Coliform, Fecal and Total | 100 ml, Sterile P | Cool 4 °C, 0.1 mL of 10% $Na_2S_2O_3$ | 30 hours from time of collection |
| **Inorganic Tests** | | | |
| Alkalinity | 200 ml, P, G | Cool, 4 °C | 14 days |
| Antimony | 500 ml, P, G | Conc $HNO_3$ to pH <2 | 6 months |
| Arsenic | 500 ml, P, G | Conc $HNO_3$ to pH <2 | 6 months |
| Asbestos | 1000 ml, P, G | Cool, 4 °C | - |
| Barium | 500 ml, P, G | Conc $HNO_3$ to pH <2 | 6 months |
| Beryllium | 500 ml, P, G | Conc $HNO_3$ to pH <2 | 6 months |
| Cadmium | 500 ml, P, G | Conc $HNO_3$ to pH <2 | 6 months |
| Calcium | 500 ml, P, G | Conc $HNO_3$ to pH <2 | 6 months |
| Chloride | 200 ml, P, G | None | 28 days |
| Chromium | 500 ml, P, G | Conc $HNO_3$ to pH <2 | 6 months |
| Copper | 500 ml, P, G | Conc $HNO_3$ to pH <2 | 6 months |
| Cyanide | 500 ml, P, G | NaOH to pH >12, cool 4° C, 0.6 g ascorbic acid | 14 days |
| Fluoride | 500 ml, P, G | None | 1 month |
| Free Chlorine Residual | 100 ml, P, G | None | Analyze immediately |
| Lead | 500 ml, P, G | Conc $HNO_3$ to pH <2 | 6 months |
| Mercury | 500 ml, P, G | Conc $HNO_3$ to pH <2 | 28 days |
| Nickel | 500 ml, P, G | Conc $HNO_3$ to pH <2 | 6 months |
| Nitrate N | 500 ml, P, G | Cool, 4 °C | 28 days |
| Total Nitrate/Nitrite | 500 ml, P, G | Cool, 4 °C, $H_2SO_4$ to pH <2 | 28 days |
| Nitrite N | 500 ml, P, G | Cool 4 °C | 48 hours |
| *o*-Phosphate | 500 ml, P, G | Filter immediately, Cool 4 °C | 48 hours |
| pH | 500 ml, P, G | None | Analyze immediately |
| Selenium | 500 ml, P, G | Conc $HNO_3$ to pH <2 | 6 months |
| Silica | 500 ml, P | Cool 4 °C | 28 days |
| Sodium | 500 ml, P, G | Conc $HNO_3$ to pH <2 | 6 months |
| Temperature | 500 ml, P, G | None | Analyze immediately |

Continued on next page.

---

[62] Polyethylene (P) or Glass (G).

**Table 1-28.** **Drinking water holding time, preservation and sample container requirements from** *Manual for the Certification of Laboratories Analyzing Drinking Water - Criteria and Procedures Quality Assurance* **Third Edition, Change 2 EPA-814B-92-002, September 1992**, *continued*

| Parameter | Sample Volume & Container | Preservation | Max. Holding Time |
|---|---|---|---|
| **Inorganic Tests,** *continued* | | | |
| Thallium | 500 ml, P, G | Conc HNO$_3$ to pH <2 | 6 months |
| Total Filterable Residue (TDS) | 500 ml, P, G | Cool 4 °C | 7 days |
| Turbidity | 500 ml, P, G | Cool 4 °C | 48 hours |
| **Organic Tests (method)** | | | |
| EDB & DBPC (504) | 40 mL glass with Teflon cap liner | 3 mg sodium thiosulfate, HCl to pH <2, Cool 4 °C | 28 days to extraction, analyze immediately |
| Chlorinated pesticides (505) | 40 mL glass with Teflon cap liner | 3 mg sodium thiosulfate, Cool 4 °C | 14 days to extraction, analyze immediately |
| Phthalates and Adipates (506) | 1 L amber glass with Teflon cap liner | 60 mg/L sodium thiosulfate, Cool 4 °C | 14 days to extraction, 14 days to analysis |
| NP pesticides (507) | 1 L amber glass with Teflon cap liner | 10 mg/L mercuric chloride, 80 mg/L sodium thiosulfate, Cool 4 °C | 7 days to extraction, 14 days to analysis |
| Chlorinated pesticides (508) | 1 L glass with Teflon cap liner | 10 mg/L mercuric chloride, 80 mg/L sodium thiosulfate, Cool 4 °C | 7 days to extraction, 14 days to analysis |
| PCB (508A) | 1 L glass with Teflon cap liner | Cool 4 °C | 14 days to extraction, 30 days to analysis |
| Herbicides (515.1) | 1 L amber glass with Teflon cap liner | 10 mg/L mercuric chloride, 80 mg/L sodium thiosulfate, Cool 4 °C | 14 days to extraction, 28 days to analysis |
| BNA (525.1) | 1 L glass with Teflon cap liner | 40-50 mg/L sodium sulfite, HCl to pH <2, Cool 4 °C | 7 days to extraction, 30 days to analysis |
| Carbamates (531.1) | 1 L glass with Teflon cap liner | Monochloroacetic acid to pH 3, 80 mg/L sodium thiosulfate, Cool 4 °C until storage at -10 °C | 28 days with storage at -10 °C |
| Glyphosate (547) | 1 L amber glass with Teflon cap liner | 100 mg/L sodium thiosulfate, Cool 4 °C | 14 days |
| Endothall (548 and 548.1) | 1 L glass with Teflon cap liner | Cool 4 °C | 7 days to extraction, 1 day to analysis |
| Diquat & Paraquat (549) | 1 L amber high density PVC or silanized amber glass | 100 mg/L sodium thiosulfate, sulfuric acid to pH <2, Cool 4 °C | 7 days to extraction, 21 days to analysis |
| PAH (550 or 550.1) | 1 L amber glass with Teflon cap liner | 100 mg/L sodium thiosulfate, 6N HCl to pH <2, Cool 4 °C | 7 days to extraction, 40 days to analysis |

Continued on next page.

**Table 1-28.** **Drinking water holding time, preservation and sample container requirements from** *Manual for the Certification of Laboratories Analyzing Drinking Water - Criteria and Procedures Quality Assurance* **Third Edition, Change 2 EPA-814B-92-002, September 1992,** *continued*

| Parameter | Sample Volume & Container | Preservation | Max. Holding Time |
|---|---|---|---|
| **Organic Tests (method)** | | | |
| Dioxins (1613) | 1 L amber glass with Teflon cap liner | 80 mg/L sodium thiosulfate, Cool 4 °C | 40 days |
| TTHM (501.1 or 501.2) | 40 mL glass with Teflon lined septa | 3 mg sodium thiosulfate or sodium sulfite | 14 days |
| VOC (502.1, 502.1, or 503.1) | 40 mL glass with Teflon lined silicon septa | 25 mg ascorbic acid or 3 mg sodium thiosulfate, 1:1 HCl to pH <2, Cool 4 °C | 14 days |
| VOC (524.1 or 524.2) | 40 mL glass with Teflon lined silicon septa | 25 mg ascorbic acid, 1:1 HCl to pH <2, Cool 4 °C | 14 days |
| **Radiological Tests**[63] | | | |
| Gross alpha | 1 L, P, G | Conc. HCl or $HNO_3$ to pH <2 | - |
| Gross beta | 1 L, P, G | Conc. HCl or $HNO_3$ to pH <2 | - |
| Strontium-89 | 1 L, P, G | Conc. HCl or $HNO_3$ to pH <2 | - |
| Strontium-90 | 1 L, P, G | Conc. HCl or $HNO_3$ to pH <2 | - |
| Radium-226 | 1 L, P, G | Conc. HCl or $HNO_3$ to pH <2 | - |
| Radium-228 | 1 L, P, G | Conc. HCl or $HNO_3$ to pH <2 | - |
| Cesium-134 | 1 L, P, G | Conc. HCl to pH <2 | - |
| Iodine-131 | 2 L, P, G | None | - |
| Tritium | 1 L, P, G | None | - |
| Uranium | 1 L, P, G | Conc. HCl or $HNO_3$ to pH <2 | - |
| Photon emitters | P, G | Conc. HCl or $HNO_3$ to pH <2 | - |

---

[63] *Prescribed Procedures for Measurement of Radioactivity in Drinking Water,* EPA-600/4-80-032 1980.

**Table 1-29.  Holding times, containers and preservatives for wastewater
samples.  From 40 CFR 136, Table II, as amended 31 Jan 1994,
59 FR 4504**

| Parameter | Sample volume & Container[64] | Preservation[65,66] | Max. Holding Time[67] |
|---|---|---|---|
| **Bacterial Tests** | | | |
| Coliform, Fecal and Total | 100 ml, Sterile P or G | Cool 4 °C, 0.008% $Na_2S_2O_3$[68] | 6 hours from time of collection |
| Fecal streptococci | 100 ml, Sterile P or G | Cool 4 °C, 0.008% $Na_2S_2O_3$[68] | 6 hours from time of collection |
| **Inorganic Tests** | | | |
| Acidity | 500 ml, P, G | Cool 4 °C | 14 days |
| Alkalinity | 500 ml, P, G | Cool 4 °C | 14 days |
| Ammonia | 500 ml, P, G | Cool 4 °C, $H_2SO_4$ to pH <2 | 28 days |
| BOD | 1000 ml, P, G | Cool, 4 °C | 48 hours |
| Bromide | 500 ml, P, G | None required | 28 days |
| CBOD | 1000 ml, P, G | Cool, 4 °C | 48 hours |
| COD | 500 ml, P, G | Cool 4 °C, $H_2SO_4$ to pH <2 | 28 days |
| Chloride | 500 ml, P, G | None required | 28 days |
| Chlorine, total residual | 500 ml, P, G | None required | Analyze immediately |
| Color | 500 ml, P, G | Cool 4 °C | 48 hours |

Continued on next page.

---

[64]  Polyethylene (P) or Glass (G).

[65]  Sample preservation should be performed immediately upon sample collection.  For composite chemical samples each aliquot should be preserved at the time of collection.  When use of an automated sampler makes it impossible to preserve each aliquot, then chemical samples may be preserved by maintaining at 4 °C until compositing and sample splitting is completed.

[66]  When any sample is to be shipped by common carrier or sent through the US Postal System, it must comply with the Department of Transportation Hazardous Materials Regulations (49 CFR 172).  The person offering such material for transportation is responsible for ensuring such compliance.  For the preservation requirements of the Table, the Office of Hazardous Materials, Materials Transportation Bureau, Department of Transportation has determined that the Hazardous Materials Regulations do not apply to the following materials:  Hydrochloric acid (HCl) in water solutions at concentrations of 0.04% by weight or less (pH about 1.96 or greater);  Nitric acid in water solutions of 0.15% by weight or less (pH about 1.62 or greater);  Sulfuric acid ($H_2SO_4$) in water solutions at concentrations of 0.35% by weight or less (pH about 1.15 or greater); and Sodium Hydroxide (NaOH) in water solutions at concentrations of 0.080% by weight or less (pH about 12.30 or less).

[67]  Samples should be analyzed as soon as possible after collection.  The times listed are the maximum times that samples may be held before analysis and still be considered valid.  Samples may be held for longer periods only if the permittee, or monitoring laboratory, has data on file to show that the specific types of samples under study are stable for longer time, and has received a variance from the Regional Administrator under 40 CFR 136.3(e).  Some samples may not be stable for the maximum time period given in the Table.  A permittee, or monitoring laboratory, is obligated to hold the sample for a shorter time if knowledge exists to show that this is necessary to maintain sample stability.  See 40 CFR 136.3(e) for details.

[68]  Should only be used in the presence of residual chlorine.

**Table 1-29. Holding times, containers and preservatives for wastewater samples. From 40 CFR 136, Table II, as amended 31 Jan 1994, 59 FR 4504,** *continued*

| Parameter | Sample volume & Container[69] | Preservation[70,71] | Max. Holding Time[72] |
|---|---|---|---|
| **Inorganic Tests,** *continued* | | | |
| Cyanide, total and amenable to chlorination | P, G | Cool 4 °C, NaOH to pH >12, 0.6 g ascorbic acid[73] | 14 days[74] |
| Fluoride | P | None required | 28 days |
| Hardness | P, G | $HNO_3$ to pH <2, $H_2SO_4$ to pH < 2 | 6 months |
| Hydrogen ion (pH) | P, G | None required | Analyze immediately |
| Kjeldahl and organic nitrogen | P, G | Cool 4 °C, $H_2SO_4$ to pH <2 | 28 days |
| **Metals**[75] | | | |
| Boron | P(PTFE) or quartz | $HNO_3$ to pH <2, | 6 months |
| Chromium VI | P, G | Cool 4 °C | 24 hours |
| Mercury | P, G | $HNO_3$ to pH <2, | 28 days |
| Metals, other | P, G | $HNO_3$ to pH <2, | 6 months |
| Nitrate | P, G | Cool 4 °C | 48 hours |
| Nitrate-nitrite | P, G | Cool 4 °C, $H_2SO_4$ to pH <2 | 28 days |
| Nitrite | P, G | Cool 4 °C | 48 hours |
| Oil and grease | G | Cool 4 °C, HCl or $H_2SO_4$ to pH <2 | 28 days |
| Organic carbon | G | Cool 4 °C, HCl, $H_2SO_4$ or $H_3PO_4$ to pH <2 | 28 days |
| Orthophosphate | P, G | Filter immediately, Cool 4 °C | 48 hours |
| Oxygen, dissolved probe | 500 ml, G | None required | Analyze immediately |
| Oxygen, dissolved Winkler | 300 ml, G | Fix on site and store in dark | 8 hours |
| Phenols, total | 500 ml, G | Cool 4 °C, $H_2SO_4$ to pH <2 | 28 days |

Continued on next page.

[69] See footnote 64.
[70] See footnote 65.
[71] See footnote 66.
[72] See footnote 67.
[73] Should only be used in the presence of residual chlorine.
[74] Maximum holding time is 24 hours when sulfide is present. Optionally, all samples may be tested with lead acetate paper before pH adjustments in order to determine if sulfide is present. If sulfide is present, it can be removed by the addition of cadmium nitrate powder until a negative spot test is obtained. The sample is filtered, and then NaOH is added to pH 12.
[75] Samples should be filtered immediately on-site before adding preservative for dissolved metals.

**Table 1-29. Holding times, containers and preservatives for wastewater samples. From 40 CFR 136, Table II, as amended 31 Jan 1994, 59 FR 4504,** *continued*

| Parameter | Sample volume & Container[76] | Preservation[77,78] | Max. Holding Time[79] |
|---|---|---|---|
| **Metals,** *continued* | | | |
| Phosphorous (elemental) | 500 ml, G | Cool 4 °C | 48 hours |
| Phosphorous, total | 500 ml, P, G | Cool 4 °C, $H_2SO_4$ to pH <2 | 28 days |
| Residue, total (TS) | 500 ml, P, G | Cool 4 °C | 7 days |
| Residue, Filterable (TDS) | 500 ml, P, G | Cool 4 °C | 7 days |
| Residue, Nonfilterable (TSS) | 500 ml, P, G | Cool 4 °C | 7 days |
| Residue, settleable | 1000 ml, P, G | Cool 4 °C | 48 hours |
| Residue, volatile | 500 ml, P, G | Cool 4 °C | 7 days |
| Silica | 500 ml, P or quartz | Cool 4 °C | 28 days |
| Specific conductance | 500 ml, P, G | Cool 4 °C | 28 days |
| Sulfate | P, G | Cool 4 °C | 28 days |
| Sulfide | P, G | Cool 4 °C, add zinc acetate and NaOH to pH >9 | 7 days |
| Sulfite | P, G | None required | Analyze immediately |
| Surfactants | P, G | Cool 4 °C | 48 hours |
| Temperature | P, G | None required | Analyze immediately |
| Turbidity | P, G | Cool 4 °C | 48 hours |
| **Organic Tests (method)** | | | |
| Purgeable halocarbons (601, 624, or 1624) | 40 mL glass, Teflon lined silicon septum | Cool 4 °C, 0.008% $Na_2S_2O_3$[80] | 14 days |
| Purgeable aromatic hydrocarbons (602, 624, or 1624) | 40 mL glass, Teflon lined silicon septum | Cool 4 °C, 0.008% $Na_2S_2O_3$[80], HCl to pH 2[81] | 14 days |
| Acrolein and acrylonitrile (603, 624, or 1624) | 40 mL glass, Teflon lined silicon septum | Cool 4 °C, 0.008% $Na_2S_2O_3$[80], adjust pH to 4-5[82] | 14 days |

Continued on next page.

---

[76] See footnote 64.
[77] See footnote 65.
[78] See footnote 66.
[79] See footnote 67.
[80] Should only be used in the presence of residual chlorine.
[81] Sample receiving no pH adjustment must be analyzed within 7 days of sampling.
[82] The pH adjustment is not required if acrolein will not be measured. Samples for acrolein receiving no pH adjustment must be analyzed within 3 days of sampling.

**Table 1-29. Holding times, containers and preservatives for wastewater samples. From 40 CFR 136, Table II, as amended 31 Jan 1994, 59 FR 4504,** *continued*

| Parameter | Sample volume & Container[83] | Preservation[84,85] | Max. Holding Time[86] |
|---|---|---|---|
| Organic Tests (method), *continued* | | | |
| Phenols[87] (604, 625, or 1625) | 1L glass with Teflon lined cap | Cool 4 °C, 0.008% $Na_2S_2O_3$[88] | 7 days until extraction, 40 days after extraction |
| Benzidine[89] (605, 625, or 1625) | 1 L, glass with Teflon lined cap | Cool 4 °C, 0.008% $Na_2S_2O_3$[88] | 7 days until extraction[90] |
| Phthalates (606, 625, or 1625) | 1 L, glass with Teflon lined cap | Cool 4 °C | 7 days until extraction, 40 days after extraction |
| Nitrosamines[91] (607, 625, or 1625) | 1 L, glass with Teflon lined cap | Cool 4 °C, 0.008% $Na_2S_2O_3$[88], store in dark | 7 days until extraction, 40 days after extraction |
| PCB (608 or 625) | 1 L, glass with Teflon lined cap | Cool 4 °C | 7 days until extraction, 40 days after extraction |
| Nitroaromatics and isophorone (609, 625 or 1625) | 1 L, glass with Teflon lined cap | Cool 4 °C, 0.008% $Na_2S_2O_3$[88], store in dark | 7 days until extraction, 40 days after extraction |
| PAH (610, 625 or 1625) | 1 L, glass with Teflon lined cap | Cool 4 °C, 0.008% $Na_2S_2O_3$[88], store in dark | 7 days until extraction, 40 days after extraction |
| Haloethers (611, 625 or 1625) | 1 L, glass with Teflon lined cap | Cool 4 °C, 0.008% $Na_2S_2O_3$[88] | 7 days until extraction, 40 days after extraction |

Continued on next page.

---

83   See footnote 64.
84   See footnote 65.
85   See footnote 66.
86   See footnote 67.
87   When the extractable analytes of concern fall within a single chemical category, the specified preservative and maximum holding time should be observed for optimum safeguard of sample integrity. When the analytes of concern fall within two or more chemical categories, the sample may be preserved by cooling to 4 °C, reducing residual chlorine with 0.008% sodium thiosulfate, storing in the dark, and adjusting the pH to 6-9; samples preserved in this manner may be held for 7 days before extraction and for 40 days after extraction. Exceptions to this optional preservation and holding time procedure are noted in footnote 68 (re: the requirement for thiosulfate reduction of residual chlorine) and footnotes 86 and 87 (re the analysis of benzidine).
88   Should only be used in the presence of residual chlorine.
89   If 1,2-diphenylhydrazine is likely to be present, adjust the pH of the sample to 4.0 ± 0.2 to prevent rearrangement to benzidine.
90   Extracts may be stored for up to 7 days if storage is conducted under an inert (oxidant-free) atmosphere.
91   For the analysis of diphenylnitrosamine, add 0.008% sodium thiosulfate and adjust pH to 7-10 with sodium hydroxide within 24 hours of sampling.

**Table 1-29.** **Holding times, containers and preservatives for wastewater samples. From 40 CFR 136, Table II, as amended 31 Jan 1994, 59 FR 4504,** *continued*

| Parameter | Sample volume & Container[92] | Preservation[93,94] | Max. Holding Time[95] |
|---|---|---|---|
| **Organic Tests (method),** *continued* | | | |
| Chlorinated hydrocarbons (612, 625 or 1625) | 1 L, glass with Teflon lined cap | Cool 4 °C | 7 days until extraction, 40 days after extraction |
| TCDD (613) | 1 L, glass with Teflon lined cap | Cool 4 °C, 0.008% $Na_2S_2O_3$[96] | 7 days until extraction, 40 days after extraction |
| Chlorinated pesticides[97] (608 or 625) | 1 L, glass with Teflon lined cap | Cool 4 °C, pH 6-9 | 7 days until extraction, 40 days after extraction |
| **Radiological Tests** | | | |
| Alpha, beta and radium[98] | 1L P or G | $HNO_3$ to pH <2 | 6 months |

[92]  See footnote 64.
[93]  See footnote 65.
[94]  See footnote 66.
[95]  See footnote 67.
[96]  Should only be used in the presence of residual chlorine.
[97]  The pH adjustment may be performed upon receipt at the laboratory and may be omitted if samples are extracted within 72 hours of collection. For the analysis of aldrin, add 0.008% sodium thiosulfate.
[98]  *Prescribed Procedures for Measurement of Radioactivity in Drinking Water,* EPA-600/4-80-032 1980.

**Table 1-30** **Preservation, holding times and sample containers for aqueous matrices, Table 2-21 from Chapter 2, SW-846, Third Edition, Revision 1, July, 1992**

| Parameter | Container[99] | Preservation | Max. Holding Time |
|---|---|---|---|
| **Bacterial Tests** | | | |
| Coliform, total | P, G | Cool 4 °C, 0.008% $Na_2S_2O_3$ | 6 hours |
| **Inorganic Tests** | | | |
| Chloride | P, G | None required | 28 days |
| Cyanide, total and amenable to chlorination | P, G | If oxidizing agents are present add 0.6 g ascorbic acid per liter; adjust pH >12 with 10N NaOH, Cool 4°C | 14 days |
| Hydrogen ion (pH) | P, G | None required | Analyze immediately |
| Nitrate | P, G | Cool 4 °C | 48 hours |
| Sulfate | P, G | Cool 4 °C | 28 days |
| Sulfide | P, G | Cool 4 °C, add zinc acetate | 7 days |
| Metals | | | |
| Chromium VI | P, G | Cool 4 °C | 28 hours |
| Mercury | P, G | $HNO_3$ to pH <2 | 38 days glass 13 days plastic |
| Other metals | P, G | $HNO_3$ to pH <2 | 6 months |
| **Organic Tests** | | | |
| Oil & Grease | G | Cool 4 °C; adjust pH to <2 with HCl, $H_2SO_4$ or solid $NaHSO_4$ | 28 days |
| TOC | P, G | Cool 4 °C; adjust pH to <2 with HCl, $H_2SO_4$ or solid $NaHSO_4$ | 28 days |
| Purgeable halocarbons | Glass with Teflon lined septum | Cool 4 °C[100] | 14 days |
| Purgeable aromatic hydrocarbons | Glass with Teflon lined septum | Cool 4 °C; adjust pH to <2 with HCl, $H_2SO_4$ or solid $NaHSO_4$[101] | 14 days |
| Acrolein and acrylonitrile | Glass with Teflon lined septum | Cool 4 °C, 0.008% $Na_2S_2O_3$, adjust pH to 4-5 | 14 days |
| Phenols | Glass with Teflon lined cap | Cool 4 °C, 0.008% $Na_2S_2O_3$ | 7 days until extraction, 40 days after extraction |
| Benzidines | Glass with Teflon lined cap | Cool 4 °C, 0.008% $Na_2S_2O_3$ | 7 days until extraction, 40 days after extraction |

Continued on next page.

[99] Polyethylene (P) or Glass (G).
[100] Free chlorine must be removed by appropriate addition of sodium thiosulfate.
[101] Free chlorine must be removed by appropriate addition of sodium thiosulfate, prior to acidification.

**Table 1-30  Preservation, holding times and sample containers for aqueous matrices, Table 2-21 from Chapter 2, SW-846, Third Edition, Revision 1, July, 1992,** *continued*

| Parameter | Container[102] | Preservation | Max. Holding Time |
|---|---|---|---|
| **Organic Tests,** *continued* | | | |
| Phthalate esters | Glass with Teflon lined cap | Cool 4°C | 7 days until extraction, 40 days after extraction |
| Nitrosamines | Glass with Teflon lined cap | Store in dark, Cool 4 °C, 0.008% $Na_2S_2O_3$ | 7 days until extraction, 40 days after extraction |
| PCBs | Glass with Teflon lined cap | Cool 4°C | 7 days until extraction, 40 days after extraction |
| Nitroaromatics and cylic ketones | Glass with Teflon lined cap | Store in dark, Cool 4 °C, 0.008% $Na_2S_2O_3$ | 7 days until extraction, 40 days after extraction |
| PAH | Glass with Teflon lined cap | Store in dark, Cool 4 °C, 0.008% $Na_2S_2O_3$ | 7 days until extraction, 40 days after extraction |
| Haloethers | Glass with Teflon lined cap | Cool 4 °C, 0.008% $Na_2S_2O_3$ | 7 days until extraction, 40 days after extraction |
| Chlorinated hydrocarbons | Glass with Teflon lined cap | Cool 4 °C, 0.008% $Na_2S_2O_3$ | 7 days until extraction, 40 days after extraction |
| Dioxins and furans | Glass with Teflon lined cap | Cool 4 °C, 0.008% $Na_2S_2O_3$ | 7 days until extraction, 40 days after extraction |
| TOX | Glass with Teflon lined cap | Cool 4 °C; adjust pH to <2 with HCl, $H_2SO_4$ or solid $NaHSO_4$ | 28 days |
| Pesticides | Glass with Teflon lined cap | Cool 4 °C, pH 5-9 | 7 days until extraction, 40 days after extraction |
| **Radiological Tests** | | | |
| Alpha, beta and radium | P, G | $HNO_3$ to pH <2 | 6 months |

---

[102]  Polyethylene (P) or Glass (G).

## Table 1-31. Sample containers, preservatives and holding times for hazardous waste samples analyzed by SW-846 methods

| Parameter | Container[103] | Preservation | Max. Holding Time |
|---|---|---|---|
| **Metals**[104] | | | |
| Aqueous, Total | 600 mL, P, G | Cool 4 °C, $HNO_3$ to pH < 2 | 6 months |
| Aqueous, Dissolved | 600 mL, P, G | Filter on site, Cool 4 °C, $HNO_3$ to pH <2 | 6 months |
| Aqueous, Suspended | 600 mL, P, G | Filter on site, Cool 4 °C | 6 months |
| Solid, Total | 200 g, P, G | Cool 4 °C | 6 months |
| Chromium VI, aqueous | 400 mL, P, G | Cool 4 °C | 24 hours |
| Chromium VI, Solid | 200 g, P, G | Cool 4 °C | As soon as possible |
| Mercury, aqueous, total | 400 mL, P, G | Cool 4 °C, $HNO_3$ to pH < 2 | 38 days G<br>13 days P |
| Mercury, aqueous, dissolved | 400 mL, P, G | Filter, Cool 4 °C, $HNO_3$ to pH <2 | 38 days G<br>13 days P |
| Mercury, solid | 200 g, P, G | Cool 4 °C | 28 days |
| **Organic Tests**[105] | | | |
| VOA, concentrated waste samples | 8 oz (125 mL) wide mouth glass with Teflon cap liner | None | 14 days |
| VOA, liquid sample | 2 x 40 mL glass with Teflon lined septum cap | Adjust to pH <2 with $H_2SO_4$, HCl or solid $NaHSO_4$, Cool 4 °C | 14 days |
| VOA, liquid sample, chlorine residual present | 2 x 40 mL glass with Teflon lined septum cap | Collect sample in 4 oz container with 4 dps 10% $Na_2S_2O_3$, dispense into 40 mL vials, Adjust to pH <2 with $H_2SO_4$, HCl or solid $NaHSO_4$, Cool 4 °C | 14 days |
| VOA, soil, sediment or sludge | 4 oz (125 mL) wide mouth glass with Teflon cap liner | Cool 4 °C | 14 days |
| Acrolein and acrylonitrile, liquid sample | 2 x 40 mL glass with Teflon lined septum cap | Adjust to pH 4-5, Cool 4 °C | 14 days |
| Semivolatile, concentrated waste | 8 oz (125 mL) wide mouth glass with Teflon cap liner | None | 14 days before extraction, analyzed within 40 days after extraction |

Continued on next page.

---

[103]  Polyethylene (P) or Glass (G).
[104]  Table 3-1, Chapter 3, page 3, SW-846, Revision 1, July, 1992 and proposed Revision 2, November, 1992.
[105]  Table 4-1, Chapter 4, page 6-7, SW-846, Revison 1, July, 1992.

**Table 1-31. Sample containers, preservatives and holding times for hazardous waste samples analyzed by SW-846 methods,** *continued*

| Parameter | Sample volume & Container[106] | Preservation | Max. Holding Time |
|---|---|---|---|
| **Organic Tests**[107], *continued* | | | |
| Semivolatile, water sample | 1 gal or 2 x 0.5 gal amber glass with Teflon cap liner | Cool 4 °C | 7 days before extraction, analyzed within 40 days after extraction |
| Semivolatile, water sample, chlorine residual present | 1 gal or 2 x 0.5 gal amber glass with Teflon cap liner | 3 mL 10% $Na_2S_2O_3$, per gal, Cool 4 °C | 7 days before extraction, analyzed within 40 days after extraction |
| Semivolatile, soil, sediment or sludge sample | 8 oz (125 mL) wide mouth glass with Teflon cap liner | Cool 4 °C | 14 days before extraction, analyzed within 40 days after extraction |
| **TCLP, Method 1311**[108] | | | |
| Volatiles | Glass with Teflon lined septum | Cool 4 °C and minimal headspace before and after TCLP | 14 days to TCLP, 14 days after TCLP to analysis |
| Semi-volatiles | Glass with Teflon lined cap | Cool 4 °C before and after TCLP | 14 days to TCLP, 7 days after TCLP to extraction, 40 days after extraction to analysis |
| Mercury | P, G | Preserve with $HNO_3$ to pH <2 after TCLP | 28 days to TCLP, 28 days after TCLP to analysis |
| Other metals | P, G | Preserve with $HNO_3$ to pH <2 after TCLP | 180 days to TCLP, 180 days after TCLP to analysis |

---

[106] Polyethylene (P) or Glass (G).
[107] Table 4-1, Chapter 4, page 6-7, SW-846, Revison 1, July, 1992.
[108] Method 1311, SW-846, Third Edition, Revision 0, July, 1992.

**Table 1-32. Sampling and preservation procedures for groundwater detection monitoring, Table 11-1, Chapter 11, page 7, SW-846, Third Edition, Revision 0, September, 1986**

| Parameter | Sample Volume & Container[109] | Preservation | Max. Holding Time |
|---|---|---|---|
| pH | 25 mL, T, P, G | None | Analyze immediately |
| Specific Conductance | 100 mL, T, P, G | None | Analyze immediately |
| TOC | 4 x 15 mL, Glass, Teflon lined cap | Cool 4 °C, HCl to pH < 2 | 28 days |
| TOX | 4 x 15 mL, Amber glass, Teflon lined cap | Cool 4 °C, 1 mL of 1.1 M sodium sulfite | 7 days |
| Chloride | 50 mL, T, P, G | Cool 4 °C | 28 days |
| Metals, Total[110] | 1000 mL, T, P[111] | Field acidified to pH < 2 with $HNO_3$ | 6 months |
| Metals, Dissolved[112] | 1000 mL, T, P[113] | Field filtration (0.45 mm) then acidify to pH < 2 with $HNO_3$ | 6 months |
| Phenols | 500 mL, G | Cool 4 °C, $H_2SO_4$ to pH < 2 | 28 days |
| Sulfate | 50 mL, T, P, G | Cool 4 °C | 28 days |
| Fluoride | 300 mL, T, P | Field acidified to pH < 2 with $HNO_3$ | 28 days |
| Nitrate | 1000 mL, T, P, G | Cool 4 °C, $H_2SO_4$ to pH < 2 | 14 days |
| Chlorinated pesticides and herbicides | 2000 mL, T, G | Cool 4 °C | 7 days |
| Radium, Gross alpha, and Gross beta | 1 gal, P, G | Field acidified to pH < 2 with $HNO_3$ | 6 months |
| Coliform bacteria | 200 mL, Sterilized PP or G | Cool 4 °C | 6 hours |
| Cyanide | 500 mL, P, G | NaOH to pH >12, Cool 4 °C | 14 days |
| Oil & Grease | 100 mL, G | $H_2SO_4$ to pH < 2, Cool 4 °C | 28 days |
| Semivolatile, volatile organics | 1000 mL, T, G | Cool 4 °C | 7 days |

---

[109]  Teflon (T), Polyethylene (P), Polypropylene (PP) or Glass (G).
[110]  Includes iron, manganese, arsenic, barium, cadmium, chromium, lead, mercury, selenium, sodium and silver.
[111]  Silver sample is collected in a dark bottle.
[112]  Includes iron, manganese, arsenic, barium, cadmium, chromium, lead, mercury, selenium, sodium and silver.
[113]  Silver sample is collected in a dark bottle.

**Table 1-33. Sample container, preservation and holding time requirements in CLP-SOW**

| Parameter | Container[114] | Preservative[115] | Max. Holding Time |
|---|---|---|---|
| **Inorganic Tests[116]** | | | |
| Metals, other than mercury, aqueous samples | P, G | $HNO_3$ to pH < 2 | 180 days |
| Metals, other than mercury, soil/sediment samples | P, G | Cool 4 °C | 180 days |
| Mercury, aqueous samples | P, G | $HNO_3$ to pH < 2 | 26 days |
| Mercury, soil/sediment samples | P, G | Cool 4 °C | 26 days |
| Cyanide, total and amenable to chlorination, aqueous samples | P, G | 0.6 g ascorbic acid[117], NaOH to pH >12, Cool 4 °C | 12 days |
| Cyanide, total and amenable to chlorination, soil/sediment samples | P, G | Cool 4 °C | 12 days |
| **Organic Tests[118]** | | | |
| VOA, all samples | Glass | Protected from light and cool 4 °C | 10 days of sample receipt |
| SV, water samples | Glass | Protected from light and cool 4 °C | Extraction begun within 5 days of receipt, analysis within 40 days from extraction |
| SV, soil/sediment samples | Glass | Protected from light and cool 4 °C | Sonication complete within 10 days of receipt, analysis within 40 days from extraction |
| Pesticides, water samples | Glass | Protected from light and cool 4 °C | Extraction started within 5 days of receipt, analysis completed within 40 days of extraction |
| Pesticide, soil/sediment samples | Glass | Protected from light and Cool 4 °C | Sonication complete within 10 days of receipt, analysis complete within 40 days of extraction. |

---

[114] Polyethylene (P), or Glass (G).

[115] Sample preservation is performed by the sampler immediately upon sample collection.

[116] USEPA CLP-SOW for inorganic analysis, multi-media, multi-concentration, Document Number ILM03.0.

[117] Only used in the presence of residual chlorine.

[118] USEPA CLP-SOW for organics analysis, multi-media, multi-concentration, Document Number OLM02.1, November, 1993.

**Table 1-34. USACE Sample Containers, Preservatives and Holding Times, Low Concentration Samples[119]**

| Parameter | Container[120] | Preservative[121, 122] | Max. Holding Time |
|---|---|---|---|
| **Water Matrix** | | | |
| Volatiles | 2 x 40 mLG, Septa vial | Ice to 4 °C, 4 drops conc, HCl or $NaHSO_4$ to pH < 2 | 14 days |
| BNA | 2 x 1 L[123] amber G | Ice to 4 °C | 7 days to extraction, 40 days after extraction to analysis |
| PCBs, Pesticides | 2 x 1 L amber G | Ice to 4 °C | 7 days to extraction, 40 days after extraction to analysis |
| Metals[124] | 1 x 1 L P | $HNO_3$ to pH < 2 | 6 months |
| Total Recoverable Petroleum Hydrocarbons (TRPH) | 2 x 1 L G | Ice to 4 °C, HCl to pH < 2 | 28 days |
| Common anions[125] | 1 x 1 L G | Ice to 4 °C | 28 days |
| Explosives | 2 x 1 L G (amber) | Ice to 4 °C | 7 days to extraction, 40 days after extraction to analysis |
| Cyanide | 1 x 1 L P | NaOH to pH >12, Ice to 4 °C | 14 days |
| **Soil/Sediment Matrix** | | | |
| Volatiles | 2 x 40 mL G or 2 x 125 mL G Septa vial | Ice to 4 °C | 14 days |
| BNA, PCB, Pesticides | 1 x 8 oz G | Ice to 4 °C | 14 days to extraction, 40 days after extraction to analysis |
| Metals, Cyanide, TRPH | 1 x 8 oz G | Ice to 4 °C (Cyanide & TRPH) | 6 months (TRPH: 28 days) |
| Explosives | 1 x 4 oz G | Ice to 4 °C | 14 days to extraction, 40 days after extraction to analysis |

---

[119]  Table F-1, USACE Chemical Data Quality Management for Hazardous Waste Remediation Activities, ER 1110-1-263, 1 October, 1990, pg F-9.

[120]  All containers must have Teflon-lined seals (Teflon-lined septa for VOA vials). G = Glass; P = High density polyethylene.

[121]  Samples with residual chlorine present will be dechlorinated with sodium thiosulfate as specified in SW-846 (Third Edition).

[122]  Samples with residual chlorine present will be dechlorinated with sodium thiosulfate as specified in SW-846 (Third Edition).

[123]  Three bottles are required on at least 5-10% (but at least one) sample so that the laboratory can perform all method QC checks for SW-846 method.

[124]  Total Recoverable Metals for water samples. Holding time for mercury is 28 days in glass; for hexavalent chromium is 24 hours.

[125]  $Cl^-$, $Br^-$, $F^-$, $NO_3^-$, $NO_2^-$, $PO_4^{3-}$, $SO_4^{2-}$; 1 L for each method; orthophosphate requires filtration. Holding time for extraction is 48 hrs for $NO_2^-$, $NO_3^-$, and $PO_4^{3-}$ if not preserved with $H_2SO_4$ to pH < 2.

## Table 1-35.  USACE Sample Containers, Preservatives and Holding Times, Medium and High Concentration Samples[126]

| Parameter | Container[127] | Preservative[128, 129] | Max. Holding Time |
|---|---|---|---|
| **Medium Concentration Water Matrix** | | | |
| Volatiles | 2 x 40 mL G, Septa vial | Ice to 4 °C | 14 days |
| BNA | 2 x 32 oz wide mouth jars[130] G | Ice to 4 °C | 7 days to extraction, 40 days after extraction to analysis |
| PCBs, Pesticides | 2 x 32 oz wide mouth jars G | Ice to 4 °C | 7 days to extraction, 40 days after extraction to analysis |
| Metals[131] | 1 x 16 oz wide mouth jar, G | $HNO_3$ to pH < 2 | 6 months |
| Explosives | 2 x 1 L G (amber) | Ice to 4 °C | 7 days to extraction, 40 days after extraction to analysis |
| Cyanide | 1 x 16 oz wide mouth jar, G | Ice to 4 °C | 14 days |
| **Medium Concentration Soil/Sediment Matrix** | | | |
| Volatiles | 2 x 40 mL G or 2 x 125 mL G | Ice to 4 °C | 14 days |
| BNA, PCB, Pesticides | 1 x 8 oz G | - | 14 days to extraction, 40 days after extraction to analysis |
| Metals, Cyanide, TRPH | 1 x 8 oz G | Ice to 4 °C (Cyanide & TRPH) | 6 months (TRPH: 28 days) |
| Explosives | 1 x 4 oz G | Ice to 4 °C | 14 days to extraction, 40 days after extraction to analysis |

Continued on next page.

---

[126]  Table F-2, USACE Chemical Data Quality Management for Hazardous Waste Remediation Activities, ER 1110-1-263, 1 October, 1990, pg F-9.

[127]  All containers must have Teflon-lined seals (Teflon-lined septa for VOA vials).  G = Glass; P = High density polyethylene.

[128]  Samples with residual chlorine present will be dechlorinated with sodium thiosulfate as specified in SW-846 (Third Edition).

[129]  Samples with residual chlorine present will be dechlorinated with sodium thiosulfate as specified in SW-846 (Third Edition).

[130]  Three bottles are required on at least 5-10% (but at least one) sample so that the laboratory can perform all method QC checks for SW-846 method.

[131]  Total Recoverable Metals for water samples.  Holding time for mercury is 28 days in glass; for hexavalent chromium is 24 hours.

**Table 1-35.  USACE Sample Containers, Preservatives and Holding Times, Medium and High Concentration Samples**[132], *continued*

| Parameter | Container[133] | Preservative[134] | Max. Holding Time |
|---|---|---|---|
| **High Concentration Samples** | | | |
| Liquid - all organic and inorganic analyses | 1 x 8 oz wide mouth jar, G | - | Same as above for individual analytes |
| Solid - all organic and inorganic analyses | 1 x 8 oz wide mouth jar, G | - | Same as above for individual analytes |

---

[132]  Table F-2, USACE Chemical Data Quality Management for Hazardous Waste Remediation Activities, ER 1110-1-263, 1 October, 1990, p. F-9.

[133]  All containers must have Teflon-lined seals (Teflon-lined septa for VOA vials).  G = Glass; P = High density polyethylene

[134]  Sample preservation will be done in the field immediately upon sample collection.  If water samples are filtered in the field, differential pressure methods using 45 micron filters will be used, and preservative added after filtration.  VOA samples should never be filtered.

**Table 1-36. AFCEE requirements for containers, preservation techniques, sample volumes and holding times[135]**

| Parameter | Method | Container[136] | Preservation[137],[138] | Minimum sample volume/ weight | Maximum holding time |
|---|---|---|---|---|---|
| Alkalinity (field test) | A2320 | P,G | None required | 50 mL | Analyze immediately |
| Alkalinity (lab test) | A2320 | P,G | 4 °C | 50 mL | 14 days |
| Common anions | SW9056 | P,G | None | 50 mL | 28 days for Br, F, Cl, $SO_4$ 48 hrs for $NO_3$, $NO_2$, $PO_4$ |
| Cyanide, total and amenable | SW9010 | P,G,T | 4 °C, NaOH to pH >12, 0.6 g ascorbic acid | 500 mL or 4 oz | 14 days (water and soil) |
| Filterable residue | E160.1 | P,G | 4 °C | 100 mL | 7 days |
| Non-filterable residue | E160.2 | P,G | 4 °C | 100 mL | 7 days |
| pH (field test) | SW9040, SW9045 | P,G | None | N/A | Analyze immediately |
| Nitrate + nitrite | E353.1 | P,G | 4 °C, $H_2SO_4$ to pH < 2 | 500 mL | 28 days |
| Specific conductance (field test) | SW9050 | P,G | None | N/A | Analyze immediately |
| Temperature | E170.1 | P,G | None | N/A | Analyze immediately |
| Total organic carbon | SW9060 | P,G,T | 4 °C, HCl or $H_2SO_4$ to pH < 2 | 500 mL or 4 oz | 28 days (water and soil) |
| Chromium$^{+6}$ | SW7196 | P,G,T | 4 °C | 500 mL or 8 oz | 24 hrs[139] |
| Mercury | SW7470, 7471 | P,G,T | $HNO_3$ to pH < 2, 4 °C | 500 mL or 8 oz | 28 days |
| Metals | SW6010, SW-AA | P,G,T | $HNO_3$ to pH < 2, 4 °C | 500 mL or 8 oz | 180 days |
| Petroleum hydrocarbons | E418.1 140 | G,T | $H_2SO_4$ to pH < 2, 4 °C | 1 L or 8 oz | 28 days |

Continued on next page.

[135] *AFCEE Handbook for the Installation Restoration Program (IRP) Remedial Investigations and Feasibility Studies* (RI/FS), September, 1993.

[136] Polyethylene (P); Glass (G); Brass sleeves in the sample barrel, sometimes called California Brass (T).

[137] No pH adjustment for soil.

[138] Preservation with 0.008% sodium thiosulfate is only required when residual chlorine is present.

[139] Holding time for hexavalent chromium in soils has not been established. The recommended holding time for extracting into water is 48 hrs. The sample must be analyzed within 24 hrs of extraction.

[140] The use of method E418.1 requires specific AFCEE approval because of the use of ozone depleting reagents.

**Table 1-36. AFCEE requirements for containers, preservation techniques, sample volumes and holding times[141], *continued***

| Parameter | Method | Container[142] | Preservation[143],[144] | Minimum sample volume/ weight | Maximum holding time |
|---|---|---|---|---|---|
| Volatile fuel hydrocarbons | SW8015 modified | G, Teflon lined septum, T | 4 °C, HCl to pH < 2 | 2x40 mL or 4 oz | 14 days; 7 days if not preserved |
| Extractable fuel hydrocarbons | SW 8015 modified | G, amber, T | 4 °C | 1 L or 8 oz | water 7 days to extraction, 40 days after extraction; soil 14 days to extraction, 40 days after extraction |
| Aromatic volatile organics | SW8020 | G, Teflon lined septum, T | 4 °C, HCl to pH < 2, 0.008% Na$_2$S$_2$O$_3$ | 2x40 mL or 4 oz | 14 days; 7 days if not preserved |
| Chlorinated herbicides | SW8150 | G, Teflon lined cap, T | 4 °C, pH 5-9 | 1 L or 8 oz | water 7 days to extraction, 40 days after extraction; soil 14 days to extraction, 40 days after extraction |
| Pesticides and PCBs | SW8080, 8140 | G, Teflon lined cap, T | 4 °C, pH 5-9 | 1 L or 8 oz | water 7 days to extraction, 40 days after extraction; soil 14 days to extraction, 40 days after extraction |
| Phenols | SW8040 | G, Teflon lined cap, T | 4 °C, 0.008% Na$_2$S$_2$O$_3$ | 1 L or 8 oz | water 7 days to extraction, 40 days after extraction; soil 14 days to extraction, 40 days after extraction |
| Semivolatile organics | SW8270 | G, Teflon lined cap, T | 4 °C, 0.008% Na$_2$S$_2$O$_3$ | 1 L or 8 oz | water 7 days to extraction, 40 days after extraction; soil 14 days to extraction, 40 days after extraction |

Continued on next page.

---

141 See footnote 131.
142 See footnote 132.
143 See footnote 133.
144 See footnote 134.

**Table 1-36. AFCEE requirements for containers, preservation techniques, sample volumes and holding times[145],** *continued*

| Parameter | Method | Container[146] | Preservation[147, 148] | Minimum sample volume/ weight | Maximum holding time |
|---|---|---|---|---|---|
| Volatile organics | SW8240, 8015 modified, 8010, 8260 | G, Teflon lined septum, T | 4 °C, HCl to pH < 2 for aromatic volatiles by 8240 or 8260, 0.008% $Na_2S_2O_3$ | 2x40 mL or 4 oz | 14 days; 7 days if not preserved |
| PAH | SW8310 | G, Teflon lined cap, T | 4 °C, 0.008% $Na_2S_2O_3$, store in dark | 1 L or 8 oz | water 7 days to extraction, 40 days after extraction; soil 14 days to extraction, 40 days after extraction |
| Carbamate pesticides | SW8314 | G, Teflon lined cap, T | 4 °C, 0.008% $Na_2S_2O_3$ | 1 L or 8 oz | water 7 days to extraction, 40 days after extraction; soil 14 days to extraction, 40 days after extraction |
| Dioxins | SW8280, 8290 | G, Teflon lined cap, T | 4 °C, 0.008% $Na_2S_2O_3$ | 1 L or 8 oz | 30 days until extraction, 45 days after extraction |
| 1,2-dibromoethane | E504 | G, Teflon lined septum, T | 4 °C, 0.008% $Na_2S_2O_3$ | 2x40 mL | 28 days |
| alpha, beta and radium | SW9310, 9315, 9320 | G,P,T | $HNO_3$ to pH < 2 | 2 L or 16 oz | 180 days |
| TCLP | SW1311 | G, Teflon lined cap, T | 4 °C | 1 L or 8 oz | See footnote[149] |
| Explosive residues | SW8330 | P,G,T | 4 °C | 1 L or 8 oz | Water - 7 days to extraction; Soils - 14 days to extraction; Analysis within 40 days after extraction |

---

[145]   See footnote 131.
[146]   See footnote 132.
[147]   See footnote 133.
[148]   See footnote 134.
[149]   Volatiles - 14 days to TCLP extraction, 14 days after extraction; Semivolatiles - 14 days to TCLP extraction, 40 days after prep. extraction; Mercury - 28 days to TCLP extraction, 28 days after extraction; Metals - 180 days to TCLP extraction, 180 days after extraction.

**Table 1-37. Holding times, preservatives, containers and minimum sample size for HAZWRAP[150]**

| Parameter | Matrix | Holding time | Container | Preservative | Min. sample size[151] |
|---|---|---|---|---|---|
| **CLP methods** | | | | | |
| Volatile organics | water | 14 days | 2 x 40 mL with Teflon lined cap | 4 drops conc. HCl | 40 mL |
| | soil | 14 days | Brass or Teflon core tube sealed on both ends | 4 °C | 10 g |
| Extractable organics | water | 7 days extraction, 40 days to analysis | 1 L glass with Teflon liner | 4 °C | 1000 mL |
| | soil | 14 days extraction, 40 days to analysis | Glass jar with Teflon liner or core tube | 4 °C | 50 g |
| Metals, except Hg | water | 180 days | polyethylene or glass | $HNO_3$ to pH <2 | 100 mL |
| | soil | 180 days | ditto | 4 °C | 10 g |
| Mercury | water | 28 days | polyethylene or glass | $HNO_3$ to pH <2 | 100 mL |
| | soil | 28 days | ditto | 4 °C | 10 g |
| Cyanide | water | 14 days | polyethylene or glass | 0.6 g ascorbic acid, NaOH to pH >12, 4 °C | 100 mL |
| | soil | 14 days | ditto | 4 °C | 10 g |
| **Other methods** | | | | | |
| Volatile organics[152] | water, no res. chlorine | 14 days | 2 x 40 mL vials with Teflon lined septum caps | 4 drops conc. HCl, 4 °C | 40 mL |
| | water, res. chlorine pres. | 14 days | 2 x 40 mL vials with Teflon lined septum caps | 4 drops 10% $Na_2S_2O_3$, 4 dps conc. HCl, 4°C | 40 mL |
| | soil/ sediments and sludges | 14 days | Brass or Teflon core tube sealed on both ends | 4 °C | 10 g |
| Acrolein and acrylonitrile[153] | water | 14 days | 2 x 40 mL vials with Teflon lined septum caps | Adjust to pH 4-5, 4 °C | 40 mL |

Continued on next page.

---

[150] HAZWRAP requirements for quality control of analytical data, Document DOE/HWP-65/R1, July, 1990, Tables 6.1-6.5.

[151] Additional samples must be collected for matrix spike/matrix spike duplicate samples or matrix spike/duplicate.

[152] Methods 601, 602, 8010, 8015 or 8020.

[153] Methods 603 or 8030.

**Table 1-37. Holding times, preservatives, containers and minimum sample size for HAZWRAP[154], *continued***

| Parameter | Matrix | Holding time | Container | Preservative | Min. sample size[155] |
|---|---|---|---|---|---|
| Extractable organics[156] | water, no res. chlorine | 7 days to extraction, 40 days to analysis | 1 L glass with Teflon liner | 4 °C | 1 L |
| | water, res. chlorine present | 7 days to extraction, 40 days to analysis | 1 L glass with Teflon liner | 1 mL 10% $Na_2S_2O_3$ per liter, 4 °C | 1 L |
| | soil/ sediments and sludges | 14 days to extraction, 40 days to analysis | Glass jar with Teflon liner or core tube | 4 °C | 50 g |
| Dioxins/ furans[157] | water | 30 days to extraction, 45 days to analysis | 1 L glass | 4 °C | 1000 mL |
| | soil/waste | 30 days to extraction, 45 days to analysis | core tube | 4 °C | 50 g |
| Petroleum hydrocarbons as gasoline[158] | water | 14 days | 2 x 40 mL vials with Teflon liners | 4 °C, HCl to pH < 2 | 40 mL |
| | soil/waste | 14 days | core tube | 4 °C | 50 g |
| Petroleum hydrocarbons as gasoline[159] | water | 14 days to extraction, 40 days to analysis | 1 L glass | 4 °C, HCl to pH < 2 | 500 mL |
| | soil/waste | ditto | core tube | 4 °C | 50 g |
| Petroleum hydrocarbons as diesel[160] | water | 14 days to extraction, 40 days to analysis | 1 L glass | 4 °C | 500 mL |
| | soil/waste | 14 days to extraction, 40 days to analysis | core tube | 4 °C | 50 g |
| Petroleum hydrocarbons (TPH)[161] | water | 28 days | 1 L glass | 4 °C, HCl to pH <2 | 1000 mL |
| | soil | 28 days | glass jar with Teflon liner or core tube | 4 °C | 50 g |

Continued on next page.

---

154   See footnote 146.
155   See footnote 147.
156   Methods 604, 606, 608, 610, 614, 615, 632, 8040, 8060, 8080, 8140, 8150, or 8310.
157   Method 8280.
158   TPH-gasoline by purge and trap, Leaking Underground Fuel Tank Manual (LUFT).
159   TPH-gasoline extractable (LUFT).
160   TPH-diesel extractable (LUFT).
161   TPH-IR method 418.1.

**Table 1-37.** **Holding times, preservatives, containers and minimum sample size for HAZWRAP[162], *continued***

| Parameter | Matrix | Holding time | Container | Preservative | Min. sample size[163] |
|---|---|---|---|---|---|
| ICP metals[164] | water | 6 mo | polyethylene | $HNO_3$ to pH < 2 | 100 mL |
| | soil/waste | 6 mo | core tube/glass jar | 4 °C | 10 g |
| Arsenic[165] | water | 6 mo | polyethylene | $HNO_3$ to pH < 2 | 100 mL |
| | soil/waste | 6 mo | core tube/glass jar | 4 °C | 10 g |
| Mercury[166] | water | 28 days | polyethylene | $HNO_3$ to pH < 2 | 100 mL |
| | soil/waste | 28 days | core tube/glass jar | 4 °C | 10 g |
| Selenium[167] | water | 6 mo | polyethylene | $HNO_3$ to pH < 2 | 100 mL |
| | soil/waste | 6 mo | core tube/glass jar | 4 °C | 10 g |
| Thallium[168] | water | 6 mo | polyethylene | $HNO_3$ to pH < 2 | 100 mL |
| | soil/waste | 6 mo | core tube/glass jar | 4 °C | 10 g |
| Lead[169] | water | 6 mo | polyethylene | $HNO_3$ to pH < 2 | 100 mL |
| | soil/waste | 6 mo | core tube/glass jar | 4 °C | 10 g |
| Chromium VI[170] | water | 24 hrs | polyethylene | 4 °C | 100 mL |
| | soil/waste | 24 hrs | core tube/glass jar | 4 °C | 10 g |

---

[162] See footnote 146.
[163] See footnote 147.
[164] Methods 200.7 or 6010.
[165] GFAA methods 206.2 or 7060.
[166] Cold vapor methods 245.1, 7470 or 7471.
[167] GFAA methods 270.2 or 7740.
[168] GFAA methods 279.2 or 7841.
[169] GFAA methods 239.2 or 7421.
[170] Methods 218.4, 218.5, 7196 or 7197.

## IV. QUALITY ASSURANCE AND QUALITY CONTROL

Quality assurance and quality control (QA/QC) are often spoken of as if they are synonomous terms. In the environmental industry, however, they are quite distinct. Quality control is defined as a single step or procedure that is performed to evaluate a single aspect of the analysis or test. Examples of quality controls are PE samples, matrix spikes and analysis of blanks. Quality assurance is defined as the sum of all the quality controls performed in the laboratory plus everything else that is done with respect to producing reliable data. The quality assurance program used in an environmental laboratory attempts to satisfy two general criteria for acceptance of results. The first criteria assesses the ability of the laboratory and the analytical method to perform an analysis within set tolerances. This is described as data that are analytically valid. The second criteria assesses the legality of the reported results, i.e., are the results defensible in United States court of law? This legal criteria is met through the chain of documents that accompany the sample and verify the actual analysis. This criteria is generally termed the legally defensible aspect of the data.

The intent of the quality program in the laboratory from the analytical validity viewpoint is to recognise, quantitate, and minimize errors. Errors are classified as either random or systematic. Random errors are inherent parts of any analysis, although steps are taken to minimize their magnitude. Random errors are associated with an even distribution of results around the mean of the results. On the molecular level the Heisenburg uncertainty principle is a recognition of random error in the measurement of an electron's simultaneous position (x) and momentum (p):

$$\Delta x \Delta p > \frac{h}{4\pi}$$

where $h$ is Planck's constant $6.63 \times 10^{-34}$ Js. Random errors are composed of two parts. The first part of random error is associated with the background or instrument noise from the test. The second part of random error results from the spread of results around the true value of the sample. Random errors affect the reproducibility of an analysis. Systemic errors arise from a bias in the method of analysis or the instrument. They always tend to cluster on one side or another of the actual value for the test. Systemic errors can also be caused by the particular matrix of a sample.

The laboratory's quality assurance program is documented in the Quality Assurance Manual. The QA Manual is a legal document of the laboratory and is commonly the first point of examination of the lab by regulators, state and federal certification/validation officers and attorneys. The QA Manual is also the single most useful sales tool of the laboratory. Legally defensible QA Manuals are not produced in an afternoon's worth of work, but are the result of close examination of the lab by the QA Manager or consultant, documentation of the findings and then periodic review to insure that the QA Manual in fact reflects and accurately describes the activities of the lab. Although there is no universally applicable standard format for QA Manuals, most of the required formats, for example those of the State of Florida, the Contract Laboratory Program, and the U.S. Army Environmental Center, are minor variations on a general theme. For those individuals or organizations receiving EPA grants, 40 CFR 30.503 has specific requirements for the contents of a QA project plan as presented in Table 1-38. The generalized contents of a more comprehensive QA Manual, are presented in Table 1-39.

**Table 1-38. Contents for a Quality Assurance Project Plan in compliance with 40 CFR 30.503**

| Section | Contents |
|---|---|
| 1 | Title of project and name of principal investigators |
| 2 | Table of Contents |
| 3 | Project description |
| 4 | Project organization and responsibilities |
| 5 | Quality assurance objectives and criteria for determining precision, accuracy, completeness, representativeness, and comparability of data |
| 6 | Sampling procedures |
| 7 | Sample custody |
| 8 | Calibration procedures and frequency and traceability of standards |
| 9 | Analytical procedures |
| 10 | Data reduction, validation and reporting |
| 11 | Internal quality control checks |
| 12 | Performance and system audits |
| 13 | Preventative maintenance |
| 14 | Specific standard operating procedures used to assess data precision, accuracy, representativeness, and comparability |
| 15 | Corrective action for out-of-control situations |
| 16 | Quality assurance reporting procedures |

**Table 1-39. Generalized contents for a Quality Assurance Manual**

| Section | Title and Description |
|---|---|
| 1 | Title Page with authorization signatures and dates |
| 2 | Table of Contents |
| 3 | Statement of QA Policy |
| 4 | Organizational tables and job descriptions for supervisory positions |
| 5 | Data quality objectives for accuracy, precision, and method detection limits for each test, target analyte and sample matrix |
| 6 | Sampling procedures, field equipment lists, field decontamination protocols and documentation |
| 7 | Sample custody procedures and documentation |
| 8 | Analytical methods variances, glassware washing protocols, etc. |
| 9 | Equipment and instrument lists and calibration procedures along with documentation descriptions and acceptance criteria |
| 10 | Preventative maintenance schedules and documentation description for each analytical instrument |
| 11 | Quality control procedures and frequency for each test for determination of laboratory contamination, accuracy, precision and method detection limits along with acceptance criteria |
| 12 | Data reduction, validation, reviews and reporting procedures |
| 13 | Standard corrective action procedures for QC failures in Sections 9 and 11 |
| 14 | Performance and system audit procedures and example documentation |
| 15 | Frequency and content of QA reports |
| 16 | Resumes of key personnel |
| Appendices | References, glossary of terms and miscellaneous information |

A frequently encountered requirement for QA Manuals and for Standard Operating Procedures (SOP) is document control. This labels each page of each section as part of a known number of pages of a specified revision and date. This information is commonly supplied in a page header such as that illustrated in Figure 1-3.

| | |
|---|---|
| Analytical Services Inc. | Section No. 2 |
| Quality Assurance Manual | Revision No. 2 |
| | Date 15 December, 1993 |
| | Page 2 of 3 |

**Figure 1-3.  Example of a page header to establish document control.**

## A.  Calibration

Calibration is the process where an initial analytical response is related to an amount of analyte present in the sample. Examples of analytical responses include volume of titrant, millivolts/potential, picoamps/current, peak area, peak height, absorbance of light, emission of light, generation of heat, and mass of residue. Although several EPA procedures, in particular analyses using titration, allow a single point calibration, for the majority of the methods multi-point calibrations are required.

All multi-point calibrations in EPA methods have common characteristics, which are illustrated in Figure 1-4, a calibration generated from the data in Table 1-40. The first characteristic is lower and upper ends to the calibration curve (no calibration curves are open ended), which defines the calibrated range. The second characteristic is saturation at both the lower and upper ends of the calibration curve. Saturation is defined for two different cases. The first is no change in response with decreasing amounts of analyte, and the second is no change in response with increasing amounts of analyte. These cases cover situations with either positive or negative slopes to the calibration and the background noise from the instrument not allowing calibration at lower levels. The calibration presented in Figure 1-4 has a positive slope and exhibits saturation at the upper levels of the curve.

**Table 1-40.  General calibration example**

| Response | Amount |
|:---:|:---:|
| .100 | .100 |
| .200 | .200 |
| .300 | .300 |
| .400 | .400 |
| .500 | .500 |
| .580 | .600 |
| .640 | .700 |
| .650 | .800 |
| .650 | .900 |

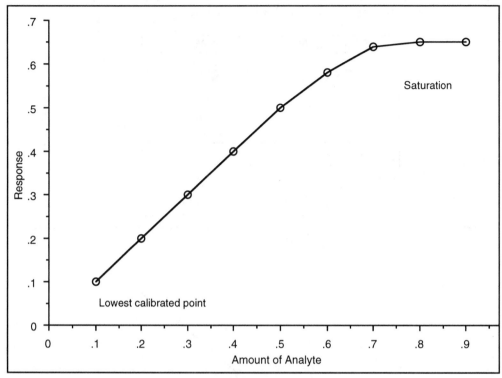

**Figure 1-4.  Generalized point-to-point calibration curve**

For any calibration there are highest and lowest calibrated points that define the range of the calibration.  It is legally non-defensible and poor analytical practice to report concentrations of target analytes that are either below or above the range of the calibration unless steps have been taken to either concentrate or dilute the solution of the target analyte, and a re-analysis result has been obtained within the calibration range.  The re-analysis result is then adjusted for the concentration or dilution factor, and the fact of the concentration or dilution reported on the laboratory worksheet.  This requires that if the laboratory is reporting below detection limit (BDL) results for target analytes, then a calibrated point at the concentration of the detection limit must be included on each calibration curve.

## 1. Calibration Curves by Point-to-Point Curve Fitting

Point-to-point calibration curves are quite common and are very useful.  They are plotted on graph paper and read by finding the appropriate response level, moving horizontally until the curve is intersected, then moving down vertically until the concentration axis is intersected.  Graphing programs on personal computers make the technique even easier.

**Table 1-41.** Calibration of sulfate analysis by EPA method 375.4 using spectrophotometric analysis at 420 nm

| Sulfate mg/L | ABS |
|:---:|:---:|
| 0.1 | .004 |
| 0.5 | .024 |
| 1.0 | .079 |
| 1.5 | .138 |
| 2.0 | .202 |
| 2.5 | .272 |
| 3.0 | .367 |
| 4.0 | .513 |
| 5.0 | .642 |

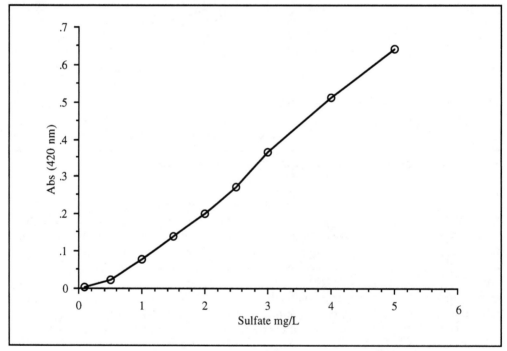

**Figure 1-5.** Non-linear point-to-point calibration curve for sulfate analysis in Table 1-41.

## 2. Calibration Curves by Linear Regression

Linear regresssion is a more rigorous approach to generating a calibration that employs statistical techniques to smooth the random error from the analysis. The most commonly used regression procedure is least squares, however other regression techniques are available in various computer statistics packages[167]. A general diagram of

---

167  Birkes, D. and Y. Dodge, *Alternative Methods of Regression.* 1993. Wiley Interscience, New York, NY. ISBN 0-471-56881-3.

the method is illustrated in Figure 1-6. The major value of the technique is the generation of a calibration equation that can be used in computerized instruments to result in a direct read-out of concentration data by the instrument. A second benefit is a quantitative measure of the "goodness-of-fit" of the calibration.

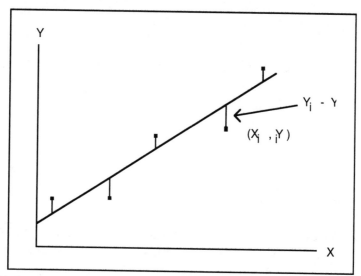

**Figure 1-6. Linear regression calculation.**

The idea is to construct the best straight line through the points, which minimizes the separation of the points from the line. The equation of the line for a linear regression takes the form:

$$Y = a + bX$$

If

$$x_i = X_i - X_{ave} ;$$

where $x_i$ is the separation of the observed value $X_i$ from the mean value $X_{ave}$; and

$$y_i = Y_i - Y_{ave} ;$$

with similar meaning, then the appropriate values for a and b become:

$$b = \frac{\sum_{i=1}^{n} x_i y_i}{\sum_{i=1}^{n} x_i^2} ; \text{ and } a = Y_{ave} - bX_{ave}$$

The goodness of fit of the regression line to the observed data points is expressed by the correlation coefficient, r, where :

$$r = \frac{\displaystyle\sum_{i=1}^{n} x_i y_i}{\sqrt{\displaystyle\sum_{i=1}^{n} x_i^2 \sum_{i=1}^{n} y_i^2}}$$

r is related to the coefficient of determination, $r^2$, by squaring r. $r^2$ is also directly accessible through the following:

$$r^2 = \frac{b \displaystyle\sum_{i=1}^{n} x_i y_i}{\displaystyle\sum_{i=1}^{n} y_i^2}$$

The absolute values of r lie between 0 and 1, with the higher values indicating a greater correlation. A negative value for r indicates a line with a negative slope, rather than the more common positive slope.

The following machine formulas are used by computers in performing the calculations:

$$\sum_{i=1}^{n} x_i^2 = \sum_{i=1}^{n} X_i^2 - \frac{\displaystyle\sum_{i=1}^{n} X_i \sum_{i=1}^{n} X_i}{n}$$

$$\sum_{i=1}^{n} y_i^2 = \sum_{i=1}^{n} Y_i^2 - \frac{\displaystyle\sum_{i=1}^{n} Y_i \sum_{i=1}^{n} Y_i}{n}$$

$$\sum_{i=1}^{n} x_i y_i = \sum_{i=1}^{n} X_i Y_i - \frac{\displaystyle\sum_{i=1}^{n} X_i \sum_{i=1}^{n} Y_i}{n}$$

Application of the linear regression technique to the data in Table 1-41 generates the calibration in Figure 1-7.

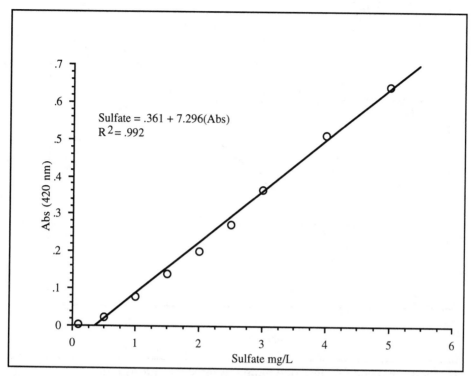

**Figure 1-7. Linear regression calibration curve for sulfate analysis in Table 1-41.**

## 3. Calibration Curves by Polynomial Regression

Just as a linear regression results in an equation of the form $y = a + bx$, a polynomial regression of the second degree results in an equation of the form:

$$y = a + bx + cx^2$$

allowing an actual curve in the calibration. Some methods, particularly in the 500 and 600 series allow these type calibrations if the RF fit is not linear. However, one must be cautious in the polynomial regression application. The major reason is that any three points can be fit with a polynomial curve with a correlation coefficient of $r = 1.00$. As a rule of thumb, five different concentration standards should be analyzed before attempting to calibrate with a second degree polynomial regression. Application of second and third degree polynomial regressions to the sulfate data (Table 1-41) are illustrated (Figures 1-8 and 1-9, respectively). In most situations a higher than second degree regression fit is probably unwarranted for applications in environmental analysis. However in this example the third degree polynomial gives a very accurate description of the calibration curve and further suggests that the upper levels of the calibration are possibly approaching saturation.

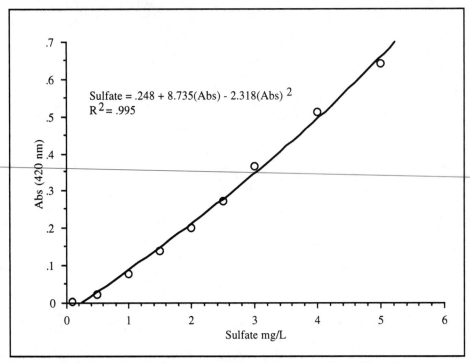

**Figure 1-8. Sulfate second degree polynomial regression calibration.**

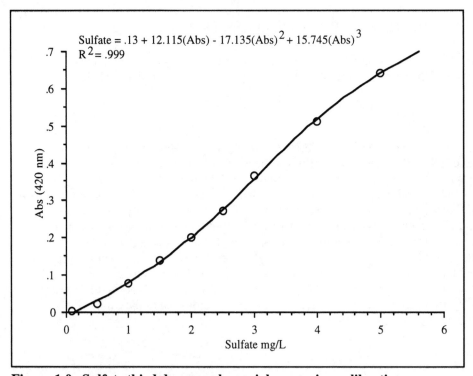

**Figure 1-9. Sulfate third degree polynomial regression calibration.**

## 4. Calibration Factor Calibrations

A calibration factor (CF) is a derived number used to multiply the raw response and give the analytical concentration as follows:

Result = CF x response

This type of calibration is found in many different types of tests such as titration analyses and other wet chemistry procedures and some organic analyses by GC. The calibration factor may be based on a combination of theoretical considerations of the involved chemistry and experimental standardizations, such as occurs in titrations, or it may be derived as an average of testing calibration standards at a series of concentrations. Regardless of the derivation, use of the calibration factor requires the explicit assumption that the relation between the concentration of the target analyte and the analytical response is exactly linear, and the line passes through the origin. For most applications in wet chemistry, these assumptions are probably valid over the calibrated range. However, when applied to organic instrumental determinations by GC, these assumptions are often not valid.

The use of calibration factors in GC analysis arises from the external standard cali-bration procedure. In this technique a known volume of a known concentration of the target analyte is injected into the GC, and the resulting peak area tabulated and related to the amount of analyte. The procedure is repeated for the set of calibrations standards (3 to 5 or more), then the mean of the individual CF's is determined and the %RSD. The %RSD is evaluated against the acceptance criteria of the method, with examples from chlorinated hydrocarbon pesticide analysis procedures by GC-ECD: 508 CF %RSD <20%; 608 CF %RSD <10%; 8080 CF %RSD <20%; and CLP-SOW OLM03.0 CF %RSD <20% (except $\alpha$-BHC, $\delta$-BHC and surrogates). If the acceptance criteria are met the calibration factor is considered constant over the calibrated range, however see 5. Response Factor Calibrations below for some of the consequences of this assumption.

$$CF = \frac{Area_{analyte}}{Amount_{analyte}}$$

## 5. Response Factor Calibrations

Response factors (RF) are commonly used in organic analysis by gas chromatography (GC) or gas chromatography-mass spectrometry (GC-MS). They often are calculated in conjunction with the use of internal standards. Internal standards are known amounts of compounds that are added to each sample immediately before instrumental analysis. The response of the internal standard is used to establish a standard response for the instrument. Each analyte is calibrated against the internal standard(s), generating the response factors.

$$RF = \frac{Area_{analyte} \times Amount_{internal\ standard}}{Area_{internal\ standard} \times Amount_{analyte}}$$

The idea behind the use of average RF is that the relative response of internal stan-dard and target analytes remains constant across the calibrated range. Although this may be a valid assumption for detectors such as the flame ionization detector, when applied to the mass spectrometer the justification is simply not present. Reduced analyte response in mass spectrometers at increasing concentration is a fact of life and can be attributed to the initial inefficiency of the ionization, reduced mean free path, reduced relative ion throughput in the mass analyzer, and counting rate limitations in the ion detector and the associated software. If the internal standard is very similar to the calibrated analyte, such as crysene-$d_{12}$ and crysene, the above effects are essentially constant for the two compounds, whereas when the internal standard and analyte are very different chemically, these effects become pronounced.

The acceptance of the average RF is assessed quantitatively by calculating the percent relative standard deviation (%RSD) for the set of RF's generated from the calibrated concentrations and then applying an acceptance criteria to the %RSD. The acceptance criteria vary from method to method: 525 %RSD <30; 625 %RSD <35; 8270 %RSD <15 except for CCC where %RSD <30. The data for the example are presented in Table 1-42.

$$\%RSD = 100 \text{ x } \frac{S_{RF}}{RF_{ave}}$$

where:      %RSD is the percent relative standard deviation,
                     $S_{RF}$ is the standard deviation of the RFs, and
                     $RF_{ave}$ is the average RF of the calibration standards.

Using the criteria for acceptance of the RF calibration from method 625, all three of the example compounds would be treated as exhibiting a linear calibration. The plot in Figure 1-10 illustrates that the RF calibration for chrysene (%RSD = 5.5) is linear across the concentrations, however, the other two examples exhibit a pronounced downward slope. This becomes of greater concern with the issue of continuing calibration acceptance. Method 625 allows continuing calibration RF's to vary up to ± 20% from the initial calibration. Some data systems calculate the daily continuing calibration RF and, if it is acceptable, replace the initial calibration RF with the daily value. What this in effect does is replace a three to five point calibration curve with a one point calibration, and is another example of poor analytical practice. The possible allowed day-to-day variation on RF is illustrated in Figure 1-11 for bis(2-chloroisopropyl) ether.

**Table 1-42.**   **Raw areas and RFs of compounds and associated internal standards *vs.* concentration (ng/uL)**

| Compound | Concentration (ng/uL) | | | | | Ave RF | % RSD |
|---|---|---|---|---|---|---|---|
| | 20 | 50 | 80 | 120 | 160 | | |
| 1,4-Dichlorobenzene $D_4$ | 67626 | 46894 | 56641 | 59557 | 58943 | | |
| bis(2-chloroisopropyl) ether | 89307 | 150720 | 235334 | 324271 | 318733 | | |
| As/Ais | 1.321 | 3.214 | 4.155 | 5.445 | 5.407 | | |
| RF | 2.641 | 2.571 | 2.077 | 1.815 | 1.352 | 2.091 | 25.7 |
| Acenaphthene $D_{10}$ | 98841 | 79437 | 90211 | 93294 | 90856 | | |
| Diethyl phthalate | 89892 | 171722 | 275156 | 384749 | 393958 | | |
| As/Ais | 0.909 | 2.162 | 3.050 | 4.124 | 4.336 | | |
| RF | 1.819 | 1.729 | 1.525 | 1.375 | 1.084 | 1.506 | 19.5 |
| Chrysene $D_{12}$ | 80918 | 71426 | 73597 | 75327 | 75816 | | |
| Chrysene | 40668 | 80933 | 127936 | 213813 | 277181 | | |
| As/Ais | 0.503 | 1.133 | 1.738 | 2.838 | 3.656 | | |
| RF | 1.005 | 0.906 | 0.869 | 0.914 | 0.928 | 0.928 | 5.5 |

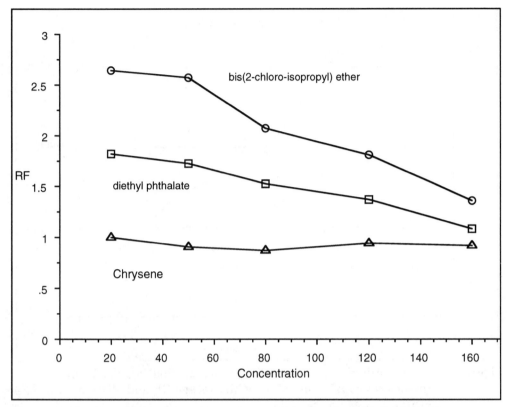

**Figure 1-10. Plot of RF *vs*. concentration (ng/uL) for data in Table 1-42.**

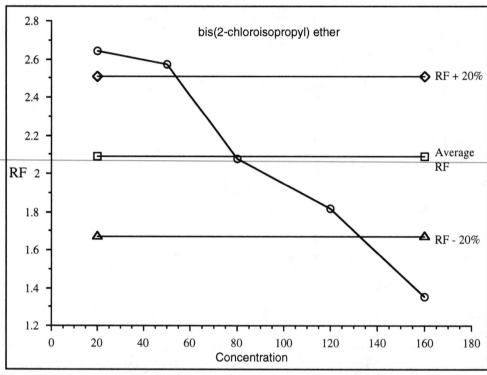

**Figure 1-11. Plot of initial calibration RF *vs*. concentration (ng/uL) for bis(2-chloroisopropyl) ether along with average RF and allowed daily RF variations by method 625.**

Allowed variations to the average RF calibration are manual or computer plotting of RF or concentration *vs.* the area ratio of the target analyte to the internal standard (As/Ais).  This is illustrated in Figure 1-12.

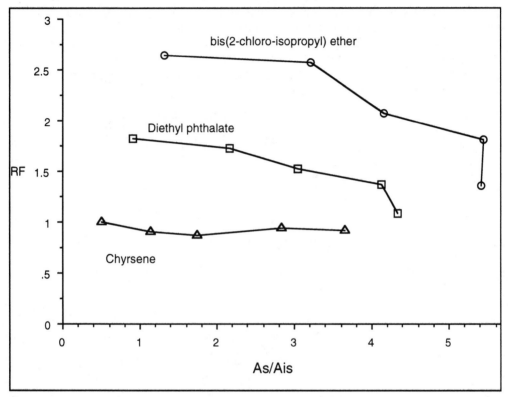

**Figure 1-12.  Plot of RF *vs*. As/Ais for manual calibration.**

More accurate calibrations can be obtained by performing regression analyses on the RF *vs.* As/Ais data. Figure 1-13 illustrates the results of a linear regression analysis applied to the first two compounds in Table 1-42. Figure 1-14 shows a second degree polynomial regression of the same data, while Figures 1-15 and 1-16 illustrate third degree polynomial regressions. The latter plot demonstrates the necessity for a visual checking of the calibration plot, because the result in this instance is clearly nonsense, even though it exhibits a desirable correlation coefficient. Considering the large amount of analytical error associated with GC and GC-MS determinations of semivolatile organics after extractive sample preparation, it is probably not warranted to use regression calibrations of greater than linear degree.

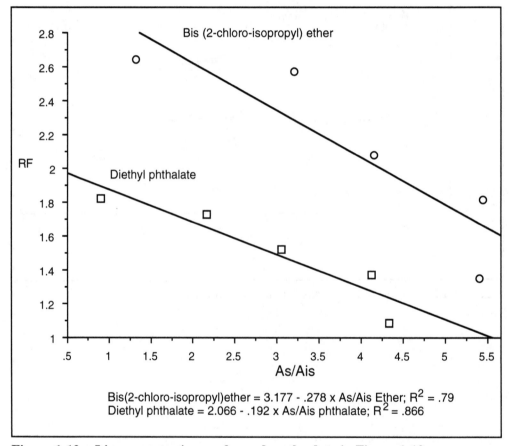

**Figure 1-13. Linear regression performed on the data in Figure 1-12.**

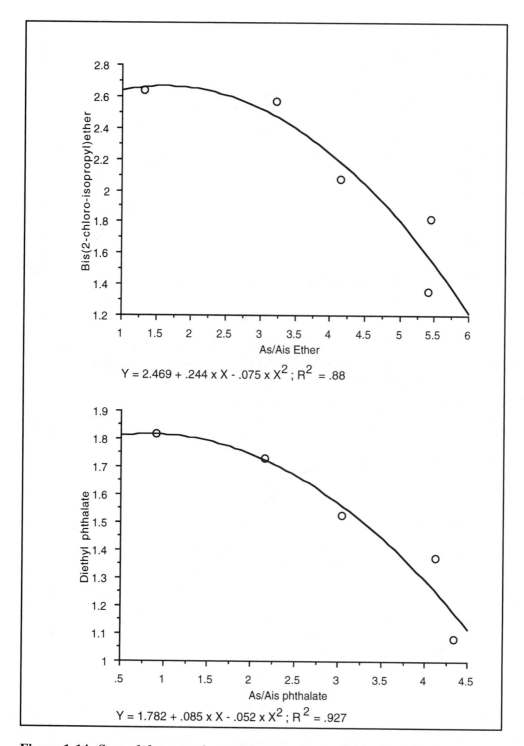

**Figure 1-14. Second degree polynomial regression performed on the data in Figure 1-12.**

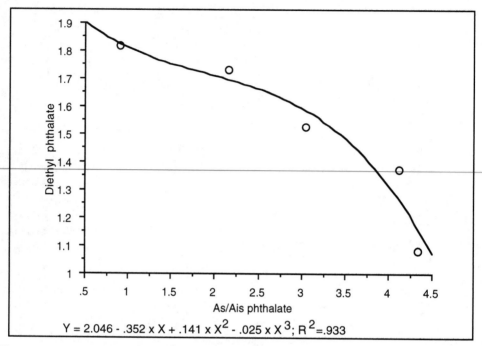

**Figure 1-15. Third degree polynomial regression performed on the diethyl phthalate data from Table 1-42.**

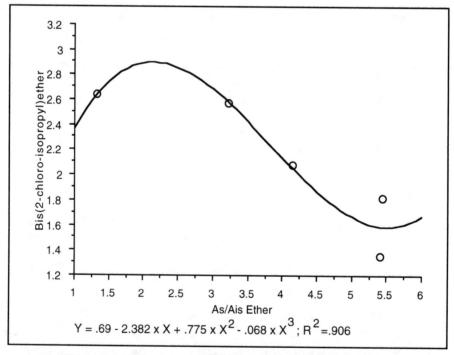

**Figure 1-16. Third degree polynomial regression performed on the bis(2-chloroisopropyl) ether data from Table 1-42.**

## 6. Multi-peak Target Analytes.

A number of the pesticide target analytes of methods 508, 608, 8080, and 8081 are composed of a variety of compounds. Examples are chlordane, toxaphene, and the PCBs and PCTs. Several techniques can be used to identify these analytes[168], the most common being a visual pattern recognition although computerized algorithims are available. Quantitation can be performed either by selected indicator peaks (area or peak height) or by total area under the analyte envelope. The latter method suffers when more than one multi-peak analyte is present, the envelopes overlap and the same peaks show up in two or more target analytes, or the target analyte is subject to selective losses of some of the lighter or more reactive components (weathering).

A simplified approach for dealing with overlapping target analytes is to calibrate each of the indicator peaks as an independant measure of the target analyte. For example, considering PCB 1242, six peaks may be calibrated in a single calibration table for PCB 1242. The sample chromatogram is quantitated against the calibration table, and if the target analyte is uncontaminated, all six indicator peaks should give very similar values as PCB 1242. If another PCB, for example 1248, is also present, the six peaks will give a range of substantially different values as PCB 1242. The sample chromatogram is then quantitated against the 1248 calibration table.

---

[168]  Erickson, M.D. *Analytical Chemistry of PCBs*. 2nd Edition, 1997. CRC Press, Boca Raton, FL.

---

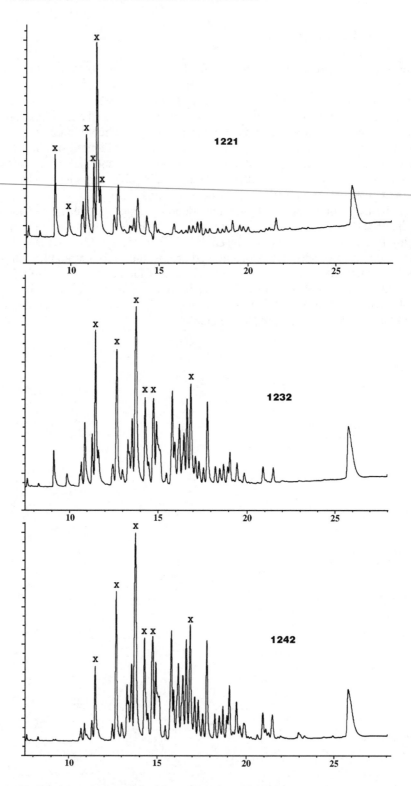

**Figure 1-17. Multi-component target analytes (PCBs)**

On the other hand target analytes such as the petroleum hydrocarbon fuels are difficult to quantitate based on indicator peaks, as these vary greatly in abundance from one manufacturer to the next. Once the sample is identified, the most practical method of quantitation is total area above the baseline from the beginning to the end of the analyte's elution pattern. See Section 3 for a more detailed discussion.

## 7. Multiple Standard Addition

Multiple standard addition is a calibration technique used most commonly in metals analysis by AA, however it can be applied in many areas of the laboratory. It serves to correct for matrix effects in the sample. Aliquots of a digested or extracted sample are spiked with at least three different concentrations of a standard. The solutions are analyzed, and the responses recorded and plotted on graph paper. A linear regression is performed on the responses, and the line extended down to the zero response intercept. The concentration of the sample is then read off as the absolute value at the intercept or by setting the response equal to zero in the regression equation. For the example shown, the sample concentration would be 1.50.

The technique works best when the response of the instrument is known to be linear, and the standard additions are chosen to bracket the expected unknown sample concentration. In the CLP (ILM03.0) the linearity requirement is determined by having a correlation coefficient of at least 0.995. In cases where the IDL of the analysis is known, the IDL value on the response axis would be chosen for the intercept rather than zero.

**Table 1-43. Example of MSA data**

| Response | Amount |
|----------|--------|
| 0.246    | 1.00   |
| 0.461    | 3.00   |
| 0.644    | 5.00   |

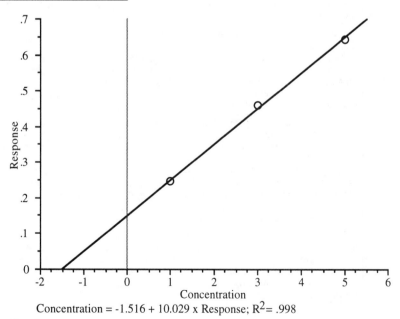

Concentration = -1.516 + 10.029 x Response; $R^2$= .998

**Figure 1-18. Graph of MSA example.**

## B. Data Quality Objectives

Data quality objectives (DQO) can be defined as what the analyst expects to obtain from the analysis. Or maybe a more realistic definition is what the data reviewer expects to obtain as a result of the technician's work. The EPA Region IV definition is, "Data Quality Objectives are qualitative and quantitative statements which specify the quality of the data required to support Agency decisions during remedial response activities." Data quality objectives are composed of written expectations for accuracy, precision, and detection limits for each analyte for each test and for each different analytical matrix. EPA also adds written expectations for completeness, comparability and representativeness. Completeness is defined as the percentage of samples that meet or exceed all the DQOs for accuracy, precision, and detection limits. Representativeness is the degree to which the results of the analysis reflect the target analyte concentrations in the site sampled. Comparability is the degree of confidence with which results from two or more data sets, or two or more laboratories may be compared. Comparability, completeness and representativeness are difficult to quantitate, and most numbers quoted for them are strictly guesses.

Data Quality Objectives for a specific project will depend on what information is required and how it will be used. Five levels of data quality are generally recognized as defined in Table 1-44.

### Table 1-44. Data Quality Levels

| Level I | Field based analytical screening procedures using organic vapor analyzers, and other essentially non-calibrated instruments. Reportable data includes method, detection limit, result, date, time, and person conducting analysis. |
|---|---|
| Level II | Field based analyses using instruments that are calibrated and blanks are performed to ascertain contamination. May include data from field GCs and other advanced screening methods. Reportable data include method, detection limit, results, date, time, and person conducting analysis, and may include information on blanks. |
| Level III | Laboratory based batch analyses that use calibration and continuing calibration, blanks, QC procedures to determine accuracy and precision, MDL studies are documented, and the data is of sufficient quality to satisfy most regulatory reporting requirements. Report includes method, detection limit, results, and external chain-of-custody. Summaries of QC data, such as date, time and person conducting analysis and batch blanks, surrogate recoveries, accuracy, and precision may be supplied with Final Analytical Reports. |
| Level IV | Laboratory based analyses that comply with all requirements and provide full documentation as stated in the appropriate CLP-SOW. Data package is capable of surviving the most rigorous legal examination. Final report includes a case narrative and method, detection limit, and results for each sample along with a data package. Reported data in the package includes chain-of-custody copy, initial and continuing calibration data, blank results, system monitoring compound results, accuracy and precision results, surrogate recoveries, daily tuning results, extraction and sample preparation log copies, internal standard area and RT summaries, run log copies, TIC results and mass spectra copies, raw data, and quantitation reports in both hardcopy and electronic media. |
| Level V | Laboratory analyses that utilize or seek to validate non-standard methods. Detailed descriptions of all analytical procedures used are provided along with data that indicate single laboratory precision, accuracy, and MDL obtained from multiple determinations of the target analytes. May include comparison data to a promulgated method. |

## 1. Accuracy and Precision

Accuracy and precision are two measures of the reliability of an analytical result. Accuracy is the degree with which the obtained result agrees with the actual result, often expressed as recovery. In mathematical terms accuracy is the average of the results from repeated analysis of the same sample, compared to the actual amount of analyte in the sample. Precision is the ability to generate the same result in repeated tests of the same sample. In mathematical terms precision is the percent difference of the results from re-analysis of a sample. Graphic representations of accuracy and precision are shown in Figure 1-19. The desire of all analysts is to obtain results that are both highly accurate and highly precise. However in the cases where one or the other is not present, the prefered situation is a highly precise analysis. If the analysis is precise then the "sights" can be adjusted to give the desired accuracy. The other situations are useless.

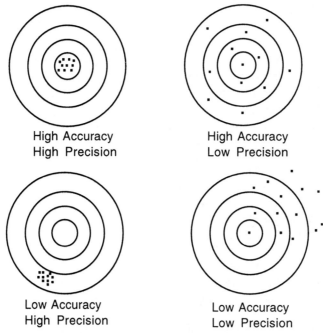

High Accuracy
High Precision

High Accuracy
Low Precision

Low Accuracy
High Precision

Low Accuracy
Low Precision

**Figure 1-19.  Accuracy and precision.**

Accuracy is calculated as follows for spikes into laboratory water:

$$\%R = 100 \text{ x } \frac{\text{Observed value}}{\text{Known value}}$$

where:    %R is the percentage recovery
Observed value is the analytical result, and
Known value is the concentration of the spike.

For calculation of accuracy of spikes into natural matrices:

$$\%R = 100 \text{ x } \frac{\text{Observed value - Background value}}{\text{Known value}}$$

where:         %R is the percentage recovery.
               Observed value is the analytical result after spiking.
               Background value is the analytical result of the matrix before spiking, and
               Known value is the concentration of the spike.

The following calculations for the average percent recovery and the standard deviation of the recovery are used in generation of DQOs. The standard deviation can be calculated by one of two procedures, the machine formula and the manual formula. The manual formula requires first calculation of the average from the data set, then on a second pass going back through the data and determining the difference between the average and each datum. The machine formula gives the exact same result for the standard deviation; however, it requires only one pass through the data set and is much faster when dealing with large data sets. The manual formula can be derived from the machine formula by expanding and collecting the terms.

$$\%R_{ave} = \frac{\sum\limits_{i=1}^{n} \%R_i}{n}$$

where:         $\%R_{ave}$ is the average percent recovery,
               $\%R_i$ is the percent recovery of observation $i$, and
               n is the number of observations.

The machine formula used in computers for calculating standard deviation is:

$$S_{\%R} = \sqrt{\frac{\sum\limits_{i=1}^{n} \%R_i^2 - [\sum\limits_{i=1}^{n} \%R_i]^2 / n}{n-1}}$$

where:         $S_{\%R}$ is the standard deviation of percent recovery,
               $\%R_i$ is the percent recovery of observation $i$, and
               n is the number of observations.

The manual formula for calculating standard deviation is:

$$S_{\%R} = \sqrt{\frac{\sum\limits_{i=1}^{n} [\%R_{ave} - \%R_i]^2}{n-1}}$$

Precision is assessed through the following calculation:

$$RPD = \frac{2 [A-B]}{A+B} \times 100$$

where:         RPD is the relative percent difference between duplicate determinations,
               A and B are the analytical results for the duplicate determinations, and
               [A - B] is the absolute difference between the determinations.

The concepts of percent difference and standard deviation are somewhat similar and many times confused. The distinction between the two concepts is that percent difference (RPD) is limited to an actual comparison of two and only two values, while standard deviation is a statistical concept that attempts to relate the spread of values in a small subset of data to the width of the distribution of values in an entire population of data. The RSD for two points is not the same as the RPD as can be seen as follows.

$$RSD = \frac{\sqrt{2}\,[A-B]}{A+B} \times 100$$

where:     RSD is the relative standard deviation calculated from duplicate determinations,

A and B are the analytical results for the duplicate determinations, and

[A - B] is the absolute difference between the determinations.

## 2. Calculation of Data Quality Objectives for Accuracy and Precision

Data quality objectives for both accuracy and precision for a laboratory test represent a statistically derived 95% confidence level. Mathematically this is a range of plus and minus 2 standard deviations from the mean.

**Table 1-45.  Oil and grease batch data for DQO calculation**

| DATE | MS | MSD | True Value | %R1 | %R2 | %R ave | Precision |
|------|------|------|------|------|------|------|------|
| 5-11-92 | 42.0 | 37.6 | 51.0 | 82.3 | 74.0 | 78.0 | 10.3 |
| 5-12-92 | 39.2 | 40.0 | 51.0 | 77.0 | 78.0 | 77.5 | 1.3 |
| 5-14-92 | 39.6 | 39.8 | 51.0 | 77.6 | 78.0 | 77.8 | 0.5 |
| 5-18-92a | 41.4 | 42.0 | 51.0 | 81.0 | 82.2 | 81.6 | 1.5 |
| 5-18-92b | 42.0 | 36.4 | 51.0 | 82.0 | 71.0 | 76.5 | 14.4 |
| 5-20-92 | 40.0 | 40.6 | 51.0 | 78.4 | 79.6 | 79.0 | 1.5 |
| 5-21-92 | 40.4 | 34.4 | 51.0 | 79.0 | 67.5 | 73.0 | 15.8 |
| 5-26-92 | 42.8 | 43.0 | 51.0 | 84.0 | 84.3 | 84.2 | 0.4 |
| 5-28-92 | 44.2 | 43.0 | 51.0 | 86.7 | 84.3 | 85.5 | 2.8 |
| 5-29-92 | 39.6 | 46.2 | 51.0 | 77.6 | 90.6 | 84.1 | 15.5 |
| 6-02-92 | 43.0 | 43.8 | 51.0 | 84.3 | 85.9 | 85.1 | 1.9 |
| 6-04-92 | 40.8 | 39.2 | 51.0 | 80.0 | 76.9 | 78.5 | 3.9 |
| 6-08-92 | 39.6 | 36.8 | 51.0 | 77.6 | 72.4 | 74.9 | 7.2 |
| 6-09-92 | 48.4 | 42.4 | 51.0 | 94.9 | 83.0 | 89.0 | 13.4 |
| 6-11-92 | 41.4 | 42.0 | 51.0 | 81.2 | 82.4 | 81.8 | 1.5 |
| | | | | | Mean | 80.43 | 6.12 |
| | | | | | SD | 4.32 | 5.82 |

For example, repeat duplicate analysis of a mid-range standard for Oil & Grease gives %$R_{ave}$ of 80.43 with $S_{\%R}$ of 4.32 (Table 1-45). The data quality objective for accuracy is:

%$R_{ave}$ - 2$S_{\%R}$  to  %$R_{ave}$ + 2$S_{\%R}$, or

80.43 - 2(4.32) to 80.43 + 2(4.32), or

71.8 - 89.1.

Precision for the Oil & Grease example generates $RPD_{ave}$ 6.12 and $S_{RPD}$ 5.82. The data quality objective for precision is:

$RPD_{ave}$ - $2S_{RPD}$ to $RPD_{ave}$ + $2S_{RPD}$ , or

6.12 - 2(5.82) to 6.12 + 2(5.82), or

0 - 17.8

A negative value for precision is nonsense, and so zero is always the lower value for the range. Although it is possible for the lower value to be some other positive value than zero, in general zero is used because the analyst never wants to eliminate the possibility that he can get exactly the same answer twice in a row as an acceptable result. It is important to realize that DQOs are statistical ranges and that under normal operating conditions around 5% of test results will fall outside these ranges. Data quality objectives should be updated at least on an annual basis if not more frequently. Within the laboratory, it is possible to calculate DQOs for each analyst for each test, however when providing DQOs to end users of the data, it is probably more representative of the laboratory's capabilities to report a composite value from all the technicians performing a test.

## 3. Instrument Detection Limits

In Figure 1-20 the question arises as to whether the signal at point A indicates the presence of an analyte or is just instrument noise. Instrument detection limit (IDL) is a measure of the normal instrument noise. It provides a guide to what is noise and what is a real signal and is an evaluation of the maximum sensitivity of an analytical instrument to perform an analysis. It is set at three times the standard deviation of the instrument noise level. IDL is determined by the following procedure (EPA 40 CFR Part 136, Appendix B, July 1993):

1. Prepare a calibration curve for the test with standards.
2. Analyze seven (7) laboratory water blanks.
3. Record the response of the test for the blanks.
4. Prepare the mean ($\%R_{ave}$) and standard deviation ($S_{\%R}$) of the results from the blanks as above.
5. The IDL is three times the $S_{\%R}$ on the calibration curve (Figure 1-21).

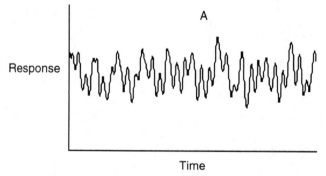

**Figure 1-20. Instrument detection limit problem.**

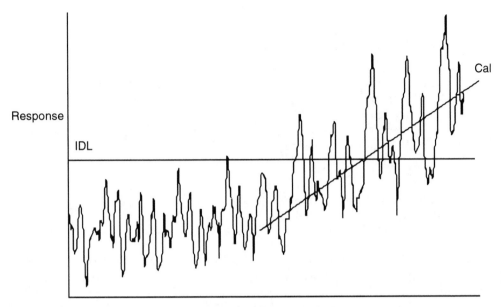

**Figure 1-21. Intersection of IDL with calibration curve.**

The major function of the IDL is to separate noise from analyte responses. The presence of a signal above the IDL is most often real and serves to eliminate the false positive (Type I) error at the 99% confidence level. See Figure 1-22.

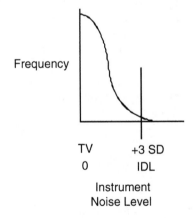

**Figure 1-22. Distribution of instrument noise levels.**

## 4. Method Detection Limits

There are many different manners in which laboratories report results for low concentrations of target analytes. Some are as follows[169]:

---

[169] Berthouex, P.M. 1993. "A Study of the Precision of Lead Measurements at Concentrations Near the Method Limit of Detection." *Water Environment Research.* 65(5). pp. 620-629.

1. Trace
2. ND (not detected)
3. Numerical value of MDL
4. A "less than" the numerical value of the MDL (BDL)
5. Zero
6. Some value between zero and the MDL, for example, half the MDL
7. Actual measured value, even if below the MDL
8. Actual measured value, followed by MDL in parentheses
9. Actual measured value with an estimate of precision, for example $2 \pm 4$ ug/L, where the estimate of error can be the MDL.

Additional reporting forms are:

10. A number followed by Estimated Maximum Possible Concentration (EMPC)
11. Detected but less than MDL
12. Detected but less than PQL

The plethora of reporting techniques results in a real problem for some of the end users of the data. Those who wish to know whether their effluent is above or below a regulatory limit do not really care about the exact value of a parameter when it's on the safe side; however other users, especially those who input the results into mathematical models for site assessments, are very exacting in their data requirements. For these latter applications "Not Detected" is quite different from a "Detected, but less than the MDL" or "Below Detection Limits." It is somewhat imperative for the laboratory to develop a dialog with the end user to determine the exact requirements of the data.

Method detection limits (MDL) are the minimum level of an analyte that can be determined with 99% confidence. Once an IDL has been determined, it is readily apparent that for samples that have target analyte present at the IDL, at least half the analyses of the sample will result in responses below the IDL (Figure 1-21). The objective of the analyst becomes a determination of how high on the calibration curve one must go so that all signals will be above the IDL, in other words, no false negatives will be reported. The MDL attempts to answer this question. The procedure that follows is again drawn from EPA 40 CFR Part 136, Appendix B. The analyst should consult the 40 CFR reference, as there are a number of specific conditions and choices that must be made during the MDL procedure. In brief the method is as follows:

1. Prepare a spike of the analyte into laboratory water that is very close (2 to 5 times) to the IDL obtained above.
2. Take seven aliquots of this spiked solution and process each through the sample clean-up and preparation procedure.
3. Analyze each of the prepared aliquots in the exact same manner as prescribed in the Method used.
4. Calculate the standard deviation ($S_{\%R}$) of the aliquot results as described above.
5. The MDL is equal to the one-tailed t-statistic at a 99% confidence level for the performed number of samples times the standard deviation:

$$MDL = t_{0.99,n} \times S_{\%R} \quad \text{or in this case} \quad MDL = 3.143 \, S_{\%R}$$

For other numbers of repetitions in the MDL study, the appropriate value of $t_{0.99}$ can be found in Table 1-46.

**Table 1-46.   One-tailed t-statistic at 99% confidence level for a variety of repetitions**

| Repetitions | $t_{0.99}$ | Repetitions | $t_{0.99}$ |
|---|---|---|---|
| 3 | 6.965 | 15 | 2.624 |
| 4 | 4.541 | 16 | 2.602 |
| 5 | 3.747 | 17 | 2.583 |
| 6 | 3.365 | 18 | 2.567 |
| 7 | 3.143 | 19 | 2.552 |
| 8 | 2.998 | 20 | 2.539 |
| 9 | 2.896 | 21 | 2.528 |
| 10 | 2.821 | 22 | 2.518 |
| 11 | 2.764 | 23 | 2.508 |
| 12 | 2.718 | 24 | 2.500 |
| 13 | 2.681 | 25 | 2.492 |
| 14 | 2.650 | 26 | 2.485 |

In practice, determination of MDLs is quite challenging.  If the spike level is too high, the resulting standard deviation will be so small, that the calculated MDL can actually be below the instrument detection level.  On the other hand, if the spike level is too low, the standard deviation can be so high that the calculated MDL is useless for most regulatory purposes.  Due to the considerable time that can be spent on these procedures, most analysts seek only to verify the MDLs listed in most of the published regulatory methods.  This practice in itself causes problems for end users who have exacting data requirements.

The determination of the MDL for total suspended solids is illustrated in Table 1-47. In the first trial, the spike level was 12 mg/L while for the second trial the spike was increased to 16 mg/L.  The EPA expected MDL for this test is 5 mg/L.  Trial 1 gives an MDL that is not usable for the most part, while the second trial verifies the EPA MDL, yet there is only a slight difference in the spike level.

**Table 1-47.  MDL example for Total Suspended Solids in mg/L**

|  | Trial 1 | Trial 2 |
|---|---|---|
|  | 12.5 | 14.5 |
|  | 17 | 16 |
|  | 15.5 | 18.5 |
|  | 13 | 17 |
|  | 8 | 15.5 |
|  | 16 | 16 |
|  | 13.5 | 16 |
|  | 17 | 15 |
|  | 16 | 16 |
| Mean | 14.28 | 16.06 |
| SD | 2.89 | 1.16 |
| MDL | 8.37 | 3.36 |

In all analyses there is a spread of results around the true value (TV). The MDL eliminates the false positive by having the reporting level generally several standard deviations above the IDL, thus any signal seen is real. However for analyte spikes at the MDL itself, 50% of the obtained results are going to be less than the MDL (the shaded area in the graph), and not reporting them constitutes a Type II error, a false negative[170]. To avoid the problem many labs use Practical Quantitation Levels (PQL), which are set at a variety of amounts, the most common being 12 times the standard deviation resulting from the MDL procedure. Three different types of result now can be given by the laboratory: a numerical value above the PQL, a detect but less than the PQL, or a non-detect. See Figures 1-23 and 1-24.

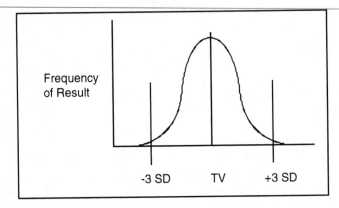

**Figure 1-23. Distribution of results around a true value.**

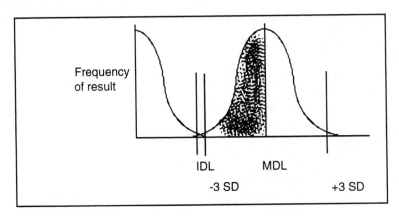

**Figure 1-24. False negative determinations at the MDL.**

MDLs are always linked to a standard sample size such as 200.0 mL of sample titrated for alkalinity (310.1), 1.00 L of sample extracted and concentrated to 1.00 mL for semivolatile organics analysis (8270), or 5.00 mL sparged for GC-MS analysis (8260). Attempts to lower MDLs through increasing the processed sample size are generally not productive due to the simultaneous increase in background interferences.

170   L. Keith, *Environmental Laboratory*, June/July 1992. pp. 58-61.

The reduction of standard sample size is commonly done as a measure to reduce interference and permit a determination in the presence of severe backgrounds. This effectively serves to increase the MDL by the same degree in which the sample size is reduced. Thus decreasing the sample size by one half, doubles the MDL. Reducing the sample size by 10, multiplies the MDL by 10.

The physical characterization of solids in samples as total solids (TS), total dissolved solids (TDS) and total suspended solids (TSS) have an absolute requirement of a minimum of 2.5 mg of residue detected. For 50 mL of sample processed the MDL will be 50 mg/L, while for 500 mL sample the MDL is 5 mg/L. As samples are quite variable in filtering ability, in a sample batch there will often be a wide range of MDLs.

A final problem with the use of MDL as currently defined, concerns those analyses in which there is not 100% recovery of target analyte. By its very definition the MDL is a measure of the precision of an analysis and no account is taken of accuracy[171]. Quite erratic results and misinterpretations of results are possible by data reviewers if this aspect of the MDL is not recognized. Remember that the MDL is determined using reagent water, so it is not surprising that MDL levels usually cannot be achieved when complex samples of wastewater, soils, fish, etc., are analyzed by a lab.

## C. Reporting Units and Common Conversions

Scientific results are almost always reported in metric units such as grams, kilograms, liters, etc. SI prefixes are used to indicate variations on the basic units of grams, liters, moles and others, as indicated in the table.

**Table 1-48. SI prefixes**

| Prefix | Abbv | Multiplier | Prefix | Abbv | Multiplier |
|--------|------|------------|--------|------|------------|
| zepto- | z | $10^{-21}$ | zetta- | Z | $10^{21}$ |
| atto- | a | $10^{-18}$ | exa- | E | $10^{18}$ |
| femto- | f | $10^{-15}$ | peta- | P | $10^{15}$ |
| pico- | p | $10^{-12}$ | tera- | T | $10^{12}$ |
| nano- | n | $10^{-9}$ | giga- | G | $10^{9}$ |
| micro- | u (μ) | $10^{-6}$ | mega- | M | $10^{6}$ |
| milli- | m | $10^{-3}$ | kilo- | k | $10^{3}$ |
| centi- | c | $10^{-2}$ | hecta- | h | $10^{2}$ |
| deci- | d | $10^{-1}$ | deca- | da | 10 |

Environmental results are often expressed in the units of parts per million (ppm), parts per billion (ppb), and parts per trillion (ppt). These have different meanings depending on the sample matrix. With liquids and solids the units are in terms of mass/volume and mass/mass respectively, and are often interchanged based on the assumption that the density of water is 1.000 g/mL (1.000 kg/L), although this is strictly true only at 4 °C. For massively contaminated samples, the concentrations are expressed as parts per hundred or percents (%) with 1000 ppm being equal to 0.10%.

---

[171] Kimbrough, D.E., and J. Wakakuwa. "Method Detection Limits in Solid Waste Analysis." *Environ. Sci. Technol.* 1993. 27(13). pp. 2692-2699.

**Table 1-49.  Common environmental reporting units**

| Unit | Liquids | | | Solids | |
|---|---|---|---|---|---|
| % | – | g/100 mL | – | – | g/100 g |
| ppm | mg/L | ug/mL | ng/uL | mg/kg | ug/g |
| ppb | ug/L | ng/mL | pg/uL | ug/kg | ng/g |
| ppt | ng/L | pg/mL | fg/uL | ng/kg | pg/g |

A number of common conversions from the English system of weights and measures to the Metric system are encountered in the environmental business as indicated in the Table 1-50.

**Table 1-50.  Commonly encountered conversions and definitions**

| Unit | Definition |
|---|---|
| 1.000 mL | volume of 1.000 g of water at 4 °C |
| 1.000 calorie | amount of heat necessary to raise the temperature of 1.000 g of water 1 °C |
| 1.000 BTU | amount of energy necessary to raise the temperature of 1.000 lb of water 1 °F |
| 1.000 calorie | equal to 4.184 joules |
| 1.000 BTU | equal to 1055 joules or 252 calories |
| 1.000 atmosphere of pressure | equal to 14.7 psi |
| ppm | equal to gallons/million gallons |
| ppm x 8.34 | equal to pounds/million gallons |

## D. Volumetric Measurements

Most analytical procedures in the lab require accurate measurement of amounts of samples, reagents, and standards.  The most frequently used methods of measurement commonly depend on the materials being in a solution of known concentration and then dispensing the solution.  Burets, volumetric pipets, and volumetric flasks are the tools of precise volume measurements.  They are produced by a number of manufacturers in a variety of grades.  The only grade present in an analytical laboratory should be Class A.  Class A standards for volumetric measuring devices are set by ASTM.  ASTM E287 covers standards for burets; E969-83 covers volumetric pipets; E288, E542 and E694 cover volumetric flasks; and E694 and E542 are for graduated cylinders.  Graduated cylinders are not precise volumetric measuring devices, although commonly used for this purpose, especially for aliquoting samples.  Table 1-51 lists the allowed tolerances under the Class A designation for volumetric devices and compares these with the most accurate graduated cylinders commercially available.  Note that Erlenmeyer flasks, beakers and other miscellaneous laboratory glassware are not measuring devices.  The volume markings on the sides of these containers are approximate with a tolerance of from ± 5 to 10%.

**Table 1-51. Class A tolerances for volumetric measuring devices**

| Capacity mL | Buret | Graduated Cylinder | Volumetric Flask | Volumetric Pipet |
|---|---|---|---|---|
| 0.5 | - | - | - | ±0.006 |
| 1 | - | - | ±0.01 | ±0.006 |
| 2 | ±0.01 | - | ±0.015 | ±0.006 |
| 3 | - | - | - | ±0.01 |
| 4 | - | - | - | ±0.01 |
| 5 | ±0.01 | - | ±0.02 | ±0.01 |
| 6 | - | - | - | ±0.02 |
| 7 | - | - | - | ±0.02 |
| 8 | - | - | - | ±0.02 |
| 9 | - | - | - | ±0.02 |
| 10 | ±0.02 | ±0.08 | ±0.02 | ±0.02 |
| 15 | - | - | - | ±0.03 |
| 20 | - | - | - | ±0.03 |
| 25 | ±0.03 | ±0.14 | ±0.03 | ±0.03 |
| 50 | ±0.05 | ±0.2 | ±0.05 | ±0.05 |
| 100 | ±0.10 | ±0.35 | ±0.08 | ±0.08 |
| 200 | - | - | ±0.10 | - |
| 250 | - | ±0.65 | ±0.12 | - |
| 500 | - | ±1.1 | ±0.20 | - |
| 1000 | - | ±2.0 | ±0.30 | - |
| 2000 | - | ±4.0 | ±0.50 | - |

Also missing from the list of Class A volumetric measuring devices are syringes and automatic disposable tip pipettors, although these are used throughout the laboratory industry. To be used in a legally defensible manner these must be calibrated and the calibration documented. The most common method of calibration is to dispense a volume of reagent grade water from the syringe or pipettor onto an analytical balance. The density of water is affected by the temperature and the atmospheric pressure, however the second effect is quite small and normally ignored. The density of water at various temperatures is listed in Table 1-52. Intermediate values can be obtained through extrapolation.

**Table 1-52. Density of reagent water at different temperatures**

| Temp °C | Density g/mL | Temp °C | Density g/mL |
|---|---|---|---|
| 10 | 0.99970 | 24 | 0.99730 |
| 12 | 0.99950 | 26 | 0.99678 |
| 14 | 0.99924 | 28 | 0.99623 |
| 16 | 0.99894 | 30 | 0.99565 |
| 18 | 0.99860 | 32 | 0.99503 |
| 20 | 0.99820 | 34 | 0.99437 |
| 22 | 0.99777 | 36 | 0.99369 |

## E. Significant Figures

Significant figures are an important concept in analytical chemistry as they give an implicit indication of the degree of confidence of the results. This becomes of greater impact in these closing years of the twentieth century due to the prominent use of electronic calculators and computers in the laboratory to perform data conversions while at the same time many older model measuring devices are still being used to obtain the data. Suppose that the analyst needs to multiply 2.13 times 4.67 and uses a calculator to obtain 9.9471. Does the precision implied by the last number reflect the precision of the numbers used to derive it?

In analytical chemistry the uncertainty implied in a number is a variation of $\pm 1$ in the final decimal place, unless otherwise explicitly stated. When the number 2.13 is reported, the analyst means that the value 2.13 is the best estimate of a result that exists somewhere in the range 2.12 to 2.14. Compare the ranges of the following numbers and how increasing numbers of significant figures imply greater degrees of measurement precision.

| Reported number | Implied precision |
|:---:|:---:|
| 2 | 1 to 3 |
| 2.0 | 1.9 to 2.1 |
| 2.00 | 1.99 to 2.01 |
| 2.000 | 1.999 to 2.001 |

The consequence of this definition and use of significant figures is that when the notation of 5 mL is seen on a benchsheet when refering to a sample aliquot, the immediate interpretation is a dispensing of 4 to 6 mL by the technician and an implied initial error in the analysis of 20%. On the other hand if a Class A volumetric pipet was used to dispense that sample the number should be recorded as 5.00 mL with a significant decrease in initial analytical error (0.2%).

The number of significant figures allowed in a final result is limited by the maximum inaccuracy in the measuring tools used. For example suppose we want to multiply 1.7 times 2.4 and we are limited to an old instrument called a slide rule. The calculation is illustrated in Figure 1-25, where the positions of 1.7, 2.4 and the result 4.1 are estimated and to the limits of our measurement, 4.1 is a pretty good estimate of the range 4.0 to 4.2. On the other hand, use of a calculator gives the exact answer of 4.08 with the implied estimate range 4.07 to 4.09, which is a misrepresentation of the accuracy possible from the slide rule.

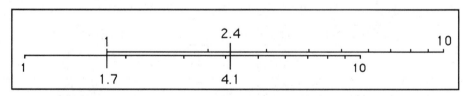

**Figure 1-25. Multiplication of two numbers using an old fashioned slide rule.**

Most environmental laboratories use Class A glassware for volume measurements, and this places a limitation on the number of significant figures reportable. For example preparation of a standard by dilution of a 5.00 mL aliquot of a 21.00 mg/L standard solution to 100.0 mL limits the concentration of the working standard to three significant figures, 1.05 mg/L not 1.050 mg/L. This in turn limits any final results reported from this analysis to three significant figures. In general three significant figures is the maximum number that can be reported from any environmental analytical procedure.

There was a metals section in a laboratory that always reported recovery data with four significant figures (93.12%). An audit of the procedure was performed and Class A glassware was found to be used in all parts of the analysis except one. This one excepted use was in adding matrix spike solutions to the samples where a 20 µL disposable tip pipettor was employed. These type devices in the hands of an experienced technician are accurate to ± 1 µL which translates to a ± 5% variation in the amount of matrix spike added to the sample. Following this error through the procedure and into the recovery calculations suggests that the recovery data reported had a built in variation of ± 5% or allowable reporting values of 90% or 95%, not the figure provided. When questioned about this, the technician was aware of the problem, however the computer that processed the QC data was programmed to report all numbers with 2 decimal places, regardless of the input data.

## F. Record Keeping and File Management

Many records are required to be kept to support the legally defensible aspect of the data reported from the lab. Possible records that need to be maintained include, but are not limited to, the following list. Most of these records do not have a set format, however, they should all supply the answers to the questions, who did what to which sample, how was it done and when? Some of the forms have formats specified in the most recent CLP SOWs. In laboratories with LIMS, the forms are computer generated, and the laboratory establishes a format that is the most compatible with the computers in use.

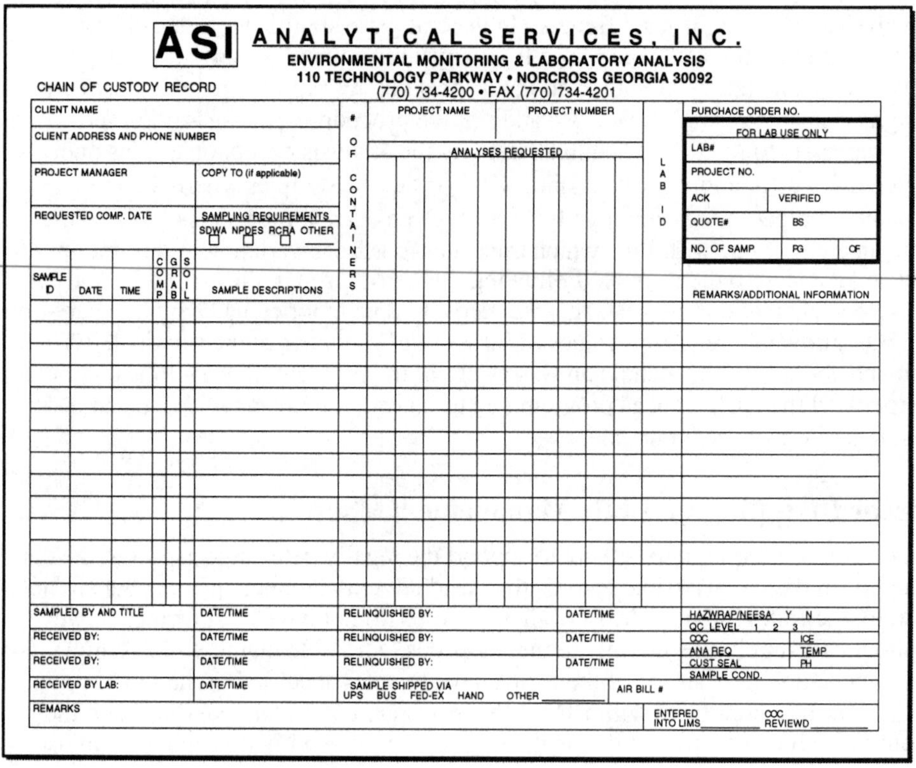

ASI ANALYTICAL SERVICES, INC.
ENVIRONMENTAL MONITORING & LABORATORY ANALYSIS
110 TECHNOLOGY PARKWAY • NORCROSS GEORGIA 30092
(770) 734-4200 • FAX (770) 734-4201

CHAIN OF CUSTODY RECORD

CLIENT NAME
CLIENT ADDRESS AND PHONE NUMBER
PROJECT MANAGER | COPY TO (if applicable)
REQUESTED COMP. DATE | SAMPLING REQUIREMENTS: SDWA NPDES RCRA OTHER
# OF CONTAINERS
PROJECT NAME | PROJECT NUMBER
ANALYSES REQUESTED
LAB ID
PURCHACE ORDER NO.
FOR LAB USE ONLY: LAB# | PROJECT NO. | ACK | VERIFIED | QUOTE# | BS | NO. OF SAMP | PG | OF

SAMPLE ID | DATE | TIME | COMP | GRAB | SOIL | SAMPLE DESCRIPTIONS | REMARKS/ADDITIONAL INFORMATION

SAMPLED BY AND TITLE | DATE/TIME | RELINQUISHED BY: | DATE/TIME
RECEIVED BY: | DATE/TIME | RELINQUISHED BY: | DATE/TIME
RECEIVED BY: | DATE/TIME | RELINQUISHED BY: | DATE/TIME
RECEIVED BY LAB: | DATE/TIME | SAMPLE SHIPPED VIA UPS BUS FED-EX HAND OTHER | AIR BILL #
REMARKS | ENTERED INTO LIMS | COC REVIEWD

HAZWRAP/NEESA Y N | QC LEVEL 1 2 3 | COC | ICE | ANA REQ | TEMP | CUST SEAL | PH | SAMPLE COND.

**Figure 1-26. Chain of custody form.**

**Chain of Custody forms** - These are used to document the custody of a sample as it travels from the person collecting the sample through the transportation process until its receipt in the laboratory. It has spaces for signatures and times of persons having custody. See Figure 1-26.

**Field monitoring reports and worksheets -** These are all of the items of documentation that verify the field operations and field analysis.

**Sample receipt logbooks** - These document the arrival and condition of the sample at the laboratory. They also serve as the primary documentation of what field sample number corresponds to what laboratory sample number.

**Work assignments** - Most commonly produced from LIMS, these list the samples and their location for a test parameter to be performed by the technician.

## WORK ASSIGNMENT

| Analyst: LMB | Date: 10-29-96 | Test: TSS (mg/L)(EPA 160.2) | |
|---|---|---|---|
| Sample # | Location | Due Date | Client |
| 43012-1 | C7 | 11-07-96 | Springfield Power Plant |
| 43012-2 | C7 | 11-07-96 | Springfield Power Plant |
| 43012-3 | C7 | 11-07-96 | Springfield Power Plant |
| 43012-4 | C7 | 11-07-96 | Springfield Power Plant |
| 43012-5 | C7 | 11-07-96 | Springfield Power Plant |
| 43013 | H1 | 11-06-96 | Springfield Dairy |
| 43014-3 | R2 | 11-11-96 | Springfield Fire Department |

**Figure 1-27.  Work assignment for TSS.**

**Bench worksheets** - These are often bound into books or spiral bound and serve to record the preparation and analysis of the samples.  Each benchsheet is generally limited to a single analytical batch and documents the QC measures such as blanks, sample duplicates, calibration checks, matrix spikes, etc. that were performed with the batch. Operational information of the test such as times, temperatures, and amounts and sources of reagents and standards can also be listed on the benchsheet.  A sample benchsheet is shown in Figure 1-28.

# GRAVIMETRIC ANALYSIS BENCHSHEET

ANALYST_____     DATE/TIME_____

METHOD NUMBER_____ _____     TEST_____ _____

INITIAL OVEN TEMPERATURE_____     FINAL OVEN TEMPERATURE_____ ___

Thermometer Certification Number:

| SAMPLE | CLIENT | TARE | TOTAL | NET | DRY 1 TOTAL | NET | DRY 2 TOTAL | NET | NOTES |
|---|---|---|---|---|---|---|---|---|---|
| BLANK | | | | | | | | | |
| Check Sample | | | | | | | | | |
| | MS | | | | | | | | |
| | MSD | | | | | | | | |
| | Duplicate | | | | | | | | |
| | | | | | | | | | |
| | | | | | | | | | |
| | | | | | | | | | |
| | | | | | | | | | |
| | | | | | | | | | |
| | | | | | | | | | |
| | | | | | | | | | |
| | | | | | | | | | |
| | | | | | | | | | |
| | | | | | | | | | |
| | | | | | | | | | |
| | | | | | | | | | |
| | | | | | | | | | |
| | | | | | | | | | |
| | | | | | | | | | |
| | | | | | | | | | |
| | | | | | | | | | |
| | | | | | | | | | |
| | | | | | | | | | |

**Figure 1-28. Example of a bench worksheet.**

**Sample preparation logbooks** - These are particular to procedures that involve separate sample preparation and instrument analysis. The most common forms are extraction logs in the organics area and digestion logs in metals analysis.

**Instrument maintenance and run logs** - The instrument maintenance logs serve to document that the instrument is operating per maunfacturer's specifications. They document both preventative maintenance performed by the instrument operator and service calls by factory technicians. The run log documents every sample that has been tested on the instrument and what data file the information is stored under. Instruments often maintain an internal run log in the computer memory that should duplicate the manual run log kept by the technician.

**Raw data from the analysis (chromatograms, strip charts, absorbances, etc.)** - Often kept as computer records, hardcopy should be maintained and filed in such a fashion as to be readily available for a period of at least 5 years.

**Sample result calculation worksheets** - These records may be part of the raw data from the analysis, with the transformation of the raw data to the final result included as part of the document. Often a single detailed calculation is illustrated on the worksheet. The assumption is made that all the calculations were performed in the same manner. A laboratory may chose to attach detailed calculations for each result to the analysis benchsheet.

**Calibration curves and the raw data** - Instruments and procedures must be calibrated and documentation kept supporting the calibration. Many instruments maintain this data as computer memory on tape or disk. Manual procedures may require hand-plotting of the calibration curve, however, a better solution is to use a statistics package on a PC and have the computer draw the calibration curve and at the same time calculate the correlation coefficient (r). Some procedures require a coefficient of at least 0.995 for acceptance of the calibration. If several technicians are performing the same test, each must prepare and maintain his/her calibrations. Most test methods specify the frequency of recalibration, ranging from each use to once a year. "Calibrations" should indicate who performed it, when, the specific test or instrument, and the correlation coefficient. All instruments must be calibrated. There are several commercial instruments on the market for spectrophotometric analysis of water pollutants that have a built-in factory-set calibration. None of these instruments are known to be approved for regulatory reporting. The calibration curve must be checked immediately prior to beginning analysis of a batch, and the check documented.

**Analytical balance daily calibration check logbook** - The analytical balance is the most important instrument in the laboratory. It is used for weighing samples and standards, and in gravimetric analysis, it is the determinative instrument. The calibration of the balance should be adjusted by a service technician at least twice a year and the service call documented. The calibration should be checked on a daily basis by weighing a set of Class S weights and recording the results (Figure 1-29). There are a variety of calibration masses available commercially. ASTM (standard E617) and NIST have established tolerances for different class weights as in Table 1-53.

**ANALYTICAL BALANCE DAILY CALIBRATION CHECK**

Balance Serial Number: _____     Date: _____

Analytst: _____     Page: _____

Class S Weight Serial Number: _____

| Nominal Class S Weight | Acceptance Range | Result |
|:---:|:---:|:---:|
| 10 mg | 0.0099-0.0101 | |
| 20 mg | 0.0199-0.0201 | |
| 50 mg | 0.0495-0.0505 | |
| 100 mg | 0.0990-0.1010 | |
| 200 mg | 0.1990-0.2010 | |
| 500 mg | 0.4900-0.5050 | |
| 1 g | 0.9990-1.0010 | |
| 5 g | 4.9990-5.0010 | |
| 10 g | 9.9990-10.0010 | |
| 100 g | 99.9900-100.0100 | |

**Figure 1-29. Analytical balance daily calibration logbook.**

**Internal chain of custody** - The internal chain of custody is most commonly maintained as a computer record in the LIMS. It may rely on manual entry of the sample numbers, time, date and the name of the technician acquiring or relinquishing custody or it may be driven with a bar code reader.

**Sample result worksheets** - These forms are the working draft of the final analytical report. They may be computer generated as a result of the sample receipt process, or they may be hand typed. They serve as a summary of information about the sample, the test parameters required, methods required, and have space for the technicians to enter the result, their MDL for the test, and their initials. The forms may be color coded according to a priority of testing scheme, such as orange for 24-hour turn-around, or blue for regular turn-around. When the technicians have entered all the sample results onto these forms, they are reviewed and initialed by the supervisors and laboratory managers before being sent on for final report generation. See Figure 1-30.

**Table 1-53.    Tolerances (in mg) of various ASTM and NIST Classes of Standard Weights**

| Mass | ASTM Class 1 | NIST Class S | NIST Class S-1[172] | NIST Class P[173] | NIST Class C | NIST Class F |
|------|------|------|------|------|------|------|
| 1 mg | 0.010 | 0.014 | 0.025 | 0.050 | 0.04 | 0.10 |
| 2 mg | 0.010 | 0.014 | 0.025 | 0.050 | 0.05 | 0.12 |
| 5 mg | 0.010 | 0.014 | 0.028 | 0.055 | 0.10 | 0.17 |
| 10 mg | 0.010 | 0.014 | 0.030 | 0.060 | 0.15 | 0.21 |
| 20 mg | 0.010 | 0.014 | 0.035 | 0.070 | 0.20 | 0.26 |
| 50 mg | 0.010 | 0.014 | 0.042 | 0.085 | 0.35 | 0.35 |
| 100 mg | 0.010 | 0.025 | 0.050 | 0.10 | 0.5 | 0.43 |
| 200 mg | 0.010 | 0.025 | 0.060 | 0.12 | 0.7 | 0.54 |
| 500 mg | 0.010 | 0.025 | 0.080 | 0.16 | 1.5 | 0.72 |
| 1 g | 0.034 | 0.054 | 0.10 | 0.20 | 2 | 0.90 |
| 2 g | 0.034 | 0.054 | 0.13 | 0.26 | 3 | 1.1 |
| 5 g | 0.034 | 0.054 | 0.18 | 0.36 | 5 | 1.5 |
| 10 g | 0.050 | 0.074 | 0.25 | 0.50 | 7 | 2.0 |
| 20 g | 0.074 | 0.074 | 0.35 | 0.70 | 10 | 4.0 |
| 50 g | 0.12 | 0.12 | 0.60 | 1.2 | 20 | 10 |
| 100 g | 0.25 | 0.25 | 1.0 | 2.0 | 30 | 20 |

[172]   Equivalent to ASTM Class 3.
[173]   Equivalent to ASTM Class 4.

**Final analytical reports** - These are the written reports sent to the client that convey the results of the analysis. Information that should be included is a description of the sample, where it came from, the time and date of sampling, the client's name and address, the parameters reported, test method, test results, detection limits of the test, and any data qualifiers. The report must be signed by an official of the laboratory. A modern innovation is to submit final reports on computer readable media such as tapes or disk, or over data transmission lines. However, each final report submitted on computer media should also be duplicated and sent as hardcopy to the client. See Figure 1-2 for an example.

**Sample container logs** - These records take the form of a bound logbook that, for manual cleaning, contains a written description of the cleaning process along with the date, time and initials of the person performing the cleaning. The page number of the log accompanies the sample container through the sampling process and should appear in the field notebook, the chain of custody and the sample receipt logbook. For precleaned sample containers the logbook has pasted into it the manufacturer's certificate of analysis, the lot number and references the in-house container blank QA results. Either the lot number or logbook page should appear in the field notebook, chain of custody, and the sample receipt logbook.

**Standard receipt logs** - These are logbooks that document the receipt of analytical standards in the laboratory. They take many forms but should include the time and date of receipt, the source of the standard and lot number, and the storage location. These records may be maintained in the purchasing office rather than in the laboratory.

**Standard preparation logs** - These records document the preparation of standards used for instrument calibrations. They must be linked by reference to the calibration and the manufacturer's certificate of analysis. They include the time and date of preparation, the vendor, manufacturer, and lot number of the standard, the volume or weight of standard used, the calculation of final concentration of the standard, the storage container and location, and the expiration date of the standard. The log must be countersigned and dated by the section supervisor. See Figure 1-31.

**Sample disposition logs** - Most samples have a required 30-day holding time after analysis and before disposal. As samples are logged out from the laboratory, they are removed from the sample storage locations and transfered to a holding location. A LIMS can handle the paperwork documenting this function very easily by generating a purge list each morning for all samples completed on the previous day. The receipt technicians go find all the samples (and extracts and digestates), marking off on the list all that they find and moving the purge samples to the holding area with the purge list attached to the shelf. The list is dated, and 30 days from its issuance the technicians remove the samples from the holding area and either safely dispose of the benign samples or return the hazardous samples to the client. The LIMS can facilitate this process by placing an asterisk next to each sample that tested hazardous and needs to be returned to the client. The hazardous determination is normally made during the report review process.

Priority **3**  Due 12/12/96  Sample # 9999-1,2

Notes:  Metals not Preserved

Phone: 619-285-0386 ext 4439

Springfield Power Plant  Date Received: 10-25-96
PO Box 1234  PO #
1st St.
Springfield, Ohio  # Samples = 2  # Containers = 6


ATTN:  Mr. Homer Simpson


Location:  **C 3**


Description:
Water, grab, 435Z, 10-18-96, Time, received 10-25-96

| TEST | Result | Detection | By |
|---|---|---|---|
| **Sample 1** | | | |
| Total Lead (Pb)(mg/L)(EPA 239.2) | _____ | 0.005 | _____ |
| Total Copper (Cu)(mg/L)(EPA 220.2) | _____ | 0.002 | _____ |
| **Sample 2** | | | |
| Chemical Oxygen Demand (COD)(mg/L)(EPA 410.1) | _____ | 5 | _____ |
| Total Phosphorous (P)(mg/L)(EPA 365.1) | _____ | 0.02 | _____ |
| Total Kjeldahl Nitrogen (N)(mg/L)(EPA 351.3) | _____ | 0.1 | _____ |
| Total Suspended Solids (mg/L)(EPA 160.2) | _____ | 40 | _____ |
| Total Zinc (Zn)(mg/L)(EPA 200.7) | _____ | 0.02 | _____ |

DATES:  Completed:  Typed:  Mailed:

Review:  Review:

Review:

**Figure 1-30.  Sample report worksheet.**

# BNA STANDARD PREPARATION LOG

| Date: | Time: |
|---|---|
| Analyst: | Page Number: |

### BASE/NEUTRAL STANDARD

| Vendor: | Manufacturer: |
|---|---|
| Catalog Number: | Lot Number: |
| Receipt Date: | Expiration Date: |
| Dilution Solvent: | Dilution Solvent Lot Number: |
| Volume used: | Final Volume: |
| Final Concentration: | Storage location and expiration date: |

### ACID STANDARD

| Vendor: | Manufacturer: |
|---|---|
| Catalog Number: | Lot Number: |
| Receipt Date: | Expiration Date: |
| Dilution Solvent: | Dilution Solvent Lot Number: |
| Volume used: | Final Volume: |
| Final Concentration: | Storage location and expiration date: |

### CALCULATIONS

| B/N | Acid |
|---|---|
|  |  |

Supervisor verification:             Date:

**Figure 1-31. Standard preparation log.**

# G. Quality Control Procedures for Sampling

**Container blanks** - Analyte free water placed in random samples from a vendor's lot number of containers, then analyzed for the target parameters. BDL results for the target analytes indicate the lot is appropriate for use in sampling.

**Blank samples** - Analyte free water placed in a container in the field, preservatives added and the sample submitted with the rest of the samples from that field operation. Serves to check on the preservatives and laboratory water used in the field, along with incidental contamination that may be present at the sampling site.

**Blank preservatives** - Similar to the container blank, it concentrates upon the purity of the preservatives. May be performed in the laboratory if preservatives are purchased in single-use sealed ampules by vendor's lot number.

**Equipment blanks** - Equipment is rinsed with laboratory water immediately prior to use in sampling, and the rinsings submitted to the laboratory as a sample for analysis. This is especially pertinent if equipment is cleaned between uses in the field.

**Trip blanks (VOA only)** - VOA vials are filled with laboratory water at the lab and sealed. These go to the field and return where they are analyzed as a regular sample. They check for permeation of volatile contaminants through the container septum. A recent example that detected hydrocarbon contamination in the trip blank was traced to the technician storing the VOC samples in a box over a running truck's exhaust tailpipe for several hours.

**Field duplicate samples** - The sample is split into two or more containers, which are then analyzed as regular samples. Checks for consistency in sampling and analysis.

# H. Quality Control Procedures for Sample Preparation

**Spikes and recovery (matrix spikes)** - A matrix spike is the addition of a known amount of a target analyte to a sample. Analysis of the sample and the matrix-spiked sample generate recovery numbers. These recovery numbers give an indication of the accuracy of the analytical procedure for the particular sample. Matrix spike results are normally reported on a batchwise basis. In test procedures where the target analyte is infrequently found in samples, realistic evaluations of precision are best obtained through performance of a matrix spike and matrix spike duplicate.

## SEMIVOLATILE BNA SPIKE RESULTS
## AQUEOUS SAMPLES

| Data Quality Objectives | %Recovery | RPD |
|---|---|---|
| Phenol | 12-89 | 0-42 |
| 2-Chlorophenol | 27-123 | 0-40 |
| 1,4-Dichlorobenzene | 36-97 | 0-28 |
| N-Nitrosodipropylamine | 41-116 | 0-38 |
| 1,2,4-Trichlorobenzene | 44-142 | 0-28 |
| 4-Chloro-3-methylphenol | 23-97 | 0-42 |
| Acenaphthene | 46-118 | 0-31 |
| 2,4-Dinitrotoluene | 24-96 | 0-38 |
| 4-Nitrophenol | 10-80 | 0-50 |
| Pentachlorophenol | 9-103 | 0-50 |
| Pyrene | 26-127 | 0-31 |

| Compound | %R1 | %R2 | %R$_{ave}$ | RPD | Notes |
|---|---|---|---|---|---|
| Phenol | | | | | |
| 2-Chlorophenol | | | | | |
| 1,4-Dichlorobenzene | | | | | |
| N-Nitrosodipropylamine | | | | | |
| 1,2,4-Trichlorobenzene | | | | | |
| 4-Chloro-3-methylphenol | | | | | |
| Acenaphthene | | | | | |
| 2,4-Dinitrotoluene | | | | | |
| 4-Nitrophenol | | | | | |
| Pentachlorophenol | | | | | |
| Pyrene | | | | | |

Batch Number:

File Name (MS):                 File Name (MSD):

Analyst:                      Date:

**Figure 1-32. Batch matrix spike results for BNA analysis.**

**Surrogates** - Surrogates are compounds added to every single QC, blank, and analytical sample. They are calibrated just like target analytes. The surrogates are present to evaluate the success or lack of success of the sample preparation. Surrogates are chosen to expose sample preparation problems, thus they must be very similar chemically to the target analytes. Since they are added to every sample, they must never be found naturally in a sample. For this reason surrogates are often isotope-labeled target analytes such as toluene-$D_8$, where all the hydrogens have been replaced with deuterium.

## VOA BATCH SURROGATE RECOVERY SUMMARY
### WATER SAMPLES
#### % Recovery Objectives

| | | |
|---|---|---|
| S1 | 1,2-Dichloroethane-D4 | 76-114 |
| S2 | Toluene-D8 | 88-110 |
| S3 | 4-Bromofluorobenzene | 86-115 |

| Sample | File | S1 | S2 | S3 | Notes |
|---|---|---|---|---|---|
| Blank | | | | | |
| MS | | | | | |
| MSD | | | | | |
| Duplicate | | | | | |
| QC Check | | | | | |
| | | | | | |
| | | | | | |
| | | | | | |
| | | | | | |
| | | | | | |
| | | | | | |
| | | | | | |
| | | | | | |
| | | | | | |
| | | | | | |
| | | | | | |

Analyst:          Batch:          Date:

**Figure 1-33. Batch surrogate recovery form.**

**Sample duplicates** - Sample duplicate analysis must be performed at a rate varying from 1 every 10 samples to 1 every 20 samples, depending on the regulatory agency. When performing tests for target analytes that are often found in the sample, such as nutrients, duplicates should be used for the determination of precision results and DQOs. In cases where the target analytes are seldom present, the duplicate analysis is still performed; however, precision is calculated from matrix spike duplicate analysis.

**Reagent blanks** - Reagent blanks are the first test performed in any batch to determine the level of laboratory contamination in reagents, solvents, glassware, etc. The blank must give BDL results for each target analyte before continued sample analysis is allowed.

In an analysis[174] of results reported from groundwater samples obtained from over 500 RCRA and CERCLA sites distributed over all 10 EPA Regions, out of 425 total contaminants detected, the most frequently reported volatile organic contaminant found was dichloromethane, and the most frequently reported semi-volatile organic compound was bis (2-ethylhexyl) phthalate. Ranking the results by individual sites or by individual analyses did not change this observation. The list[175] of the top 50 chemicals in production contains methyl-*tert*-butyl ether, vinyl chloride, benzene, ethyl benzene, styrene, xylene, toluene, cumene, phenol, vinyl acetate, acrylonitrile, acetone, and *n*-butyl alcohol, which are also prominent on various target compound lists as environmental contaminants. Although methylene chloride and bis(2-ethylhexyl) phthalate are important industrially, they are not that overwhelmingly prevalent in the environment, with the above list of compounds probably present in greater frequency, simply based on the amounts in existence. Instead these analytical results must be viewed as an indication of the pervasiveness of laboratory contamination as a problem to environmental laboratories.

Virtually every solvent used in the organics laboratory, except methanol, is a listed target analyte of one or more EPA methods. Examples of listed solvents include acetone, hexane, methylene chloride, toluene, ethyl ether, methyl ethyl ketone and methyl isobutyl ketone. Other common lab contaminants found in the volatiles lab are naphthalene (old fashioned mothballs) and para-dichlorobenzene (new formulation mothballs). Limonene and citral can be present from floor waxes and cleaning formulations. Acrylonitrile and other compounds are found in carpet glue and backing. Methyl and ethylmethacrylate are common in fingernail polishes.

These can normally be minimized in the volatiles lab by situating the lab up-wind and in an independant building from the semi-volatiles extraction laboratory. However we have seen the wind shift 180° from the prevailing direction and at a distance of 100 yards, the VOA GC-MS background starts to register increased levels of methylene chloride within an hour. Housing the volatiles lab under the same roof as the rest of the laboratory creates the need for either a completely separate ventilation system effectively isolating the VOA area, or arranging the HVAC ducting so that all the exchange air in the building enters through the volatiles lab, creating a positive air pressure in the room.

The situation is different in the semi-volatiles extraction laboratory where the biggest contaminants are a variety of phthalates found in almost all products manufactured in the USA. The most common culprits are di-*n*-butyl phthalate and bis(2-ethylhexyl) phthalate although benzylbutyl-, di-*n*- octyl- and diethylphthalate can be a problem at times. The list of products that contribute these contaminants in the lab are impressive, ranging from plastic bags used to hold 25 kg lots of anhydrous sodium sulfate to the gloves the technicians wear to protect their hands. A survey was conducted in a laboratory to determine sources of phthalate contamination. The results are in Table 1-54.

---

174   Plumb, R. H. Jr., "The Importance of Volatile Organic Compounds as a Disposal Site
       Monitoring Parameter." in *Groundwater Contamination and Analysis at Hazardous Waste Sites*.
       S. Lesage and R.E. Jackson (Eds), Marcel Dekker, Inc, 270 Madison Ave, New York, NY
       10016. 1992. pp. 173-197.
175   *Chemical and Engineering News*. April 11, 1994. p. 13.

Other contaminants seen in the semi-volatiles lab arise from the solvents[176] that are used in the extraction process. Methylene chloride and other chlorinated solvents are subject to free-radical degradation initiated by ultraviolet light. Degradation products include hydrochloric acid, phosgene, and a variety of hydrocarbons and chlorinated hydrocarbons of increasing chain-length. Free-radical scavengers used to stabilize chlorinated solvents include amylene and ethanol (up to 1%). Phosgene is of particular interest, not only because it is toxic (it was employed as one of the first chemical warfare agents during World War I) but also because it is extremely reactive toward alcohols, phenols and amines that originally may be in the sample. Reaction with phosgene can transform target analytes into unrecognizable by-products.

Ether solvents are prone to formation of hydroperoxides, initiated by exposure of the solvent to air and ultraviolet light. Not only are hydroperoxides famous for their instability, old opened bottles of ether and tetrahydrofuran have been known to spontaneously explode, but the peroxides are effective oxidizing agents of target analytes. Ether solvents are stabilized by addition of either BHT or ethanol, and by packaging the solvent in a light-proof container under a nitrogen atmosphere. Bottles or cans of ether solvents should be purchased in the minimum size needed for weekly analysis use. Any excess should be disposed of properly. Containers that have been opened and stored more than 30 days should be suspected as having peroxides present. The presence of peroxides can be checked by shaking a 5 mL portion of the solvent with 1 mL of a 10% potassium iodide solution. Any formation of a yellow to brown or purple color in the solvent layer is interpreted as indicating that peroxides are present.

Ketone solvents such as acetone or methylethyl ketone (MEK) can form peroxides; however, the more frequently noted mode of degradation is condensation of two or more molecules of the solvent in the aldol reaction. 4-Hydroxy-4-methyl-2-pentanone (diacetone alcohol) is found as a contaminant in almost every instance when acetone has been used in the glassware washing process. Acetone and MEK can also condense with anilines and other aromatic amines to form very stable imines ($Ph-N=C[CH_3]_2$) that change the retention time and mass spectum of the target analyte.

**Table 1-54. Phthalates and other contaminants found in common laboratory items. Amounts are in ng/uL injected into the GC-MS from 1.0 mL final volume of extract**

| Item and number | Contaminant found | Amount |
|---|---|---|
| sodium sulfate | di-*n*-butyl phthalate | 5-100 |
| 1 g glass wool | di-*n*-octylphthalate | 2 |
| 1 sheet of paper towel roll | di-*n*-butyl phthalate | 36.5 |
| | N,N-dimethyl-9-octadecenamide | - |
| | 4,4'-butylidenebis[2-(1,1-dimethylethyl)-5-methyl] phenol | - |
| | pentatriacontane | - |
| #4 filter paper | di-*n*-butyl phthalate | 139 |
| | butylbenzyl phthalate | 0.8 |
| | Bis(2-ethylhexyl) phthalate | 1.1 |
| | di-*n*-octyl phthalate | 0.2 |
| | decamthylcyclopentasiloxane | - |

Continued on next page.

---

[176] Seaver, C., J. Przybytek, and N. Roelofs, 1995. "Solvent Selection, Part III - Solvent Life and Degradation." *LC-GC*, 13(11). pp. 860-864. November, 1995.

---

**Table 1-54. Phthalates and other contaminants found in common laboratory items. Amounts are in ng/uL injected into the GC-MS from 1.0 mL final volume of extract,** *continued*

| Item and number | Contaminant found | Amount |
|---|---|---|
| Acrodisk PTFE 0.45 mm filter disk (15) | di-*n*-butyl phthalate | 3.8 |
| Safeskin glove | di-*n*-butyl phthalate | 1.1 |
| | Bis(2-ethylhexyl) phthalate | 12.2 |
| | butylbenzyl phthalate | 2.4 |
| | N,N-bis(2-hydroxyethoxy)-dodecamide | - |
| | octadecadienal | - |
| | octadecene | - |
| | hydrocarbon oils | - |
| Triclean glove | Bis(2-ethylhexyl) phthalate | 4.3 |
| | butylbenzyl phthalate | 11.4 |
| | 4-chloro-3-methyl phenol | 6.5 |
| | N,N-bis(2-hydroxyethoxy)-dodecamide | - |
| | Hexadecanoic acid | - |
| | 4,4'-butylidene bis[2-(1,1-dimethylethyl)-5-methyl]phenol | - |
| | octadecadienal | - |
| N-Dex nitrile glove | di-*n*-butyl phthalate | 6.3 |
| | benzyl alcohol | 56.8 |
| | Bis-(2-ethylhexyl) phthalate | 4.6 |
| | 3,3'-imino bis propanenitrile | - |
| | 2-mercaptobenzothiazole | - |
| | hydrocarbon oils | - |
| | 4,4'-butylidene bis[2-(1,1-dimethylethyl)-5-methyl]phenol | - |
| Chemsolve (1 g) | hexamethylcyclotrisiloxane | - |
| | pentamethyldisiloxane | - |
| | octamethylcyclotetrasiloxane | - |
| | 2-[2-[4-(1,1,3,3-tetramethylbutyl)phenoxy]ethoxy]ethanol | - |
| | di-*n*-octylphthalate | 1.4 |
| HDPE container (500 mL) | 2,5,8,11,14-pentaoxahexadecan-16-ol and other alcohols | - |
| Rubber suction bulb (large) | large amounts of hydrocarbon oils | - |
| Latex suction bulb (3) | 4 unknown compounds | - |
| 1 Alumina PrepSep column | (none detected) | |
| Tygon R-3603 tubing (41 inches) | Bis(2-ethylhexyl)phthalate | 44,000 |
| Fisher disposable Pasteur pipets (12) | (none detected) | |
| Soxhlet extraction thimble | di-*n*-butyl phthalate | 9.3 |
| | unidentified phthalate | - |
| | unidentified adipate | - |
| Silastic tubing (27") | diethyl phthalate | 6.0 |
| | phenanthrene | 2 |
| | anthracene | 1.9 |
| | di-*n*-butyl phthalate | 5.1 |
| | Bis(2-ethylhexyl) phthalate | 15.5 |
| | ethanol, 2-(2-butoxyethoxy)-acetate | - |
| | unidentified siloxane polymer series | - |
| Aluminum foil | (none detected) | |
| Baker C18 SPE | Bis(2-ethylhexyl) phthalate | 2.7 |
| | unidentified siloxane polymer series | - |
| McDonald's fingers | $C_{12}$-$C_{18}$ Fatty acid series | varies |

Reagent blanks normally substitute reagent or laboratory water for the sample volume. In the case of marine (seawater) samples, a more representative blank can be prepared using a preparation in either 40 CFR 796.1860 for synthetic seawater, EPA method 350.1 for substitute ocean water, or *Standard Methods* 19th Edition 4500-NH$_3$ G and 8010 E, summarized in Table 1-55. The 796.1860 preparation results in a solution of 34 ± 0.5 g/kg salinity and pH 8.0 ± 0.2. These solutions are also suitable for matrix spike, laboratory control samples or standard preparation.

**Table 1-55. Preparation of 1 L of synthetic seawater**

| Reference Method | 350.1[177] | 4500-NH$_3$ G | SM 8010E | 796.1860 |
|---|---|---|---|---|
| Chemical | Amounts | | | |
| NaF | 3 mg | 3 mg | 3 mg | 3 mg |
| SrCl$_2$•6H$_2$O | 30 mg (anh) | 30 mg (anh) | 20 mg | 20 mg |
| H$_3$BO$_3$ | 30 mg | 30 mg | 30 mg | 30 mg |
| KBr | 100 mg | 100 mg | 100 mg | 100 mg |
| KCl | 700 mg | 700 mg | 700 mg | 700 mg |
| CaCl$_2$•2H$_2$O | 1.16 g (anh) | 1.16 g (anh) | 1.470 g | 1.47 g |
| Na$_2$SO$_4$ | 4.09 g | 4.09 (anh) | 4.00 g | 4.00 g |
| MgCl$_2$•6H$_2$O | 5.20 (anh) | 5.20 (anh) | 10.780 g | 10.78 g |
| NaCl | 24.53 g | 24.53 g | 23.500 g | 23.50 g |
| Na$_2$SiO$_3$•9H$_2$O | - | - | 20 mg | 20 mg |
| NaHCO$_3$ | 200 mg | 200 mg | 200 mg | 200 mg |
| Na$_4$EDTA | - | - | 1 mg | - |

Freshwater blank matrices can be generated from laboratory purified water using a recipe in *Standard Methods* 19th Edition 8080E for synthetic freshwater. ASTM has generated a standard specification for substitute wastewater, ASTM D5905, that is useful for determination of the ruggedness of proposed test procedures.

**Table 1-56. Synthetic freshwater recipe amounts in mg/L**

| Water type | NaHCO$_3$ | CaSO$_4$•2H$_2$O | MgSO$_4$ | KCl |
|---|---|---|---|---|
| Very Soft | 12 | 7.5 | 7.5 | 0.5 |
| Soft | 48 | 30 | 30 | 2.0 |
| Mod. Hard | 96 | 60 | 60 | 4.0 |
| Hard | 192 | 120 | 120 | 8.0 |
| Very Hard | 384 | 240 | 240 | 16.0 |

**QC check standards (lab control standards or samples)** - These QC measures are used to determine if the sample preparation for the batch is successful on an ideal sample. The ideal sample can consist of a matrix spike into analyte-free water, in which case it is called a laboratory control sample. It could also be one of a variety of commercially available check samples where the level of target analytes are known and provided with the sample, in which case it is called a QC check sample. The recovery of the target analytes must be within the laboratory's DQO for the test. Specific DQOs for the lab control samples may be established.

---

[177] Anhydrous (anh) weight of salt.

## I. Quality Control Procedures during Analysis

**Operator Certification** - The certification may be general for laboratory operations, such as a wastewater laboratory analyst certificate, or specific for each test, for example, passing a PE sample. The certificate may be for attending a formal training course at an instrument manufacturer's facility. Many methods have a one-time demonstration of ability the analyst must pass before being allowed to test samples. All of these must be documented and copies of the documentation placed in the employee's training file. Having an SOP for employee training is a required part of the QA program under a number of laboratory certification programs.

**Calibration curves** - These are required for each analyst performing the test and are updated on a regular basis. Calibration curves must be immediately verified with testing of a mid-level calibration standard that comes from a different manufacturer than that of the standards used for the calibration. This procedure is called an initial calibration verification (ICV).

**Calibration checks** - The calibration curve must be checked on a batchwise basis to verify if it is still valid. The normal check is testing of one of the original mid-level calibration standards and verifying that the RPD is within the acceptance range of the method. The procedure is called a continuing calibration verification (CCV).

**QC check standards** - These are often repeat analysis of the ICV standard on a batchwise basis or at least 5% of the samples in the batch.

**Post digestion spikes (PDS) or post extraction spikes (PES)** - These procedures are used to specifically separate sample preparation problems from sample analysis problems. The PDS consists of adding matrix spike to the final analytical volume of analyte-free water. The PES is formed by taking an aliquot of surrogate mixture, diluting to the final analytical volume with the appropriate solvent, adding internal standard if required by the test, and then analyzing. The procedures allow verification that the instrument and the spike or surrogate solutions are within specifications.

**Duplicate analysis** - Sample duplicate analysis must be performed at a rate varying from 1 every 10 samples to 1 every 20 samples, depending on the regulatory agency. When performing tests for target analytes that are often found in the sample, such as nutrients, duplicates should be used for the determination of precision results and DQOs. In cases where the target analytes are seldom present, the duplicate analysis is still performed, however, precision is calculated from matrix spike duplicate analysis.

**Blind check samples** - These are samples inserted into the normal laboratory workload by the lab manager or QC manager. The samples have known target analyte concentrations and serve as an evaluation tool of the laboratory.

**Laboratory certification samples** - These blind samples, also known as Performance Evaluation or PE samples, are sent to the laboratory by another party. Analyte concentrations in the samples are known by the sender but not by the laboratory, and the laboratory's results are compared to the true value or acceptance range.

**Internal performance and system audits** - These audits are performed by either the QA Manager or the Laboratory Director and are an intense examination of a particular function or test procedure in the lab. The audits may be strictly observational, or they may include detailed examination of paperwork or even the use of blind laboratory check samples. The results of these audits are written and included in the QA record. Most regulatory agencies require at least an annual audit of each functioning area in the lab.

**EPA, OSHA, state, third party, and client audits** - Formal announced or surprise visits by a variety of interested parties are the norm for most environmental labs. They range from cursory visits to exhaustive investigations of analytical procedures, facilities, personnel, and especially documentation. These visits are almost always followed by a written report to which the laboratory is given a set amount of time to respond, again in writing.

**Sample splits** - Sample splits are performed by outside parties where a single well-mixed sample is divided into two samples, and the samples sent to different laboratories for analysis. The results from the laboratories are compared.

**Florida DER minimum QC procedures** - In the absence of specified quality control procedures, the Florida Department of Environmental Regulation (DER) recommends the following minimum QC procedures:

1. Method reagent blanks analyzed at a rate of one every set of samples.
2. Matrix spikes analyzed at a rate of at least one or 5% of the samples with the same matrix in a sample set. Each different type of matrix in a sample set should be spiked.
3. Reagent water or reagent matrix spikes analyzed at a rate of 5% of the samples analyzed.
4. Quality control check samples analyzed in duplicate as blind samples at least twice a year.
5. Quality control check standards analyzed at a rate of 5% of the samples in a set.
6. Duplicate samples or matrix spike duplicates analyzed at a rate of at least one or 5% of the samples of differing matrix types in a sample set.
7. Continuing calibration standards analyzed at a rate of 5% of the samples in a sample set. (Item 5 may substitute for this procedure.)

# J. Control Charts

Control charts were developed in the 1920's by Dr. Walter A. Shewhart of Bell Labs. Originally designed to monitor manufacturing processes with set tolerance limits, they have been generalized to many process control situations. In analytical chemistry, control charts are used to monitor accuracy and precision of analytical methods.

A control chart can be maintained for any individual repetitive quality control checks such as analysis of a constant concentration matrix spike and a matrix spike duplicate at a rate of 5% of the analytical samples. Charts for accuracy and precision can be maintained for these QC measures. After 10 repeats of the QC check, the mean and standard deviation of the %R and RPD are calculated and the control charts established. The ±Warning Level is set at the Mean ±2 standard deviations and the Control level at the Mean ±3 standard deviations. Daily plotting of new points on the control chart gives the type figures shown in Figures 1-34 and 1-35, which are termed "I" charts for the individual plotted observations.

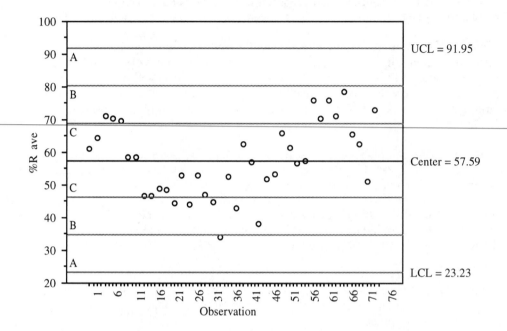

**Figure 1-34. I chart of average recovery for trichlorobenzene.**

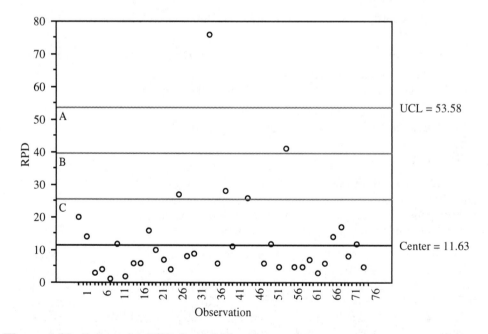

**Figure 1-35. I chart for RPD for trichlorobenzene.**

The control chart assumes that the distribution of values around the mean is binomial, thus the following distribution should be obtained:

Mean ±1 sd = 68% of observations

Mean ±2 sd = 95% of observations (Warning Level)

Mean ±3 sd = 99.7% of observations (Control Level)

It is expected that 5% of the QC results will fall between the Warning and Control Levels, however two points in a row outside the Warning Level± should be investigated. Three out of 1000 observations are expected to fall outside the Control level. Two points outside control within a short period of time are definite signs for concern. The 600 series EPA methods call for updating control charts every 5 to 10 additional QC results.

Another control chart method generates X-bar and R charts. Instead of treating each quality control in a batch as an independant observation, these charts group the quality controls in a batch as a single observation, or what is termed a subgroup. The X-bar chart plots and calculates the %$R_{ave}$ on a batch basis, then determines control limits based on the average range. The range is defined as the absolute difference between the two observations in the batch and is used instead of RPD as an indicator of precision. Examples of the X-bar and R charts are presented in Figures 1-36 and 1-37 for the same data plotted in Figures 1-34 and 1-35.

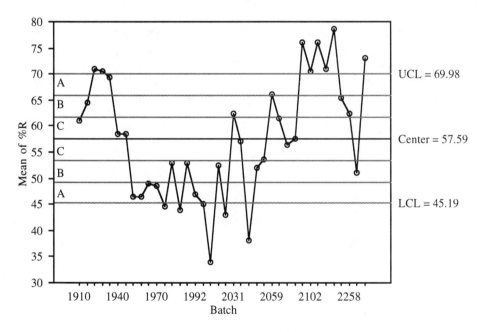

**Figure 1-36. X-bar chart for recovery of trichlorobenzene.**

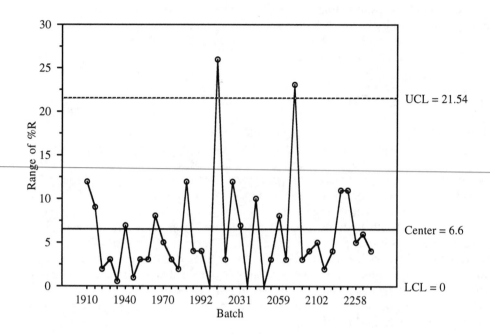

**Figure 1-37. R chart for recovery of trichlorobenzene.**

The U.S. Army Environmental Center (USAEC, formerly USATHAMA) requires control charts to be maintained and copies submitted with each sample result[178]. These control charts have control limits that are updated for every day of operation and extend back through the last 39 batches. Control limits are established based on the average range. An example of a USAEC X-bar control chart with moving limits using the above data for trichlorobenzene is presented in Figure 1-38. The USAEC also allows for control chart preparation that uses control limits based on 3-day moving averages.

---

178  *U.S. Army Environmental Center Guidelines for Implementation of ER1110-1-263 for USAEC Projects.* May 1993.

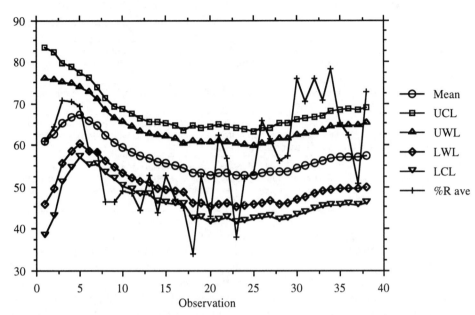

**Figure 1-38. X-bar chart for recovery of trichlorobenzene with daily moving limits.**

There is a list of eight standard tests[179] that have been used to evaluate control charts, Table 1-57. The applicability of all eight to analytical processes in the laboratory is uncertain as there are oftentimes short-term shifts in the mean or standard deviation of the procedure that are inconsequential in the longer term for analytical validity. BOD tests are famous for these small, short-lived trends, as are other tests with high degrees of variablity such as instrumental organic procedures. Statistical packages for personnel computers are increasingly used for generation of control charts, and several have automatic flagging of the data based on the Western Electric Rules. The USAEC has established a simplified set of rules for evaluation of control charts. Out-of-control situations are indicated by a point outside the control limit, 7 consecutive points on the same side of the mean, 5 consecutive points in the same direction, a cyclical pattern of control values, or two points between the UCL and UWL or LCL and LWL.

**Table 1-57. Western Electric rules for evaluating control charts**

| Test | Analysis |
|------|----------|
| 1 | 1 point beyond 3 SD - detects a shift in the process mean, an increase in the estimated standard deviation or a single aberration. |
| 2 | 9 consecutive points above or below the centerline - detects a shift in the process mean. |
| 3 | 6 consecutive increasing or decreasing points - detects a trend or drift in the process mean. |
| 4 | 14 consecutive alternating points - detects systematic alternating effects, such as alternating use of different machines, operators or materials. |

Continued on next page.

---

[179] Western Electric Co., Inc. 1956. *Statistical Quality Control Handbook*. Western Electric Co. Inc., Newark, NJ.

**Table 1-57.   Western Electric rules for evaluating control charts,** *continued*

| Test | Analysis |
|------|----------|
| 5 | 2 of 3 consecutive points beyond 2 SD - detects a shift in the process mean, or an increase in the standard deviation.  The two points must be on the same side of the centerline. |
| 6 | 4 of 5 points beyond 1 SD - detects a shift in the process mean.  The 4 points must be on the same side of the centerline. |
| 7 | 15 consecutive points within 1 SD - detects stratification within subgroups when the observations in a single subgroup come from various sources with different means.  The points must be on both sides of the centerline. |
| 8 | 8 consecutive points beyond 1 SD - detects stratification of subgroups when the observations in one subgroup come from a single source, but subgroups come from different sources with different means.  The points must lie on both sides of the centerline. |

Control charts can also be established for preventative maintenance purposes. Examples are the plotting of internal standard areas for GC-MS batches and the plotting of weekly calibrations of automatic dispensing pipets.  Although it is possible to develop control and warning limits for these purposes, the value of the time spent in the calculation will probably not be recovered in the use of the chart, as all the analyst is looking for is a significant change as a sign for needed cleaning or repair.  Further the act of maintenance often creates a new norm of operations that can be quite different from the previous norm, and the first set of points collected may be out-of-control as compared to the previous limits, although in actuality the system may be in perfect working order.

When the analyst or QA personnel are updating control limits on the charts, the question of data censoring must be answered.  This boils down to whether all collected data points are used in the update, or only those points obtained under complete control operations.  An example is RPD calculated from 1 and 3 %R results as compared to a 95 and 105 %R batch.  Intuitively, both sets of points are in control as far as reproducibility is concerned but the RPDs are 100 and 10 respectively.  An RPD of 100 may be fine for a recovery of 2%, but totally unacceptable for a 100% average recovery.  What is being seen is a severe matrix effect on the recovery, which may be a very common occurance in the lab.  The problem lies in the decision as to whether the control limits are to reflect all data from the lab and give a realistic insight on the performance or if only perfect conditions are to be allowed.

## K. Performance Evaluation (PE) samples

Performance evaluation (PE) samples measure the ability of the lab to correctly identify and quantitate unknown target analytes in samples. PE samples are also called quality control check samples or validation samples. They are an essential "final exam" on the laboratory. PE samples can be obtained from the EPA (WP, WS and DMR series), from state laboratories (North Carolina and Wisconsin, for example), other government agencies (USACE, etc.) or from commercial vendors (ASI, APG, and ERA, for example). PE sample analysis is an essential part of laboratory certification and accreditation by most regulatory agencies. While ability to pass PE samples may not be a completely accurate measure of the lab's competence, failure to pass PE samples is a distinctly bad sign that will doom a laboratory to a very short life as a profitable company.

Most often PE samples are obtained as concentrates in sealed glass ampules, or as powders in sealed serum vials. Directions accompany the PE samples detailing how to prepare the sample by dilution for analysis. PE samples rarely come as ready-prepared solutions. An example of the ready-prepared PE samples are those provided by the U.S. Army Corps of Engineers (USACE). PE samples should always be prepared and analyzed in duplicate.

The regularly scheduled EPA PE samples consist of twice-annual drinking water (WS or Water Supply) and wastewater (WP or Water Pollution) sets. During 1996 EPA combined the WP and the Discharge Monitoring Report QA studies (DMR) samples. For each study, the number of concentrations was reduced from two to one. Prior to 1996, DMR QA Study participants were completely segregated from the WP participants, however, now, if a laboratory participates in the WP studies, all the DMR participant has to do is inform the EPA Study Coordinator of which lab is doing the work. The idea behind the change was to reduce the large number of duplicate PE samples that each commercial laboratory was receiving (the WP ampules and one set of DMR QA Study ampules from each of the lab's clients).

**Table 1-58.  WP Analytes in WP035**

| Ampule(s) | Analytes |
|---|---|
| Trace Metals | Aluminum, Arsenic, Beryllium, Cadmium, Cobalt, Chromium, Copper, Iron, Mercury, Manganese, Nickel, Lead, Selenium, Vanadium, Zinc, Antimony, Silver, Thallium, Molybdenum, Strontium, Titanium |
| Minerals | pH, Specific Conductivity, TDS, Hardness, Calcium, Magnesium, Potassium, Sodium, Alkalinity, Chloride, Fluoride, Sulfate |
| Nutrients | Ammonia, Nitrate, Orthophosphate, Kjeldahl nitrogen, Total phosphorus |
| Demand | COD, 5 day BOD, TOC, 5 day carbonaceous BOD |
| PCBs in Water | 1016/1242, 1232, 1248, 1254, 1260 |
| PCBs in Transformer Oil | 1016/1242, 1254, 1260 |
| Pesticides | Chlordane, Aldrin, Dieldrin, DDD, DDE, DDT, Heptachlor, Heptachlor epoxide |

Continued on next page.

**Table 1-58. WP Analytes in WP035,** *continued*

| Ampule(s) | Analytes |
|---|---|
| Volatile Halocarbons | 1,2-Dichloroethane, Chloroform, 1,1,1-Trichloroethane, Trichloroethene, Carbon tetrachloride, Tetrachloroethene, Bromodichloromethane, Dibromochloromethane, Bromoform, Methylene chloride, Chlorobenzene |
| Volatile Aromatics | Benzene, Ethylbenzene, Toluene, 1,2-Dichlorobenzene, 1,3-Dichlorobenzene, 1,4-Dichlorobenzene |
| Cyanide | Total cyanide |
| Residue | TSS |
| Phenolics | Total phenolics (4-AAP) |
| Oil & Grease | Oil & Grease |
| Chlorine | Total Residual Chlorine |

Figure 1-39 is an example of the reporting form. The blocks labeled MC are for entering the Method Code of the analysis.

| CHEMISTRY DATA | | | | | | Page 2 of 8 | | |
|---|---|---|---|---|---|---|---|---|

| Study Number | | | | EPA Lab I.D. | | Results | | |
|---|---|---|---|---|---|---|---|---|
| W : S : 0 : 3 : 8 | | | | : : : : : : | | | | |
| Analyte Number & Name | | | | Sample # | MC | < / > | Quantity | |

| | | | |
|---|---|---|---|
| **TRACE METALS** | | | |
| 140 | Antimony | 2 | µg/L |
| 001 | Arsenic | 1 | µg/L |
| 002 | Barium | 2 | µg/L |
| 141 | Beryllium | 1 | µg/L |
| 226 | Boron | 2 | µg/L |
| 003 | Cadmium | 1 | µg/L |
| 004 | Chromium | 1 | µg/L |
| 091 | Copper | 1 | µg/L |
| 005 | Lead | 1 | µg/L |
| 236 | Manganese | 1 | µg/L |
| 006 | Mercury | 1 | µg/L |
| 237 | Molybdenum | 2 | µg/L |
| 142 | Nickel | 1 | µg/L |
| 007 | Selenium | 1 | µg/L |
| 143 | Thallium | 2 | µg/L |
| 239 | Zinc | 1 | µg/L |
| **NITRATE & NITRITE & FLUORIDE & ORTHOPHOSPHATE** | | | |
| 009 | Nitrate as N | 1 | mg/L |
| 092 | Nitrite as N | 1 | mg/L |
| 010 | Fluoride | 1 | mg/L |
| 261 | Orthophosphate as P | 1 | mg/L |

EPA-359 (Cin) Rev. 8-96. Previous editions are obsolete. (Note: The Data Report Form is continued on the next page.)

**Figure 1-39.  Example of WP sample reporting form.**

The WS PE samples test the laboratory's ability to perform the tests required for monitoring of the primary and secondary drinking water parameters. Similar to the WP samples, only a single concentration level is provided.

**Table 1-59. WS Analytes in WS038**

| Ampule(s) | Analytes |
|---|---|
| Trace Metals | Antimony, Arsenic, Barium, Beryllium, Boron, Cadmium, Chromium, Copper, Lead, Manganese, Mercury, Molybdenum, Nickel, Selenium, Thallium, Zinc |
| Nitrate/Nitrite/Fluoride | Nitrate, Nitrite, Fluoride. Orthophosphate |
| Insecticides | Alachlor, Atrazine, Chlordane, Endrin, Heptachlor, Heptachlor epoxide, Hexachlorobenzene, Hexachlorocyclopentadiene, Lindane, Methoxychlor, Metolachlor, Metribuzin, Prometon, Simazine, Toxaphene, Trifluralin, Aldrin, Butachlor, Dieldrin, Propachlor |
| Carbamates and Vydate | Aldicarb, Aldicarb sulfone, Aldicarb sulfoxide, Carbofuran, Methomyl, Oxamyl (Vydate) |
| Herbicides | 2,4-D, 2,4,5-TP, Dalapon, Dicamba, Dinoseb, DCPA, Pentachlorophenol, Picloram, Acifluorifen |
| PCBs | Decachlorobiphenyl |
| PAHs | Benzo(a)pyrene |
| Adipates/Phthalates | Di(2-ethylhexl)phthalate, Di(2-ethylhexyl)adipate, |
| Miscellaneous SOCs | Diquat, Endothall, Glyphosate |
| Trihalomethanes | Bromodichloromethane, Dibromochloromethane, Bromoform, Chloroform, Total Trihalomethane |
| Regulated VOCs | Benzene, Carbon tetrachloride, Chlorobenzene, 1,2-Dichlorobenzene, 1,4-Dichlorobenzene, 1,2-Dichloroethane, 1,1-Dichloroethene, cis-1,2-Dichloroethene, trans-1,2-Dichloroethene, 1,2-Dichloropropane, Ethylbenzene, Styrene, Tetrachloroethene, Toluene, 1,1,1-Trichloroethane, Trichloroethene, Vinyl chloride, Xylenes |
| Unregulated VOCs | Bromobenzene, Bromochloromethane, Bromodichloromethane, Bromoform, Bromomethane, n-Butybenzene, sec-Butylbenzene, tert-Butylbenzene, Chlorodibromomethane, Chloroethane, Chloroform, Chloromethane, 2-Chlorotoluene, 4-Chlorotoluene, DBCP, Dibromomethane, 1,3-Dichlorobenzene, Dichlorodifluoromethane, 1,1-Dichloroethane, Dichloromethane, 1,3-Dichloropropane, 2,2-Dichloropropane, 1,1-Dichloropropene, cis-1,3-Dichloropropene, trans-1,3-Dichloropropene, EDB, Fluorotrichloromethane, Hexachlorobutadiene, Isopropylbenzene, 4-Isopropyltoluene, Naphthalene, n-Propylbenzene, 1,1,1,2-Tetrachloroethane, 1,1,2,2-Tetrachloroethane, 1,2,3-Trichlorobenzene, 1,2,4-Trichlorobenzene, 1,1,2-Trichloroethane, 1,2,3-Trichloropropane, 1,2,4-Trimethylbenzene, 1,3,5-Trimethylbenzene |
| Organic Disinfection By-products | Chloral hydrate, Dibromoacetic acid, Dichloroacetic acid, Monobromoacetic acid, Monochloroacetic acid, Trichloroacetic acid, Bromochloroacetic acid |
| Inorganic Disinfection By-products | Bromate, Chlorate, Chlorite, Bromide |
| Miscellaneous Analytes | Residual Free Chlorine, Turbidity, Total cyanide, Sulfate, pH, Alkalinity, Sodium, Total Dissolved Solids, Calcium Hardness, Ethylene thiourea, Dioxin, Asbestos, TOC |

The reporting forms for the WS samples are virtually identical to those for the WP samples.

Interpretation of the WS and WP results when the programs were initiated were very straight forward. The analyst was to prepare a single dilution of the PE sample ampule contents to a specified volume, then analyze the sample, possibly in duplicate along with the regular sample load of the laboratory. There were to be no special procedures or measures taken on the sample that were different from what was routinely done with any other sample in the lab. When performed in this fashion, a statistical distribution of results can be assumed for all the tests within a PE sample study, and a good performance by the laboratory would be to get at least 80 to 85% of the individual analytes in the study correct. However, due to the emphasis that has been placed on acceptable laboratory PE results by clients and state and federal laboratory certification programs, the manner in which these samples are handled in the laboratory has been changed. What actually happens with them is that the laboratory technicians are alerted and ready well in advance of the arrival of the PE samples. The most capable technicians are assigned to spend a substantial amount of time analyzing and re-analyzing the samples. Techniques, such as direct injection of the concentrate or a dilution into the analytical instrument, preparation and analysis of a variety of dilutions, matrix spikes on the samples, microextractions, use of multiple methods, and other techniques proposed by the analysts, are employed to insure that an acceptable result is generated. Many laboratories will share their results with other laboratories to help insure that the results are comparable. Some laboratories have been known to sub-contract analysis of the PE samples to other labs. In all, the PE samples are treated as anything but what a typical sample receives. The consequence of these actions is that the evaluation is not of the average performance of the laboratory but of the best answer that the lab can possibly generate. Major dislocations in the practice of the analysis of the samples from the original intents are obvious from the historical trends in scores and the distribution of scores for any of the recent tests[180]. It should not be surprising that the passing score for a good laboratory is now better than 95% of the analyte results being correct, with 100% correct being common.

Holders of Federal- or State- issued NPDES permits are required to participate annually in the analysis of DMR QA Study samples. Facilities permitted by cities or other POTWs do not receive DMR PE samples nor do they submit monthly reports on EPA Form 3320. The permit holder forwards to the EPA QA Study Coordinator the name and EPA identification number of the laboratory that normally does the permitees testing. It is an expected courtesy for the laboratory to provide the permit holder the QA Study results at no cost for the lab's regular clients. There is now only one concentration level for each target analyte in the DMR QA study and the ampules are identical to those used in the WP Study. In addition to the chemical target analytes, the DMRs add acute and/or chronic toxicity testing samples. Organisms calibrated against the samples include fathead minnow, *Ceriodaphnia, Mysidopsis bahia, Menidia beryllina*, sheepshead minnow, *Daphnia magna, Daphnia pulex*, and rainbow trout. Figure 1-40 is an example of the reporting form.

---

[180]  Burton, A.G., and D.E. Lawver, 1995. Evaluating Lab Performance. *Environmental Lab*, February, 1995. pp. 28-33.

**Table 1-60. DMR QA Study 16 (1996) Chemical Analytes**

| Ampule(s) | Analytes |
|---|---|
| Trace Metals | Aluminum, Arsenic, Beryllium, Cadmium, Cobalt, Chromium, Copper, Iron, Mercury, Manganese, Nickel, Lead, Selenium, Vanadium, Zinc |
| Minerals | pH |
| Nutrients | Ammonia, Nitrate, Orthophosphate, Kjeldahl nitrogen, Total phosphorous |
| Demand | COD, 5 day BOD, TOC, 5 day carbonaceous BOD |
| Cyanide | Total cyanide |
| Residue | TSS |
| Phenolics | Total phenolics (4-AAP) |
| Oil & Grease | Oil & Grease |
| Chlorine | Total Residual Chlorine |

| Analyte Name | EPA Use | Analyte No. | Sample No. | USEPA Labcode | Voluntary Analyte | Method Code | < / > | Quantity | |
|---|---|---|---|---|---|---|---|---|---|
| | | | | **DMR-QA Study 16**<br>**CHEMISTRY DATA** | | | | | |
| | | | | **TRACE METALS** | | | | | |
| Aluminum | XC | 001 | 1 | | | | | | µg/L |
| Arsenic | XC | 002 | 1 | | | | | | µg/L |
| Beryllium | XC | 003 | 1 | | | | | | µg/L |
| Cadmium | XC | 004 | 1 | | | | | | µg/L |
| Chromium | XC | 006 | 1 | | | | | | µg/L |
| Cobalt | XC | 005 | 1 | | | | | | µg/L |
| Copper | XC | 007 | 1 | | | | | | µg/L |
| Iron | XC | 008 | 1 | | | | | | µg/L |
| Lead | XC | 012 | 1 | | | | | | µg/L |
| Manganese | XC | 010 | 1 | | | | | | µg/L |
| Mercury | XC | 009 | 1 | | | | | | µg/L |
| Nickel | XC | 011 | 1 | | | | | | µg/L |
| Selenium | XC | 013 | 1 | | | | | | µg/L |
| Vanadium | XC | 014 | 1 | | | | | | µg/L |
| Zinc | XC | 015 | 1 | | | | | | µg/L |

facsimile of EPA-422 (Cin) Rev. 3-96. Previous editions are obsolete. Page 3 of 4

**Figure 1-40. Example of the DMR QA Study 16 result reporting form.**

There are differences in how the WP/DMR and WS QA studies are scored. The WP/DMR results obtained from the EPA Regional labs and selected state labs are used to generate Warning Limits and Acceptance Limits for the results for each target analyte. The Warning Limits are ±2 standard deviations from the mean and represent the 95% confidence level while the Acceptance Limits are ±3 standard deviations from the mean and represent the 99% confidence level. The possible evaluations that the lab receives for each analyte are "Acceptable," "Check for error," or "Not acceptable."

The WS PE samples scoring is described in 40 CFR 141 and is wrapped into the drinking water laboratory certification programs administered for the most part by the states. The true value is based on the quantity of analyte weighed out to prepare the check sample. In cases where the mean of the results obtained by the EPA regional and selected state labs does not match-up with the calculated true value, such as happened with fluoride in WS037, the analyte is deleted from the affected study. The only two possibilities for results for individual analytes in WS studies are "Acceptable" or "Not acceptable."

**Table 1-61.  WS QA study acceptance criteria based on true value (40 CFR 141)**

| Analyte | Acceptance criteria |
|---|---|
| Antimony | ±30% |
| Barium | ±15% |
| Beryllium | ±15% |
| Cadmium | ±20% |
| Chromium | ±15% |
| Copper | ±10% |
| Lead | ±30% |
| Mercury | ±30% |
| Nickel | ±20% |
| Selenium | ±20% |
| Thallium | ±30% |
| Cyanide | ±25% |
| Fluoride | ±10% |
| Nitrate | ±10% |
| Nitrite | ±15% |
| Total Trihalomethanes | ±20% |
| Regulated VOC | ±20% if >10 ug/L<br>±40% if <10 ug/L |
| Alachlor | ±45% |
| Atrazine | ±45% |
| Carbofuran | ±45% |
| Chlordane | ±45% |
| 2,4-D | ±50% |
| Dalapon | 2 Std. Deviations[181] |

Continued on next page.

[181]  Two standard deviations based on the results of the reference laboratories used in the QA Study. The reference labs are the EPA Regional labs and selected Primacy State labs.

**Table 1-61. WS QA study acceptance criteria based on true value (40 CFR 141),**
*continued*

| Analyte | Acceptance criteria |
|---|---|
| Dibromochloropropane (DBCP) | ±40% |
| Dinoseb | 2 Std. Deviations |
| Diquat | 2 Std. Deviations |
| Endothall | 2 Std. Deviations |
| Endrin | ±30% |
| Ethylenedibromide (EDB) | ±40% |
| Glyphosate | 2 Std. Deviations |
| Heptachlor | ±45% |
| Heptachlor epoxide | ±45% |
| Lindane | ±45% |
| Methoxychlor | ±45% |
| Oxamyl | 2 Std. Deviations |
| Pentachlorophenol | ±50% |
| Picloram | 2 Std. Deviations |
| Simazine | 2 Std. Deviations |
| Toxaphene | ±45% |
| 2,4,5-TP (Silvex) | ±50% |
| Hexachlorobenzene | 2 Std. Deviations |
| Hexachlorocyclopentadiene | 2 Std. Deviations |
| Benzo(a)pyrene | 2 Std. Deviations |
| PCB (as DCB) | 0-200% |
| Di(2-ethylhexyl)adipate | 2 Std. Deviations |
| Di(2-ethylhexyl)phthalate | 2 Std. Deviations |

During 1996, EPA made the decision that it could no longer bear the costs associated with preparation, administration and evaluation of the WP/DMR and WS PE samples. Instead the laboratory community would pay for the programs. A series of public meetings were held to address questions concerning the future of the programs. As of the time of this writing the plans have not been finalized.

## L. Evaluation of Laboratory Data

A review of performance evaluation (PE) sample results and the laboratory's quality assurance program are measures that should be performed prior to any contracted analysis with the laboratory. Although these reviews may lead to expectations that the candidate lab is competent to generate both analytically valid and legally defensible data, the reviews themselves give no indication as to the quality of the data that are reported on the specific samples. Evaluation of chemical laboratory data is the subject of a recent book[182]. Evaluation of radiological data has been the subject of recent articles[183] and

---

[182] Berger, W., H. McCarty and R.-K. Smith, 1996. *Environmental Laboratory Data Evaluation*, Genium Publishing, Schenectady, NY.
[183] Grega, K.K., and R.J. Vitale, 1995. "Validating Radiological Data." *Environmental Lab.* November, 1995. 7(7). pp. 14-18.

ANSI/ANS is preparing a guidance document[184]. In general, laboratory data are evaluated by comparison of the quality control results against data quality objectives that may be generic to the particular lab or they may be project specific. It must be emphatically stated as a basic premise that without quality control data there can be no confidence in analytical results. There are many instances in the literature of environmental research where completely unwarranted hypotheses and conclusions have been proposed that are based on laboratory data that are highly suspect due to laboratory contamination or other artifacts of analysis[185]. It is also very rare that researchers will publish retractions of their work when they do find out that the data are spurious.

Within the framework of the environmental industry, laboratory data must reflect correct identification and quantitation of target pollutants present in the sample while at the same time being obtained in compliance with the dictates of an approved method of analysis. To evaluate data, it is necessary for the reviewer to be familiar with both the project data needs and the referenced analytical methods.

---

[184] Rucker, T.L., S.R. Salaymen, J. Griggs, C.K. Liu, D.E. McCurdy, A. Rosencrance, D.E. Vance, R. Wells, and R.W. Holloway. 1996. "ANSI/ANS Standard for Radioanalytical Data Validation. In *Proceedings of the Twelth Annual Waste Testing and Quality Assurance Symposium*, EPA/ACS, Washington Hilton & Towers, Washington, D.C. 23-26 July, 1996. pg 88.

[185] Wallace, J.C., I. Basu, and R.A. Hites, 1996. "Sampling and Analysis Artifacts Caused by Elevated Indoor Air Polychlorinated Biphenyl Concentrations". *Environ. Sci. Technol.* 30(9). pp. 2730-2734.

# Physical, Biological and General Chemical Parameters

## I. PHYSICAL PARAMETERS
### A. Solids (SM$_{18}$ 2540, Reference 39[*]; EPA 160, Reference 20[*])

Solids (also called residues) are an important characterization of drinking and waste-water, and one or another of the tests are normally required in all DMRs of NPDES permits. Conceptually simple tests, in practice the determinations can be tedious when attempting to dry the solid to a constant weight, the biggest problem stemming from bound water. Various classes of bound water are associated with solids, the difficulty in removing them decreases as one goes down the list:

- Chemically combined water such as in calcium hydroxide
- Water of crystallization, water occupying fixed positions in the crystal structure
- Water of hydration, water hydrogen bonded onto the crystal structure
- Occluded water, droplets of water encased by a solid coating
- Absorbed water, water in the body of the solid, also called pore water
- Adsorbed water, water on the surface of the solid

Solids are divided into classes with the class defined by how the test is performed. The general classes are total solids (TS), total suspended solids (TSS), total dissolved solids (TDS), total volatile solids (TVS), total volatile dissolved solids (TVDS), total volatile suspended solids (TVSS), settleable solids, and ash (fixed solids). It might be expected that total solids should equal total suspended solids plus total dissolved solids, TS = TSS + TDS, however this seldom works out in practice as the TS and TSS values are obtained from a 104 °C drying and the TDS at 180 °C. The volatile fractions are determined by the difference between the dried fraction and the ashed fraction and are often held to represent the organic part of the solid. However, loss of $CO_2$ from carbonates and bicarbonates and loss of volatile inorganic salts can give very misleading results. Other derivative measures, such as sludge volume index (SVI), are calculated from these fractions. The MDL of the analysis is dependent upon not only the volume or mass of the sample tested but also the minimum residual mass of the solid required. For example TS requires at least 2.5 mg residue, which, based on a 100 mL sample, gives a MDL of 25 mg/L. The MDL can be lowered by evaporating successive 100 mL portions in the same dish; however; the principle of diminishing returns quickly applies.

**TS (SM$_{18}$ 2540 B, EPA 160.3)** - A weighed portion is poured into a tared crucible and dried to a constant weight at 104 ± 1 °C. A minimum of 2.5 mg residue is required.

---

[*] This and other references cited in titles refer to the reference number found in Appendix D of this book.

**Settleable solids (SM$_{18}$ 2540 F, EPA 160.5)** - A known volume, generally a liter, is allowed to sit in a graduated cone (Imhoff cone) for an hour. The settleable solids are read off in mL at the bottom of the cone.

**TSS (SM$_{18}$ 2540 D, EPA 160.2)** - Non-filterable (suspended) solids are determined by filtering a known volume through a tared glass fiber filter in a vacuum filtration apparatus, then drying the filter to a constant weight at $104 \pm 1$ °C. Recent WP series PE samples have included floating solids as part of the TSS check sample. Great care had to be taken to get the floating particles onto the glass fiber filter. A minimum of 2.5 mg residue is required for a detection of TSS.

**TDS (SM$_{18}$ 2540 C, EPA 160.1)** - Filterable (dissolved) solids are determined by evaporating a known volume of the filtrate from the TSS test in a tared crucible and drying at $180 \pm 2$ °C to a constant weight. A minimum of 2.5 mg residue is required. TDS detection limits are particularly sensitive to the 2.5 mg minimum residue because in many cases it is impossible to filter more than about 25 mL of water through the glass fiber filter. This results in MDLs of 100 mg/L and even higher in some cases.

**Ash (SM$_{18}$ 2540 E, EPA 160.4)** - Ignite TS residue at $550 \pm 50$ °C in a muffle furnace.

**Volatile solids (SM$_{18}$ 2540 E, EPA 160.4)** - This is the difference between the dried solids and the same sample further ignited at $550 \pm 50$ °C. Thus TVS = TS - ash. TVSS = TSS - TSS$_{ash}$. TVDS = TDS - TDS$_{ash}$.

**SVI (SM$_{18}$ 2710 D)** - A calculation that divides the result of the settleable solids (measured after 30 minutes) value by TSS. The units are mL/g.

Soils and dirts often need to be classified. Aside from the chemical composition, the size distribution of the soil particles affects the physical behavior. Sieving is a convenient method of characterization. A well-dried sample of the soil is shaken through a graded series of sieves, and the mass retained on each sieve is used to calculate the size distribution. Standard sieve sizes are listed in Table 2-1.

**Table 2-1.   Standard sieve sizes**

| Sieve No. | Tyler Mesh No. | Millimeters | Inches |
|-----------|----------------|-------------|--------|
| 4 | 4 | 4.7 | 0.185 |
| 6 | 6 | 3.33 | 0.131 |
| 8 | 8 | 2.36 | 0.093 |
| 10 | 9 | 2.0 | 0.078 |
| 13 | 10 | 1.65 | 0.065 |
| 16 | 14 | 1.17 | 0.046 |
| 20 | 20 | 0.833 | 0.033 |
| 30 | 28 | 0.589 | 0.023 |
| 40 | 35 | 0.417 | 0.016 |
| 50 | 48 | 0.295 | 0.012 |
| 60 | 60 | 0.25 | 0.01 |
| 70 | 65 | 0.208 | 0.008 |
| 80 | 70 | 0.177 | 0.007 |
| 100 | 100 | 0.149 | 0.006 |

Continued on next page.

**Table 2-1. Standard sieve sizes,** *continued*

| Sieve No. | Tyler Mesh No. | Millimeters | Inches |
|-----------|----------------|-------------|--------|
| 130 | 150 | 0.104 | 0.004 |
| 140 | 170 | 0.088 | 0.0035 |
| 200 | 200 | 0.074 | 0.0029 |
| 400 | 400 | 0.038 | 0.0015 |

The USDA standard size classifications of soils are: Gravel >2mm, sand particles 2-0.074 mm, silt 0.074-0.002 mm and, clay <0.002 mm[1]. The silts and clays are combined into "fines" in the ASTM classification. Other characteristics of soils include porosity, penetrability, compressibility, gas flux and diffusivity, and a large variety of water and hydraulic parameters[2].

Particle size is a parameter that relates to not only part of the characterization of soil samples, but is a necessary consideration in practical aspects of dealing with samples in the lab. For example, filtration is a common means of separating solids from liquids, and filter paper is frequently used. Knowing what will pass through the filter paper and what will be retained, ignoring any adsorption phenomena, is helpful in making the correct choice of paper size. The chart in Figure 2-1 relates size measurements to some items and concepts for which people have an inate feeling of "big" and "small."

[1]  Winegardner, D.L. *Introduction to Soils for Environmental Professionals.* 1996. CRC Press, Boca Raton, FL.
[2]  Klute, A. *Methods of Soil Analysis, Part 1 Physical and Mineralogical Methods*, 2nd Edition. 1986. ASA and SSSA, Madison, WI.

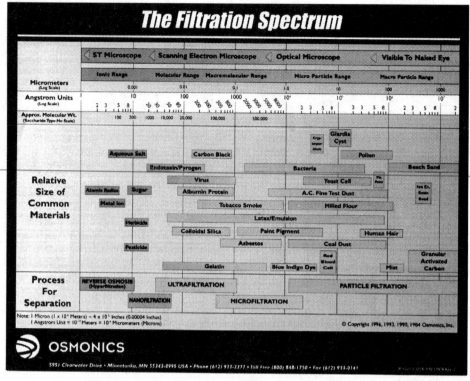

Provided Courtesy of Osmonics, Minnetonka, Minnesota USA

**Figure 2-1 Size of common objects.**

# B. Moisture

The moisture content of samples is of interest when the results are to be reported on a dry weight basis. This determination involves weighing a portion of the sample in a tared crucible, drying to a constant weight at $104 \pm 1$ °C and then calculating the percent moisture by:

$$\text{percent moisture} = 100 - \left( \frac{\text{dry weight}}{\text{wet weight}} \times 100 \right)$$

$$\text{fraction solids} = \frac{\text{dry weight}}{\text{wet weight}}$$

$$\text{percent solids} = \frac{\text{dry weight}}{\text{wet weight}} \times 100$$

The reporting of results on a dry weight basis is performed by taking the test result and dividing by the fraction of solids.

$$\text{dry weight basis} = \frac{\text{wet result}}{\text{fraction solids}}$$

Some test methods, for example explosives residues in soils (Method 8330), dry the sample in the open air overnight prior to measuring out a portion for analysis. The final weight of the dried sample that is obtained depends on the local relative humidity. Samples dried in the arid Rocky Mountain regions will lose more water than the same samples dried in the very humid Southeast part of the United States. This sometimes will affect the comparability of the results from one laboratory to the next, and occasionally between duplicate determinations in the same laboratory. Drier samples result in higher target analyte values. Up to a two-fold difference in sample results have been noted that are attributable to this effect.

Often received in the laboratory are non-aqueous samples that require determination of water content. Gross amounts of water (greater than 1%) may be determined by weighing a portion of the sample, then doing azeotropic distillation with toluene in a Dean-Starke trap.

Amounts of water less than 1% down to the ppm level can be determined by Karl Fisher titration[3]. There are two versions of KF titration; the protic and the aprotic. Both are based upon the oxidation of sulfur dioxide to sulfate ion coupled with the reduction of iodine to iodide, a process that requires water to supply the oxygen atom for the sulfate product.

In the protic titration, the base most commonly used is pyridine, however any tri-substituted nitrogen base can be substituted. One of the oxygen atoms on the final sulfate product comes from the alcohol solvent. The commercially available stench-free titrant solutions use bases other than pyridine, but the chemistry is the same.

| | |
|---|---|
| Solvolysis | $2ROH + SO_2 \longrightarrow RSO_3^- \ ROH_2^+$ |
| Buffer | $Base + RSO_3^- \ ROH_2^+ \longrightarrow BaseH^+RSO_3^- + ROH$ |
| 1:1 Redox titration | $H_2O + I_2 + BaseH^+RSO_3^- + 2\ Base \longrightarrow$ |
| | $BaseH^+RSO_4^- + 2BaseHI$ |

The aprotic procedure has fewer reagents, but is a bit more technically involved and has a 2:1 titration. Both oxygen atoms on the sulfate arise from water.

| | |
|---|---|
| 2:1 Redox titration | $2H_2O + SO_2 + I_2 \longrightarrow H_2SO_4 + 2HI$ |

Normal interferences include $NH_3$ , RSH, $Tl^+$, $Sn^{2+}$, $In^+$, $S_2O_2^{2-}$ (thiosulfite anion), ascorbic acid, $HONH_2$ (hydroxylamine), all of which can reduce $I_2$. Other interferences include hydroxy and aminophenols and naphthols that are oxidized to quinoid structures.

Detection is performed by a number of techniques. The oldest is volumetric titration, which relies on the visual presence of excess $I_2$ for determination of the endpoint. Potentiometric detection is performed with two electrodes that sense the potential difference in $2e^- + I_2 \longleftrightarrow 2I^-$. With $H_2O$ present there is no $I_2$, and a large potential difference exists. Without $H_2O$ present the $I_2$ builds in concentration, and the potential difference drops to zero, a deadstop titration. Amperometric detection is possible as

---

3    MacLeod, S.K. "Moisture Determination Using Karl Fisher Titrations." *Analytical Chemistry.* 1991. 63(10). pp. 557A-566A; Margolis, S.M., "Amperometric Measurement of Moisture in Transformer Oil Using Karl Fisher Reagents." *Anal. Chem*, 1995. 67(23). pp. 4239-4246; Cedergren, A., "Comparison Between Bipotentiometric and True Potentiometric End-point Detection using Rapidly Reacting Karl Fischer Reagents." *Anal. Chem.* 1996. 68(20). pp. 3679-3681; Cedergren, A., "Coulometric Study of Reaction Rates of Water in Pyridine- and Imidazole-Buffered Methanolic Karl Fischer Reagents Containing Chloroform." *Anal. Chem.* 68(20). pp. 3682-3687.

---

there is no current flow without excess $I_2$ present and a "kickoff" endpoint current flow when $I_2$ becomes present.

The method is calibrated through titration of a known amount of sodium tartrate dihydrate, or better (if you happen to work in a pharmaceutical laboratory), Lincomycin HCl monohydrate. The common practice of adding water to anhydrous methanol with a microsyringe is quite imprecise.

## C. Temperature (SM$_{18}$ 2550; Reference 39)

Temperature is a parameter that must be measured immediately after sampling. The thermometer must be either a certified thermometer or calibrated annually against an NIST traceable thermometer. It is suggested that glass thermometers be contained in metal thermometer holders. Glass thermometers come in two types: red fluid filled and silver mercury filled. The red fluids vary from alcohol to glycol mixtures depending on the temperature range of the thermometer. There is not much hazard associated with breaking these thermometers. However, the mercury-filled thermometers, which are generally regarded as more accurate, release dangerous mercury fumes on breaking. This presents a real problem with high background contamination if the lab is performing mercury analysis and the mercury-filled thermometer breaks indoors. There are also digital thermometers that operate on the thermocouple principle. These need to be calibrated just like the glass thermometers.

Temperature is a common monitoring parameter in the laboratory. Samples must be stored at the proper temperature, most often 4 °C. Waterbaths and ovens must be at the proper temperature for the performance of the various tests to be in compliance with the regulatory methods. These include mercury digestions, solids determinations, fecal coliform and BOD incubations, etc. The thermometers that monitor these temperatures must either be certified or calibrated against a certified NIST traceable thermometer at least annually. Temperature monitoring logs are kept for each instrument, which must be maintained at a set temperature. Figure 2-2 is an example of such a log.

## TEMPERATURE MONITORING LOG

Device Monitored:                                    Set-point/acceptance range:

Thermometer certificate or calibration number:

| Date | AM reading | Initials/Time | PM reading | Initials/Time | Notes |
|------|-----------|---------------|------------|---------------|-------|
|      |           |               |            |               |       |
|      |           |               |            |               |       |
|      |           |               |            |               |       |
|      |           |               |            |               |       |
|      |           |               |            |               |       |
|      |           |               |            |               |       |
|      |           |               |            |               |       |
|      |           |               |            |               |       |
|      |           |               |            |               |       |
|      |           |               |            |               |       |

**Figure 2-2. Temperature monitoring log.**

## D. Turbidity (Nephelometry) (SM₁₈ 2130, Reference 39; EPA 180.1, Reference 20)

Turbidity is defined as suspended particulate matter in water. Acidic water is normally crystal clear, while basic/neutral water is turbid. The reason is that the oxides, hydroxides and carbonates of heavy metal ions found in basic conditions are insoluble substances, while the nitrates, chlorides and sulfates of the same metal ions present under acidic conditions are soluble. Further, acidic conditions are toxic to algae and other organisms, which can survive in very basic pH waters, creating turbidity.

Turbidity was originally measured with the Jackson candle turbidimeter. Test water is added to a tube until light from a standard candle at the bottom is extinguished. The minimum turbidity is 25 JTU (Jackson Turbidity Units).

More modern techniques use Nephelometers that measure scattered light at 90° to incident light with a photodetector. See Figure 2-2. The readings are in NTU's (Nephelometric Turbidity Units), which have no direct correlation with JTU's. Samples are quantitated *vs.* standards of freshly prepared polymer (hydrazine + hexamethylene-tetraamine, 1:10 w/w in water, 25 °C ± 3 °C, 24 hrs) or standard styrene divinylbenzene copolymer beads. The formazin is more repeatable. See Figure 2-3.

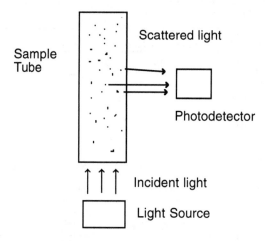

**Figure 2-3. Schematic of a nephelometer instrument for measuring turbidity.**

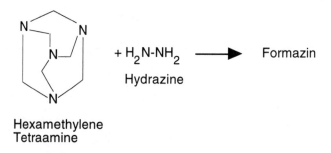

**Figure 2-4. Formazin polymer formation.**

# E. Conductivity (SM$_{18}$ 2510, Reference 39; EPA 120.1, Reference 20)

Conductivity is the inverse of resistance, which is the actual measured quantity in the lab. The units of measurement within the EPA complex are in umhos/cm. The international units of conductivity are in millisiemens (mS) per meter, and some conductivity meters read in uS/cm. 1.0 uS/cm is exactly equal to 1.0 umhos/cm. Freshly distilled water has a conductivity of 0.5 to 2.0 umhos/cm, increasing on storage to 2 to 4 umhos/cm due to dissolution of $CO_2$ and to a lesser degree $NH_3$. Potable water has values from 50 to 1500 umhos/cm, while wastewaters may range to 10,000 umhos/cm. Salt water exhibits a range of conductivity from 1000 to 100,000 umhos/cm. Conductivity is a measure of ions present in the water, their charge, mobility, valence and relative concentration. The mobility of the ion is related to the concept of ionic atmosphere; the number and orientation of the solvent molecules in the immediate vicinity of the ion. Some ions have very highly structured atmospheres, and the physical movement of the ion and the atmosphere is retarded through the rest of the solvent. The ions $H^+$ and $OH^-$, on the other hand, have very high conductances in water solution as compared to other solvents due to the ability of the water molecules to dissociate into the ions. Thus transference of a charge due to $H^+$ or $OH^-$ within water from one location to another does not require significant physical movement of the ion. Conductivity changes depend on the temperature of the sample. The temperature effect is complex with the exact nature of the ions in the sample affecting the magnitude of the temperature coefficient. These can range from 0.96 percent change/°C for a 5% sulfuric acid solution to 5.64 percent change/°C for a sugar syrup solution. Organic pollutants are generally not detected by conductivity measurements; however, a large organic content in the sample can severely depress the conductivity, conpared to pure water solutions of similar ion concentration.

Measurement of conductivity is performed in a cell where the electrodes are rigidly fixed a constant distance from each other. The ideal cell has two electrodes of 1 cm$^2$ surface area fixed 1 cm apart. This ideal cell has a cell constant of 1.0/cm. Cells with small, widely separated electrodes will have cell constants > 1.0/cm, while closely spaced large electrodes will have cell constants < 1.0/cm. Electrodes with cell constants >1.0 are used for measurement of large conductivity. Electrodes with cell constants <1.0 are used for measurement of samples with low conductivity values.

The cell constant was important in the early days of conductivity measurement, where the direct reading of inverse resistance from the meter had to be multiplied by the cell constant to obtain the specific conductance of the sample.

Conductance = Reading x Cell Constant.

The cell constant was obtained by measuring the inverse resistance of a standard solution of known conductance, then dividing the known conductance value by the measured value. Today, in most approved regulatory methods, the conductivity values of the sample are given as a direct readout of the meter, calibrated by the measurement of standards immediately prior to the analysis. The cell constant is actually the slope of the calibration line. Although regular determination of the cell constant can serve as a preventative maintenance evaluation of the condition of the electrode, the daily calculation and recording of the cell constant serves no practical purpose.

## II. BIOLOGICAL PARAMETERS
### A. Fecal coliform *Escherichia coli*

The bacterial quality of water and its effect on public health is one of the original driving forces behind government supervision of water supplies. In the later part of the 1800's, water-borne diseases such as typhoid resulted in annual mortalities of approximately 35 per 100,000 population, with epidemics running at much higher rates. By the 1960's when disinfection of water systems was widely practiced, the annual death rate for typhoid had dropped to less than 10 for the whole population of the US (around 200,000,000).

The identification of pathogenic bacteria is a tedious and expensive process. Instead of testing for a suite of specific disease-causing organisms, examination of the water for an indicator organism is used to screen the sample. The coliform bacteria are characterized by being anaerobic and aerobic, gram negative, non-spore forming, rod shaped bacteria that ferment lactose within 48 hrs at 35 °C, producing carbon dioxide and acid (see Figure 2-5). The fecal coliforms exist in nature as part of the normal flora in the intestines of mammals and thus serve as an indicator that fecal contamination of the water has occured. Normally what is intended when fecal coliform is mentioned is *Escherichia coli.*, however other coliform genera that live in mammalian intestinal tracts include *Enterobacter, Klebsiella, Citrobacter* as well as the *Escherichia*. The coliforms are more hardy than almost all disease-causing bacteria, thus the absence of coliforms is a good indication of the lack of other pathogenic bacteria. The presence of coliforms indicates the possibility of other pathogens being present, but it is not diagnostic. When specific identification of *Escherichia coli* is needed there is a specific set of biochemical tests that can be performed for confirmation ($SM_{18}$ 9225). Commercially available kits are commonly used for these identifications, for example Enterotube® II from Becton Dickinson; however, the logic of spending a lot of time to absolutely confirm the identity of a specific indicator organism is somewhat fuzzy when the objective is to reduce the presence of pathogenic organisms.

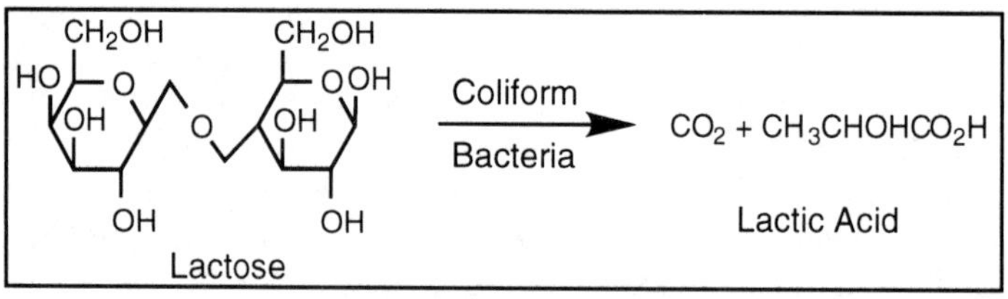

**Figure 2-5.   Fermentation of lactose by coliforms.**

## B.  MPN tube tests ($SM_{18}$ 9221, Reference 39)

The presumptive test consists of 5 repetitions of incubations in sterilized test tubes containing an inverted vial and a set volume (1.0 or 10.0 mL) of wastewater with 10.0 mL lauryl tryptose broth, which contains lactose. At least three decade (1:10 and 1:100) dilutions and repetitions are prepared. The minimum number of tubes used per test is 15. The inoculate is incubated at 35 °C ± 0.5 °C for 24 ± 2 hrs and examined for gas production, then incubated for a total of 48 ± 3 hrs and examined. Each positive tube (gas producing) is subjected to the confirmed test by transfer to a tube containing Brilliant Green Bile broth and incubated at 35 °C ± 0.5 °C for 24 ± 2 hrs and examined for gas production, then incubated for a total of 48 ± 3 hrs and examined. Positives are confirmed for fecal coliform by transfer to EC nutrient broth for $24 \pm 2$ hrs and $48 \pm 3$ hrs at $44.5\ ^\circ C \pm 0.2\ ^\circ C$. Positives are indicated by production of gas in an inverted vial. Most Probable Number of present organisms is determined from tables and depends on how many repetitions of which dilutions are confirmed positive. The completed test requires streaking a Eosin methylene blue agar plate with broth from a positive Brilliant Green Bile tube, incubation at $35\ ^\circ C \pm 0.5\ ^\circ C$ for $24 \pm 2$ hrs, then transfer of a typical colony (nucleated with or without a metallic sheen) to a lauryl tryptose fermentation tube and incubation for up to $48 \pm 3$ hrs and transfer of a typical colony to either a nutrient or plate count agar slant for up to $48 \pm 3$ hrs at $35\ ^\circ C \pm 0.5\ ^\circ C$. A positive completed test is indicated by gas production and gram negative rods.

**Table 2-2.** **Formulations of common culture media for Coliforms**

| Lauryl Tryptose Broth | |
|---|---|
| Tryptose or Trypicase Peptone | 20 g |
| Lactose | 5.0 g |
| $K_2HPO_4$ | 2.75 g |
| $KH_2PO_4$ | 2.75 g |
| NaCl | 5.0 g |
| Sodium lauryl sulfate | 0.1 g |
| Preparation | 35.6 g to 1 L |

| Eosin Methylene Blue agar | |
|---|---|
| Peptone | 10.0 g |
| Lactose | 10.0 g |
| $K_2HPO_4$ | 2.0 g |
| Agar | 15.0 g |
| Eosin Y | 0.4 g |
| Methylene Blue | 0.065 g |
| Preparation | 37.5 g to 1 L |

| Plate Count Agar | |
|---|---|
| Tryptone or Trypticase Peptone | 5.0 g |
| Yeast Extract | 2.5 g |
| Dextrose | 1.0 g |
| Agar | 15.0 g |
| Preparation | 23.5 g to 1 L |

| Brilliant Green Bile | |
|---|---|
| Peptone | 10.0 g |
| Lactose | 10.0 g |
| Oxgall or bile | 20.0 g |
| Brilliant green | 0.33 g |
| Preparation | 40 g to 1 L |

| EC Nutrient Broth | |
|---|---|
| Tryptose or Trypticase Peptone | 20.0 g |
| Lactose | 5.0 g |
| Bile Salts #3 or Bile Salts mixture | 1.5 g |
| $K_2HPO_4$ | 4.0 g |
| $KH_2PO_4$ | 1.5 g |
| NaCl | 5.0 g |
| Preparation | 37 g to 1 L |

| Nutrient agar | |
|---|---|
| Peptone | 5.0 g |
| Beef extract | 3.0 g |
| Agar | 15.0 g |
| Preparation | 23 g to 1 L |

For drinking water analysis, 10 tubes of double strength broth with 10.0 mL sample in each are tested. Positives are subjected to confirmation as above. A special MPN table for drinking water is used, however the MPN number can be calculated using the following:

$$\text{MPN/100 mL} = \frac{\text{no. of positive tubes x 100}}{\sqrt{\text{mL sample in neg. tubes x mL sample in all tubes}}}$$

**Table 2-3. MPN values for drinking water**

| Number of positive tubes | MPN/100 mL | 95% confidence limits |
|:---:|:---:|:---:|
| 0 | <1.1 | 0-3.0 |
| 1 | 1.1 | 0.03-5.9 |
| 2 | 2.2 | 0.26-8.1 |
| 3 | 3.6 | 0.69-10.6 |
| 4 | 5.1 | 1.3-13.4 |
| 5 | 6.9 | 2.1-16.8 |
| 6 | 9.2 | 3.1-21.1 |
| 7 | 12.0 | 4.3-27.1 |
| 8 | 16.1 | 5.9-36.8 |
| 9 | 23.0 | 8.1-59.5 |
| 10 | >23.0 | 13.5-infinite |

**Table 2-4. MPN/100 mL for five tube, three dilution series (10, 1.0, 0.1 mL)[4]**

| Positives | MPN/100 mL | 95% limits |
|:---:|:---:|:---:|
| 0-0-0 | <2 | - |
| 0-0-1 | 2 | <0.5-7 |
| 0-1-0 | 2 | <0.5-7 |
| 0-2-0 | 4 | <0.5--11 |
| 1-0-0 | 2 | <0.5-7 |
| 1-0-1 | 4 | <0.5-11 |
| 1-1-0 | 4 | <0.5-11 |
| 1-1-1 | 6 | <0.5-15 |
| 1-2-0 | 6 | <0.5-15 |
| 2-0-0 | 4 | <0.5-13 |
| 2-0-1 | 7 | 1-17 |
| 2-1-0 | 7 | 1-17 |
| 2-1-1 | 9 | 2-21 |
| 2-2-0 | 9 | 2-21 |
| 2-3-0 | 12 | 3-28 |
| 3-0-0 | 8 | 1-19 |
| 3-0-1 | 11 | 2-25 |
| 3-1-0 | 11 | 2-25 |
| 3-1-1 | 14 | 4-34 |
| 3-2-0 | 14 | 4-34 |
| 3-2-1 | 17 | 5-46 |
| 4-0-0 | 13 | 3-31 |

Continued on next page.

---

[4] Table II-C-4, Microbiological Methods for Monitoring the Environment. EPA-600/8-78-017. December, 1978.

**Table 2-4.  MPN/100 mL for five tube, three dilution series (10, 1.0, 0.1 mL)[5],**
*continued*

| Positives | MPN/100 mL | 95% limits |
|---|---|---|
| 4-0-1 | 17 | 5-46 |
| 4-1-0 | 17 | 5-46 |
| 4-1-1 | 21 | 7-63 |
| 4-1-2 | 26 | 9-78 |
| 4-2-0 | 22 | 7-67 |
| 4-2-1 | 26 | 9-78 |
| 4-3-0 | 27 | 9-80 |
| 4-3-1 | 33 | 11-93 |
| 4-4-0 | 34 | 12-93 |
| 5-0-0 | 23 | 7-70 |
| 5-0-1 | 30 | 11-89 |
| 5-0-2 | 40 | 15-110 |
| 5-1-0 | 30 | 11-93 |
| 5-1-1 | 50 | 16-120 |
| 5-1-2 | 60 | 21-150 |
| 5-2-0 | 50 | 17-130 |
| 5-2-1 | 70 | 23-170 |
| 5-2-2 | 90 | 28-220 |
| 5-3-0 | 80 | 25-190 |
| 5-3-1 | 110 | 31-250 |
| 5-3-2 | 140 | 37-340 |
| 5-3-3 | 170 | 44-500 |
| 5-4-0 | 130 | 35-300 |
| 5-4-1 | 170 | 43-490 |
| 5-4-2 | 220 | 57-700 |
| 5-4-3 | 280 | 90-850 |
| 5-4-4 | 350 | 120-1000 |
| 5-5-0 | 240 | 68-750 |
| 5-5-2 | 500 | 180-1400 |
| 5-5-4 | 1600 | 640-5800 |

## C.  Membrane filter test (SM$_{18}$ 9222, Reference 39)

Sample volumes (100 mL for drinking water, less amounts are filtered for more contaminated wastewater samples) are filtered through a 0.45 um pore membrane with drawn grids.  The membranes are incubated in a water bath on an absorbent pad soaked with M-FC (44.5 °C ± 0.2 °C for 24 ± 2 hrs and 48 ± 3 hrs) or M-Endo broth (35 °C ± 0.5 °C for 24 ± 2 hrs and 48 ± 3 hrs).  Positive FC colonies are blue in color with a distinct metallic sheen on the M-FC nutrient.  Positive coliform colonies are pink to dark red with a metallic sheen on the M-Endo nutrient.  At least five presumptive coliform

[5]  Table II-C-4, Microbiological Methods for Monitoring the Environment. EPA-600/8-78-017. December, 1978.

colonies must be confirmed by transfer to lauryl tryptose broth for incubation and examination for gas production.

**Table 2-5.  Media formulations for Fecal Coliforms**

| M-FC | |
|---|---|
| Tryptose or Biosate Peptone | 10.0 g |
| Proteose Peptone #3 or Polypeptone | 5.0 g |
| Yeast Extract | 3.0 g |
| NaCl | 5.0 g |
| Lactose | 12.5 g |
| Bile Salts #3 or Bile Salts mixture | 1.5 g |
| Aniline Blue | 0.1 g |
| Preparation | 37 g to 1L |

| M-Endo | |
|---|---|
| Tryptose or Polypeptone | 10.0 g |
| Thiopeptone or Thiotone | 5.0 g |
| Casitone or Trypticase | 5.0 g |
| Yeast Extract | 1.5 g |
| Lactose | 12.5 g |
| NaCl | 5.0 g |
| $K_2HPO_4$ | 4.375 g |
| $KH_2PO_4$ | 1.375 g |
| Sodium Lauryl Sulfate | 0.050 g |
| Sodium desoxycholate | 0.1 g |
| Sodium Sulfite | 2.1 g |
| Basic Fuchsin | 1.05 g |
| Preparation | 48 g to 1L + 20 mL 95% ethanol |

## D.  Presence-absence (P-A) Coliform Test (SM$_{18}$ 9221 D, Reference 39)

This is a one-step screening test using lauryl tryptose broth with bromocresol purple added as an acid-base indicator and 100 mL sample.  Presence of coliform bacteria is suggested by a yellow color from the presence of acid in the broth after incubation.  The test must be confirmed if positive.

**Table 2-6.  Presence-absence media formulation**

| P-A broth | |
|---|---|
| Dehydrated lactose broth | 13.0 g |
| Dehydrated tryptose broth | 17.5 g |
| Bromocresol purple | 0.0085 g |
| Preparation | 21.5 g to 1 L |

## E.  Colilert™ Chromogenic Substrate Coliform Test (SM$_{18}$ 9223, Reference 39)

A patented, EPA approved (40 CFR part 141.21, *Federal Register*, Wednesday, 10 June, 1992, Vol. 57, No. 122, pp. 24744-24747) one step P-A or MPN test for fecal coliforms.  The sample is added to a dry mixture of *o*-Nitrophenyl-ß-D-galactopyranoside (ONPG), 4-Methylumbelliferyl-ß-D-glucuronide (MUG), either HEPES (4-[2-hydroxyethyl]-1-piperazineethanesulfonic acid) or phosphate buffer and essential nutrient salts, then incubated at 35-37 °C for 24 hrs.  A yellow color indicates formation of ONP from digestion of ONPG (presence of the enzyme ß-D-galactosidase) and a blue fluorescence under 366 nm UV light indicates formation of 4-methylumbelliferone from MUG (presence of enzyme ß-glucuronidase). These are the only sources of food for the bacteria in the medium, and fecal coliforms are the only bacteria capable of using both. For drinking water the test can be run on one 100 mL sample with results interpreted as in the P-A test, or on 10 tubes of 10 mL sample with results interpreted as in the MPN test. For wastewater the test is run in the same fashion as the MPN procedure.

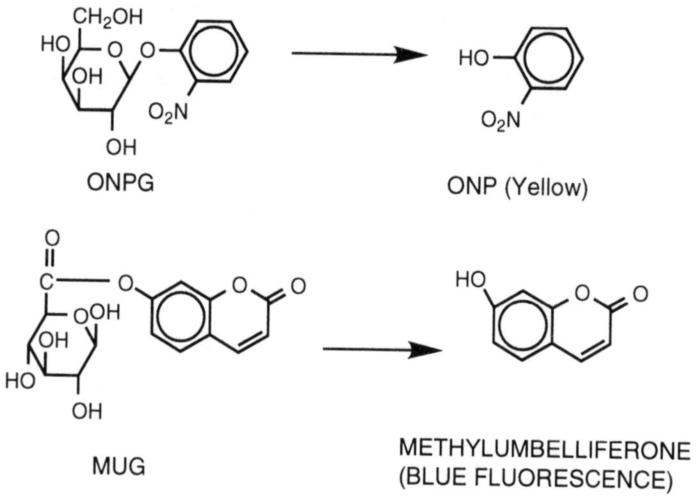

**Figure 2-6. Chemistry of the Colilert P-A test.**

Another approved version of this test is marketed as the Colisure™ test. It differs from Colilert by replacing the ONPG with chloro phenol red ß-galactopyranoside. Digestion of this material by bacteria containing ß-galactosidase is indicated by development of a red to magenta color from the original yellow. The presence of MUG in Colisure serves the same purpose as in Colilert.

## F. Toxicity testing (SM$_{18}$ 8010, Reference 39, EPA Methods 1001.0-1009.0)

These types of tests are completely different from most other EPA evaluation procedures in that they are not looking for a specific target analyte. Instead they measure the overall effects of the wastewater on living creatures. Toxic effects that are found are not only lethal effects (organism dies) but also reproductive- and growth-related. The effects may be irreversible or reversible, that is, permanent or the organism may recover. If a toxic effect is found, then there are established procedures to isolate and identify the toxicant[6]. The use of toxicity testing for required NPDES monitoring has been increasing and will continue to do so. The following are a number of terms used in toxicity testing.

---

[6] *Methods for Aquatic Toxicity Identification Evaluations.* Phase I EPA/600/6-91/003, Phase II EPA/600/3-88/035, Phase III EPA/600/3-88/036; and *Characterization of Chronically Toxic Effluents.* Phase I EPA/600/6-91/005F.

- Toxicant (poison) - A substance that is harmful to living organisms due to detrimental effects on tissue, organs, or biological processes.

- Toxicology - The study of poisons.

- DoseResponse curves - Dose is the amount of toxicant (mg/kg of body weight, or dilution factor) the organism is challenged with response is the biological effect on organism, most commonly death. The curves are a plot of % response vs. log dose. One standard deviation on the curve runs from $LD_{16}$ to $LD_{84}$. See Figure 2-6 for a general example.

- $LD_5$ - Dose at which 5% of the test population perishes, individuals in this 5% are called hypersensitive.

- $LD_{50}$ - Dose at which 50% of the test population dies.

- $LD_{95}$ - Dose at which 95% of the test population has died. Individuals surviving this dose are termed hyposensitive, probably have some genetic difference from the rest of the population that allows them to survive and are the source of resistance mechanisms.

- Lethal concentration (LC) - Normally the toxicant concentration that kills 50% of the test organisms after a set observation time, expressed as 48-h $LC_{50}$, for example.

- Acute toxicity - Short term lethal effects, generally 4 days or less for fish and 2 days for smaller organisms.

- Chronic toxicity - Longer term lethal or reproductive effects than acute toxicity. The response to a particular dose of a toxicant will vary from species to species. Doses for chronic effects may be found at as little as $10^{-6}$ times the dose that results in acute effects.

- Immunity - Ability of a single organism to adjust metabolism to combat future exposures to a toxicant. Generally involves manufacture of antibodies that neutralize bacteria or viruses.

- Resistance - Shifting of the gene frequency in a population through attrition of susceptible individuals to leave only resistant organisms. The gene for resistance exists within the population prior to any exposure to the toxicant.

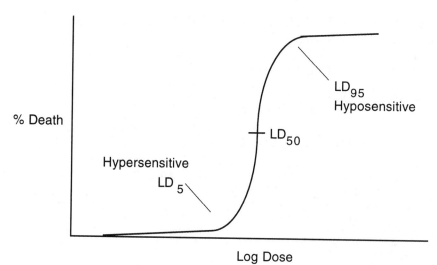

**Figure 2-7.   Generalized log dose-response curve.**

Common test subjects for toxicity testing are the microcrustaceans represented by *Dafnia* sp. water fleas (fresh) ($SM_{19}$ 8711).  These organisms are very sensitive to pollutants in water and have been used for over a century.  Another common group of test organisms are fish ($SM_{19}$ 8910) represented by *Pimephales promelas* fathead minnows, *Salmo gairdneri* rainbow trout, and *Cyprinodon variegatus* sheepshead minnows.

Certain chronic toxic effects are of particular concern when humans are exposed to toxicants.  These include:

- Mutagenesis - inheritable traits result from alteration of DNA; chemicals that cause mutations are known as mutagens.  Often the traits are considered birth defects or give rise to cancer.

- Carcinogenesis - uncontrolled replication and growth of the organism's own cells.  Most mutagens are also carcinogens.  Biological alkylating and arylating chemicals such as guanidine can cause cancer.  Most cancer-causing agents require metabolic activation and are thus classed as precarcinogens.  Dioxin (2,3,7,8-tetrachlorodibenzodioxin) is probably a precarcinogen.  Primary carcinogens require no activation.

- Teratogenesis - birth defects resulting from exposure to xenobiotics.  Mutations in germ cells may give rise to teratogenesis, however the most common cause is damage to embryonic or fetal cells.

Commonly used is the Ames Test for carcinogens: Mutant histidine requiring *Salmonella* bacteria are exposed to a mixture of homogenized liver tissue and the test chemical on an agar media that contains no histidine.  The liver tissue serves to test for precarcinogens, compounds that are metabolically altered in the body to an active mutagen.  If the test chemical is or becomes a mutagen, the bacteria mutate back to the ability to synthesize histidine and prosper, resulting in visible colonies on the agar surface.  A 90% correlation exists between the ability to synthesize histidine and the actual mutagenic ability of the test compound.

Several manuals are available from EPA that detail the test procedures for toxicity testing. These include the documents in Table 2-7.

**Table 2-7.   EPA toxicity testing procedural manuals**

| |
|---|
| *Short-term Methods for Estimating the Chronic Toxicity of Effluents and Receiving Water to Freshwater Organisms,* Third Edition. July, 1994. EPA-600-4-91-002. |
| *Short-term Methods for Estimating the Chronic Toxicity of Effluents and Receiving Water to Marine and Estuarine Organisms,* Second Edition. July, 1994. EPA-600-4-91-003. |
| *Methods for Assessing the Toxicity of Sediment-Associated Contaminants with Estuarine and Marine Amphipods.* June, 1994. EPA/600/R-94/025. |
| *Methods for Measuring the Toxicity and Bioaccumulation of Sediment-Associated Contaminants with Freshwater Invertebrates.* June, 1994. EPA/600/R-94/024. |
| *Manual for the Evaluation of Laboratories Performing Aquatic Toxicity Tests.* January, 1991. EPA/600/4-90/031. |
| *Methods for Measuring the Acute Toxicity of Effluents to Freshwater and Marine Organisms,* Fourth Edition. 1993. EPA/600/4-90/027F. |

## III.  CHEMICAL PARAMETERS

### A.  pH (SM$_{18}$ 4500-H⁺, Reference 39; EPA 150.1, Reference 20)

pH is defined as:  pH = - log [H⁺].  The scale in water ranges from 1 to 14, with 6 to 8 considered normal, or neutral.  A more correct definition uses the activity of the hydrogen ion ($a_H$), which is equal to the single ion activity coefficient of the hydrogen ion ($\gamma_H$) times the molality ($m_H = \dfrac{mol}{kg}$ ).

$$pH = - \log (a_H) \ = \ - \log (\gamma_H m_H)$$

pH is measured either by electrodes attached to a pH meter or by pH-indicating paper.

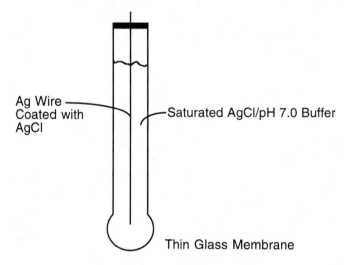

Ag Wire
Coated with
AgCl

Saturated AgCl/pH 7.0 Buffer

Thin Glass Membrane

**Figure 2-8.   Single pole pH electrode.**

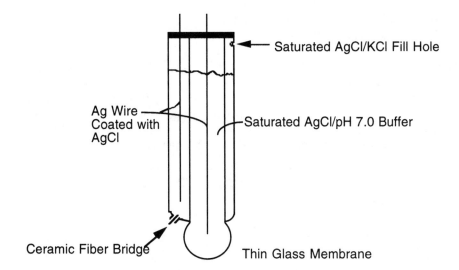

**Figure 2-9. Combination pH electrode.**

The best explanation for the operation of the thin glass membrane pH electrode is that the glass acts as a weak acid (GlassH). The existence of the pH 7.0 buffer inside the membrane maintains the inside of the membrane with a set number of anionic sites. When the outside of the membrane is placed in a solution at a different pH, the glass is either deprotonated or protonated relative to the inside of the glass. This sets up a potential across the membrane that is detected against the reference electrode and is proportional to the pH. The potential reading *vs* the reference electrode is sensitive to temperature, and the pH meter must be re-calibrated immediately before use.

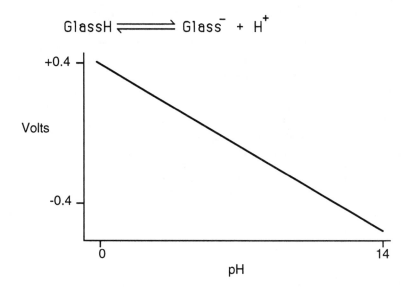

**Figure 2-10. pH plotted against potential for a pH electrode.**

There are three effects of temperature upon the measurement of pH using an electrode. The first is an intrinsic relationship between temperature and the ionization constant of water (see Figure 4-1 in Section 4). The pH value of a neutral solution changes with temperature as presented in Table 2-8. This interdependence of temperature and ionization is also seen in the variation of the true pH value of the buffer solutions used for the calibration of the pH meter. Most commercially available buffers will have on the side of the label a chart of temperature *vs* true pH value.

**Table 2-8. Temperature dependent pH variation of a neutral water solution**

| Temp°C | Neutral pH |
|--------|------------|
| 0 | 7.49 |
| 20 | 7.09 |
| 25 | 7.00 |
| 30 | 6.92 |
| 40 | 6.77 |
| 60 | 6.51 |
| 70 | 6.40 |

The second effect relates to the relationship between temperature and measured potential differences[7]. A modification of the Nernst equation in simplistic form describes a direct temperature dependence that amounts to about 3.4% slope measurement difference for every 10 °C temperature change.

$$E_{measured} = E_{reference} - \frac{RT}{F} \log[H^+]$$

The third effect relates to the temperature dependent solubility of the salts contained in the buffer solution of the reference electrode. Calomel ($Hg_2Cl_2$) and silver chloride (AgCl) are the two most common salts found in reference electrodes. The reference voltage of the electrode is inversely related to the concentration of these salts in the filing solution and the concentration increases with increasing temperature. The effect is illustrated in Table 2-9.

**Table 2-9. Reference electrode voltage variation with temperature due to increased solubility of silver chloride**

| Temp °C | Reference electrode mV |
|---------|------------------------|
| 10 | 231 |
| 30 | 219 |
| 50 | 204 |
| 70 | 188 |
| 90 | 170 |

In most situations in the environmental laboratory, the extremes of pH (<2 for acidic conditions, and >12 for basic conditions) are not found in samples. Most natural water

---

[7] Frant, M., "The Effect of Temperature on pH Measurements." *American Laboratory*. July, 1995. pp. 18-23.

has a slightly acidic pH due to carbon dioxide saturation at pH = 6.35. See the following discussion on alkalinity for a more detailed look at carbon dioxide in water. Many tests in the lab require pH control, which is achieved through the use of buffers. A buffer is formed from either a weak acid and a salt of the acid, or a weak base and a salt of the base.

For a weak acid:  $HA \longleftrightarrow H_3O^+ + A^-$

$$K_a = \frac{[H_3O^+][A^-]}{[HA]} \quad ; \quad pK_a = -logK_a$$

$$pH = pK_a - log\frac{[HA]}{[A^-]} \quad \text{Henderson-Hasselbalch Equation}$$

Many different buffer systems are created and used in the laboratory. Table 2-10 gives a few of the more common. The pH of the equimolar solution is indicated as the $pK_a$. For other pH values that can be created from the buffer chemicals, the Henderson-Hasselbalch equation is used. However, the more common practice is to make an equimolar solution of the buffer chemicals then add acid or base as necessary to adjust the pH while it is being monitored with a pH meter.

**Table 2-10.  Common laboratory buffer systems and their $pK_a$**

| Acid/conjugate base | $pK_a$ |
|---|---|
| $H_3PO_4$ / $KH_2PO_4$ | 2.15 |
| $H_3$Citric Acid / $NaH_2$Citrate | 3.13 |
| $NaH_2$Citrate / $Na_2H$Citrate | 4.76 |
| HOAc / NaOAc | 4.76 |
| $H_2CO_3$ / $HCO_3^-$ | 5.38 |
| $Na_2H$Citrate / $Na_3$Citrate | 6.40 |
| $KH_2PO_4$ / $Na_2HPO_4$ | 7.20 |
| $Tris^+HCl$ / Tris | 8.08 |
| $H_3BO_3$ / $Na_3BO_3$ | 9.23 |
| $NH_4Cl$ / $NH_3$ | 9.25 |
| $NaHCO_3$ / $Na_2CO_3$ | 10.33 |
| $Na_2HPO_4$ / $Na_3PO_4$ | 12.4 |

Indicators are chemicals that exhibit a visual color change as the pH of the solution is varied. The operation of pH paper is dependent upon indicators absorbed on the paper. There is an equation similar to the Henderson-Hasselbalch equation for buffer solutions, which describes acid-base indicator transitions, based on $pK_{In}$.

$$pH = pK_{In} + log\frac{[\text{Base form}]}{[\text{Acid form}]}$$

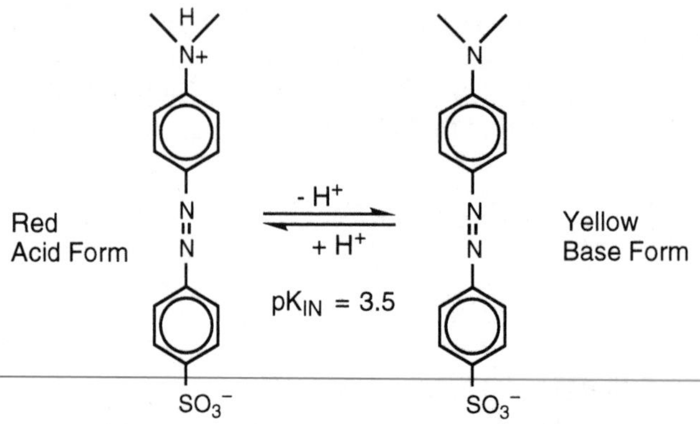

**Figure 2-11. Chemistry of the common indicator Methyl Orange.**

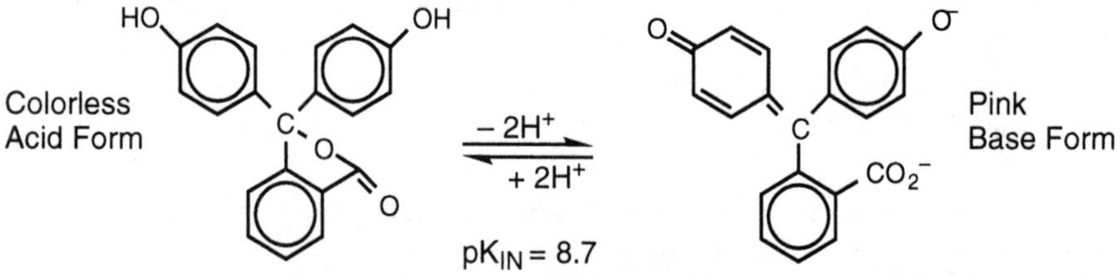

**Figure 2-12. Chemistry of the common indicator phenolphthalein.**

pH meters require calibration. Laboratories will often purchase calibration solutions at pH 4.0, 7.0, and 10.0 to use with the pH meter. These solutions and a number of other pH standards can be easily prepared from readily available compounds in the laboratory.

**Table 2-11. Primary standards for pH calibration[8]**

| Primary Standard | Conditions | pH at 25 °C |
|---|---|---|
| Potassium hydrogen tartrate | saturated solution at 25 °C | 3.557 |
| Potassium dihydrogen citrate | 0.10 mol/kg | 3.776 |
| Potassium hydrogen phthalate | 0.05 mol/kg | 4.005 |
| $Na_2HPO_4 + KH_2PO_4$ | 0.025 mol/kg + 0.025 mol/kg | 6.865 |
| $Na_2HPO_4 + KH_2PO_4$ | 0.03043 mol/kg + 0.008695 mol/kg | 7.413 |
| Disodium tetraborate | 0.010 mol/kg | 9.180 |
| $NaHCO_3 + Na_2CO_3$ | 0.025 mol/kg + 0.025 mol/kg | 10.012 |

8    Kristensen, H. B., A. Salomon and G. Kokholm. "International pH Scales and Certification of pH." *Anal. Chem.* 1991. 63(18). pp. 885A-891A.

## B. Alkalinity (SM$_{18}$ 2320, Reference 39; EPA 310.1, Reference 20)

Alkalinity is defined as the acid-neutralizing capability of water. It is reported as due to $HCO_3^-$, $CO_3^{-2}$, and $OH^-$, although borates, phosphates, ammonia, amines, silicates, organic carboxylates, and phenates (in humus) and other basic anions may contribute. Samples are titrated with standard $H_2SO_4$ or $HCl$ (0.02$N$ or 0.1$N$) to pH 8.3 (phenolphthalein or metacresol purple) for "carbonate" alkalinity and pH 4.5 (bromocresol green) for "bicarbonate" alkalinity. Results are expressed as "The alkalinity to pH ____ = _____ mg $CaCO_3$/L."

$$CO_{2(air)} <=> CO_{2(aq)} <=> HCO_3^-{}_{(aq)} <=> CO_3^{2-}{}_{(aq)} <=> CO_3^{2-}{}_{(solid)}$$

$$CO_{2(aq)} + H_2O \longleftrightarrow H_2CO_{3(aq)} \qquad K = \frac{[H_2CO_3]}{[CO_2]} = 2 \times 10^{-3} \text{ at } 25\,°C$$

$$CO_2(aq) + H_2O \longleftrightarrow HCO_3^- + H^+ \quad K = \frac{[H^+][HCO_3^-]}{[CO_2]} = 4.45 \times 10^{-7}$$

$$pK_{a1} = 6.35$$

$$HCO_3^- \longleftrightarrow CO_3^{2-} + H^+ \qquad K = \frac{[H^+][CO_3^{2-}]}{[HCO_3^-]} = 4.69 \times 10^{-11}$$

$$pK_{a2} = 10.33$$

**Figure 2-13. Equilibrium chemistry of carbon dioxide in water.**

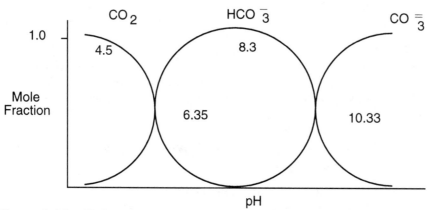

**Figure 2-14. pH dependence of the mole fraction of carbonate, bicarbonate and carbon dioxide.**

$CO_2$ saturation at 25 °C is 1.146 x 10$^{-5}$ $M$ (about 500 ppm), which results in pH = 5.65, not considering any disproportionation. For illustration purposes the alkalinity titration to pH 8.3 can be visualized as:

$$H_2SO_4 + CaCO_3 \longrightarrow \frac{1}{2} CaCO_3 \text{ for the carbonate fraction, and:}$$

$$H_2SO_4 + 2OH^- \longrightarrow H_2O \text{ for the hydroxide fraction.}$$

The titration from pH 8.3 to pH 4.5 can be visualized as:

$$H_2SO_4 + \frac{1}{2}CaCO_3 \longrightarrow CO_2 \text{ for the bicarbonate fraction, or one-half the}$$

carbonate fraction if the original pH was greater than 8.3. By knowing the initial pH of the sample, the contribution of the different species can be easily determined.

A specific application of alkalinity concerns the narrow pH range (6.4 to 7.6) necessary for proper operation of an anaerobic digester. Total alkalinity to pH 4.3 includes all the bicarbonate contribution and 80% of the volatile organic acids. These contributions can be sorted by titration of the sample with acid to first pH 5.1 and then pH 3.5, using a pH meter[9]. The titration results are used to solve the following simultaneous equations:

$$A1 = \frac{[HCO_3^-]\{[H]_2-[H]_1\}}{[H]_2+K_1} + \frac{[VA]\{[H]_2-[H]_1\}}{[H]_2+K_2}$$

$$A2 = \frac{[HCO_3^-]\{[H]_3-[H]_1\}}{[H]_3+K_1} + \frac{[VA]\{[H]_3-[H]_1\}}{[H]_3+K_2}$$

where A1 and A2 are the molar amounts of the acid used to the first and second titration end-points; $[H]_{123}$ are the hydrogen ion concentrations of the initial sample and the first and second end-points, respectively; $K_1$ is the conditional dissociation constant of carbonic acid $= 6.6 \times 10^{-7}$; and $K_2$ is the combined dissociation constants of the common volatile organic acids $= 2.4 \times 10^{-5}$.

The traditional determination of volatile organic acids in anaerobic digesters involves either isolation of the organic acids using a silica gel column with $CHCl_3$-butanol eluant and titration to phenolphthalein with standard base, or a more rapid process of titrating the sample to pH 4.0, noting the volume of standard acid used, then continued titration to pH 3.3 - 3.0. The sample is then boiled for 3 minutes and allowed to cool. Titration to pH 4.0 is performed with standard base, the volume noted, then continued to pH 7.0. The initial value of volatile organic acid alkalinity is = mL 0.050 N NaOH x 2500/ mL sample used. If the calculated volatile acid alkalinity is greater than 180 mg/L, then the volatile acid content is the volatile acid alkalinity x 1.5. If the calculated volatile acid alkalinity is less than 180 mg/L, then the volatile acid alkalinity is the volatile acid alkalinity. Although very roughly determined these procedures give adequate results for wastewater plant process control.

## C. Hardness (SM18 2340, Reference 39; EPA 130, Reference 20; or 200.7, Reference 25 and 42)

Defined as the sum of the calcium and magnesium concentrations, hardness is expressed as mg $CaCO_3$/L. Hardness may be calculated based on 2.497 [Ca] + 4.118[Mg] in mg/L, obtained from individual determinations of Ca and Mg by AA, ICP or other methods. The other common method is the 0.01M ethylenediaminetetraacetic acid (EDTA) complexometric titration. The pH of the sample is adjusted to pH 10.0, Eriochrome Black T is added as an indicator, and the solution becomes wine red. EDTA is a stronger complexing agent for magnesium and calcium than Eriochrome

9    G.K. Anderson and G. Yang. "Determination of Bicarbonate and Total Volatile Acid Concentration in Anaerobic Digesters Using A Simple Titration." *Water Environment Research.* 1992. 64(1). pp. 53-59.

Black T. EDTA is used to titrate the sample. When all the ions are complexed to EDTA and none are available for the indicator, the end of the titration is signaled by the permanent blue of the uncomplexed Eriochrome Black T. The stoichiometry for EDTA to calcium and magnesium ions is 1:1.

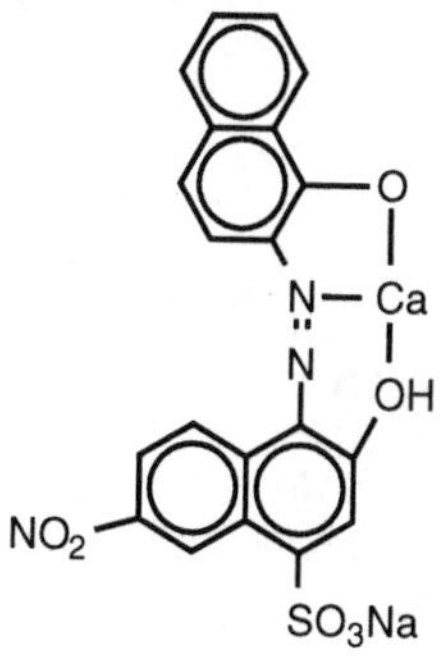

Erichrome Black T 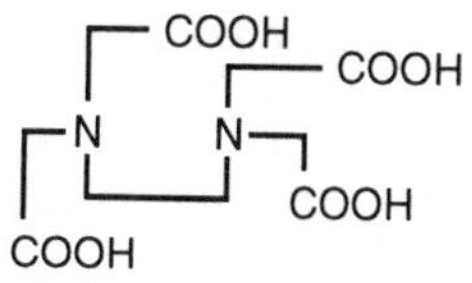                    EDTA

**Figure 2-15. Reagents used in hardness titration.**

## D. Langelier's Index

Langelier's Index is a measure of the saturation state of water with respect to calcium carbonate. A value of zero indicates that the water is in thermodynamic equilibrium with calcium carbonate. A negative value indicates that the water is corrosive with respect to precipitated calcium carbonate. A positive Langelier's Index indicates that the water is oversaturated with calcium carbonate, and it will precipitate or be "encrustive." A positive value is the desired state as the precipitated calcium carbonate tends to passivate metal water lines from dissolution of copper and lead.

The Index is calculated as follows:

$$LI = pH_{sample} - pH_{saturation}$$

$$pH_{saturation} = A + B - \log[Ca^{+2}] - \log[alkalinity]$$

where:

$[Ca^{2+}]$ and [alkalinity] are in terms of $CaCO_3$ in mg/L

A = constant for water temperature in °C

B = constant for TDS in mg/L

**Table 2-12. Langelier's Index Values for A**

| Temperature °C | A |
|---|---|
| 0 | 2.60 |
| 4 | 2.50 |
| 8 | 2.40 |
| 12 | 2.30 |
| 16 | 2.20 |
| 20 | 2.10 |

**Table 2-13. Langelier's Index Values for B**

| TDS mg/L | B |
|---|---|
| 0 | 9.70 |
| 100 | 9.77 |
| 200 | 9.83 |
| 400 | 9.86 |
| 800 | 9.89 |
| 1000 | 9.90 |

## E. Dissolved oxygen (SM$_{18}$ 4500-O, Reference 39)

Wet chemical methods exist, however, most dissolved oxygen determinations are performed using one of a variety of oxygen-specific electrodes. The older style electrodes required vigorous stirring of the sample solution, due to a net consumption of $O_2$ from the sample:

Cathode reaction $\qquad$ $O_2 + 4H^+ + 4e^- \longrightarrow 2H_2O$

Anode reaction $\qquad$ $2\,Pb + 2H_2O \longrightarrow 2PbO + 4H^+ + 4e^-$

Net $\qquad$ $O_2 + 2Pb \longrightarrow 2PbO$ $\quad$ (Clark type DO probe)

The most modern electrodes rely on the following, with no net consumption of $O_2$:

Cathode reaction $\qquad$ $O_2 + 4H^+ + 4e^- \longrightarrow 2H_2O$

Anode reaction $\qquad$ $2H_2O \longrightarrow O_2 + 4H^+ + 4e^-$

Net $\qquad$ zero

The system is separated from the sample by a polyethylene and/or fluorocarbon membrane that allows diffusion of $O_2$. Introduction of $O_2$ to the system across the membrane causes increased current to maintain the higher presence of $O_2$. The fluctuations in current are related to the DO level through calibration with a standard, either air or air-saturated water. The calibration of the electrodes is subject to local temperature and atmospheric pressure, which can fluctuate in a significant fashion during the course of a single day. The most accurate calibration is to determine the DO of a sample with the Winkler titration, then use that value to adjust the electrode.

**Winkler Method (azide modification) for DO:** $Mn(II)SO_4$ is added to the sample followed by a strongly basic solution of $NaN_3$ and KI (alkaline-azide-iodide or AIA solution). If the precipitate is white at this point, the lack of DO is indicated, a brown precipitate of $Mn^{4+}$ forms if oxygen was present. The precipitate is allowed to settle, and the sample acidified. After the addition of acid the sample is considered preserved and can be transported back to the laboratory. The released $I_2$ ($I_3^-$) is titrated with PhAsO (or thiosulfate) with starch as the indicator or until it is colorless. Most titration procedures use only a portion of the sample, generally 203 mL of the 300 mL in the BOD bottle. The odd volume is due to the addition of the 2 mL of manganous sulfate solution and 2 mL of AIA solution, which displace 4 mL of DO containing sample. 2/3 of 4 mL is rounded to 3 mL. The addition of the acid is performed after the floc has settled, which contains the information on the original DO level, and no dilution correction is necessary.

$$2Mn^{2+} + 4OH^- + O_2 \longrightarrow MnO(OH)_2 + H_2O \qquad \text{base conditions}$$

$$NaN_3 + H^+ \longrightarrow HN_3 + Na^+ \qquad \text{acid conditions}$$

$$HN_3 + NO_2^- + H^+ \longrightarrow N_2 + N_2O + H_2O \qquad \text{prevents } I^- \text{ oxidation by } NO_2^-$$

$$MnO(OH)_2 + 6I^- + 6H^+ \longrightarrow Mn^{2+} + 2I_3^- + 3H_2O \qquad \text{oxidation of iodine}$$

$$2H_2O + I_3^- + PhAsO \longrightarrow 2HI + I^- + PhAs(OH)_2O \qquad \text{titration analysis}$$

**Figure 2-16. Chemistry of the Winkler DO method.**

## F. Biochemical Oxygen Demand (BOD) (SM$_{18}$ 5210, Reference 39; EPA 405.1, Reference 20)

BOD measures the amount of oxygen required for bacteria and other microorganisms to metabolise waste material in a water stream. The material metabolised may be organic substances or some inorganics such as iron(II) and sulfides. The organic material can be subdivided into carbonaceous and nitrogenous demand. Nitrogen oxidation can be inhibited through the addition of 2-chloro-6-trichloromethyl pyridine (TCMP), methylene blue or allylthiourea[10]. If nitrogen inhibition is performed the test is called CBOD (carbonaceous biochemical oxygen demand). A subscript is added to the initials to indicate the length of time in days the test was conducted; BOD$_5$ is the standard. In short the test calls for measurement of the DO, incubation for 5 days at constant temperature (20 °C) in the dark, measurement of DO, and comparison of the before and after values of DO to give BOD. Distilled water at 20 °C is saturated with oxygen at approximately 9 mg/L. The BOD of wastewater normally exceeds this by a factor of 10 to 10,000, thus dilutions are performed to obtain usable results.

Samples are stored at 4 °C with no preservative, for a limit of 48 hours. Samples are warmed to 20 °C, neutralized to pH 6.5 - 7.5 with H$_2$SO$_4$ or NaOH of such a strength that the volume does not exceed 0.5% of the sample. Na$_2$SO$_3$ can be added to destroy residual chlorine and other oxidizers. (Excess Na$_2$SO$_3$ will exert a BOD). Dilutions are prepared with neutralized distilled water containing nutrients and saturated with DO. Range of dilutions is 1.0% or less for strong industrial wastes, 1 to 5% for raw and settled wastewater, 5 to 25% for biologically treated effluent, 25% to 100% for polluted river waters. In BOD bottles (300 mL capacity, tapered water seal stopper) the sample is placed along with nutrients (Ca, Mg, Fe salts, and phosphate buffer), DO saturated dilution water and a multi-organism seed. DO is measured. Bottles are sealed and incubated in the dark for 5 days at 20 °C ± 1 °C. DO is again measured after 5 days. The BOD requirement of the seed is subtracted, then the BOD calculated. Usable dilutions have initial DO 7-9 mg/L and final values >1 mg/L. A minimum corrected depletion between initial and final DO of 2.0 mg/L is required to calculate the BOD.

A novel variation on the traditional BOD procedure has been reported[11] that uses an immobilized microorganism coupled with an oxygen sensor to yield a biosensor capable of determining a value up to approximately 110 mg/L BOD. Although the results were not identical with the traditional BOD, a correlation could be demonstrated. The quick

---

[10] Young, J.C., "Chemical Methods for Nitrification Control." *J. Water Pollution Control Fed.* 1973. 45. p. 639.

[11] Preininger, C., I. Klimant and O.S. Wolfbeis. "Optical Fiber Sensor for Biological Oxygen Demand." *Analytical Chemistry.* 1994. 66(11). pp. 1841-1846.

determination of the results makes this type of instrument very attractive for process control.

A major technical problem of the $BOD_5$ procedure results from the initial limited amount of oxygen in the sample. A modification of the procedure[12] uses a headspace in the sealed system to replenish the oxygen consumed in the sample and gives a much longer dynamic range for each test bottle. Thus headspaces of 5, 10 and 15 mL give ranges of 8-51, 18-120 and 36-241 mg/L BOD for a 28 mL container. The performance of the modified test is essentially the same as the traditional procedure with measured parameters of headspace volume and oxygen saturation at the beginning of the test and dissolved oxygen at the end of the test. The mathematics of this procedure are somewhat more involved, having to take into account the initial and final number of moles of oxygen in the system and the Henry's Law constant for oxygen.

$$HBOD = \frac{V_g M p_i 10^3}{[V - V_g]RT} (1 - c_f/c_{sat}) + (c_i - c_f)$$

where:

V is the total volume of the sealed system,

$V_g$ is the volume of the headspace,

M is the molecular mass of oxygen,

$p_i$ is the initial partial pressure of oxygen,

R is the gas constant, 0.0821 Latm/molK,

T is temperature in Kelvins, and,

$c_i$, $c_f$, and $c_{sat}$ are the initial, final, and saturation levels of dissolved oxygen.

Many factors influence $BOD_5$ results. These include the presence of toxic materials in the sample and the exact nature of the seed. Further, metabolised material may be toxic at high concentrations, while a nutrient at lower levels. It is possible to control the method by using glucose-glutamic acid or KHP as the standard and thus QC can be applied in a rigorous fashion. A 300 mg/L GGA standard gives a $BOD_5$ of $198 \pm 30.5$ mg/L, and a $CBOD_5$ of $164 \pm 30.7$ mg/L.

KHP:
$$2KC_8H_5O_4 + 15O_2 + 2H^+ \longrightarrow 16CO_2 + 6H_2O + 2K^+$$

Glucose:
$$C_6H_{12}O_6 + 6O_2 \longrightarrow 6CO_2 + 6H_2O$$

Glutamic acid:
$$2C_5H_9NO_4 + 9O_2 \longrightarrow 10 CO_2 + 6H_2O + 2NH_3$$

Ammonia oxidation:
$$2NH_3 + 4O_2 \longrightarrow 2NO_3^- + 2H_2O + 2H^+$$

**Figure 2-17. Chemistry of oxidation of KHP and glucose-glutamic acid.**

---

[12] Logan, B.E. and G. A. Wagenseller "The HBOD test: A New Method for Determining Biochemical Oxygen Demand." *Water Environment Research.* 1993. 65(7). pp. 862-868.

## G. Chemical oxygen demand (COD) (SM$_{18}$ 5220, Reference 39; EPA 410.1, Reference 20)

Chemical oxidation of the sample with the strong oxidant dichromate, results in almost complete (>95%) oxidation of organic materials. Values are almost always higher than BOD values. Materials that resist chemical oxidation include some volatile chemicals (they don't remain in the oxidation flask when heated), hydrocarbons, pyridine, and ammonia. A variety of inorganic ions are also oxidized, such as $Fe^{+2}$, $S^{-2}$, $Mn^{+2}$, etc.

A sample of wastewater (20 mL) is strongly acidified with sulfuric acid containing $Ag_2SO_4$ (a catalyst). A known amount of $K_2Cr_2O_7$ is added, and mercuric sulfate ($HgSO_4$ 0.4 g/20.0 mL sample). The mercuric sulfate removes interfering chloride ions that can precipitate the silver catalyst. Chloride ion can be oxidized to chlorine by dichromate, and thus exert a COD on the sample. The mixture is refluxed for 2 hours. After cooling, ferroin indicator (1,10-phenanthroline ferrous sulfate) is added, and the residual dichromate titrated with ferrous ammonium sulfate (FAS). The ferroin indicator forms an intense color in the presence of ferrous ions ($Fe^{+2}$), and is colorless with only $Fe^{+3}$ present. The titration end-point is indicated by the solution change from greenish blue to orange brown. Each mL of a 0.25$N$ solution of $K_2Cr_2O_7$ (22.259 g/1.0 L) consumed is equivalent to 2.0 mg/L COD if a 20.0 mL sample is used.

The test can also be performed with a spectrophotometer by measuring either the decrease in absorbance of the dichromate ion or the increase in absorbance of the $Cr^{+3}$ ion (SM$_{18}$ 5220 D, Reference 39; EPA 410.4, Reference 20). The reaction is exactly the same as the titrimetric method; however, it is conducted in a screwtop test tube or cuvette. The reflux is replaced by heating the closed test tube in a heating block. The colorimetric method is preferred these days because of the decreased amount of hazardous reagents (chromium, mercury and silver, and the associated disposal costs) and reduced sample size used in the test with an improvement in detection level and precision. Use of greater than 1 cm cells can reduce MDL to be equivalent to titration.

Oxidation equivalents; one mole of dichromate is equivalent to 1.5 mole of $O_2$:
$$Cr_2O_7^{2-} + 8H^+ \longrightarrow 2Cr^{3+} + 4H_2O + 3(O°) \ ;$$

Titration reaction:
$$Cr_2O_7^{2-} + 14H^+ + 6Fe^{2+} \longrightarrow 2Cr^{3+} + 6Fe^{3+} + 7H_2O$$

**Figure 2-18. Chemistry of COD reaction and titration.**

The COD reaction is standardized by using potassium hydrogen phthalate as the test material. The COD procedure is one of the few tests that uses a primary standard as the major reagent and is standardized against a primary standard (KHP). Potassium dichromate is a primary standard and available in very high purity at a reasonable cost as is KHP. Primary standards are very precious materials in analytical chemistry because there are so few. Primary standards have the following properties:

- They are chemically stable and have very long shelf lives at room temperature.
- They are readily available.
- They are solids and easily purified.
- Their chemistry is well defined.
- They do not form hydrates upon storage nor tend to absorb water.

---

$$2KC_8H_5O_4 + 10K_2Cr_2O_7 + 41H_2SO_4 \longrightarrow 16CO_2 + 46H_2O + 10Cr_2(SO_4)_3 + 11K_2SO_4$$

**Figure 2-19. Reaction of KHP in the COD procedure.**

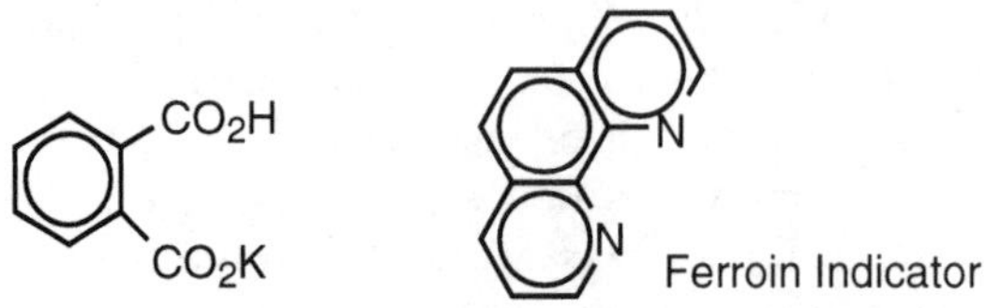

Ferroin Indicator

**Figure 2-20. Structures of potassium hydrogen phthalate (KHP) and ferroin indicator.**

**Table 2-14. KHP used as a 300 mg/L solution as standard for a number of tests**

| Test | Analytical Value |
|------|-----------------|
| BOD$_5$ | 240 mg/L |
| Dichromate COD | 353 mg/L |
| TOC | 141 mg/L |
| Total Acidity | 74 mg/L (as CaCO$_3$) |
| Normality | 0.00149 $N$ |
| Total Solids | 300 mg/L |
| Fixed Solids | 100 mg/L |
| Volatile Solids | 200 mg/L |
| Potassium | 57.5 mg/L |
| Conductivity at 25 °C | 168 |
| pH | 4.4 |

# H. Metals (SM$_{18}$ 3000s, Reference 39; EPA 200s and 7000s, References 20, 25 and 41)

**1. Preparation (digestion)** - All samples for metals analysis, except for drinking water samples, must be subjected to one of a variety of digestion procedures. (To achieve the drinking water MDLs, which are based on the MCLs, may require up to a 10-fold concentration.) A very informative reference[13] describes many types of digestions including open and closed systems, fusions, sintering, thermal procedures, gas streams, gaseous halogens and hydrogen halides, and pyrohydrolysis.

**a. Open Air (Hotplate) Digestions** – The most commonly used digestion procedure is a hotplate digestion exposed to the atmosphere with nitric acid (SM$_{18}$ 3030E). Other additives used in the procedure include:

- Nitric and hydrochloric acids (SM$_{18}$ 3030F)
- Nitric and sulfuric acids (SM$_{18}$ 3030G)
- Nitric and perchloric acids (SM$_{18}$ 3030H)
- Nitric, perchloric, and hydrofluoric acids (SM$_{18}$ 3030I).

---

[13] Sulcek, Z, and P. Ponondra. *Methods of Decomposition in Inorganic Analysis.* 1989. CRC Press. Boca Raton, FL.

The corresponding EPA approved methods (Reference 41) include nitric acid (EPA 3005), nitric and hydrochloric acids (EPA 3010), nitric and hydrochloric acids, and hydrogen peroxide (EPA 3050).

The digestion procedure is frequently the place of procedural breakdown when samples produce erratic results as indicated by poor spike recoveries or lack of precision when comparing duplicate determinations. Contrary to most beliefs, metals are not totally inert and stable solids. At temperatures slightly higher than 150 to 200 °C, readily achieved on a hotplate or other heating surface, many metal analytes will volatize and be lost. Technicians who allow their digestions to boil dry, with a little bit of dark brown crud left in the bottom of the container, may be astonished to know that the brown residue frequently consists of mainly polymerized organic humic debris, rather than a quantitative recovery of the metal target analytes. Further, the residue, when it does contain the target analytes, may have transformed them into an insoluble form, that simple dilution to volume with reagent grade water will not solubilize.

## Method 3050: Acid Digestion of Sediments, Sludges and Soils.

One to two grams of material is heated with 10 mL of 1:1 $HNO_3$, then heated with two additional portions of 5 mL concentrated $HNO_3$, then the volume reduced to 5 mL. Two mL water and 3 mL 30% $H_2O_2$ is added and the sample heated. Additional peroxide is added in 1 mL increments, with heating, to no more than 10 mL total. For some metal analytes concentrated HCl is added, and the sample heated. The digestate is filtered and diluted to 100 mL for analysis. The method is applicable to most metals by ICP, flame or graphite furnace AA. A recent article has suggested that the methodology is not universally applicable due to the insolubility of several metal forms[14]. The observations on the solubilization of lead, silver, antimony, chromium, molybdenum, and selenium are especially interesting because, if proven correct, the EPA methods 3020 and 3050 may be completely inappropriate for digestion of these metals.

The digestion of silver from solid samples using a variety of different procedures was examined[15]. Factors found to be important included maintenance of the digestion temperature at 95 °C and use of an excess of hydrochloric acid in the solution. The prefered conditions are those of the ASTM D3974 procedure, where 1 g of sample is reacted in 20 mL of water with 0.5 mL nitric acid and 5.0 mL hydrochloric acid, a 1:10 ratio of acids rather than the 1:1 ratio specified in the EPA procedures. The requirement for a large excess of HCl is attributed to the $HCl-H_2O$ azeotrope boiling point of 109 °C as compared to the BP of the nitric acid azeotrope (121 °C).

Digestions for arsenic in ore samples are described in Methods 108A, 108B and 108C of 40 CFR 61, Appendix B of the Air regulations. The first method uses nitric and hydrofluoric acids in a bomb, and the second a combination of nitric, hydrochloric, hydrofluoric, and perchloric acids in Teflon beakers on a hotplate, both followed by instrumental analysis. Method 108C describes a digestion procedure with nitric, hydrochloric, hydrofluoric, perchloric, and sulfuric acids in an Erlenmeyer flask on a hotplate, followed by distillation of arsenic as the chloride and analysis by a molybdenum blue colorimetric method.

---

[14] Kimbrough, D.E. and J. Wakakuwa. "A Study of the Linear Dynamic Ranges of Several Acid Digestion Procedures." *Environ. Sci. Technol.* 1992. 26(1). pp. 173-178.

[15] Cohen, R.J., A.J. Meyer, E. O'Bryan, J. Kunze and S. Kunze. "An Improved Digestion Method for Silver Analysis in Solid Samples." *Am. Environ. Lab.* 1996. 6/96. pp. 28-29.

**b.  Microwave Digestions –** Other variations use a microwave oven to affect the digestion with acid (EPA 3015 and 3051).  The major advantages to the microwave digestion lie in the very rapid heating to a suitable digestion temperature and the use of a closed system, which minimizes losses of volatile target analytes such as arsenic and selenium[16].  The EPA methods offer a procedure for calibrating the power output of the oven by measuring the temperature increase of a plastic vessel of water in the oven.  The power output is then related to the desired temperature increase in the digestion vessels.  Figure 2-21 is a diagram of a microwave digestion vessel.  This technique in practice gives erratic digestion results, particularly when differing numbers of samples are digested in different batches, and a variety of different acid mixtures are used.  As the EPA methods specify a set temperature objective during the digestion, use of either a temperature-sensing thermocouple or a pressure-sensing transducer as a positive indicator of successful digestion is well worth the slight additional initial investment.  Temperature monitoring is discussed in the EPA methods, but no mention of pressure monitoring is made, and no conversion data from temperature set points to pressure set points are provided.  Table 2-15 of water pressures in psi and mm Hg for pure water at a variety of temperatures can be used as a guide for the pressure set points for aqueous samples.  Since the aqueous digestion solution is dilute acid rather than pure water, 5 psi are subtracted from the pure water value to approximate the desired digestion temperature[17].

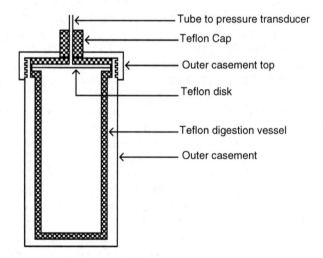

Tube to pressure transducer

Teflon Cap

Outer casement top

Teflon disk

Teflon digestion vessel

Outer casement

**Figure 2-21.  Microwave digestion vessel.**

---

[16]  Kingston, H.M., and C.B. Jassie. "Introduction to Microwave Sample Preparation Theory and Practice."  American Chemical Soc. Washington, DC. 1988. ISBN -0-8412-1450-6.

[17]  As of 1 July, 1993, Microwave digestion is allowed for wastewater samples for aluminum, arsenic, chromium, copper, lead, nickel, iron, selenium, zinc, barium and a few other metals. 40 CFR 136, Table 1B, footnote 36.

**Table 2-15. Vapor pressure of pure water at a variety of temperatures**

| °C | mm Hg | psi | °C | mm Hg | psi |
|----|-------|------|-----|-------|------|
| 20 | 17.5 | 0.34 | 110 | 1075 | 20.8 |
| 30 | 31.8 | 0.62 | 120 | 1489 | 28.8 |
| 40 | 55.3 | 1.07 | 130 | 2026 | 39.2 |
| 50 | 92.5 | 1.79 | 140 | 2711 | 52.4 |
| 60 | 149 | 2.88 | 150 | 3570 | 69.0 |
| 70 | 234 | 4.53 | 160 | 4636 | 89.6 |
| 80 | 355 | 6.87 | 170 | 5941 | 115 |
| 90 | 526 | 10.2 | 180 | 7520 | 145 |
| 100 | 760 | 14.7 | 190 | 9413 | 182 |

For example the first setpoint for the aqueous microwave digestion using nitric acid (method 3015) is 160 °C for 10 minutes. The corresponding pressure from the Table is 90 psi, which is reduced by 5 psi to 85 psi, which becomes the first setpoint. The second setpoint is 170 °C, which corresponds to 110 psi as the setpoint.

The solids digestion (method 3051) is performed in constant boiling nitric acid (120 °C) with setpoints of 175 °C and 180 °C with a pressure peak of less than 6 atmospheres (88 psi). The vapor pressure curve of the 70% nitric acid is very similar to that of pure water, but offset 20 °C. The pressure of the 70% nitric acid is 14.7 psi at 120 °C, which is the same as that of pure water at 100 °C. We have found that the subtraction of 5 psi from the pure water setpoint works very well for solids digestion. Thus a setpoint of 85 psi for 10 minutes duration gives very good results.

There are some metal target analytes that are more efficiently recovered under basic conditions rather than acidic. A recipe for basic digestions in the microwave has been published[18].

## Method 3051: Microwave Assisted Acid Digestion of Sediments, Sludges, Soils and Oils.

Up to 0.5 grams of material is digested in 10 mL $HNO_3$ in a Teflon® vessel for 10 minutes in a microwave. Either temperature or pressure must be monitored to determine successful digestion. The digestate is suitable for analysis of a number of metals as indicated in Table 2-16. Modifications of the method suggested by the microwave vendors include a nitric-hydrochloric acid digestion and a nitric-hydrochloric-hydrofluoric acid digestion. SW-846 draft method 3052 describes the latter digestion procedure. It is recognized that the digestion procedure in method 3051 does not recover all the metals in a sample, and the results are defined by the test. The hydrofluoric acid mixture is a more vigorous digestion, reducing the silicon- and aluminum- based soil matrix to the soluble state. The digestate is reflective of total metals content, except for several metals, such as calcium, which forms insoluble fluorides, and boron, as borate is added as the final reagent in the process.

---

[18] Zehr, B., J.P. VanKuren, and H.M. McMahon. "Inorganic Microwave Digestions Incorporating Bases." *Anal. Chem.* 1994. 66(13). pp. 2194-2196.

**Table 2-16. Metals That Can Be Digested by Microwave Techniques**

| Aluminum | Cadmium | Iron | Molybdenum | Sodium |
|---|---|---|---|---|
| Antimony | Calcium | Lead | Nickel | Strontium |
| Arsenic | Chromium | Magnesium | Potassium | Thallium |
| Boron | Cobalt | Manganese | Selenium | Vanadium |
| Barium | Copper | Manganese | Silver | Zinc |
| Beryllium | | | | |

**c. Volatilization of Metal Analytes from Samples** – In the above discussion of sample preparation techniques, the purpose is to obtain and retain the target analytes in a solution for ease of introduction by pipetting or suction into the instrument. Some analytes such as selenium, arsenic and antimony are quite challenging to keep in the solution due to inadvertent volitalization from the digestable mixture. By altering the sample introduction part of the instrument to allow analysis of gas streams, techniques of sample preparation that intentionally generate the metal analytes in volatile forms can be used effectively. These procedures, in general, must be tailored to the individual analyte but have the great advantage of a substantial reduction in the level of background noise and matrix interferences from the sample. This can allow routine analysis of certain metals at the part per trillion and lower levels.

The most frequent application of this idea is the cold vapor analysis of mercury from samples. Mercury has the property of existing in the elemental state as a relatively volatile liquid at room temperature and can easily be purged from the sample, discussed further below. All the other encountered metal analytes exist in the elemental form as relatively non-volatile solids. However, select compounds of other metal analytes are volatile and can be purged from the rest of the sample by an inert gas stream. Candidate compounds[19] are select metal hydrides (As[20], Bi[21], Ge, Sb, Sn, Se, Pb[22], Tl[23], In[24], Cd[25] and Cu[26]), chlorides (Bi, Cd, Ge, Mo, Pb, Sn, Tl, As, and Zn), fluorides (W, Mo, U, V, Re, and Ge), diketonates (Cr, Fe, Zn, Co, Mn, Cu, Ni, and Pb), and

---

[19] Reviews: Yan, P.-X., and Z.-M. Ni. *Anal. Chim. Acta.* 1994. 291. pp. 89-105; Dedina, J., and D.L. Tsalev. *Hydride Generation Atomic Absorption Spectrometry*, 1995. John Wiley & Sons, New York, NY.

[20] Chen, H., I.D. Brindle and X-C. Le. "Prereduction of Arsenic(V) to Arsenic (III), Enhancement of the Signal and Reduction of Interferences by L-Cysteine in the Determination of Arsenic by Hydride Generation." *Anal. Chem.* 1992. 64(6). pp. 667-672.

[21] Hahn, M.H., K.A. Wolnik, F.L. Ficke and J.A. Caruso. "Hydride Generations/Condensation System with an Inductively Coupled Plasma Polychromator for Determination of Arsenic, Bismuth, Germanium, Antimony, Selenium, and Tin in Foods." 1982. *Anal. Chem.* 54(7). pp. 1046-1052.

[22] Valdes-Hevia y Temprano, M.C., B.A. Fernandez, M.R. Fernandez de la Campa, and A. Sanz-Medel. *Anal. Chim. Acta.* 1993. 283. pp. 175-182.

[23] Ebdon, J., P. Goodall, S.J. Hill, P. Stockwell, and K.C. Thompson. *J. Anal. At. Spectrom.* 1995. 10. pp. 317-320.

[24] Liao, Y. and A. Li. *J. Anal. At. Spectrom.* 1993. 8. pp. 633-636.

[25] Sanz-Medel, A., M.C. Valdes-Hevia y Temprano, N. B. Garcia, and M.R.F. de la Campa. *Anal. Proc.* 1995. 32. pp. 49-52; Xiao-Wei, G., and G. Xu-Ming. *J. Anal. At. Spectrom.* 1995. 10. pp. 987-991. Sanz-Medel, A., MC. Valdes-Hevia y Temprano, N.B. Garcia, and M.R.F. de la Campa. "Generation of Cadmium Atoms at Room Temperature Using Vesicles and its Application to Cadmium Determination by CVAA." *Anal. Chem.* 1995. 67(13). pp. 2216-2223.

[26] Sturgeon, R.E., J. Liu, V.J. Boyko, and V.T. Luong. "Determination of Copper in Environmental Matrices Following Vapor Generation." *Anal. Chem.* 1996. 68(11). pp. 1883-1887.

dithiocarbamates (Co and Cu), as well as several organometallic materials (tetraethyl-Pb[27] and diethyl-Cd[28]). Determinative techniques have ranged from the traditional colorimetric method for arsenic to cold vapor AA, FLAA, GFAA, ICP-AES and ICP-MS. Environmental methods have been promulgated for analysis of antimony (EPA method 7062), arsenic (EPA 206.3 and 7061A, SM 3114) and selenium (EPA 270.2 and 7741A, SM 3114) as the hydrides; however, as the above list of metals demonstrates, the possibilities have been barely touched.

## 2. Instrument Analysis

**a. Atomic absorption (AA) spectrometry** - A low temperature method that uses a flame to atomize elements up to 2000 °C. This is a very good technique for easily atomized metals such as the alkali and alkaline earth metals. AA is used to directly determine calcium and magnesium for hardness. Various combustion gas combinations are in use with air - acetylene being the most common. Higher temperatures can be obtained through use of nitrous oxide - acetylene. The AA is also used with a quartz cell in place of the burner head for determination of mercury by the cold vapor technique and selenium, arsenic, and several other metals by the volatile hydride technique. The cell is heated to about 900 °C for determination of metal hydrides. $AsH_3$ can be determined by using $NaBH_4$ in a highly automated method[29].

**Table 2-17. Method numbers for FLAA (Direct Aspiration) metals procedures**

| Metals | W/WW Method | SW-846 Method |
|---|---|---|
| Aluminum | 202.1 | 7020 |
| Antimony | 204.1 | 7040 |
| Barium | 208.1 | 7080 |
| Beryllium | 210.1 | 7090 |
| Cadmium | 213.1 | 7130 |
| Calcium | 215.1 | 7140 |
| Chromium | 218.1 | 7190 |
| Cobalt | 219.1 | 7200 |
| Copper | 220.1 | 7210 |
| Iron | 236.1 | 7380 |
| Lead | 239.1 | 7420 |
| Lithium | - | 7430 |
| Magnesium | 242.1 | 7450 |
| Manganese | 243.1 | 7460 |
| Molybdenum | 246.1 | 7480 |
| Nickel | 249.1 | 7520 |
| Potassium | 258.1 | 7610 |
| Silver | 272.1 | 7760 |

Continued on next page.

[27] Sturgeon, R.E., S.N. Willie, and S.S. Berman. *Anal. Chem.* 1989. 61. pp. 1867-1869; Edbon, L., P.Goodall, S.J. Hill, P. Stockwell, and K.C. Thompson. *J. Anal. At. Spectrom.* 1994. 9. pp. 1417-1421.

[28] D'Ulivo, A., and Y. Chen. *J. Anal. At. Spectrom.* 1989. 4. pp. 319-322.

[29] Chen, H., I.D. Brindle and X-C. Le. "Prereduction of Arsenic (V) to Arsenic (III), Enhancement of the Signal and Reduction of Interferences by L-Cysteine in the Determination of Arsenic by Hydride Generation." *Anal. Chem.* 1992. 64(6). pp. 667-672.

**Table 2-17. Method numbers for FLAA (Direct Aspiration) metals procedures,** *continued*

| Metals | W/WW Method | SW-846 Method |
|--------|-------------|---------------|
| Sodium | 273.1 | 7770 |
| Strontium | - | 7780 |
| Thallium | 279.1 | 7840 |
| Tin | 282.1 | 7870 |
| Titanium | 283.1 | - |
| Vanadium | 286.1 | 7910 |
| Zinc | 289.1 | 7950 |

**Graphite Furnace Atomic Absorption (GFAA)** - Uses a small graphite tube with electrothermal heating to atomize the metals. Usable temperature range is up to 2800 to 3000 °C. The heating can be programmed to achieve a thermal ashing of the sample prior to atomization. Detection limits are 100 to 10,000 times lower than with flame AA for many metals due to elimination of the flame as a background interferent. Interferences that are seen include creation of smoke clouds and the resulting non-specific absorption due to improper choice of ashing and vaporization temperature programs. Background correction is normally required due to interferences from high solids content and spectral interferences. Common techniques for background correction are the deuterium continuum source correction and Zeeman background correction. The advantages of the Zeeman system over the deuterium system have been discussed in detail with examples of actual analytical situations[30]. In general, the deuterium background correction is ineffective when there are high levels of organic materials in the sample digestate. Although EPA and *Standard Methods* procedures require the use of liquid digestates of samples for analysis, techniques for direct analysis of solids have been published[31].

**Table 2-18. Method numbers for GFAA metals procedures**

| Metals | W/WW Method | SW-846 Method |
|--------|-------------|---------------|
| Aluminum | 202.2 | - |
| Antimony | 204.2 | 7041 |
| Arsenic | 206.2 | 7060 |
| Barium | 208.2 | 7081 |
| Beryllium | 210.2 | 7091 |
| Cadmium | 213.2 | 7131 |
| Chromium | 218.2 | 7191 |
| Cobalt | 219.2 | 7201 |
| Copper | 220.2 | 7211 |
| Iron | 236.2 | 7381 |
| Lead | 239.2 | 7421 |
| Manganese | 243.2 | 7461 |

Continued on next page.

---

[30] Flajnik-Rivera, C., and F. Delles. "Evaluation of Deuterium and Zeeman Background Correction with the Presence of Spectral Interferences." *Am. Environ. Lab.* 1996. 3/96. pp. 24-27.

[31] Freedman, Y., D. Ronen, and G.L. Long. "Determination of Cu and Cd Content of Groundwater Colloids by Solid Sampling GFAA." *Environ. Sci. Technol.* 1996. 30(7). pp. 2270-2277.

**Table 2-18. Method numbers for GFAA metals procedures,** *continued*

| Metals | W/WW Method | SW-846 Method |
|---|---|---|
| Molybdenum | 246.2 | 7481 |
| Nickel | 249.2 | - |
| Selenium | 270.2 | 7740 |
| Silver | 272.2 | 7761 |
| Sodium | 273.2 | - |
| Thallium | 279.2 | 7841 |
| Tin | 282.2 | - |
| Titanium | 283.2 | - |
| Vanadium | 286.2 | 7911 |
| Zinc | 289.2 | 7951 |

Sensitivity for determination of specific elements can be increased dramatically through use of the GFAA in a fluorescence mode, where excitation of analyte atoms in the furnace occurs at one wavelength and detection is performed at another. Lead has been determined[32] using the technique at the 10 pg/L level. The excitation source was a laser tuned to 283.3 nm while detection was performed at the lead fluorescence line at 405.7 nm.

**b. Inductively Coupled Argon Plasma (ICP or ICAP) Emission Spectrometry and Mass Spectrometry** - Operating in the 6000 to 10,000 °C range for excitation of the analyte atoms, two instrument designs are commercially available for analysis of the emission lines, the sequential and the simultaneous. The sequential is the slower but can examine many more elements by passing the diffracted emission spectrum across a photodetector. The simultaneous ICP has set detectors along the optical bench; however, automatic movement of the spectrum shifter for background correction results in small scans around each detector. Elements that have emission lines falling within the range of the spectrum shifter can also be analyzed. Normally a 28-element instrument can be programmed to assay up to 50 elements or more. Newer design plasma emission in-struments use a photo diode array to simultaneously obtain a complete emission spec-trum from a sample (TJA IRIS instruments). The ability to identify and quantitate elements from a large set of emission lines offers improved accuracy in analysis. It is possible to examine certain difficult elements such as thallium, selenium, and arsenic on the more modern ICP instruments, however the common practice is to perform these by GFAA.

ICP emission spectrometry is subject to many interferences[33] due to the large number of emission lines that most elements exhibit. Interference correction factors are widely employed to control these spectral overlaps. These are used by measuring the amount of interferring element in the sample, multiplying the amount by the correction factor and subtracting (or in some cases adding) the result from the apparent amount of the target element. A number of generic correction factors are presented in Table 2-19.

---

[32] Wagner, E.P., B.W. Smith and J.D. Winefordner. "Ultratrace Determination of Lead in Whole Blood Using Electrothermal Atomization Laser-Excited Atomic Fluorescence Spectrometry." *Anal Chem.* 1996. 68(18). pp. 3199-3203.

[33] Olesik, J.W. "Fundamental Research in ICP-OES and ICPMS." *Anal. Chem.* 1996. 68(15). pp. 469A-474A.

**Table 2-19. Generic ICP interference correction factors**

| | | Interferent Element | | | | | | | | | |
|---|---|---|---|---|---|---|---|---|---|---|---|
| Analyte | nm | Al | Ca | Cr | Cu | Fe | Mg | Mn | Ni | Ti | V |
| Al | 308.22 | - | - | - | - | - | - | 0.21 | - | - | 1.4 |
| Sb | 206.83 | 0.47 | - | 2.9 | - | 0.08 | - | - | - | 0.25 | 0.45 |
| As | 193.696 | 1.3 | - | 0.44 | - | - | - | - | - | - | 1.1 |
| Ba | 455.40 | - | - | - | - | - | - | - | - | - | - |
| Be | 313.04 | - | - | - | - | - | - | - | - | 0.04 | 0.05 |
| B | 249.77 | 0.04 | - | - | - | 0.32 | - | - | - | - | - |
| Cd | 226.50 | - | - | - | - | 0.03 | - | - | 0.02 | - | - |
| Ca | 317.93 | - | - | 0.08 | - | 0.01 | 0.01 | 0.04 | - | 0.03 | 0.03 |
| Cr | 267.72 | - | - | - | - | 0.003 | - | 0.04 | - | - | 0.04 |
| Co | 228.62 | - | - | 0.03 | - | 0.005 | - | - | 0.03 | 0.15 | - |
| Cu | 324.75 | - | - | - | - | 0.003 | - | - | - | 0.05 | 0.02 |
| Fe | 259.94 | - | - | - | - | - | - | 0.12 | - | - | - |
| Pb | 220.35 | 0.17 | - | - | - | - | - | - | - | - | - |
| Mg | 279.08 | - | 0.02 | 0.11 | - | 0.13 | - | 0.25 | - | 0.07 | 0.12 |
| Mn | 257.61 | 0.005 | - | 0.01 | - | 0.002 | 0.002 | - | - | - | - |
| Mo | 202.03 | 0.05 | - | - | - | 0.03 | - | - | - | - | - |
| Ni | 231.60 | - | - | - | - | - | - | - | - | - | - |
| Se | 196.03 | 0.23 | - | - | - | 0.09 | - | - | - | - | - |
| Si | 288.16 | - | - | 0.07 | - | - | - | - | - | - | 0.01 |
| Na | 588.99 | - | - | - | - | - | - | - | - | 0.08 | - |
| Tl | 190.86 | 0.30 | - | - | - | - | - | - | - | - | - |
| V | 292.40 | - | - | 0.05 | - | 0.005 | - | - | - | 0.02 | - |
| Zn | 213.86 | - | - | - | 0.14 | - | - | - | 0.29 | - | - |

Reference : USEPA Method 6010, SW-846, 3rd Edition, September, 1986

The weakness in this approach is the neccesity to measure the interferring element, which is itself subject to interferences and may not even be an analytical line on the instrument. The published methods in general only mention a few of the most common interferences. A frequent occurrence is that the analytical lines listed in the method for the target elements are different from those on the instrument, and reference lists of described spectral overlaps should be available for consultation. The operational software for the instrument often have interference lists imbedded in them. A common technique to check for spectral interferences in a sample is to perform a wavelength scan and visually inspect each signal to see if there are overlapping emission lines at either the analytical signal or at the background correction point. This can take up to 5 minutes for each sample and most production labs are not willing to take this additional time for the analysis. Although it is possible to optimize the sensitivity of the ICP emission spectrometer through better optics, diffraction gratings, and plasma viewing designs, in the end it is the overwhelming problems of spectral interferences that places a limit on how low the detection levels can go.

In addition to the spectral interferences, the sample introduction into the plasma torch has a great bearing on the results. Two areas of special concern are samples with high dissolved solids content and viscosity (percent acid content) matching of the sample and calibration standards. Most sample introduction devices use a high velocity carrier gas to blast the entering liquid sample stream into a fine mist (the nebulizer). Baffles or skimmers are placed in the path of the mist to collect the larger droplets and allow only a very fine mist to reach the torch. The solids content and viscosity of the sample affect the efficiency of the nebulization and the interaction of the formed mist with the baffles. There can be great differences in the amount of sample actually introduced into the torch from one sample to the next. The solids content of the mist reaching the plasma can also effect the temperature profile within the torch. The volatilization of the solids from the particles can create local cold spots and decrease the emission efficiency of the analyte elements. Droplets with very high solids content can actually crystallize around a microdroplet of water (occluded water) then explode within the torch creating a significant disturbance in the plasma flow dynamics.

The alternative detector for the ICP is to introduce the atoms from the plasma into a mass spectrometer (EPA methods 200.8 and 6020). The mass range of the elements extends from 1 to around 250, so that, compared to the mass spectrometer used for organics analysis, more time is available for acquiring data for each mass, resulting in excellent sensitivity. Most elements can be detected. However, the ICP-MS is not interference free. Isotopes of different elements can have the same mass (isobaric interference), although the interference can be detected by examining ratios of the isotope peaks of the target element. Polyatomic isobaric interferences also occur where atom clusters with the appropriate mass/charge ratio can coincide with the mass of the target analyte. Some of these are listed in Table 2-20. Another problem is that not all elements enter the mass spectrometer as single atoms, and the ratio of the various forms of the element that reach the mass analyzer can be concentration dependent. Ion transmission efficiencies through the mass analyzer are concentration dependent and serve as a source of interference. Internal standards of scandium-45, yttrium-89, indium-115, terbium-159 and bismuth-209 are used to minimize the sample introduction and ion transport variations.

**Table 2-20. Examples of polyatomic interferences found in ICP-MS**

| Ion Cluster | Mass | Ion Cluster | Mass |
|---|---|---|---|
| $NH^+$ | 15 | $OH^+$ | 17 |
| $OH_2^+$ | 18 | $C_2^+$ | 24 |
| $CN^+$ | 26 | $CO^+$ | 28 |
| $N_2^+$ | 28 | $N_2H^+$ | 29 |
| $NO^+$ | 30 | $NOH^+$ | 31 |
| $O_2^+$ | 32 | $O_2H^+$ | 33 |
| $^{36}ArH^+$ | 37 | $^{38}ArH^+$ | 39 |
| $^{40}ArH^+$ | 41 | $CO_2^+$ | 44 |
| $CO_2H^+$ | 45 | $ArC^+$ | 52 |
| $ArO^+$ | 52 | $ArN^+$ | 54 |
| $ArNH^+$ | 55 | $ArO^+$ | 56 |
| $ArOH^+$ | 57 | $ArAr^+$ | 76, 78, 80 |
| $ClO^+$ | 51, 53 | $ClOH^+$ | 52, 54 |
| $ArCl^+$ | 75, 77 | $SO^+$ | 48, 50 |
| $SOH^+$ | 49, 51 | $SO_2^+, S_2^+$ | 64 |
| $ArS^+$ | 72, 74 | $PO^+$ | 47 |
| $POH^+$ | 48 | $PO_2^+$ | 63 |
| $ArP^+$ | 71 | $ArNa^+$ | 63 |
| $ArK^+$ | 79 | $ArCa^+$ | 80 |
| TiO | 62-66 | ZrO | 106-112 |
| MoO | 108-116 | | |

**c. Anodic stripping voltametry** – Anodic stripping voltametry is a two part electro-chemistry process[34]. The first part is an electrolysis that serves to reduce the metal ions and deposit them as an amalgam in a mercury cathode. This serves a concentration function by removing the analyte ions from solution and placing them in the confines of the tiny mercury electrode. The polarity of the cell is then reversed so that the mercury electrode is now the anode. The voltage (potential) of the cell is scanned, and the current monitored. A spike in the current will occur at the dissolution potential for each of the analytes in the mercury electrode. The size of the spike is related to the original concentration of the analyte in the sample. By constructing the analytical electrode of platinum or carbon and spinning a thin film of mercury on it (rotating disk electrode) quite low detection limits can be achieved on the order of those routinely observed with GFAA. A distinct advantage is the ability to determine a number of different analytes in one procedure. Use of a gold electrode allows determination of mercury in ASV.

Quantitative results obtained with the technique depend on exact duplication of conditions for calibration standards and samples. Buffer control of pH can prevent some problems due to precipitation of insoluble hydroxides. Unexpected cations, such as gold, in the sample can lead to formation of alloys other than the desired amalgams. Dissolution potentials for these alloys, for example AuCd, $Au_3Cd$ and AuZn, can lead to spurious peaks in the current-potential profile. As with most analyses, use of regular matrix spikes, especially with unfamiliar samples, can help detect anomalous results.

Anodic stripping voltametry methods have been published by EPA for arsenic (7063) and mercury (7472).

**d. Ion Selective Electrodes and Optodes** – Optodes are devices used in conjunction with a spectrophotometer or colorimeter to measure metal cation concentrations. The sensor consists of an organic polymer film that is in direct contact with the aqueous sample. The film contains a neutral ionophore that is capable of selectively chelating the target cation, and a chromoionophore, a colored pH indicator in disguise. The pH indicator is initially in the $H^+$ state. When the ionophore removes an analyte cation from the aqueous sample, the pH indicator gives up an $H^+$ to the aqueous sample so that the organic polymer remains electrically constant. The chromoionophore is chosen to have a distinct change in absorbance related to loss of the $H^+$. The optode is mounted in the lightpath of the colorimeter, and a selected wavelength used to monitor the absorption of the chromoionophore. Changes in the absorbance in the chromoionophore correspond indirectly to target analyte concentration in the aqueous sample. The sample is buffered to a value suitable to the $pK_a$ of the chromoionophore. An ionophore and chromo-ionophore used for silver ion detection are illustrated in Figure 2-22. Recent publications have discussed the development of optodes for $Ag^{35}$, $Pb^{36}$, $Hg^{37}$ and $U^{38}$ ions in solution as continuous monitoring devices.

[34] Rieger, P.H. *Electrochemistry*, 2nd Edition, Chapman & Hall, New York, NY. 1994.
[35] Lerchi, M., F. Orsini, Z. Cimerman, E. Pretsch, D.A. Chowdhury and S. Kamata. "Selective Optical Sensing of Silver Ions in Drinking Water." *Anal Chem*. 1996. 68(18). pp. 3210-3214.
[36] Lerchi, M., E. Bakker, B. Rusterholz and W. Simon. "Lead-Selective Optodes Based on Neutral Ionophores with Subnanomolar Detection Limits." *Anal. Chem*. 1992. 64(14). pp. 1534-1540.
[37] Lerchi, M., E. Reitter, W. Simon, E. Pretsch, D.A. Chowdhury, and S. Kamata, 1994. "Bulk Optodes Based on Neutral Dithiocarbamate Ionophores with High Selectivity and Sensitivity for Silver and Mercury Cations." *Anal. Chem*. 66(10). pp. 1713-1717.
[38] Lerchi, M., E. Reitter, and W.Simon. *Fresenius J. Anal. Chem*. 1994. 348. pp. 272-276.

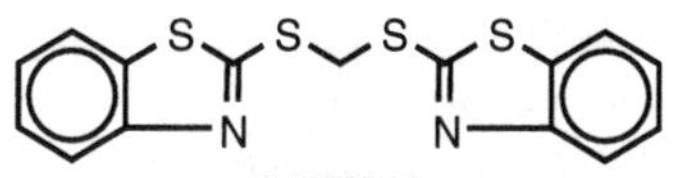

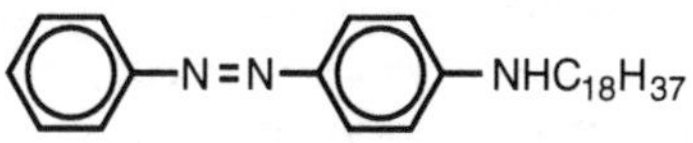

MBTBT

ETH 5315

**Figure 2-22. Ionophore (MBTBT) and chromoionophore (ETH 5315) used in an optode for silver ion detection.**

**e. Metal analyte speciation** – One aspect of speciation of metal analytes is determination of the dissolved fraction as compared to the total content of the sample. Traditionally this has been accomplished by filtration of the sample through a 0.45 um pore size membrane, followed by either direct analysis by AA, ICP-AES, or ICP-MS. Aside from the normal concerns of contamination associated with having an additional step in sample processing,[39] a recent paper[40] has addressed the question of what is actually being measured.

The determination of hexavalent chromium ($Cr^{6+}$) as compared to the amount of total chromium in the sample has for many years been a compliance monitoring parameter. Hexavalent chromium is recognized as a potent carcinogen, while other forms of chromium, such as the frequently found trivalent chromium ($Cr^{3+}$), are essential nutrients and, while not benign, present substantially less of a hazard. Hexavalent chromium can be determined using diphenylcarbazide in a simple colorimetric test (EPA methods 218.5 and 7196A), ion chromatography (EPA methods 218.6, 1636 and 7199), differential pulse polarography (EPA method 7198) and a chelation/extraction AA procedure (EPA methods 218.4 and 7197).

The term speciation means determination of the different states of the analyte that are present in the sample. The potential states of interest could include the zero-valent state (elemental), and different valence states of both inorganic and organometallic compounds of the analyte. Mercury presents a case where elemental, inorganic and organic forms can easily co-exist in the same sample[41]. Other than chromium, there are not a lot of promulgated procedures for speciation of metal analytes. The available few include methods EV-024/EV-025 for total and organotin in wastewater, and methods 1 and 2 of 40 CFR Part 80, App. B for lead in gasoline.

Although the concept of speciation is easy to understand, the analytical protocols that need to be used are not as simple as represented by hexavalent chromium determination. For many of the potential analytes, the different valence states can be easily interconverted, especially during the sample preparation. Further colorimetric tests, although specific for a particular metal valence, may not offer sufficient sensitivity to be of any use for trace contaminant determination.

---

[39] In 1995, the primary supplier of a popular membrane realized that the membranes were contaminated with antimony and had to adjust their manufacturing process.

[40] Horowitz, A.J., K.R. Lum, J.R. Garbarino, G.E.M. Hall, C. Lemieux, and C.R. Demas. "Problems Associated with using Filtration to Define Dissolved Trace Element Concentrations in Natural Water Samples." *Environ. Sci. Technol.* 1996. 30(3). pp. 954-963.

[41] Galbreath, K.C., and C.J. Zygalicke, 1996. "Mercury Speciation in Coal Combustion as Gasification Flue Gases." *Environ. Sci. Technol.* 30(8). pp. 2421-2426, and many references therein.

Most efforts in the speciation of metals have been directed toward direct analysis of aqueous samples with minimal sample preparation, relying instead upon a chromatographic separation of the analytes of interest followed by a variety of detection schemes. LC-ICPMS[42] and ion exchange chromatography-MS[43] have been proven useful for speciation of Pb, Hg, As, Se, and Cr. HPLC-AA has been used for As[44]. Capillary electrophoresis with amperometric detection or coupled to ICP-AES[45] or ICP-MS[46] has been used successfully for the speciation of mercury[47], organotins[48], arsenic and selenium. GC-AES has been reported as a useful tool for analysis of organomercury species[49].

When sample preparation has been addressed, supercritial fluid extraction of solid samples using carbon dioxide modified with dithiocarbamates, diketones or tributyl-phosphate, was found to be useful for isolation of inorganic mercury and organo-mercurials, lanthanides, uranium, and thorium[50]. EPA has a speciation method for mercury (EPA draft method 3200) under consideration that uses a sequential series of extractions with toluene and then acidic water solutions of increasing oxidizing strength.

[42] Shum, S.K.C., H.M. Pang, and R.S. Houk. "Speciation of Mercury and Lead Compounds by Microbore Column LC-ICPMS with Direct Injection Nebulization." *Anal. Chem.* 1992. 64. pp. 2444-2450; Shum, S.K.C., R. Neddersen, and R.S. Houk. *Analyst.* 1992. 117. pp. 577-582; Gjerde, D.T., D.R. Wiederin, F.G. Smith, and B.M. Mattson. *J. Chromatogr.* 1993. 640. pp. 73-78; Shum, S.C.K., and R.S. Houk. "Elemental Speciation by Anion Exchange and Size Exclusion Chromatography with Detection by ICPMS with Direct Injection Nebulization." *Anal. Chem.* 1993. 65. pp. 2972-2976.

[43] Corr, J.J., and J.F. Anacleto. "Analysis of Inorganic Species by Capillary Electrophoresis-Mass Spectrometry and Ion Exchange Chromatography-Mass Spectrometry Using an Ion Spray Source." *Anal. Chem.* 1996. 68(13). pp. 2155-2163.

[44] Manning, B.A. and D.A. Martens. "Speciation of As(III) and As(V) in Sediment Extracts by HPLC-Hydride Generation AA Spectrometry." *Environ. Sci. Technol.* 1997. 31(1). pp. 171-177.

[45] Olesik, J.W., J.A. Kinzer, and S.V. Olesik, 1995. "CE-ICP Spectrometry for Rapid Elemental Speciation." *Anal. Chem.* 67(1):1-12.

[46] Lui, Y., V. Lopez-Avila, J.J. Zhu, D.R. Wiederin, and W.F. Beckert. "Capillary Electrophoresis Coupled On-Line with ICP-MS for Elemental Speciation." *Anal. Chem.* 1995. 67(13). pp. 2020-2025; Lu, Q., S.M. Bird, and R.M. Barnes. "Interface for Capillary Electrophoresis and ICP-MS." *Anal. Chem.* 1995. 67(7). pp. 2949-2956.

[47] Lai, E.P.C., and E.Dabek-Zlotorzynska. "Capillary Electrophoresis wih Amperometric Detection for Mercury Speciation." *Am. Environ. Lab.* 1996. 6/96. pp. 1,6,8.

[48] Liu, Y., V. Lopez-Avila, M. Alcaraz, and W.F. Beckert. "Determination of Organotin Environmental Samples by Supercritical Fluid Extraction and GC-AED." *J. High. Resolut. Chromatogr.* 1993. 16(2). pp. 106-112; Liu, Y., and V. Lopez-Avila. *J. High Resolut. Chromatogr.* 1993. 16. pp. 717-720.

[49] Donais, M. K., P.C. Uden, M.M. Schantz, and S.A. Wise. "Development, Validation and Application of a Method for Quantification of Methylmercury in Biological Marine Samples using GC-AES." *Anal. Chem.* 1996. 68(21). pp. 3859-3866; Cai, Y., R. Jaffe and R. Jones. "Ethylmercury in the Soils and Sediments of the Florida Everglades." *Environ. Sci. Technol.* 1997. 31(1). pp. 302-305.

[50] Smart, N., Y. Lin, and C.M. Wai,. "Supercritical Fuid Extraction of Metal Ions from Solid Samples." *Am. Environ. Lab.* 1996. 2/96. pp. 38-42; Lin, Y., R. Brauer, K.E. Laintz, and C.M. Wai. "Supercritical Fluid Extraction of Lanthanides and Actinides from Solid Materials with a Fluorinated Diketone." *Anal. Chem.* 1993. 65. pp. 2549-2551; Wai, C.M., Y. Lin, R. Brauer, S. Wang, and W.F. Beckert. "Supercritical fluid extraction of organic and inorganic mercury from Solid Materials." *Talanta.* 1993. 40. pp. 1325-1329; Lin, Y., and C.M. Wai. "Supercritical Fluid Extraction of Lanthanides with Fluorinated Diketones and Tributylphosphate." *Anal. Chem.* 1994. 66. pp. 1971-1975; Lin, Y., C.M. Wai, F.M. Jean, and R.D. Brauer. "Supercritical Fluid Extraction of Thorium and Uranium Ions From Solid and Liquid Materials with Fluorinated Diketones and Tributylphosphate." *Environ. Sci. Technol.* 1994. 28. pp. 1190-1193.

Each solution is then analyzed for total mercury. Sequential extractions and hydride AA have been used for selenium speciation[51].

Dr. Skip Kingston has recently presented an innovative (and patented) approach to speciation[52] using ion chromatography-ICP/MS as the determinative instrument. He has termed the technique "Speciated Isotope Dilution Mass Spectrometry." The method requires an available pure isotope for each of the common valence states of the analyte. Each of the isotopes is used to prepare a single pure standard of one of the valences of the element. The sample is spiked with a known amount of each of the isotopically labeled valence states. The sample is then prepared/analyzed and the amounts of each isotope in each form are determined. Based on the natural abundance of the isotopes of the analyte and the valence distribution found in the spiked sample, the original amounts of each species can be computed. This very nicely takes into account any interconversion of the analyte forms that occurs during the sample preparation. For example, chromium naturally has the abundance of $^{50}Cr$ 4.35%, $^{52}Cr$ 83.79%, $^{53}Cr$ 9.50% and $^{54}Cr$ 2.36%. A Cr(III) spike is prepared from $^{50}Cr$ with 93.1% abundance and a Cr (VI) spike from $^{53}Cr$ with 97.7% abundance. Examination of the $^{50}Cr/^{52}Cr$, $^{50}Cr/^{53}Cr$, and $^{50}Cr/^{53}Cr$ ratios for the separated Cr(III) and Cr(VI) peaks allows calculation of the original amount of the two species in the sample. Interconversion percents for the two species ranged from 14 to 40% depending on the sample matrix and how the sample was prepared.

### 3. Recent EPA Metals Methods and Monitoring Requirements

The EPA has published the *Manual for the Determination of Metals in Environmental Samples*, (Reference 25) , and a supplement[53] in a movement to consolidate methods from the various offices in EPA. Most of the methods in the supplement are updated revisions of methods in the original manual; however, Method 200.15 is entirely new.

**Table 2-21. Contents of *Manual for the Determination of Metals in Environmental Samples*. Methods marked with an \* are in the Supplement.**

| Method | Title |
|--------|-------|
| 200.1 | Determination of acid-soluble metals |
| 200.2* | Sample preparation procedure for spectrochemical determination of total recoverable elements |
| 200.3 | Sample preparation procedure for spectrochemical determination of total recoverable elements in biological tissues |

Continued on next page.

---

51  Martens, D.A., and D.L. Suarez. "Selenium Speciation of Soil/Sediment Determined with Sequential Extractions and Hydride Generation Atomic Absorption Spectrometry." *Environ. Sci. Technol.* 1997. 31(1). pp. 133-139.

52  Kingston, H.M., D. Huo, S. Chalk and P.J. Walter. "The Accurate Determination of Species by Speciated Isotope Dilution Mass Spectrometry: Exemplified by the Evaluation of Chromium (VI) in Soil." *Proceedings of the 12th Annual Waste Testing and Quality Assurance Symposium*, 23-26 July, 1996, Washington, DC. 1996. pp 112-119;  U.S. Patent Number 5,414,259, "Method of Speciated Isotope Dilution Mass Spectrometry," Granted 9 May, 1995.

53  *Methods for the Determination of Metals in Environmental Samples*, Supplement I, EPA-600/R-94/111, May 1994.

**Table 2-21. Contents of *Manual for the Determination of Metals in Environmental Samples*. Methods marked with an \* are in the Supplement, *continued*.**

| Method | Title |
|---|---|
| 200.7* | Determination of metals and trace elements in water and wastes by inductively coupled plasma - atomic emission spectrometry |
| 200.8* | Determination of trace elements in water and wastes by inductively coupled plasma - mass spectrometry |
| 200.9* | Determination of trace elements by stabilized temperature graphite furnace atomic absorption spectrometry |
| 200.10 | Determination of trace elements in marine waters by on-line chelation preconcentration and inductively coupled plasma - mass spectrometry |
| 200.11 | Determination of metals in fish tissue by inductively coupled plasma - atomic emission spectrometry |
| 200.15* | Determination of metals and trace elements in water by ultrasonic nebulization inductively coupled plasma-atomic emission spectrometry. |
| 218.6* | Determination of dissolved hexavalent chromium in drinking water, groundwater, and industrial wastewater effluents by ion chromatography |
| 245.1* | Determination of mercury in water by cold vapor atomic absorption spectrometry |
| 245.3 | Determination of inorganic mercury (II) and selected organomercurials in drinking and groundwater by HPLC with electrochemical detection |
| 245.5 | Determination of mercury in sediment by cold vapor atomic absorption spectrometry |
| 245.6 | Determination of mercury in tissues by cold vapor atomic absorption spectrometry |

The average metals laboratory that analyses environmental samples has problems with laboratory contamination. The most frequently found contaminants are zinc, nickel, iron, aluminum and copper. These analytes are ubiquitous as contaminants and can actually be used as a hallmark of the technical competence of the laboratory. Although the GFAA, ICP-AES and ICP-MS have the ability to measure very low levels of these analytes, laboratories without clean room facilities that claim routine reporting limits for copper, nickel and zinc of less than 20 ug/L or iron and aluminum limits of less than 50 ug/L are probably overstating their capabilities.

The establishment of the water quality criteria for metals as monitoring goals has run directly into the problem of laboratory contamination. A series of trace metal determination methods, 1631, 1632, and 1637 through 1640, have been distributed from the Office of Water in support of the clean metals monitoring program. Associated with these methods, EPA has distributed guidance on clean metals sampling, the establishment and maintenance of a clean-room facility in the analytical lab, and data evaluation techniques for users of lab data. These methods and guidance documents have been distributed by EPA Office of Water as a set on a 3.5" disks for use with Word Perfect. See Table 2-22.

**Table 2-22. Metals methods and associated guidance for the clean metals program**

| Method | Title |
|--------|-------|
| 1631 | Mercury in water by oxidation, purge and trap, and cold vapor atomic fluorescence spectrometry EPA 821-R-95-027, April 1995 (draft) |
| 1632 | Determination of inorganic arsenic in water by hydride generation flame atomic absorption EPA 821-R-95-028 April 1995 (draft) |
| 1636 | Determination of hexavalent chromium by ion chromatography EPA 821-R-95-029 April 1995 |
| 1637 | Determination of trace elements in ambient waters by chelation preconcentration with graphite furnace atomic absorption EPA 821-R-95-030, April 1995 |
| 1638 | Determination of trace elements in ambient waters by inductively coupled plasma-mass spectrometry EPA 821-R-95-031, April 1995 |
| 1639 | Determination of trace elements in ambient waters by stabilized temperature graphite furnace atomic absorption EPA 821-R-95-032 April 1995 |
| 1640 | Determination of trace elements in ambient waters by on-line chelation preconcentration and inductively coupled plasma-mass spectrometry EPA 821-R-95-033, April 1995 |
| - | Guidance on establishing trace metal clean rooms in existing facilities EPA 821-B-95-001 April, 1995 (draft) |
| 1669 | Sampling ambient water for determination of trace metals at EPA water quality criteria levels and Quality Control Supplement for Determination of Trace Metals at EPA Water Quality Criteria Levels using EPA Metals Methods. EPA 821-R-95-034, April 1995 |
| - | Guidance on the documentation and evaluation of trace metals data collected for clean water act compliance monitoring EPA 821-B-95-002, April 1995 |

## I. Mercury by cold vapor (SM$_{18}$ 3500-Hg B, Reference 39; EPA 245.1 and 7470, References 20, 25 and 41)

An ongoing concern in mercury analysis has concentrated on the collection and preservation of samples[54]. Unpreserved or acid-preserved samples must be collected in borosilicate glass containers with Teflon® liners to prevent loss of mercury through disproportionation and volatilization. Samples preserved with 5.0% $HNO_3$ and 0.05% $K_2Cr_2O_7$ were stable for up to 6 months in glass or 30 days in polyethylene containers. Polypropylene containers were found to be totally unsuitable unless preservation also included HCl to form the stable, soluble $HgCl_4^{-2}$.

The addition of the $H_2SO_4$, $HNO_3$, and $KMnO_4$ serve to oxidize the mercury and organomercurials to inorganic Hg(II). The oxidation is insured to go to completion through the further addition of the $K_2SO_5$. The addition of the NaCl-hydroxylamine reduces the excess permanganate without reducing the mercury and transforms the oxidized mercury to the insoluble (and non-volatile) $HgCl_2$. Final addition of the $SnSO_4$ (or $SnCl_2$) solution reduces the mercury to the volatile elemental state and allows it to be swept through the AA analysis cell.

---

[54] Hamlin, S.N. "Preservation of Samples for Dissolved Mercury." *Water Resources Bulletin.* 1989. 25(2). pp. 255-262.

---

$$\text{``Hg''} - \text{oxidized} \longrightarrow Hg^{+2}$$
$$Hg^{+2} + Sn^{+2} \longrightarrow Hg^0 + Sn^{+4}$$

Once in the cell the mercury can be determined by either atomic absorption or by the more sensitive atomic fluorescence technique, either determination improved by the gold foil amalgamation procedure. This is simply allowing the mercury atoms coming off the sample to be initially collected on a gold surface as an amalgam, then thermally desorbing the mercury into the detector. The effect of this is to turn a diffuse mercury signal that passes through the detector over a period of up to 30 seconds or more into a very tightly compressed band of mercury with a detector transit time of less than 5 seconds. This effect is analogous to the increased signal-to-noise response and resulting sensitivity improvement seen when an analyst changes from packed column to capillary column in GC and GC-MS organics analysis. Successful use of the fluorescence instrument at the low ppt levels requires strict attention to sample preparation and reduction of laboratory contamination. As a number of common laboratory procedures, for example COD, use mercury compounds as reagents, and a broken mercury thermometer can make a permanent contribution to the ambient mercury background, the attention to laboratory contamination may extend to sample preparation in positive pressure glove boxes or isolated clean rooms.

## J. Residual Chlorine (SM$_{18}$ 4500-Cl, Reference 39; EPA 330, Reference 20)

Chlorination is used to disinfect drinking water and remove some organic and nitrogen contaminants. The reaction of chlorine with certain organics leads to additional pollution problems such as chlorinated phenols and trihalomethanes. Trihalomethane (THM) potential (EPA method 510.1, Reference 27) uses 3,5-dihydroxybenzoic acid reacted with excess hypochlorite as the standard precursor for THMs in the method calibration. These reactions are illustrated in Figure 2-23. One of the most potent direct-acting mutagens ever evaluated in Ames Tester Strain TA100, 3-chloro-4[dichloromethyl]-5-hydroxy-2(5H)-furanone (MX for short) is produced in water from the action of chlorine on 3,5-dihydroxybenzaldehyde, a lignin derivative[55]. Chloroform is a side product of the reaction (Figure 2-24).

---

[55]   Kronberg, L., and R. Franzen. "Determination of Chlorinated Furanones, Hydroxyfuranones and Butenedioic Acids in Chlorine-Treated Water and in Pulp Bleaching Liquor." *Environmental Sci. Technol.* 27(9). 1993. pp. 1811-1818.

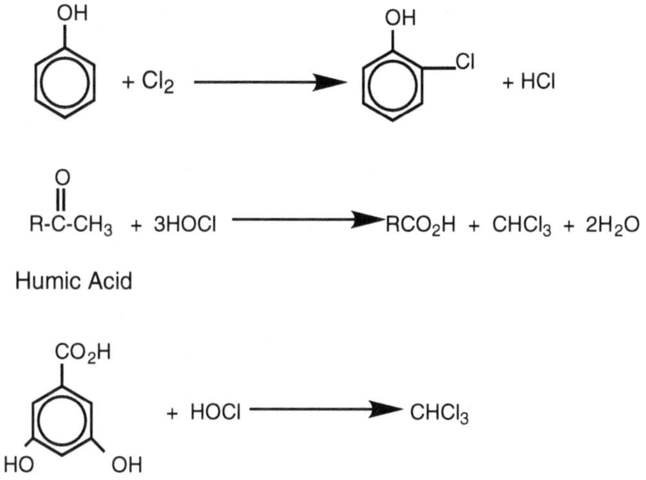

**Figure 2-23. Reactions of organic materials with chlorine to produce pollutants.**

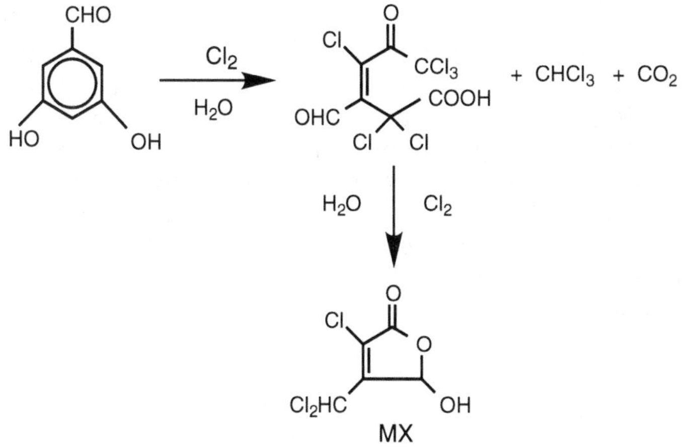

**Figure 2-24. Production of MX by reaction of chlorine with 3,5-dihydroxybenzaldehyde.**

Chemical preservation of samples often requires removal of residual chlorine to eliminate destruction of target analytes through the above types of reactions. The most common agents used for removal of residual chlorine are sodium thiosulfate, sodium sulfite and ascorbic acid. The reaction of thiosulfate with chlorine is described below and is limited to a 2:1 molar ratio, although in the presence of acid a 1:1 neutralization reaction can occur. Ascorbic acid on the other hand has a 1:1 stoichiometric initial reversible reaction with chlorine to form dehydroascorbic acid. In the presence of additional oxidant the dehydroascorbic acid irreversibly ring opens to 2,3-diketogulonic acid, which consumes further multiple equivalents of oxidant to result in a variety of five or less carbon products[56].

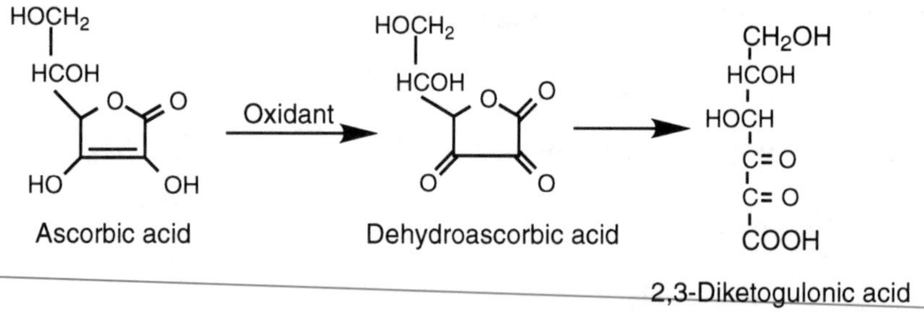

**Figure 2-25. Neutralization of residual chlorine with ascorbic acid.**

## 1. Breakpoint Chlorination

In addition to the reactions with organic chemicals and organic matter such as bacteria, algae, and viruses, chlorine is used to remove ammonia from water. The reactions of chlorine with ammonia are illustrated in Figure 2-26. Some of the intermediate compounds formed in this series are potent biocides, but not as effective as chlorine or hypochlorous acid. Mono-chloramine is an example. In many tests for residual chlorine, the mono- and di-chloramines react as if they were chlorine and contribute to the observed result. In the presence of ammonia, added chlorine reacts with it to form mono-chloramine, which tests as chlorine. When all the ammonia has been converted to mono-chloramine, the observed test results hit a maximum. Further addition of chlorine forms di-chloramine, which reacts with mono-chloramine to form nitrogen and the observed residual decreases. When all of the ammonia has been oxidized to nitrogen, the residual chlorine test hits a minimum, and with addition of more chlorine, HOCl begins to accumulate, and the breakpoint is passed.

$$Cl_2 + H_2O \longrightarrow HOCl + HCl$$

$$HOCl + NH_3 \longrightarrow NH_2Cl + H_2O$$

$$NH_2Cl + HOCl \longrightarrow NHCl_2 + H_2O$$

$$NHCl_2 + NH_2Cl \longrightarrow N_2 + 3HCl$$

**Figure 2-26. Reactions of chlorine with ammonia.**

---

[56] Deutsch, J.C, C.R. Santhosh-Kumar, K.L. Hassell, and J.F. Kolhouse. "Variation in Ascorbic Acid Oxidation Routes in $H_2O_2$ and Cupric Ion Solution as Determined by GC/MS." *Anal. Chem.* 66(3). 1994. pp. 345-350.

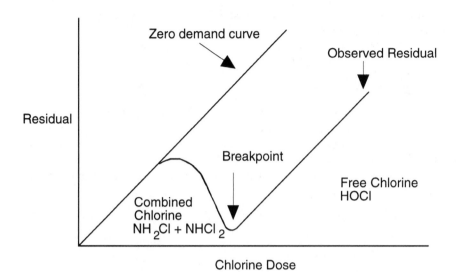

**Figure 2-27. Breakpoint chlorination curve.**

## 2. Determination of Residuals

Virtually all methods will have interference from $ClO_2$, molecular and HOX forms of bromine and iodine, permanganate, $H_2O_2$ and ozone. As mentioned above, mono-, di- and tri-chloramines will also contribute to the observed results in several of the procedures[57]. $NO_2^-$ interferes in some test procedures, particularly iodine-based methods, through both direct oxidation of iodide to iodine and in-direct involvement of dissolved oxygen in the sample in the oxidation of iodide[58].

$$2NO_2^- + 2I^- + 4H^+ \longrightarrow 2NO + I_2 + 2H_2O$$
$$O_2 + 2NO \longrightarrow 2NO_2$$
$$4H^+ + 4I^- + 2NO_2 \longrightarrow 2I_2 + 2H_2O + 2NO$$

Nitrite interference is commonly countered by the addition of sulfamic acid and phosphoric acid. However, if thiosulfate is present, competing reactions are set up with the thiosulfate winning.

$$NH_2SO_3H + HNO_2 \longrightarrow H_2SO_4 + N_2 + H_2O$$
$$2S_2O_3^{2-} + 2HNO_2 + 2H^+ \longrightarrow S_4O_6^{2-} + 2NO + 2H_2O$$

**Iodometric direct** - Potassium iodide reacts with chlorine and other oxidizers to form iodine, which is titrated with thiosulfate in the presence of a starch indicator.

$$Cl_2 + 2KI \longrightarrow I_2 + 2KCl$$
$$I_2 + 2Na_2S_2O_3 \longrightarrow 2NaI + Na_2S_4O_6 \quad \text{(1:2 titration)}$$

---

[57]  Derrigan, J., L.Y. Lin and J.N. Jensen. "Comparison of Free and Total Chlorine Measurement Methods in Municipal Wastewaters." *Water Environment Reasearch.* 1993. 65(3). pp. 205-212.

[58]  Dietz, E.A. Jr., R. Cortellucci, and M. Williams. "A Study of Analysis Errors Caused by Nitrite and Free Available Chlorine During Iodometric Titration of Total Residual Chlorine in Wastewater." *Water Environ. Res.* 1996. 68(6). pp. 974-980.

**Iodometric indirect** - A known amount of thiosulfate or phenylarsine oxide is added to the sample, then the excess, which is not required for reaction with chlorine or other oxidizing agents, is determined by titration with an iodine solution.

$$Cl_2 + PhAsO \longrightarrow 2Cl^- + PhAsO(OH)_2 \quad \text{or}$$
$$Cl_2 + 2S_2O_3^{2-} \longrightarrow 2Cl^- + S_4O_6^{2-}$$

Excess PhAsO or $S_2O_3^{2-}$ is titrated with standard $I_3^-$ or $IO_3^-$ and starch indicator. The technique is particularly prone to interferences from nitrite present in the sample and also to the exact form of residual chlorine. Thiosulfate tends to give much lower values than PAO due to some over-oxidation of the thiosulfate to sulfate[59] by free chlorine. This can be counteracted by addition of dimethylamine to the sample prior to thiosulfate reagent addition.

$$S_2O_3^{2-} + 4Cl_2 + 5H_2O \longrightarrow 2SO_4^{2-} + 8Cl^- + 8H^+$$

## 3. Iodine and thiosulfate solutions

Molecular iodine is not soluble in water to any appreciable degree. To obtain iodine in solution for titrations, the iodine is reacted with excess iodide ion to form the triiodide ion ($I_3^-$), which is very soluble and reacts as if it were molecular iodine. A handy source of iodine is from potassium biiodate, $KH(IO_3)_2$, which is a primary standard. Iodine forms in the presence of acid.

$$KH(IO_3)_2 + 10KI + 11H^+ \longrightarrow 6I_2 + 6H_2O + 11K^+$$

Excess KI reacts with the formed $I_2$ to form $I_3^-$ (triiodide ion), which titrates as if it were $I_2$. The potassium biiodate is used as a primary reference to form a known amount of $I_2$ for standardization of the thiosulfate. Thiosulfate solutions are not stable when first made. The titer seems to rise over a period of two to three days, then drop, then stabilize after two or more weeks. The reason behind this behavior is the instability of thiosulfuric acid, which forms from any acid in the water used to make the solution or from absorption of atmospheric carbon dioxide. The thiosulfurous acid decomposes to form sulfur and sulfurous acid, which reacts with iodine in a 1:1 titration instead of the 2:1 reaction of thiosulfate and the titer appears to rise. The sulfurous acid slowly reacts with dissolved oxygen to form sulfuric acid, which is inactive in the iodine titration, and the titer drops. The sulfuric acid transfers the protons to a thiosulfate ion, forming the weaker acid. The cycle continues until all the dissolved oxygen is consumed at which point the titer stabilizes, or until someone opens and shakes the bottle.

$$S_2O_3^{2-} + 2H^+ \longrightarrow H_2S_2O_3$$
$$H_2S_2O_3 \longrightarrow H_2SO_3 + S$$
$$I_2 + H_2SO_3 + H_2O \longrightarrow 2HI + H_2SO_4 \quad \text{(1:1 titration)}$$
$$2H_2SO_3 + O_2 \longrightarrow H_2SO_4 \quad \text{(inactive in } I_2 \text{ titrations and titer drops)}$$
$$H_2SO_4 + S_2O_3^{2-} \longrightarrow H_2S_2O_3 + SO_4^{2-}$$

**Figure 2-28. Chemistry of thiosulfate solutions.**

---

[59] Dietz, E.A. Jr., R. Cortellucci, and M. Williams. "A Study of Analysis Errors Caused by Nitrite and Free Available Chlorine During Iodometric Titration of Total Residual Chlorine in Wastewater." *Water Environ. Res.* 1996. 68(6). pp. 974-980.

Sodium thiosulfate solutions are also prone to developing bacterial and fungus growth. Sodium hydroxide is commonly used as an additive to the solutions to prevent growth and to neutralize any acid. Concentrated stock solutions of sodium thiosulfate are more stable toward growth and acid degradation; however, working solutions are very sensitive and need to be prepared and standardized daily.

## 4. Amperometric titration.

Two models are available. The single electrode model monitors a Pt electrode *vs.* a silver reference electrode. A small voltage is applied across the electrodes, and as long as an oxidizing agent ($Cl_2$) is present, a current flows through the cell. Phenylarsineoxide (PAO) titrant is added, and the current decreases, reaching zero when all the oxidizing agent is exhausted. A back titration is also possible by adding an excess of PAO then titrating the excess PAO with iodine until current appears. A dual electrode model is also available that operates on a steady state current flow principle: current is proportional to the concentration of oxidizing agent $Cl_2$.

$$\text{Cathode Rxn:} \quad Cl_2 + 2e^- \longrightarrow 2Cl^-$$
$$\text{Anode Rxn:} \quad 2Cl^- \longrightarrow Cl_2 + 2e^-$$

PAO, in the absence of KI, reacts only with $Cl_2$ and HOCl at pH 7, thus reading only residual chlorine. Addition of 50 mg/L KI at pH 7 allows titration of monochloramine, and addition of 250 mg/L KI at pH 4 allows titration of dichloramine. Addition of larger amounts of KI and allowing the sample to sit for several minutes makes $NCl_3$ chlorine available for titration. Stepwise analysis of the differing Cl residuals is thus possible from assay of a single sample.

Amperometric titrators are available commercially and are the standard for analysis of chlorine residuals both free and combined.

## 5. DPD Ferrous Titrimetric

N,N-diethyl phenylenediamine (DPD) is oxidized with $Cl_2$ or HOCl or $OCl^-$ ($I_2$ and other strong oxidants) to a stable red-colored radical cation called a Würster dye[60]. At pH 6.2 to 6.5 the reaction is rapid and reversible, with the red color titrated with the reducing agent ferrous ammonium sulfate, $Fe(NH_4)_2(SO_4)_2$ [FAS] to a sharp endpoint. Little interference from the combined chloramines is seen in the absence of iodide. Addition of a small crystal of KI allows titration of monochloramine. Addition of more KI gives the dichloramine contribution, similar to the amperometric titration.

The buffer is a $Na_2HPO_4/KH_2PO_4$ system with EDTA added to remove heavy metal ion catalysis interference. Oxidized manganese will interfere with the determination and is accounted for by addition of thioacetamide to remove all chlorine contribution, then addition of DPD and titration as a blank.

---

[60] Harp, D.L., "Measuring Trace Levels of Total Residual Chlorine in Wastewater." *Water Environment Laboratory Solutions*. 1994. January/February. pp. 4-5.

---

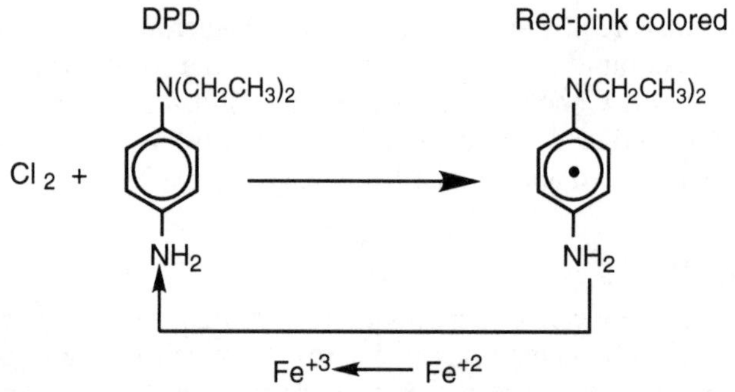

**Figure 2-29. Chemistry of DPD-FAS chlorine determination.**

## 6. DPD Colormetric

Addition of excess DPD with buffer gives a red color, the intensity of which is proportional to the concentration of $Cl_2$ or HOCl. The intensity is read on a spectrophotometer at 515 nm or compared visually to standards. There is good evidence that values of greater than 1 mg/L residual chlorine obtained from the DPD colorimetric procedure are in fact low estimates due to over oxidation of the DPD to a colorless anion[61]. The titration procedure is not affected by the overoxidation of DPD as FAS is capable of reducing the colorless anion back down to DPD.

## 7. Syringaldazine(FACTS)

Free residual chlorine ($Cl_2$ or HOCl) reacts 1:1 with 3,5-dimethoxy-4-hydroxy-benzaldazine (syringaldazine) at pH 6.5 to 6.8 to form a colored species with an absorption maximum at 530 nm. The colored product has limited solubility in water, and 2-propanol is used to keep it in solution. The only interferences in the method are $I_2$, $Br_2$ and $O_3$, and the combined chloramines are non-reactive. The method is known as the Free Available Chlorine Test, Syringaldazine (FACTS).

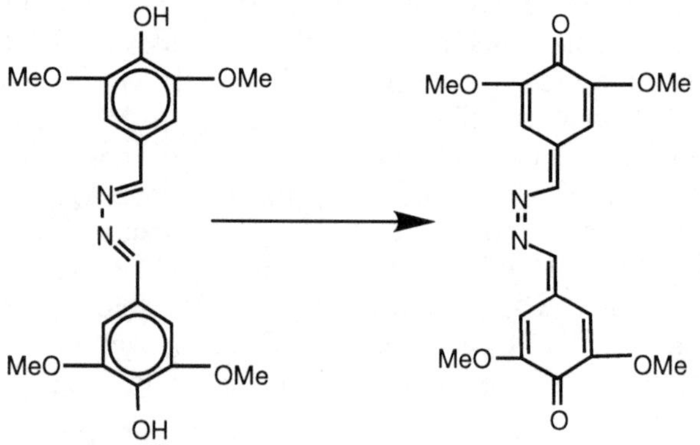

**Figure 2-30. FACTS chemistry.**

[61] Gordon, G., D.L. Sweetin, K. Smith and G.E. Pacey. "Improvements in the DPD Method for Determination of Free and Combined Residual Chlorine Through use of FIA." *Talanta.* 1991. 38(2). pp. 145-149.

## 8. Orthotolidine

Not currently used due to the toxic nature of *o*-Tolidine, it offers quick reaction with residual chlorine species to form a colored product, which is read on a spectrophotometer.

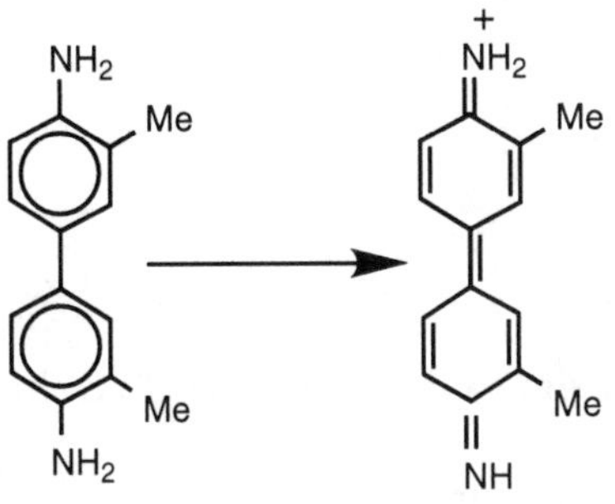

**Figure 2-31. Orthotolidine reaction with chlorine.**

## 9. Leuco Crystal Violet

Again, this is an out-dated method. LCV reacts instantly with free chlorine to develop a blue color and can be read spectroscopically within 5 minutes. Addition of $I^-$, reacts with the combined chlorine species to form $I_2$, which reacts with LCV to form Crystal Violet (Basic Violet 3), a violet color stable for days and read spectroscopically.

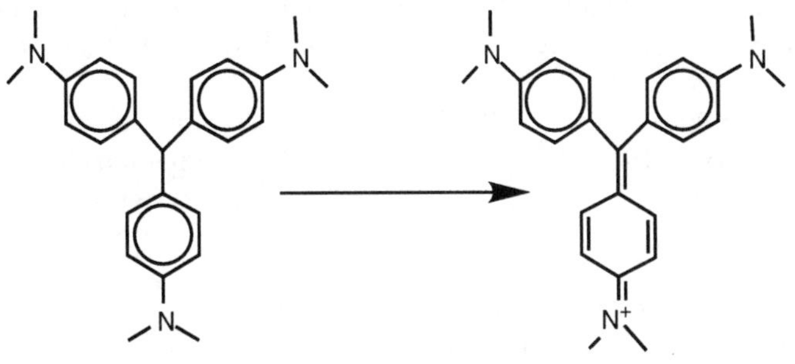

**Figure 2-32. Reaction of leuco crystal violet with chlorine.**

## 10. Methyl Orange

This is a method that in a comparison study, ranks very high in accuracy and precision for determination of chlorine free and combined residuals, yet has never caught on. Methyl Orange (Acid Orange 52, C.I. 13025, CAS 547-58-0) is decolorized instantly by free chlorine (or HOCl) on a 1:2 molar basis. The reaction is much slower with combined chlorine. The reaction can be used as a self-indicating titration method using 0.005% M.O. solution where 1.00 mL M.O. solution is equivalent to 21.9 mg $Cl_2$. The method can also be performed as a absorbance method with a spectrophotometer. M.O. is a primary standard, and solutions are stable for long periods of time, while maintaining their titer. The initial addition compound reacts further with $Cl_2$ to form nitrogen gas.

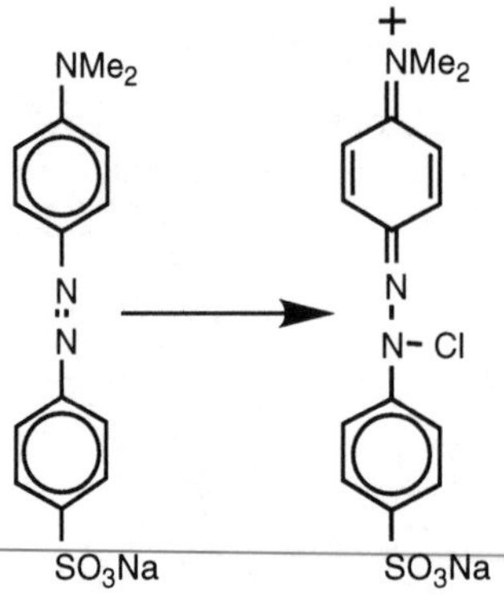

**Figure 2-33. Methyl orange determination of residual chlorine.**

## 11. Inorganic disinfection by-products

The three most common inorganic disinfection by-products of concern are chlorite ($ClO_2^-$), chlorate ($ClO_3^-$) and bromate ($BrO_3^-$). They titrate as total residual chlorine in some of the above test procedures and thus serve as interferences. They also are contaminates of concern of and by themselves in drinking water. A suitable test procedures that has been approved for use on drinking water samples is ion chromatography (EPA Method 300.0). Capillary ion electrophoresis has also been demonstrated as an effective analytical tool.

The inorganic disinfection by-products are not commonly created in the disinfection process. They are generally introduced to the water supply as co-contaminants of the disinfection chemicals, particularly the hypochlorite solutions, used to treat the water.

$$2NaClO_2 + Cl_2 \longrightarrow 2ClO_2 + 2NaCl \qquad \text{production of chlorine dioxide}$$

$$2ClO_2 + H_2O \longrightarrow 2H^+ + ClO_2^- + ClO_3^- \qquad \text{disproportionation at pH >11}$$

$$ClO_2 + e^- \longrightarrow ClO_2^- \qquad \begin{array}{l}\text{Neutral pH partial reaction with}\\\text{thiosulfate or PAO}\end{array}$$

$$ClO_2 + 4H^+ + 4e^- \longrightarrow Cl^- + 2H_2O \qquad \text{at pH of 2 or lower}$$

$$4I^- \longrightarrow 2I_2 + 4e^-$$

pH adjustment allows selective determination by FAS-DPD titration[62].

## K. Total organic carbon (TOC) (SM$_{18}$ 5310, Reference 39; EPA 415 and 9060, References 20 and 41)

Carbon fractions found in water are:

- Total Carbon (TC) - all forms of carbon, convert to $CO_2$ over heated cobalt oxide catalyst (900 °C), or persulfate -UV light oxidation to $CO_2$, determine $CO_2$ by infrared absorption or FID.
- Inorganic Carbon (IC) - carbonate, bicarbonate and dissolved $CO_2$, acidify and gas purge $CO_2$, determine by IR or FID.

---

[62]   Adam, L.C. and G. Gordon. "Direct and Sequential Potentiometric Determination of Hypochlorite, Chlorite and Chlorate Ions when Hypochlorite Ion is Present in Large Excess." *Anal. Chem.* 1995. 67(3). pp. 535-540.

- Total Organic Carbon (TOC) - covalently bonded carbon, determined as TC - IC.
- Dissolved Organic Carbon (DOC) - passes a 0.45 μm filter, assay as TC - IC.
- Nondissolved Organic Carbon (NDOC) - retained by 0.45 μm filter, assay as TC - IC.
- Purgeable Organic Carbon (POC) - fraction of TOC removed by gas stripping, determine as TC - IC - NPOC.
- Nonpurgeable Organic Carbon (NPOC) - residue after gas stripping, assay as TC.

In water IC is many times greater than TOC. IC is removed by acidifying the sample and then gas stripping to remove $CO_2$. This also results in a loss of POC. Carbon determinations after IC removal are actually NPOC values; however, POC is generally very small (negligible) in most samples, although this is not believed to be true when analyzing landfill leachates[63]. Pretreatment of the sample defines the fraction assayed.

All procedures call for the conversion of the carbon to $CO_2$ then determination of $CO_2$ by either gas chromatography (after reduction to methane and FID), nondispersive infrared spectrometry, or determination of conductance after dissolution in ultrapure water. As far as being an indicator of organic contamination, TOC is generally not very useful as a high background is normal due to the presence of large amounts of humic acids and fulvic acids. A further problem exists in interpretation of the results. Most regulated organic compounds (VOCs, pesticides, BNAs) and background organics have from 39-50% carbon, while petroleum hydrocarbons, oil, and grease exhibit above 75% carbon. TOC has been used as an alternative to BOD or COD characterization of wastewater; however, the relationship varies for every wastewater source. Assuming a relationship has been determined, TOC becomes a very rapid monitoring tool as an analysis is completed in minutes rather than hours or days.

## L. Total Organic Halide (TOX) (SM$_{18}$ 5320, Reference 39; EPA 9020, Reference 41)

Four steps are used in the analysis. The sample is introduced as a water solution of known volume into an activated carbon column. Inorganic halides (Cl, Br, and I) are removed by washing with a nitrate ion solution. The residual organic halogen compounds remaining on the column are pyrolyzed to HCl, HBr, and HI and detected with a microcoulometric titration cell. The titration cell consists of a constant concentration of silver ions in acetic acid solution maintained by a constant electric potential through a silver electrode. As the hydrogen halides dissolve in the acetic acid, solid silver halide precipitates, and the electric current rises to maintain the silver ion concentration. The applied current is integrated over the pyrolysis period and is proportional to the moles of halide on the column.

Method 9021 (SW-846) purges an aqueous sample with carbon dioxide into the pyrolysis chamber to determine the volatile total organic halide. A draft method (9023) for extractable organic halides (EOX) is currently under consideration for inclusion in SW-846. The organohalide compounds are desorbed from a solid sample by sonication in ethyl acetate, then an aliquot of the ethyl acetate solution is introduced into the pyrolysis oven.

---

63   Levine, A.D., and L.R. Kroemer. "TOC and TOX as Indicator Parameters for Organic Contaminants in Landfill Leachate." *Waste Management and Research.* 1989. 7. pp. 337-349.

## M. Surfactants (SM$_{18}$ 5540, Reference 39; EPA 425, Reference 20)

Surfactants consist of three basic types: anionic ($RSO_3^-Na$), cationic ($RMe_3N^+Cl^-$), and nonionic ($R[OCH_2CH_2]_nOH$) where R is from 10 - 20 carbons long and "n" can range to the thousands. The charged end of the molecule imparts water solubility and the organic end non-polar solubility. The presence of the ether oxygens in the non-ionic surfactants allows chelation of cationic materials and promotes further solubilization. There are also surfactants that are mixed anionic/non-ionic materials, formed by attaching a sulfate ester to the terminal hydroxy group of the non-ionic molecule. Some surfactants are noted for the production of very tenacious foams, presenting major problems in waterways downstream from effluent points. Others are designed to produce no foam, while still performing the detergent function.

Sublation is a process that removes water from the surfactant and produces a dry form of the material for analysis. The technique consists of covering a sample of surfactant containing water with ethyl acetate (a polar organic solvent) and bubbling $N_2$ gas up through the sample. The surfactant forms a foam on contact with the $N_2$ in the water, then dissolves into the organic layer as the bubbles rise. Two changes of the organic layer are sufficient to remove most of the surfactants. Evaporation of the ethyl acetate leaves the surfactant as a dried residue. The equipment is illustrated in Appendix C.

Methylene blue active substances (MBAS) are anionic surfactant specific. Methylene blue is a cationic organic dye. In the presence of an acidified solution of an anionic surfactant, the resulting ion-pair is non-polar soluble and can be extracted into chloroform. The intensity of the methylene blue in the chloroform layer is proportional to the anionic surfactants present. Carboxylic soaps are not strong enough to be extracted with methylene blue, however the sulfonate ($RSO_3^-$), sulfate ester ($ROSO_3^-$), and sulfated non-ionics ($R[OCH_2CH_2]_nOSO_3^-$) are extracted. The absorption curve at 652 nm is calibrated by extracting known amounts of linear alkylbenzene sulfonate (LAS), which is assumed to have a molecular mass of 318 g/mol. Results are reported in units of mg MBAS/L (calculated as LAS). A useful innovation is the use of microextraction for preparation of the 10-point calibration curve[64].

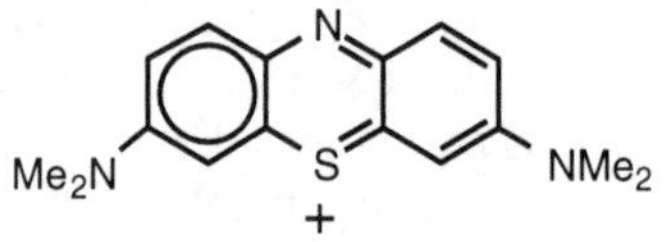

**Figure 2-34. Structure of methylene blue.**

Cobalt thiocyanate active substances (CTAS) are nonionic surfactants. Cationic and anionic surfactants are removed from the sublation residue by dissolution in MeOH and passage through a ion-exchange column containing both anionic and cationic resins. Solvent exchange to water is followed by treatment with cobalt thiocyanate and extraction with methylene chloride. Nonionic surfactants will coordinate to the cobalt and render it nonpolar soluble (the methylene chloride layer). Measurement of the absorbance of the methylene chloride cobalt solution at 620 nm is directly proportional

---

[64] Craig, C. A., and O. L. Salvador. "Microextraction for Preparing Calibration Standards for Methylene Blue Active Substances (MBAS)." *American Environmental Laboratory*. Feb., 1992. pp. 42-44.

to the molar amount of nonionic surfactant present. The method is calibrated by measuring the absorption of cobalt complexes of known amounts of a standard nonionic surfactant ($C_{12-18}[OCH_2CH_2]_{11}OH$).

There are many other techniques that can be used for surfactant analysis[65], some are substantial improvements over the MBAS and CTAS procedures. Bismuth iodide active substances (BIAS) uses Dragendorff reagent (barium tetraiodobismuthate) to form a precipitate with surfactants followed by potentiometric titration of the remaining bismuth in solution with pyrrolidine dithiocarbamate. The BIAS precipitate forms in a constant ratio of one barium to 9.8 ether oxygens and experimentally produces less variation than CTAS. The Potassium Picrate Active Substances (PPAS)[66] procedure was recently published. The sublatted reside is dissolved in ethylene dichloride, potassium picrate solution added then extracted into methylene chloride. The extract is read spectrophotometrically. The authors report a detection limit of 0.1 mg/L and fewer interferences than BIAS or CTAS. Surfactants can be qualitatively and semi-quantitatively determined by thin layer chromatography, TLC (Swisher, 1987). Gas chromatographic analytical techniques include derivatization as a trimethylsilane ester or acetate and fission with HBr (Cross, 1987). High pressure liquid chromatography, HPLC, is the most common instrumental technique[67,68]. The surfactants are reacted with phenyl isocyanate or one of a variety of acetylation reagents to form a HPLC compatible material. Detection is by UV, FID, or MS. A number of HPLC references for anionic and other surfactants are listed in *Anal. Chem.* 1992. 64(6). pp. 583-589.

Capillary electrophoresis has been examined for analysis and characterization of surfactants. Anionic sulfate and sulfonate surfactants have been determined using an naphthalenesulfonate electrolyte[69]. An alternate recipe uses a non-aqueous electrolyte[70].

Branched nonylphenol (CAS 84852-15-3) is the most common toxic degradation product of alkylphenol ethoxylates (APE), a sub-class of the non-ionic surfactants. Nonylphenol has been implicated as a significant endocrine disruptor in the environment. Analyses of APE precursors to nonylphenols are discussed above. One technique reacts the isolated surfactant to form a bromide followed by analysis by GC-MS[71]. Another technique uses acetylation with acetic anhydride (SFE extraction and acetylation for sludge and solid samples), liquid-liquid extraction and determination of the acetate by

---

[65] Talmage, S.S. *Environmental and Human Safety of Major Surfactants*, Lewis Publishers, Boca Raton, FL. 1994. ISBN 1-56670-017-5; Swisher, R.D., *Surfactant Biodegradation*, 2nd Ed, 1987. Marcel Dekker, NY; Cross, J. *Nonionic Surfactants: Chemical Analysis*. 1987. Marcel Dekker, NY; Midwidsky, B, and D.M. Gabriel. *Detergent Analysis*. 1982. Halstead Press, NY.

[66] Favretto, L., B. Stancher, and F. Tunis. "An Improved Method for the Spectrophotometric Determination of Polyoxyethylene Non-Ionic Surfactants in Waters as Potassium Picrate Active Substances." *Intl. J. Environ. Anal. Chem.* 1983. 14. pp. 201-214.

[67] Schmitt, T.M., M.C. Allen, D.K. Brain, K.F. Guin, D.E. Lemmel and Q.W. Osburn. "HPLC Determination of Ethoxylated Alcohol Surfactants in Wastewater." *J. Am. Oil Chem. Soc.* 1990. 67. pp. 103-109.

[68] Kiewiet, A.T., J.M.D. van der Steen, and J.R. Parsons. "Trace Analysis of Ethoxylated Nonionic Surfactants in Samples of Influent and Effluent of Sewage Treatment Plants by HPLC." *Anal. Chem.* 1995. 67(23). pp. 4409-4415.

[69] Shamsi, S.A. and N.D. Danielson. "Naphthalenesulfonates as Electrolytes for Capillary Electrophoresis of Inorganic Anions, Organic Acids and Surfactants with Indirect Photometric Detection." *Anal. Chem.* 1994. 66(21). pp. 3757-3764.

[70] Salimi-Moosavi, H., and R.M. Cassidy. "Application of Nonaqueous Capillary Electrophoresis to the Separation of Long-Chain Surfactants." *Anal. Chem.* 1996. 68(2). pp. 293-299.

[71] Fendinger, N.J., D.C. McAvoy, W.M. Begley and W.S. Eckhoff. "Measurement of Alkyl Ethoxylate Surfactants in Natural Waters." *Environ. Sci. Tech.* 1995. 29(4). pp. 856-863.

---

GC-MS in the SIM mode. Detection limits were estimated as 0.1 ug/L for aqueous samples and 0.1 mg/kg for solid matrices[72].

EDTA, ethylene diamine tetraacetic acid, is a small molecule chelation agent for cations and one member of a class of chelation agents. The structure is shown in Figure 2-15, in conjunction with its use as a reagent in the hardness titration. Another chelation reagent is DTPA, diethylenetriamine pentaacetic acid. These type materials exhibit human toxicity and are becoming of interest as pollutants. Analysis has been performed by HPLC[73]. Other chelation agents include the polyphosphonates, which bear the Dequest[74] trademark. Some of these materials are illustrated in Table 2-23. Capillary electrophoresis has been used for analysis[75].

**Table 2-23. Commonly encountered chelation agents**

| Name | Initials | Structure |
|---|---|---|
| Ethylenediamine tetraacetic acid | EDTA | $(HO_2CCH_2)_2NCH_2CH_2N(CH_2CO_2H)_2$ |
| Diethylenetriamine pentaacetic acid | DTPA | $(HO_2CCH_2)_2N(CH_2)_2NH(CH_2)_2N(CH_2CO_2H)_2$ |
| Nitrilo triacetic acid | NTA | $N(CH_2CO_2H)_3$ |
| Dequest[76] 2010 | HEPD | $CH_3CH(PO_3H_2)_2$ |
| Dequest 2006 | ATMP | $N(CH_2PO_3H_2)_3$ |
| Dequest 2041 | EDTMP | $(H_2O_3PCH_2)_2NCH_2CH_2N(CH_2PO_3H_2)_2$ |
| Dequest 2060 | DETPMP | $H_2O_3PCH_2N[CH_2CH_2N(CH_2PO_3H_2)_2]_2$ |
| Triethanolamine | | $N(CH_2CH_2OH)_3$ |

## N. Oil & Grease (SM$_{18}$ 5520, Reference 39; EPA 413, Reference 20; EPA 1664)

What is assayed in an oil-and-grease determination depends to a large extent on how the measurement is made. The gravimetric methods depend on solubility in 1,1,2-trichloro-trifluoroethane (Freon 113), and a lack of volatility when the sample is evaporated. The total petroleum hydrocarbon (TPH) method measures only material with C-H bonds that are soluble in Freon 113. Various classes of materials that are measured as oil & grease include fatty acids, esters and amides, animal and plant waxes, triglycerides, phosphono-lipids, chlorophylls and other synthetic and natural dyes and pigments, essential oil components, surfactants, and a range of petroleum hydrocarbon derived products.

With the gravimetric method, the sample is extracted with Freon 113, and water is removed by passage through anhydrous $Na_2SO_4$, and evaporated to dryness. The material is then measured by weight. A modification of the method using a Soxhlet

---

[72] Lee, H.-B., and T.E. Peart. "Determination of 4-Nonylphenol in Effluent and Sludge From Sewage Treatment Plants." *Anal. Chem.* 1995. 67(13). pp. 1976-1980.

[73] Nowack, B., F.G. Kari, S.U. Hilger and L. Sigg. "Determination of Dissolved and Adsorbed EDTA Species in Water and Sediments by HPLC." *Anal. Chem.* 1996. 68(3). pp. 561-566.

[74] Monsanto Co., St. Louis, MO.

[75] Shamsi, S.A. and N.D. Danielson. "Ribonucleotide Electrolytes for Capillary Electrophoresis of Polyphosphates and Polyphosphonates with Indirect Photometric Detection." *Anal. Chem.* 1995. 67(11). pp. 1845-1852.

[76] Trademark of Monsanto Company, St. Louis, MO

extractor allows processing of soils and sludges. Anhydrous $MgSO_4$ is used for drying the sludge prior to soxhlet extraction.

For the total petroleum hydrocarbons method, the sample is extracted with Freon 113, dried by passage through anhydrous $Na_2SO_4$, passed through a column of silica gel to remove non-hydrocarbons, and the absorbance measured from 3200 $cm^{-1}$ to 2700 $cm^{-1}$ on an infrared spectrophotometer *vs.* a solvent blank. Freon 113 is used because it has no IR absorbance in the analytical range. A reference oil containing iso-octane, hexadecane and chlorobenzene (37.5 : 37.5 : 25) is used to prepare a calibration curve. Omission of the silica gel column gives the "Partition - Infrared" method for determination of oil and grease. Other possibilities include the development by Buck Scientific of a quartz IR cell that uses no solvent in the IR analysis of TPH[77].

During the Summer of 1994, EPA announced draft method 1664 for oil & grease (hexane extractable material - HEM) and total petroleum hydrocarbon (silica gel treated hexane extractable material - SGT-HEM) analysis, then revised as a draft method in 1995 and 1996. The Freon 113 has been replaced by hexane, however a separatory funnel extraction remains the basis of the procedure. The method is written in a performance based modification fashion, and several possible alternates are mentioned. These consist of a continuous liquid-liquid extraction or solid phase column/disk for isolation of the target analytes, followed by elution with a suitable organic solvent. Several determinative methods are specifically excluded as allowable performance based modifications of Method 1664. Excluded are use of IR or immunoassay for determination of the residue. Method 1664 includes very strict quality control and method performance criteria as measuring sticks for what is an allowable modification and what is not. These QC include intial and continuing demonstrations of ability (IPR - Initial Precision and Recovery, and OPR - Ongoing Precision and Recovery), matrix spike, matrix spike duplicate, and blank analysis every 10 samples. The method includes specified acceptance ranges for MS/MSD and method detection/reporting limit. Once the suitable replacement technique is promulgated, all the NPDES permit holders will have to reanalyze their wastewater, and the permits will have to be rewritten to correct the discharge limits to the results of the modified test.

See Sections 3 and 4 for further information on petroleum hydrocarbon classification and analysis.

## O. Total phenols (SM$_{18}$ 5530, Reference 39; EPA 420, Reference 20)

Phenols are important industrial pollutants from a wide range of manufacturing processes. Wood, after hydrolysis, is a major source of phenols. Phenols are important because they are in themselves harmful, and during water chlorination are easily transformed into chlorophenols and then further transformed into dioxins. Phenols are organic acids and are quite soluble in mildly alkaline water. The parent compound, phenol, was the first disinfectant used in surgery by Lister (1885). Many different phenols are used in disinfectants for industrial use, in hospitals and in food preparation facilities. Phenols are often absorbed through the skin, and are active CNS agents as well as general protoplasmic poisons.

---

[77] DeMenna, G. "Determination of Oil and Grease by Evaporation of Solvent in a Quartz Cell in An Infrared Spectrophotometer." In *Oil and Grease Workshop*, EPA-821-R-93-014, Sept., 1993, p. 7 and Appendix G. As part of 16th Annual EPA Analytical Conference, May 4-6, 1993. Norfolk, Va.

Phenols can be purified (interferences removed) by extraction of a basic solution with an organic solvent such as methylene chloride or chloroform, then acidification of the water layer and steam distillation of the phenols. Phenols are detected by reaction with 4-aminoantipyrine (4-AAP) in the presence of potassium ferricyanide, $K_3Fe(CN)_6$ to give a colored antipyrine dye that is measured spectrophotometricly. The absorbance can be read directly at 500 nm in the water solution, or extracted into chloroform and read at 460 nm for increased sensitivity. A drawback to this method is that para-substituted phenols are unreactive and not measured. Further, some types of phenol, such as the nitrophenols, are deactivated toward reaction due to the ring electronics.

Phenols can be individually detected and assayed by GC, as discussed in Section 3. Some of the phenols are listed as hazardous wastes.

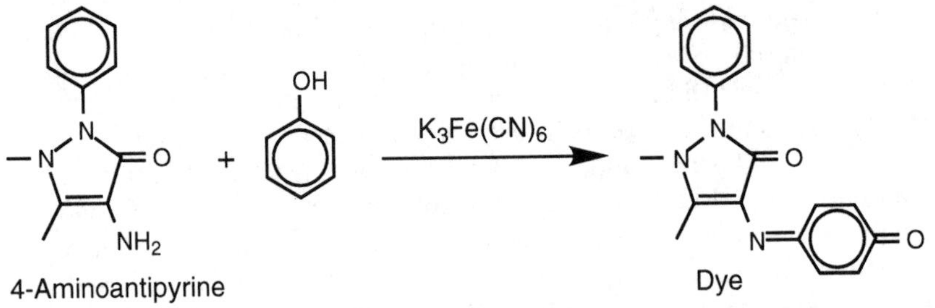

**Figure 2-35. 4-AAP reaction for analysis of total phenols.**

The preparation of standards for total phenols analysis is somewhat of a problem. Phenol itself is extremely hydroscopic with even samples that do not appear to be wet containing 8 to 10% water. After the standard is prepared according to the method (either *Standard Methods* or EPA 420.1) the concentration must be verified. *Standard Methods* offers a procedure based on the bromination of phenol. Bromate ion reacts with bromide to form free bromine. In the presence of acid and phenol, tribromophenol is formed, which precipitates. The original amount of bromate in the reaction solution is determined by titration of a portion of the mixed bromate/bromide reagent with iodine and sodium thiosulfate. The remaining bromate after the reaction has gone to completion is determined by titration and the consumed bromate determined by the difference. There is a 1:1 relation between the amount of bromate consumed and the phenol initially present in the standard.

$$BrO_3^- + 5Br^- + 6H^+ \longrightarrow 3Br_2 + 3H_2O$$

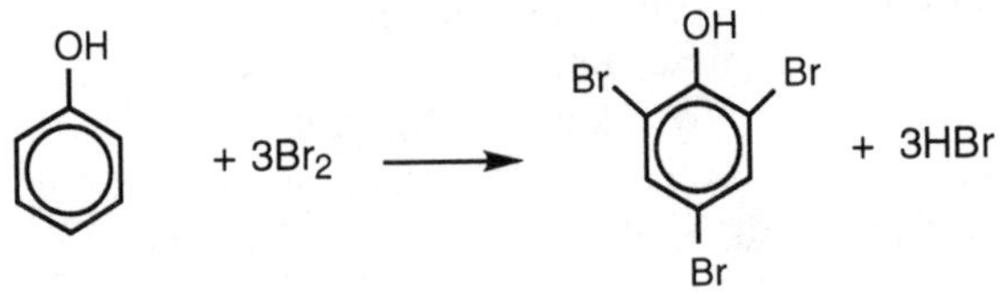

$$Br_2 + 2I^- \longrightarrow 2Br^- + I_2$$

$$I_2 + 2Na_2S_2O_3 \longrightarrow 2I^- + 2Na^+ + Na_2S_4O_6$$

**Figure 2-36. Standardization of phenol solutions**

# P. Cyanide (SM$_{18}$ 4500-CN, Reference 39; EPA 335 and 9010, References 20 and 41)

Cyanide salts and the molecular HCN are all highly poisonous, with a fatal dose for humans on the order of 50-60 mg. HCN was used during WWII for the mass exterminations in Nazi Death Camps. Fish are even more sensitive to cyanide and concentrations as low as 0.02 mg/L are fatal, whereas humans can tolerate 0.20 mg/L in drinking water. Cyanide reacts with ferricytochrome oxidase to keep the $Fe^{+3}$ active center from being reduced to $Fe^{+2}$, which is required as a first step in $O_2$ utilization in cell mitochondria. Cyanide is one of the two compounds listed under Characteristic of Reactivity in Hazardous Material Characterization 40 CFR, 261.23. The other is sulfide.

HCN is more toxic than CN$^-$, and the pH of most waters are less than the pK$_a$ of HCN, thus most of the free cyanide exists in the form of HCN. The situation is different when considering metal complexes of cyanide such as $Fe(CN)_6^{4-}$ and $Fe(CN)_6^{3-}$, which are very common forms of cyanide encountered, as most wastewater will contain some dissolved iron. The dissociation of these complexes is close to zero, and the toxic hazards are much less. Other complexes such as $Hg(CN)_2$, $Zn(CN)_4^{2-}$, $Ag(CN)_2^-$, $Cu(CN)_4^{3-}$ and $Ni(CN)_4^{2-}$ are not dissociated to any large degree in environmental samples, but are still toxic as the complex. Further, even complexes such as the relatively stable $Fe(CN)_6^{3-}$ are labile in the presence of ultraviolet radiation, such as direct sunlight, in dilute solutions.

In evaluating the health risks and thus the availability of cyanide in samples, it becomes necessary to distinguish between bound and free cyanide. Analysts use the recovery of cyanide from acidified samples as a measure of availability. The Weak Acid Dissociation (WAD) cyanide procedure, where the sample is acidified to pH 4.5 and the cyanide removed by distillation, will recover all forms of bound cyanide except mercury and iron complexes. The use of complexing ligands has also been evaluated for displacement of cyanide[78]. Ligands explored were EDTA (ethylenediamine tetraacetic acid), EGTA (ethylene bis[oxyethylenenitrilo]tetraacetic acid), CDTA (1,2-diaminocyclohexane tetraacetic acid), dithizone (diphenylthiocarbazone), TEP (tetraethylenepentaamine), and Tiron (4,5-dihydroxy-1,3-benzene disulfonic acid disodium salt). The TEP/dithizone combination was found to be effective for all WAD complexes including $Hg(CN)_2$.

Typical removal of cyanide from wastewater consists of alkaline chlorination, which proceeds through several steps to innocuous products. The first step in the process is formation of cyanogen chloride.

$$NaCN + Cl_2 \longrightarrow CNCl + NaCl$$

$$CNCl + 2NaOH \longrightarrow NaCNO + NaCl + H_2O$$

$$2NaCNO + 4NaOH + 3Cl_2 \longrightarrow 6NaCl + 2CO_2 + N_2 + 2H_2O$$

$$\text{or} \quad 2NaCNO + 6NaOH + 3Cl_2 \longrightarrow 2NaHCO_3 + 6NaCl + N_2 + 2H_2O$$

**Figure 2-37. Chlorination chemistry of cyanide.**

---

[78] Sebroski, J.R., and R.H. Ode. "Method Comparison and Evaluation for the Analysis of Weak Acid-Dissociable Cyanide." *Environ. Sci. Technol.* 1997. 31(1). pp. 52-57.

Cyanogen chloride (CNCl) is at least as toxic a gas as HCN, and of limited solubility in water. The decomposition of CNCl to cyanate ion (much less toxic) is slow at pH < 9 in the absence of excess $Cl_2$. $CNO^-$ (cyanate ion) is about 1000 times less toxic than cyanide. The removal of cyanide ion by alkaline chlorination from metal complexes such as cobalt, nickel, silver, and copper is slow at best. Intractable complexes such as $Fe(CN)_6^{-3}$ are essentially non-reactive. These complexes can be destroyed through electrolysis. The process is illustrated for removal of cyanide from a copper plating bath.

Anode
$$Cu(CN)_3^{2-} + 6OH^- \longrightarrow Cu^{2+} + 3CNO^- + 3H_2O + 7e^-$$

$$CN^- + 2OH^- \longrightarrow CNO^- + H_2O + 2e^-$$

$$CNO^- + 4H_2O \longrightarrow 2CO_2 + N_2 + 2H_2O + 6e^-$$

Cathode
$$Cu^+ + e^- \longrightarrow Cu$$

**Figure 2-38. Electrolytic decomposition of cyanide.**

It thus becomes of interest to distinguish between Total Cyanide and Cyanide Amenable to Chlorination.

## 1. Total cyanide

A sample is strongly acidified with $H_2SO_4$ and sweep distilled with $N_2$ into a NaOH solution-filled bubbler trap. The total cyanide in the trap is measured by four methods.

1) Titration with $AgNO_3$ to form the soluble complex $Ag(CN)_2^-$. The end of the titration is signaled with the silver-sensitive indicator, p-dimethylamino-benzalrhodanine, which turns from yellow in the absence of silver to salmon color in the presence of uncomplexed silver.

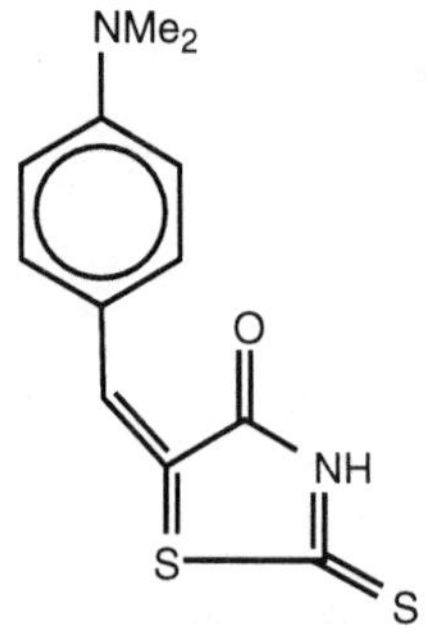

**Figure 2-39. Structure of dimethylaminobenzalrhodanine.**

2) Reaction with Chloramine-T to form CNCl, followed by reaction with pyridine-barbituric acid reagent to form a deep red-blue dye, the intensity of which is measured on a spectrophotometer at 578 nm.

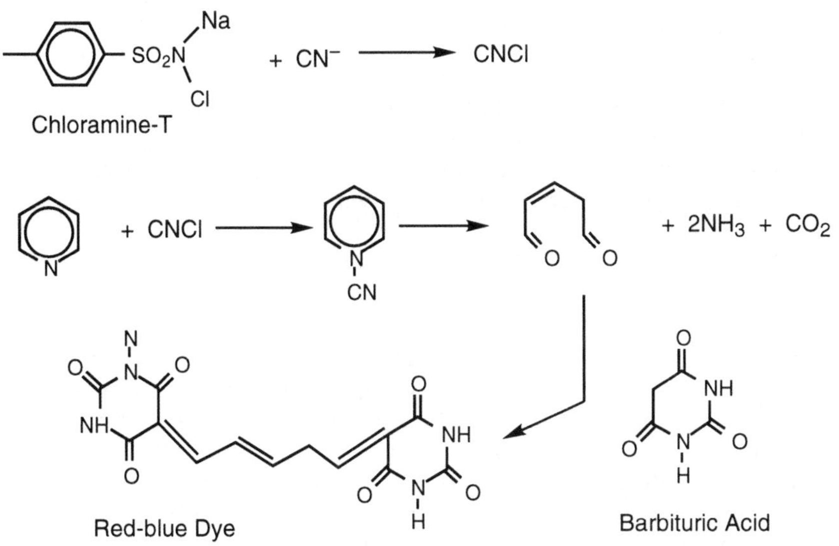

Chloramine-T

Red-blue Dye

Barbituric Acid

**Figure 2-40. Chemistry of pyridine-barbituric acid cyanide determination.**

3) Reaction with chlorine to form CNCl, followed by reaction with pyridine and pyralozone to form a blue-colored species that is measured spectrophotometricly at 612 nm.

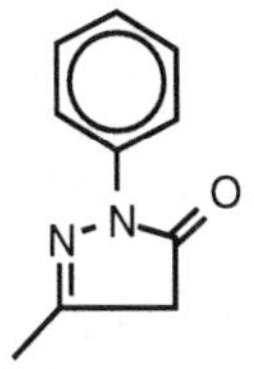

**Figure 2-41. Structure of pyralozone used in colorimetric cyanide determination.**

4) Use of $CN^-$ selective electrode to determine concentration is very rapid but subject to interferences that are removed by the distillation step above. The cyanide sensing membrane will dissolve at cyanide concentrations above 10 mg/L.

For cyanides amenable to chlorination both direct and indirect methods are used:

- The direct method is basically the same as the second method above under Total Cyanide, except the initial distillation step is skipped. Many interferences exist in this procedure with the notable inclusion of thiocyanate, which assays as cyanide. A separate $SCN^-$ determination is made, and the result subtracted from the apparent $CN^-$ result.
- The indirect method involves addition of $Ca(OCl)_2$ to the basic solution until a drop tests blue when applied to a KI-starch test paper, indicating excess chlorine present. Sodium thiosulfate is then added until the solution tests colorless with KI-starch paper. The sample is then strongly acidified and sweep distilled into a NaOH solution. The trap contents are assayed for $CN^-$ by any of the methods under Total Cyanide. The value obtained is the cyanide NOT amenable to chlorination. A concurrent sample is run for Total Cyanide. The difference between the two values is the Cyanide Amenable to Chlorination.

## Q. Sulfide (SM$_{18}$ 4500-S$^{2-}$, Reference 39; EPA 376 and 9030, References 20 and 41)

Sulfide (S$^{2-}$), is one of the species of sulfur that occur in environmental samples. Sulfide is the most reduced form of sulfur, capable of being oxidized to elemental sulfur (S$_8$) and then on to sulfite and finally sulfate. Corresponding organic forms of sulfur can also exist in a number of oxidation states and bonding schemes.

$$S^{2-} \quad \xleftarrow{\quad} 2e^- \xrightarrow{\quad} \quad S^\circ \quad \xleftarrow{\quad} 4e^- \xrightarrow{\quad} \quad SO_3{}^{2-} \quad \xleftarrow{\quad} 2e^- \xrightarrow{\quad} \quad SO_4{}^{2-}$$

$$\text{sulfide} \qquad\qquad \text{sulfur} \qquad\qquad \text{sulfite (S}^{4+}\text{)} \qquad\qquad \text{sulfate (S}^{6+}\text{)}$$

Sulfate and sulfite analyses are discussed in Section 5.

Sulfide, such as sodium sulfide, is a fairly strong base that can be converted to the volatile weak acid H$_2$S. In a waste, acid convertable sulfide, along with cyanide, are the hazardous chemicals under the Characteristic of Reactivity. H$_2$S is more toxic than HCN, with a level of 1000 ppm in air resulting in very rapid human death. H$_2$S affects the CNS, and death results from respiratory system paralysis. The gas occurs naturally in decomposition of organic matter in swamps, bogs, and tidal flats; from active volcanoes; and is a common contaminant in natural gas. In 1950, 22 people were killed in Poza Rica, Mexico when a flare used to burn-off H$_2$S from a well extinguished, releasing toxic amounts of the gas. Nine people were killed in Denver City, Texas in 1975 when H$_2$S blew out of a secondary petroleum recovery well. The gas has a foul rotten egg smell, yet fatal gassings may occur because H$_2$S incapacitates the ability to smell by irreversibly reacting with the metal atoms in the proteins responsible for odor detection. Hydrogen sulfide is a product of anaerobic bacterial metabolism of sulfate and is common in wastewater. Hydrogen sulfide is converted to sulfuric acid on contact with concrete surfaces in the presence of air and is a common cause of concrete pipe corrosion in sewer systems.

Samples for sulfide determination are collected and preserved with either Zn(OAc)$_2$, which forms the insoluble ZnS, or CdCO$_3$ to form CdS, and basified with sodium hydroxide to pH >12. The sample should be then stored, in the dark and cool, until assay. Interferences can be removed from the sample (and the sample concentrated) by carefully withdrawing the supernatant liquid from the ZnS or CdS precipitate, and either replacing the removed water with deionized water or leaving at the lesser volume for concentration. As an alternative (and required in the Reactivity Characteristic) H$_2$S can be sweep distilled from the sample by strongly acidifying the sample and trapping the H$_2$S removed in a NaOH solution in a bubbler trap.

Sulfide is assayed by one of five methods, the last two being particular to wastewater generated from the leather tanning and finishing point source category (40 CFR 425):

- S$^{2-}$ reacts with I$_2$ to produce elemental sulfur. Excess standardized I$_2$ solution is added to the sample, and the excess I$_2$ titrated with standardized sodium thiosulfate with starch as indicator. This technique is particularly prone to false positive interferences due to other reduced substances in environmental samples, however it is good method for standardizing sulfide solutions.

$$S^{2-} + I_2 \longrightarrow S^\circ + 2I^-$$

- Methylene blue method - S$^{-2}$ reacts with dimethylphenylenediamine and ferric chloride (FeCl$_3$) in a strongly acidic solution to form the dye methylene blue. The excess color due to FeCl$_3$ is removed by addition of diammonium hydrogen phosphate, (NH$_4$)$_2$HPO$_4$. Centrifugation is often required to remove the formed floc so that the test can be read colorimetrically. The color is read on a spectrophotometer at 664 nm against standards.

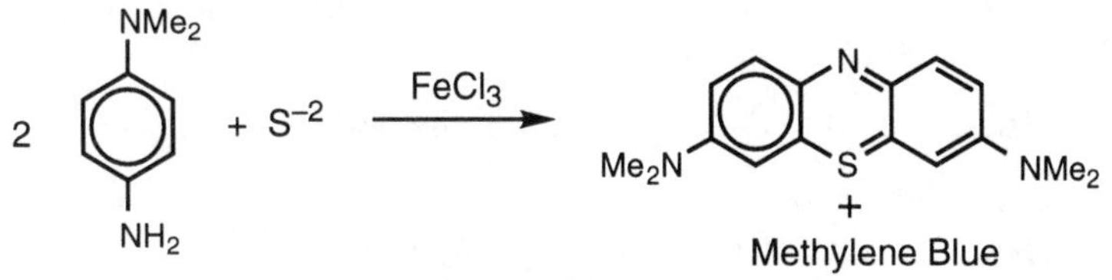

**Figure 2-42. Chemistry of methylene blue formation as a sulfide assay.**

- A newer method uses a sulfide selective electrode to determine the sulfide contents in the NaOH trap from the distillation procedure.

- The sulfide-containing sample is buffered to pH 9.3 with an ammonia buffer, then titrated with potassium ferricyanide in the presence of ferrous dimethylglyoxime indicator and barium chloride. The ferricyanide serves to oxidize the sulfide to sulfur with the endpoint indicated by permanent disappearance of the pink ferrous dimethylglyoxime color. Barium chloride serves to remove sulfite interference. (Appendix A to 40 CFR 425).

- The modified Monier-Williams method (Appendix B, 40 CFR 425) first isolates the sulfide from the sample by strong acidification and sweep-distillation with nitrogen, passes the gas through a pH 7 potassium phosphate buffered scrubber to remove interfering sulfur dioxide, and finally traps the hydrogen sulfide in an alkaline peroxide scrubber as sulfate. The sulfate is determined by either a gravimetric or a turbidimetric determination with barium chloride.

## R. Nitrogen (SM$_{18}$ 4500-N, Reference 39; EPA 351, Reference 20)

Nitrogen is an essential nutrient in biological systems. The biologically important forms of nitrogen are organic nitrogen (proteins, amino acids, DNA, etc.), ammonia, nitrite ($NO_2^-$), nitrate ($NO_3^-$), and nitrogen gas. Degradation of organic nitrogen (urea, alkaloids, aminoacids and proteins) in treatment plants proceeds in stepwise fashion to first ammonia in an anaerobic biological process. Subsequent aerobic transformations convert the ammonia biologically to nitrite by bacteria of the *Nitrosomonas* group, and then on to nitrate by members of the *Nitrobacter* group. This overall process is termed "nitrification." Under anaerobic conditions, nitrate and nitrite are converted biologically to nitrogen gas, or rarely ammonia, in the "denitrification" process. Animals can only bioassimilate organic nitrogen as a nitrogen source; however, bacteria and plants can use the other forms to make organic nitrogen[79]. Nitrite is of special interest due to the reaction with organic nitrogen to form the carcinogenic nitrosamines. Nitrite in drinking water is the cause of methemoglobinemia in human babies.

## S. Ammonia (SM$_{18}$ 4500-NH$_3$, Reference 39; EPA 350, Reference 20)

Ammonia analysis is normally performed on distilled samples, except in the case of drinking water or highly purified wastewaters. Distillation consists of addition of a pH 9 borate buffer and distillation of water and ammonia with trapping into either boric acid

---

[79] Sawyer, C.N., P.L. McCarty and G.F. Parkin. *Chemistry for Environmental Engineering*, 4th Edition. 1994. McGraw-Hill, Inc. New York, NY.

($H_3BO_3$) or sulfuric acid solution. In samples with a high organic nitrogen content the sample may be buffered to pH 7.2 - 7.4 with phosphate buffer to minimize decomposition of the organic nitrogen to ammonia. After the sample is distilled, one of four major methods is used to determine the ammonia present:

- Back titration with sulfuric acid to the original pH of the boric acid trap.

$$NH_3 + H_3BO_3 \longrightarrow NH_4^+H_2BO_3$$
$$2NH_4H_2BO_3^- + H_2SO_4 \longrightarrow H_3BO_3 + (NH_4)_2SO_4$$

- Reaction with Nessler's reagent ($K_2HgI_4$ from KI and $HgI_2$)

$$NH_3 + K_2HgI_4 + OH^- \longrightarrow NH_2Hg_2OI + KI + H_2O$$

The yellow-brown complex absorbs light over a wide range, and a number of wavelengths are used to make spectrophotometric determinations over a wide range of concentrations. Low $NH_3$ concentrations (up to 5 mg/L) are read at 400-425 nm, while values to 10 mg/L are read at 450-500 nm. Significant deviations from Lambert-Beer's Law (Abs = abc) can occur. The technique is also used for a visual determination of the ammonia levels in water. For this use permanent color standards are prepared in Nessler tubes with increasing amounts of potassium chloroplatinate ($K_2PtCl_6$) and cobalt chloride solutions. Due to waste disposal problems of the mercury reagent this method is being phased out.[80]

- The phenate method involves the reaction of ammonia with hypochlorite and alkaline phenol in the presence of $MnSO_4$ to form indophenol - a vivid blue dye which is read at 630 nm with a spectrophotometer. A variation on the method uses sodium salicylate in the presence of a nitroferricyanide catalyst to form the blue indosalicylate, that in the presence of the yellow nitroferricyanide gives a green color.

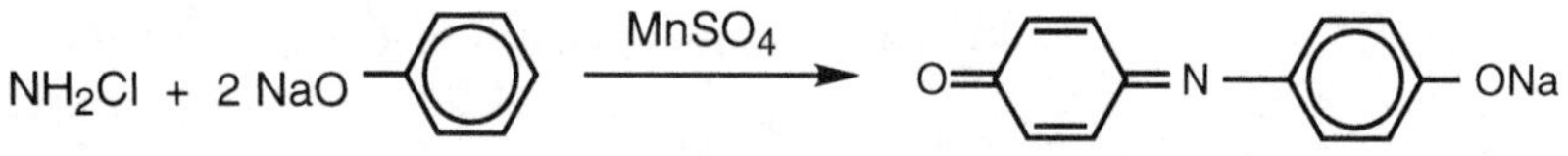

Indophenol Blue

**Figure 2-43. Phenate method for ammonia determination.**

- The ammonia-selective electrode has the widest dynamic range (0.1-1000 mg/L) of any of the methods, is the fastest method, and many samples do not need to be distilled. Wastewater and water regulations require that a comparison of distilled and non-distilled results from samples be made prior to any abandonment of the distillation. Mercury and silver ions in the sample are a distinct interference due to complexation with ammonia.

## T. Nitrite (SM$_{18}$ 4500-NO$_2$, Reference 39; EPA 354, Reference 20)

$NO_2^-$ in the presence of acid reacts with amines, particularly aromatic amines, to form diazonium salts. Diazonium salts are very reactive and can couple with other aromatic

---

[80] The 19th Edition of *Standard Methods* is dropping determination of ammonia by Nesslerization due to the mercury waste disposal problem.

systems to form colored azo-dyes. Coupling agents in current use include gentisic acid, chromotropic acid, and the very common N-napthyl-ethylenediamine dichloride (NED).

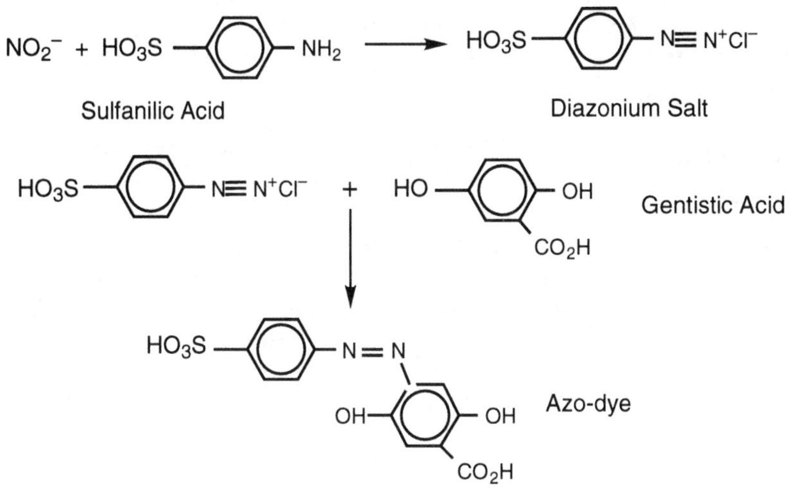

**Figure 2-44. Chemistry of nitrite colorimetric analysis.**

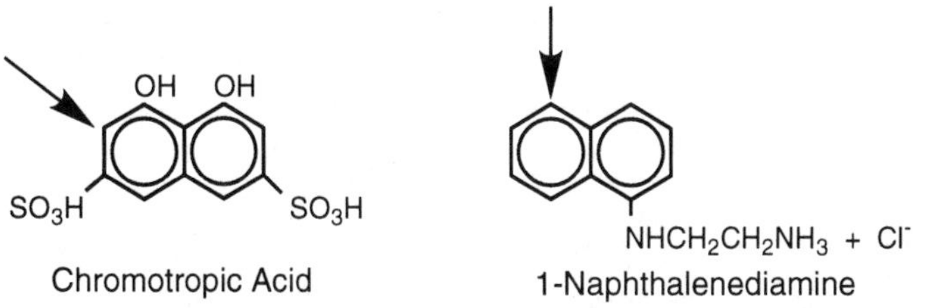

**Figure 2-45. Coupling site with other nitrite colorimetric reagents to form azo dyes.**

Nitrite can also be detected by the time-worn ferrous brown ring test.

$$2H^+ + 2FeSO_4 + 2HNO_2 \longrightarrow 2Fe^{3+} + 2NO + 2H_2O$$

$$NO + FeSO_4 \longrightarrow NOFeSO_4 \text{ (green-brown color) determined colorimetrically}$$

Nitrite has been determined in marine samples by addition of an acidic solution of 2,4-dinitrophenylhydrazine to form 2,4-dinitrophenylazide[81]. The azide reaction is complete within 5 minutes and it is then determined by HPLC with UV detection. The azide is stable for up to 4 weeks when stored cold and in the dark. Quantitation limits are reported as on the order of 5 ng/L.

## U. Nitrate (SM$_{18}$ 4500-NO$_3$, Reference 39; EPA 352, Reference 20)

Nitrate can be determined along with nitrite by ion chromatography. Nitrate ion also has a UV absorbance, that in the absence of Cr$^{6+}$, organic matter, and other interfering

---

[81] Kieber, R.J., and P.J. Seaton. "Determination of Subnanomolar Concentrations of Nitrite in Natural Waters." *Anal. Chem.* 1995. 67(18). pp. 3261-3264.

absorbers, can be used for quantification. An electrode that is somewhat selective for nitrate is also available and useful as a screening test. However most of the common nitrate quantitative tests first reduce nitrate to nitrite by Cd-Hg amalgam, Cd-Cu alloy, or hydrazine sulfate and then test for nitrite. Another procedure uses titanium chloride ($TiCl_3$) to reduce the nitrate to ammonia, then determines the ammonia with an ammonia-selective electrode.

## V. Total (Kjeldahl) (SM$_{18}$ 4500-N$_{org}$, Reference 39; EPA 351, Reference 20)

The Kjeldahl method for determining nitrogen is one of the oldest quantitative test procedures known. First published in 1883, it quantitates organic and ammonia nitrogen by conversion of the organic nitrogen to ammonia with hot concentrated sulfuric acid, catalyzed by salts of Hg, Cu, or Se (sometimes with $H_2O_2$ added). (Most organic nitrogen is in the form of amides or primary amines.) Excess NaOH is added, and the liberated $NH_3$ is distilled into a trap containing a standard amount of acid. The excess acid is back-titrated with base.

The values obtained from the TKN procedure are in terms of mass nitrogen per liter or kilogram of sample. For many years conversion factors have been used on these results to give related numbers representing protein content of the sample. Some factors are 6.25% for meat protein, 6.38% for dairy protein and 5.7% for grain protein.

Modifications of the method by addition of reducing substances prior to the digestion with sulfuric acid allow determination of azo-, nitro-, nitrite, nitrate and aromatic amine containing nitrogen compounds. An example is reaction with Devarda's metal (45% Al, 5% Zn, 50% Cu) in strongly basic media[82]:

$$3NO_3^- + 8Al + 5OH^- \longrightarrow 8AlO_2^- + 3NH_3$$

An oxidative digestion using persulfate and sulfuric acid has been used to produce nitrate as the final determinative analyte. This digestion also serves as a suitable procedure for total phosphorus determination.

## W. Phosphorus (EPA 365, Reference 20; SM$_{18}$ 4500-P, Reference 39)

Phosphorus in the phosphate oxidation state is a key nutrient in water systems. It occurs in many forms, both organic and inorganic, soluble and mineral. One of the more important insoluble phosphate minerals is hydroxyapatite - $Ca_5(PO_4)_2OH$. The monomeric phosphate anion is called orthophosphate. The phosphate ion exists as four different salts with many different names. An example of the sodium series follows.

---

[82] Method 892.01, 15th Edition of *Official Methods of Analysis*, AOAC. Volume 1. pp. 19-20.

**Table 2-24. Forms and names of mono-phosphates**

| Form | Name |
| --- | --- |
| $H_3PO_4$ | Phosphoric acid<br>Orthophosphoric acid |
| $NaH_2PO_4$ | Sodium dihydrogen phosphate<br>Sodium biphosphate<br>Sodium phosphate monobasic<br>Acid sodium phosphate<br>Monosodium orthophosphate |
| $Na_2HPO_4$ | Disodium hydrogen phosphate<br>Sodium hydrogen phosphate<br>Sodium phosphate dibasic<br>Disodium orthophosphate<br>Disodium phosphate<br>Phosphate of soda |
| $Na_3PO_4$ | Sodium phosphate tribasic<br>Trisodium phosphate<br>Sodium phosphate<br>Trisodium orthophosphate |

Linear strings of phosphates are called polyphosphates. Pyrophosphate is the simplest condensed polyphosphate. Polyphosphates up to 16 units long are common and well known. The metaphosphates are either cyclic structures or branched linear structures. The trimeta- and tetrametaphosphates are common cyclic structures, with structures known to contain up to 10 phosphate units. The common chemical sodium hexametaphosphate is not a well-defined single chemical, but rather a mixture of polymeric metaphosphates.

**Table 2-25. Forms, names, and structures of inorganic phosporus**

| Form | Name | Structure |
| --- | --- | --- |
| $PO_4^{3-}$ | ortho-phosphate | |
| $P_2O_7^{4-}$ | pyrophosphate | |
| $P_3O_{10}^{5-}$ | tripolyphosphate | |
| $P_3O_9^{3-}$ | trimetaphosphate | |

Continued on next page.

**Table 2-25. Forms, names, and structures of inorganic phosporus,** *continued*

| Form | Name | Structure |
|------|------|-----------|
| $HPO_3^{2-}$ | phosphite (phosphonate) | |
| $H_2PO_2^-$ | hypophosphite (phosphinate) | |

Organic phosphorus can have a large variety of organic attachments to the basic $PO_4$ system. Examples are DNA, RNA, phospholipids, and adenosine triphosphate (ATP).

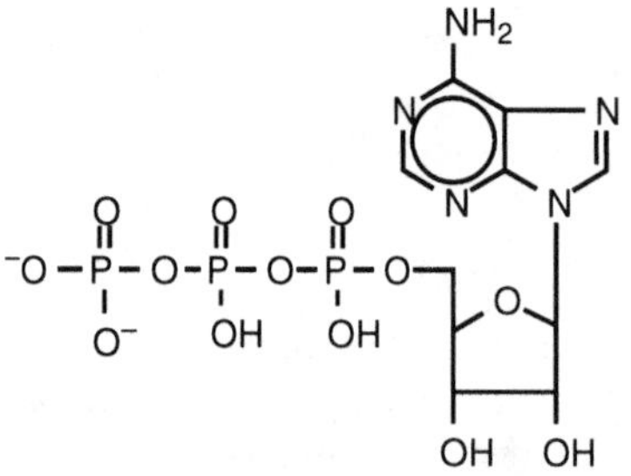

**Figure 2-46. Structure of ATP, an organic phosphate.**

The analysis of phosphate depends on the pretreatment of the sample. The simplest analysis is reaction of the sample with molybdate to form a phosphomolybdate that can be determined colorimetrically, or followed by reduction with one of a number of mild reducing agents such as $SnCl_2$, hydrazine, or ascorbic acid to form a heteropoly blue, which is determined colorimetrically. The latter procedure is the more sensitive. The direct analysis determines reactive phosphorus, which is primarily orthophosphate, but may contain some polyphosphate. The condensed phosphates can be hydrolyzed with acid and heated to orthophosphate and then determined, giving acid-hydrolyzable phosphorous; however, this also gives some of the organic phosphorus. Total phosphorus requires oxidative hydrolysis with heating to convert all phosphorus forms to orthophosphate. The persulfate oxidation is the most common and the mildest; nitric-sulfuric acid or perchloric acid digestions are more rigorous.

$$PO_4^{3-} + 12(NH_4)_2MoO_4 + 12H^+ \longrightarrow (NH_4)_3PO_4(MoO_3)_{12} + 21NH_4^+ + H_2O$$
Ammonium molybdate · · · · · · · · · · · · · · · · · · · Ammonium phosphomolybdate

$$PO_4^{3-} + (NH_4)_6Mo_7O_{24} \cdot 4H_2O \longrightarrow (NH_4)_3PO_4(MoO_3)_{12} \text{ (unbalanced reaction)}$$
Ammonium molybdate tetrahydrate

**Figure 2-47. Formation of phosphomolybdate from phosphate.**

The first step of the analysis is formation of the phosphomolybdate. The phospho-molybdate (heteropoly acid) has all the molybdenum in the +6 oxidation state. Reaction with a mild reducing agent forms the molybdenum heteropoly blue. The blue was believed to have the same structure as the heteropoly acid with two of the molybdenums in the +5 state and the other 10 molybdenums in the +6 state. Recent work has indicated that the blue actually is a huge donut-shaped poly-anion containing dozens of $MoO_3$ sub-units[83]. The blues can accommodate up to 6 extra electrons and thus are prone to over reduction. The blue color is due to the trapped electrons being loosely associated with the reduced atoms. Variations on the procedure use antimony in the formation of the phosphomolybdate (as in the EPA methods), followed by reduction.

$$PO_4^{3-} + KSbOC_4H_4O_6 + 12(NH_4)_2MoO_4 + XH^+ \longrightarrow SbOPO_4(MoO_3)_{12}$$

Another variation uses ammonium metavanadate to produce the heteropoly acid, which is directly read colorimetrically without further reduction, for a high level determination (1-20 mg/L). This is used in the Hach method and SM 4500-P C.

$$PO_4^{3-} + NH_4VO_3 + (NH_4)_6Mo_7O_{24} \cdot 4H_2O \longrightarrow PO_4VO_3Mo_{16}O_{48}^{4-}$$

The above procedures give either reactive phosphate or total phosphate as results. On the other hand the analytical task may involve characterization of a sample to determine exactly the source of the phosphate pollution. This "fingerprinting" can be accomplished by thin layer chromatography (TLC) or more definitively by ion chromatography or capillary ion electrophoresis[84].

## X. Fluoride (SM$_{18}$ 4500-F⁻, Reference 39; EPA 340, Reference 20)

There are three common techniques used for fluoride determinations, the SPADNS and complexone colorimetric methods and the ion-selective electrode method. All the techniques are subject to interferences, and complexed fluorides such as fluoroborates in general do not react well. For these reasons all samples for fluoride determination should be distilled. The distillation consists of strong acidification of the sample with concentrated sulfuric acid and addition of soft glass beads. This converts the fluoride to hexafluorosilicic acid, which is then distilled out of the sample and collected in a water solution. The addition of silver sulfate to the reaction pot serves to remove chloride interferences as silver chloride.

The SPADNS method measures the absorbance of an initial complex between zirconium ion and the dye sodium 2-(parasulfophenylazo)-1,8-dihydroxy-3,6-naphthalene disulfonate (SPADNS) and the subsequent bleaching of the complex due to reaction with fluoride ion.

---

[83] Muller, A, J. Meyer, E. Krickemeyer and E. Diemann, *Angew. Chem. Int. Ed. Engl.* 1996. 35. pp. 1206.

[84] Shamsi, S.A. and N.D. Danielson. "Ribonucleotide Electrolytes for Capillary Electrophoresis of Polyphosphates and Polyphosphonates with Indirect Photometric Detection." *Anal. Chem.* 1995. 67(11). pp. 1845-1852.

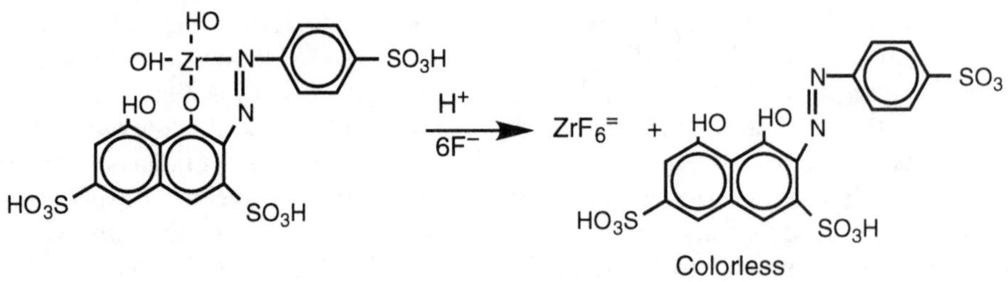

**Figure 2-48. Bleaching reaction of fluoride on zirconium-SPADNS reagent.**

The SPADNS calibration is one of the few encountered in environmental general chemical analysis that has a negative slope, *i.e.* the absorbance decreases with increasing amount of analyte. The colorimetric calibration is best set at zero with a reference blank, which contains all the reagents except the zirconium. Unfortunately the commercially available SPADNS reagent is a mixed reagent and already contains zirconium. The analyst is allowed to either set the absorbance of the blank sample at an arbitrary absorbance between 0.200 and 0.500 or to pick one of the high standards and set the absorbance at zero. Regardless of the zeroing procedure, the calibration curve has a distinct curve, being approximately linear from 0.1 mg/L to 2.0 mg/L fluoride. Since the analyst is setting the calibration, the maximum range of the calibration curve should be utilized. Absorbance values obtained from setting zero at 3.5 mg/L fluoride and the associated curve are illustrated in Table 2-26 and Figure 2-49.

**Table 2-26. Absorbance data obtained from SPADNS procedure with 3.5 mg/L fluoride standard set at zero absorbance**

| Absorbance | F⁻ mg/L |
|:---:|:---:|
| .922 | 0.00 |
| .878 | 0.10 |
| .722 | 0.50 |
| .524 | 1.00 |
| .190 | 2.00 |
| .093 | 2.50 |
| .026 | 3.00 |
| .001 | 3.50 |

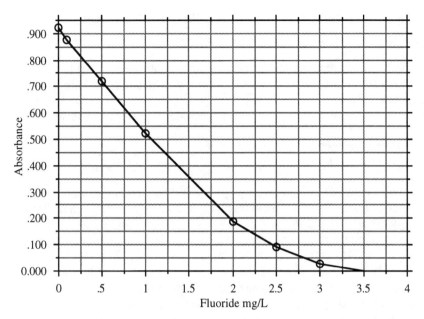

**Figure 2-49. SPADNS Fluoride calibration curve.**

The automated complexone reaction generates a colorimetric response read at 620 nm through reaction of lanthanum ion, Alizarin fluorine blue and fluoride ion. The auto-analyzers that use this chemistry all incorporate an initial distillation step.

Alizarin Fluorine Blue

**Figure 2-50. Structure of Alizarin fluorine blue**

The fluoride-selective electrode consists of a lanthanum (III) fluoride single crystal doped with trace amounts of europium (II) fluoride to serve as the electrical barrier between the inside of the electrode and the sample. The doping of the crystal is necessary to provide electrically conducting defects in the medium. The supporting electrolyte inside the electrode is sodium chloride/sodium fluoride at $0.1\ M$ each. An electrical imbalance is created across the single crystal when the outside of the crystal is immersed in a solution of different fluoride activity, which generates a measurable voltage difference. The device is sensitive to total ion activity and is particularly sensitive to hydroxide concentration. Thus a pH 5.0 buffering solution, TISB (total ion strength buffer), is added to each sample and standard. TISB also contains cyclohexylene-diaminetetracetic acid (CDTA) as a cation complexing agent to free complexed fluoride ions for determination.

## Y. Chloride (SM$_{18}$ 4500-Cl⁻, Reference 39; EPA 325, Reference 20; EPA 9250, 9251, 9252, 9253, Reference 41).

Both of the first two EPA methods depend upon removal of mercury (II) ion from a reaction mixture as the soluble, stable mercuric chloride. The automated ferricyanide methods react the chloride ion with mercuric thiocyanate to free thiocyanate ion, which further reacts with ferric ion, forming the highly colored red ferric thiocyanate ion.

$$2Cl^- + Hg(SCN)_2 \longrightarrow HgCl_2 + 2SCN^-$$
$$SCN^- + Fe^{3+} \longrightarrow Fe(SCN)^{2+}$$

In the mercuric nitrate titration, chloride reacts with the mercury ion until all the available chloride is consumed, then the excess mercuric ion reacts with an organic ligand such as diphenylcarbazone to form a highly colored mercury complex. Although chloride can react with mercury (II) ion to form a number of soluble complexes the formation constants ($K[HgCl^+] = 5.5 \times 10^6$, $K[HgCl_2] = 3.0 \times 10^6$, $K[HgCl_3^-] = 7.1$, and $K[HgCl_4^{2-}] = 10$) are rapid for formation of the neutral $HgCl_2$, while further formation constants are very slow and faster competing organic ligand reactions allow visual indication at the end of the stoichiometric titration. The complex with diphenylcarbazone has a very narrow optimum pH range (3.2-3.3) and an indicator is added (Bromophenol blue) for visual adjustment with nitric acid or sodium hydroxide to the optimum pH. Xylene cyanole FF dye is added in the case of colored interferents to sharpen the end-point color change.

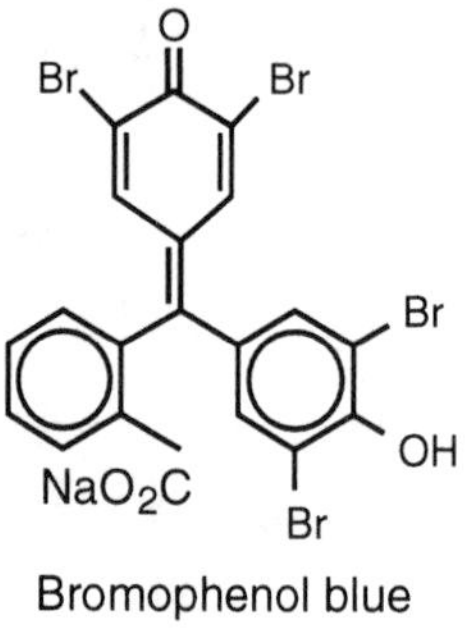

Bromophenol blue

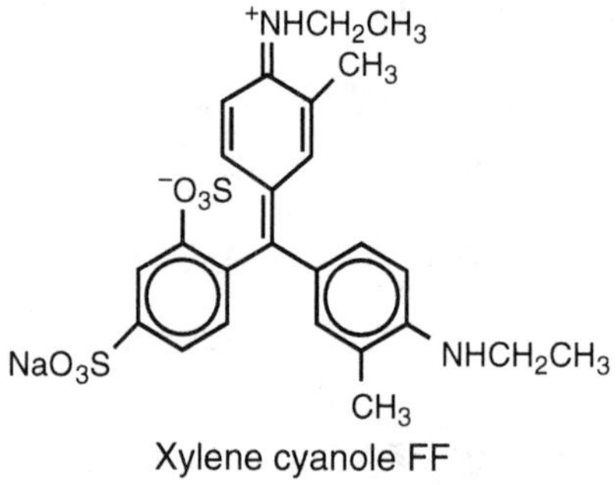

Xylene cyanole FF

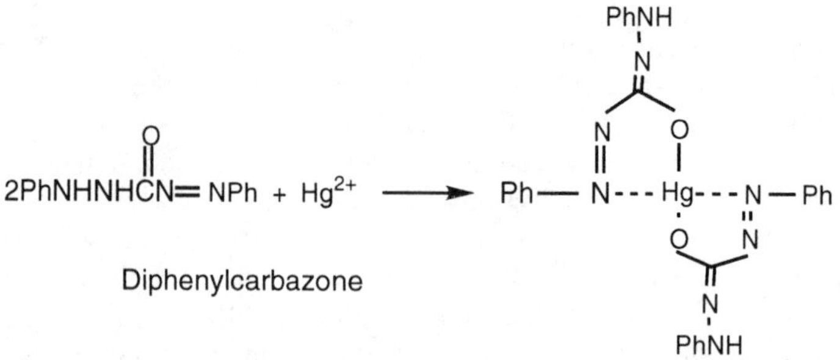

$$2PhNHNHCN \!\!=\!\! NPh + Hg^{2+} \longrightarrow$$

Diphenylcarbazone

**Figure 2-51. Chemistry of the diphenyl carbazone indication of the mercuric nitrate titration end-point.**

EPA method 9253 is the classic Mohr Agentometric titration of chloride with silver nitrate to form the white insoluble silver chloride. The endpoint of the titration is determined by addition of chromate ion, which reacts with excess silver ion to form the insoluble red-orange silver chromate. Phenolphthalein indicator is used to allow adjustment of the solution pH to the optimum of 8.3. Sulfite ion can interfere with the titration, and if its presence is suspected, it can be removed by addition of hydrogen peroxide to oxidize the sulfite to sulfate.

$$Cl^- + Ag^+ \longrightarrow AgCl$$
$$2Ag^+ + CrO_4^{2-} \longrightarrow Ag_2CrO_4$$

## Z. Ion Chromatography (EPA 300.0; EPA 9056, Reference 41; SM$_{18}$ 4110, Reference 39)

Ion chromatography[85] is an instrumental technique that can be performed in either a cationic or anionic mode. In the anion mode it relies on sequential elution of anions in the sample from a strongly basic anionic exchange resin with a bicarbonate/carbonate buffer solution. Most of the systems use conductivity detectors. The detection is made simpler by exchanging the anions into the strong acid forms after elution from the analytical column but prior to the detector module. The sample is directly injected into the instrument after filtering, and concentration of the sample is not normally performed. If the sample and the eluting liquid phase are not of the same ionic strength, a water peak appears as the first signal. The water peak often masks the eluting signal of fluoride ion and so it is not on the target analyte list. Fluoride can be determined if the sample is diluted with the elution solvent prior to injection.

Interferences that can occur are anions, other than those on the target analyte list, which can co-elute or overlap calibrated anions. Another problem is that high concentrations of an anion can shift the retention of other target analytes. This is normally corrected by diluting and re-injecting the sample.

The halides and simple oxygenated anions (nitrate, nitrite, phosphate and sulfate) are analyzed in a single injection. The inorganic disinfection by-products (chlorate, chlorite and bromate) require a different strength of bicarbonate/carbonate eluant and are analyzed on a separate column.

**Table 2-27. Target analytes of anion chromatography**

| Target analyte | MDL (mg/L) | Target analyte | MDL (mg/L) |
|----------------|------------|----------------|------------|
| Chloride | 0.02 | Bromide | 0.01 |
| Nitrate-N | 0.002 | Nitrite-N | 0.004 |
| Sulfate | 0.02 | ortho-Phosphate-P | 0.003 |
| Chlorate | 0.003 | Chlorite | 0.01 |
| Bromate | 0.02 | | |

---

[85]  Mulik, J., and E. Sawicki. 1978-79. *Ion Chromatographic Analysis of Environmental Pollutants*, Vol. I and II, Ann Arbor Science Publishers, Ann Arbor, MI; "Application Reviews for Environmental Analysis, Water Analysis, Air Pollution and Industrial Hygiene." *Analytical Chemistry*. 1993. 65(12); Bahowick, T.J., V. Murugaiah, A.W. Sulya, D.B. Taylor, R.E. Synovec, R.J. Berman, C.N. Renn, and E.L. Johnson. "Column Liquid Chromatography: Equipment and Instrumentation," *Analytical Chemistry*. 1992. 64(12). pp. 255R-270R.

## AA. Ion Selective Electrodes

A number of target analytes can be determined by ion selective electrodes (ISE) as discussed at various points in this Section. Examples include fluoride, chloride and hydrogen ion (pH). Some of the myriad procedures may entail direct determination of the concentration of the analyte in solution while others may use the ISE as an end-point indicator for a titration. An excellent reference on ISE has been published[86]. Other good reference materials are provided by the manufacturers of the devices.

ISE consist of four basic types described in the following along with their strengths and weaknesses:

- Glass body - a thin glass bulb separates the working part of the electrode from the sample. The internal part of the electrode is filled with a buffered solution matched to the working electrode element, such as AgCl for a Ag wire element. The bulb must always be kept wet, generally stored in the lowest concentration standard of the target analyte. Frequently available as a combination electrode, *i.e.* the reference is attached to the electrode as a separate compartment. Examples are the pH and sodium ISE.

- Solid state (crystal membrane) - a sealed electrode with a crystal membrane over the tip separating the sample from the sensing element. The inside of the electrode is filled with a liquid, which if gone indicates the electrode is ruined. Generally used with a separate reference electrode, although some combination electrodes are available. Can be stored dry or in a weak solution of the target analyte. The crystal should be kept polished with a soft cloth or fine abrasive. Examples are the fluoride and silver ISE.

- Polymer membrane (liquid ion exchange) - a replaceable polymer membrane impregnated with an ion exchange resin, generally used with a separate reference electode. The electrode is filled with a solution specific to the target analyte. The electrode can be stored dry or in a weak solution of the target analyte. Exposure to organic solutions or high concentrations of organics in an aqueous sample will irreversibly damage the membrane. Examples are the calcium and nitrate sensing ISE.

- Gas sensing - A replaceable gas permeable membrane is filled with a buffer solution that is in contact with a glass membrane pH sensor that has its own specific fill solution. Generally used with a separate reference electrode. Gaseous analytes diffuse from the sample across the membrane into the fill solution, that responds by changing pH. The pH change is sensed by the glass membrane electrode. The prototypical example is the ammonia electrode. The ammonia electrode should be stored by immersion in a 0.05 $M$ solution of $NH_4Cl$. Frequent replacement of the gas permeable membrane and the fill solution are necessary.

The operation of the ISE is based upon potential difference (E) measured between the ISE and a reference electrode. The absolute value of the potential will depend on which reference electrode is used in the measurement. The potential is described by the Nernst equation:

---

86    Pungor, E. *Ion-Selective Electrodes*, Akademiai Kiado, Budapest, 1989.

$$E = E° + 2.3 \frac{RT}{nF} \log [\text{analyte ion}]$$

where:   E°   is the standard potential for the analyte and the cell conditions
         R    is the gas constant
         T    is the temperature in Kelvin
         n    is the ionic charge on the analyte ions
         F    is the Faraday constant

The ratio $\frac{RT}{nF}$ is termed the "Slope Factor" and it can be used as a preventative maintenance check on the condition of the ISE. These slope factors represent the change in measured potential in millivolts (mV) as the concentration of the target ion changes by factors of ten. The ideal slope values at 25 °C for a number of common ions are presented in Table 2-28. Determining and recording the slope value when the ISE is new and in perfect working condition serves as a set-point for future evaluations of performance.

**Table 2-28.  Ideal ISE slope values for common ions at 25 °C**

| Slope value (mV) | Ion charge | Examples |
|:---:|:---:|:---:|
| 29.58 | +2 | $Ca^{2+}$, $Ba^{2+}$ |
| 59.16 | +1 | $Na^+$, $H^+$ |
| -59.16 | -1 | $Cl^-$, $F^-$, $Br^-$ |
| -29.58 | -2 | $S^{2-}$ |

Some of the many available ISE are listed in Table 2-29.

**Table 2-29.  Commonly available ISE**

| Ion | Electrode Type |
|:---:|:---:|
| Barium | Polymer membrane |
| Bromide | Solid state |
| Calcium | Polymer membrane |
| Chloride | Solid state |
| Copper | Solid state |
| Cyanide | Solid state |
| Fluoride | Solid state |
| Hydrogen | Glass |
| Iodide | Solid state |
| Nitrate | Polymer membrane |
| Potassium | Polymer membrane |
| Silver | Solid state |
| Sodium | Glass |
| Sulfide | Solid state |
| Thiocyanate | Solid state |
| Ammonia | Gas sensing |

## IV. Application to Soils and Other Matrices

Many of the methods discussed above in this Section are applicable only to aqueous samples, which is understandable since most of the procedures were developed within the context of the compliance monitoring requirements of drinking water, wastewater, and groundwater. However the need exists to determine many of these parameters in other matrices such as soil, sludge, sediment, chemical wastes, hazardous waste, and fuels.

Some methods, for example TKN, cyanide, fluoride, total metals and total phosphorus, that involve a sample pre-treatment step, can be readily modified for solid samples by simply weighing out a portion of the sample and then performing the sample digestion or distillation. On the other hand, for many common analyses, such as sulfate, chloride, and nitrate-nitrite, the target analyte must be extracted from the solid matix into an aqueous solution, then the determination can proceed as it would with water-based samples.

The environmental analytical field, in many respects is far behind other areas with respect to soil/solid analysis. The best information exists in methods developed in the agronomy and soil science areas for agricultural purposes. The standard texts and references are listed below with a general overview of the contents in Table 2-30. These methods were developed and are used to generate information related to agriculture, and the informational needs are not identical to those needed within the environmental industry.

**Table 2-30. Overview of analytical methods for soil samples**

| *Methods of Soil Analysis*, Part 1: Physical and Mineralogical Methods Second Edition, 1986 American Society of Agronomy, Inc Soil Science Society of America, Inc, 677 South Segoe Rd., Madison WI 53711 | |
|---|---|
| 1.  Errors and variability of observations | 15.  Particle-size analysis |
| 2.  Sampling | 16.  Specific surface |
| 3.  Geostatistical methods applied to soil science | 17.  Aggregate stability and size distribution |
| 4.  Extraneous values | 18.  Porosity |
| 5.  Pretreatment for mineralogical analysis | 19.  Penetrability |
| 6.  Oxides, hydroxides and aluminosilicates | 20.  Compressibility |
| 7.  Thermal analysis techniques | 21.  Water content |
| 8.  Petrographic microscope techniques | 22.  Water potential: Piezometry |
| 9.  Magnetic methods | 23.  Water potential: Tensiometry |
| 10.  Electron microprobe analysis | 24.  Water potential: Thermocouple Psychrometry |
| 11.  Infrared spectrometry | 25.  Water potential: Miscellaneous methods |
| 12.  X-ray diffraction techniques | 26.  Water retention: Laboratory methods |
| 13.  Bulk density | 27.  Water retention: Field methods |
| 14.  Particle density | 28.  Hydraulic conductivity and diffusion: Laboratory methods |

Continued on next page.

**Table 2-30. Overview of analytical methods for soil samples,** *continued*

| *Methods of Soil Analysis*, Part 1: Physical and Mineralogical Methods Second Edition, 1986, *continued* American Society of Agronomy, Inc Soil Science Society of America, Inc, 677 South Segoe Rd., Madison WI 53711 | |
|---|---|
| 29. Hydraulic conductivity and diffusion: Field methods | 40. Heat flux |
| 30. Hydraulic conductivity, diffusivity, and sorptivity of unsaturated soils: Field methods | 41. Heat of immersion |
| 31. Hydraulic conductivity of unsaturated soils: Prediction and formulas | 42. Solute content |
| 32. Intake rate: Cylinder infiltrometer | 43. Solute diffusivity |
| 33. Intake rate: Sprinkler infiltrometer | 44. Solute dispersion coefficients and retardation factors |
| 34. Intake rate: Border and furrow | 45. Water and solute flux |
| 35. Evaporation from bare soil measured with high spatial resolution | 46. Gas diffusivity |
| 36. Field capacity and available water capacity | 47. Gas flux |
| 37. Temperature | 48. Air permeability |
| 38. Heat capacity and specific heat | 49. Oxygen electrode measurement |
| 39. Thermal conductivity and diffusivity | 50. Air pressure measurement |

| *Methods of Soil Analysis*, Part 2: Chemical and Microbiological Properties Second Edition, 1982 American Society of Agronomy, Inc Soil Science Society of America, Inc, 677 South Segoe Rd., Madison WI 53711 | |
|---|---|
| 1. Dissolution for total elemental analysis | 21. Lead |
| 2. Atomic absorption and flame emission spectrometry | 22. Mercury |
| 3. Optical emission spectrometry | 23. Arsenic |
| 4. Neutron activation analysis | 24. Phosphorus |
| 5. X-ray fluorescence spectrometry | 25. Boron |
| 6. High-pressure liquid chromatography | 26. Bromine, chlorine and fluorine |
| 7. Anodic stripping voltametry and differential pulse polarography | 27. Cobalt, molybdenum and selenium |
| 8. Cation exchange capacity | 28. Sulfur |
| 9. Exchangeable cations | 29. Total carbon, organic carbon and organic matter |
| 10. Soluble salts | 30. Organic matter characterization |
| 11. Carbonate and gypsum | 31. Nitrogen - total |
| 12. Soil pH and lime requirement | 32. Nitrogen - organic forms |
| 13. Lithium, sodium and potassium | 33. Nitrogen - inorganic forms |
| 14. Magnesium, calcium, strontium and barium | 34. Nitrogen - urea |
| 15. Silicon | 35. Nitrogen - availability indices |
| 16. Aluminum | 36. Nitrogen - isotope-ratio analysis |
| 17. Iron | 37. Cultural methods for soil microorganisms |
| 18. Manganese | 38. Microscopic methods for soil microorganisms |
| 19. Nickel, copper, zinc and cadmium | 39. Most probable number method for microbial populations |
| 20. Chromium | 40. Microbial biomass |

Continued on next page.

## Table 2-30. Overview of analytical methods for soil samples, *continued*

| Methods of Soil Analysis, Part 2: Chemical and Microbiological Properties Second Edition, 1982, *continued* American Society of Agronomy, Inc Soil Science Society of America, Inc, 677 South Segoe Rd., Madison WI 53711 | |
|---|---|
| 41. Soil respiration | 48. Nitrifying bacteria |
| 42. Composition of soil atmospheres | 49. Rhizobium |
| 43. Soil enzymes | 50. Free-living dinitrogen-fixing bacteria |
| 44. Filamentous fungi | 51. Algae |
| 45. Actinomycetes | 52. Protozoa |
| 46. Anaerobic bateria and processes | 53. Nematodes |
| 47. Denitrification | 54. Mites and other soil microarthropods |

| Soil Sampling and Methods of Analysis, 1993, Lewis Publishers, Boca Raton FL Canadian Society of Soil Science 907-151 Slater St., Ottawa, Ontario K1P5H4 Canada | |
|---|---|
| 1. Site description | 30. Root nodule bacteria and nitrogen fixation |
| 2. Soil sampling for environmental assessment | 31. Microarthropods in soil and litter |
| 3. Soil handling and preparation | 32. Nematodes |
| 4. Nitrate and exchangeable ammonium Nitrogen | 33. Nitrogen mineralization potential in soils |
| 5. Ammonium acetate-extractable elements | 34. Denitrification |
| 6. Mihlich III-extractable elements | 35. Earthworms |
| 7. Sodium bicarbonate-extractable P, K, and N | 36. Total and labile polysaccharides |
| 8. Available potassium | 37. Organic forms of nitrogen |
| 9. Extraction of available sulfur | 38. Soil humus fractions |
| 10. Available P | 39. Light fraction and macroorganic matter |
| 11. DTPA-extractable Fe, Mn, Cu and Zn | 40. Water-soluble phenolic materials |
| 12. Boron, molybdenum and selenium | 41. Soil lipids |
| 13. Cd, Cr, Pb and Ni | 42. Sampling organic soils |
| 14. Lime requirement | 43. Physical properties of organic soils |
| 15. Chemical characterization of plant tissue | 44. Chemical properties of organic soils |
| 16. Soil reaction and exchangeable acidity | 45. Micromorphological methodology |
| 17. Soil solution | 46. Palynological assessments |
| 18. Soluble salts | 47. Particle size distribution |
| 19. Ion exchange and exchangeable cations | 48. Soil shrinkage |
| 20. Carbonates | 49. Soil consistency limits |
| 21. Total and organic carbon | 50. Density and compressibility |
| 22. Total nitrogen | 51. Soil water content |
| 23. Total and organic phosphorus | 52. Soil water potential |
| 24. Total and fractions of sulfur | 53. Soil water desorption curves |
| 25. Extractable Al, Fe, Mn and Si | 54. Soil porosity |
| 26. Reference materials for data quality | 55. Saturated hydraulic conductivity: Laboratory measurement |
| 27. Cultural methods for soil microorganisms | 56. Saturated hydraulic conductivity: Field measurement |
| 28. Soil microbial biomass C and N | 57. Unsaturated hydraulic conductivity and sorptivity: Laboratory measurement |
| 29. Vesicular-arbuscular mycorrhiza | 58. Unsaturated hydraulic conductivity: Estimation from desorption curves |

Continued on next page.

**Table 2-30. Overview of analytical methods for soil samples,** *continued*

| Soil Sampling and Methods of Analysis, 1993, Lewis Publishers, Boca Raton FL<br>Canadian Society of Soil Science<br>907-151 Slater St., Ottawa, Ontario K1P5H4 Canada | |
|---|---|
| 59. Unsaturated hydraulic conductivity: Field measurement | 68. Sand analysis |
| 60. Air permeability | 69. Identification and measurement of carbonates |
| 61. Aggregate stability to water | 70. Chemical methods in mineralogy |
| 62. Dry aggregate distribution | 71. Sampling frozen soils |
| 63. Soil air | 72. Hydrological properties of frozen soils |
| 64. Soil temperature | 73. Thermal properties of frozen soils |
| 65. Micromorphological methodology for inorganic soils | 74. Frost heave potential |
| 66. Soil separation for mineralogical analysis | 75. Depth of frost penetration |
| 67. Clay and silt analysis | |
| Handbook on Reference Methods for Soil Analysis, 3rd Edition, 1992<br>Council on Soil Testing and Plant Analysis<br>Georgia University Station<br>P.O. Box 2007, Athens, GA 30612-0007 | |
| Soil water pH | Phosphorus by Mehlich No. 3 extraction |
| Soil pH in 0.01M CaCl$_2$ | Ca, K, Mg and Na by Mehlich No. 3 extraction |
| Soil-paste pH and conductivity of saturated extract | Mn, Zn and Cu by Mehlich No. 3 extraction |
| Specific conductance in 1:2 soil:water solution | Boron by hot water extraction |
| Soil buffer pH by Adams-Evans lime buffer | Zn by 0.1 N HCl extraction |
| Soil buffer pH by SMP lime buffer | Acid-extractable Cu by Mehlich-Bowling |
| Exchangeable acidity and lime requirement | Ammonium bicarbonate-DTPA soil test for K, P, Zn, Fe, Mn, Cu and nitrate |
| Phosphorus by Bray P1 extraction | Zn, Mn, Fe and Cu by DTPA extraction |
| Phosphorus by Olsen's sodium bicarbonate extraction | Cd, Cu, Ni and Zn by DTPA extraction for sludge-amended soils |
| K, Mg, Ca and Na by ammonium acetate extraction | Nitrate-nitrite by ISE |
| Phosphorus by Mehlich No. 1 extraction | K, Ca, Mg and Na by water extraction |
| K, Mg, Ca and Na by Mehlich No. 1 extraction | Organic matter by wet digestion |
| Zn by Mehlich No. 1 extraction | Organic matter by loss-on-ignition |
| Phosphorus by Morgan extraction | Humic matter by NaOH extraction |
| K, Ca and Mg by Morgan extraction | Relative availabilities by small-exchange |
| pH, soluble salts, nitrate, P, Ca, Mg, Na, and Cl in greenhouse growth media (soil less mixes) | |

The analysis of inorganic anions in solid phase samples has been addressed in the US Environmental Protection Agency's National Sewage Sludge Survey[87] and in the context of analysis of agricultural soils. The EPA testing needs were addressed as one line sample preparation modifications to already existing traditional wet chemical methods for determination of the specific anions total phosphate, chloride, sulfate, nitrite and nitrate. These, for the most part, involve mixing a portion of the solid with reagent grade

---

[87] Analytical Methods for the National Sewage Sludge Survey, USEPA WH-585, September 1990; POTW Sludge Sampling and Analysis Guidance Document, USEPA August, 1989.

water, agitating on a wrist-shaker or stirring for up to 24 hours, then filtering and treating the filtrate as a normal aqueous sample.

A number of procedures are available in methods manuals[88] (Table 2-30) used by agricultural soils testing laboratories. These involve extraction of the sample with either reagent grade water alone or reagent grade water with various additives. The results from the plain water extractions are most frequently regarded by agronomists, botanists, environmental assessors and other ecology related professionals as the "bio-available" fraction of the total analyte presence in the soil, although experimental justification for such a classification is lacking. The use of water fortified with a variety of additives, such as calcium sulfate, ammonia, ethylenediamine tetraacetic acid (EDTA), and diethylenetriamine pentaacetic acid (DTPA), for the isolation of anions, generates concentration estimates that are assumed to represent "total" content. These recipes were developed with the objective of the analysis of a single anion (such as sulfate), and in many cases they only work for that select anion.

Anions exist in soil samples in a variety of micro-environments[89]. The pore water of the sample can and does contain a number of dissolved components. As long as the samples can be finely divided, providing intimate interaction and dilution of the pore water with the bulk of the extraction mixture, anions contained in this micro-environment can be easily recovered. However, when the pore water is saturated with respect to any specific anion-cation combination, the excess analyte will precipitate as either a particle suspended in the pore water or as a solid upon the surface of the soil matrix, largely an alumino-silicate substrate. Another micro-environment consists of select cations partially incorporated into the alumino-silicate matrix and strongly binding anions to the matrix.

Soils can contain varying amounts of organic material. Most of the organic content is humus derived, which exhibits largely anionic character. Inorganic anions are not expected to be strongly associated with this soil fraction.

Three techniques have been used to recover analyte from these micro-environments. The first is a simple dilution of the pore water with the extraction solution, decreasing the saturation concentration of the solid which may allow more to re-dissolve. Kinetically this is frequently a slow process, and varying recoveries can be obtained depending on the length of contact time with the solid and extracting solvent. Increasing the temperature of the extraction can serve to hasten the process. The second technique is a displacement or exchange process where the solid is suspended in a solution containing an excess of an anion that, when combined with the cation, forms a more insoluble material. For example, sulfate can be solubilized from solid calcium sulfate when the extraction solution contains an excess of carbonate. The more insoluble calcium carbonate is precipitated.

The third technique is directed toward the cation and uses active solubilizing agents such as EDTA, DTPA, cryptands or crown ethers. These agents form very strong complexes with the cation and release the associated anion to the solution. A brief

---

[88] *Handbook on Reference Methods for Soil Analysis*, Soil and Plant Analysis Council, Inc. 1992. *Wisconsin Procedures for Soil Testing, Plant Analysis and Feed & Forage Analysis,* Department of Soil Science, College of Agricultural and Life Sciences, University of Wisconsin-Extension-Madison. 1987; *Soil Sampling and Methods of Analysis*, M.R. Carter (Ed), Canadian Society of Soil Science. 1993, CRC Press, Boca Raton FL; *Methods of Soil Analysis: Part 2 - Chemical and Microbiological Properties*, 2nd Edition, American Society of Agronomy Soil Science Society of America, Madison, WI. 1982.

[89] D.L. Winegardner *Introduction to Soils for Environmental Professionals. CRC Press.* 1996. Boca Raton, FL.

---

examination of the suitability of various extraction mixtures (water, EDTA, DTPA, and, ammonia) for multi-anion analysis using capillary electrophoresis has been published.[90]

A potential approach, that has not been employed in anion analysis, would be to solubilize the soil matrix, such as is done in digestions with hydrofluoric acid for recovery of total metals.

---

[90] Smith, R.-K., J. Romano, J. Kruz, and D. Roth. Extraction of anious from Solid-Phase Samples for Capillary ion Electrophoresis. Proceeding of the Twelfth Annual Quality Assurance and Waste Testing Symposium, USEPA/ACS. Washington, D.C. 23-26 July, 1996. pp 128-138.

# Organic Parameters

An analytical process generally first determines what is present (qualitative analysis) and then determines how much (quantitative analysis). Most of the methods discussed in the previous section are highly specific for the target parameter and have relatively few interferences. Thus the qualitative and quantitative analyses are performed simultaneously. The analysis of organic parameters is much more complex than the determination of the inorganics. To a large part the complexity of the analysis is due to the small range of physical and chemical properties the different organic target analytes exhibit. Any procedure used for organic pollutant analysis will almost always result in determination of a large number of compounds. The qualitative aspects of the analysis become of foremost importance before the determination of how much is present. Most methods for organic analysis embody some sort of separation technique (GC or HPLC) for isolating target analytes and then characterize the isolates with a detector.

Once compounds are separated by some means it is necessary to translate the chemical information of the separation to some usable data form, generally electrical. There are many types of detection, based on a variety of physical properties of the target compounds. In general the explanation of the technique is much more involved than the hardware and software required to put the technique in practice.

1. Conductivity - Conductivity is the inverse of resistance, which is actually what is measured. A potential is applied across a flow of solvent and the decrease in resistance is measured as a positive signal. This can be directly applied to the eluting solvent in HPLC. In GC this technique is used in the Hall (Electrolytic Conductivity) Detector. A selective detector for halogenated compounds is made by mixing the carrier gas stream from the GC column with hydrogen and passing it through a 800 - 900 °C nickel tube. The halogens are reduced to hydrogen halides such as HCl and HBr. The gas flow is then bubbled into a non-conductive yet polar solvent such as propanol. The fluid stream then passes through the conductivity cell, and the decrease in resistance of the flow measured as an electrical signal. Appropriate modifications allow selective detection of nitrogen and sulfur compounds.

2. Spectroscopy - Electromagnetic radiation interacts with compounds in a number of ways. These techiques are often used both as qualitative and quantitative tools. The quantitative aspect is embodied in Lambert-Beers Law (A = abc), which states that absorption is equal to the product of the absorption coefficient (a), the pathlength of the sample (b) and the molar concentration (c) of the analyte. For most procedures this is a linear relationship for at least some range of concentration.

decreasing energy, increasing wavelength, decreasing frequency

---------------------------------------------------------------------->

| X-rays | Vacuum UV | Ultraviolet | Visible | Infrared | Microwave | Radiowave |
|--------|-----------|-------------|---------|----------|-----------|-----------|
| <10 nm | 10-20 nm | 200-400 nm | 400-800 nm | 2-150 um | 50 um - 30 cm | >30 cm |

**Figure 3-1. Energy spectrum.**

Quite common detectors use the X-ray, UV-Visible and the IR parts of the spectrum. The X-ray and UV-Visible end of the spectrum correspond to allowed energy transitions of electrons within the atom or molecule. The IR area of the spectrum corresponds to bond vibrations and molecular rotations. Any photon of energy emitted or absorbed by a molecule will equate to a) an exactly allowed energy transition by an electron in an atom or molecule; or b) the frequency of a periodic atomic motion.

3. UV-Visible interactions - These can be either absorption or emission events. These always involve allowed electron transitions in either atoms or molecules. The molecular electronic transitions are most often absorption events that correspond to allowed jumps of an electron from a ground or low state to a higher energy level, tested on solutions of the target analytes at room temperature. The energy of the absorbed photon ($E = h\nu$) is always equal to the energy of the electron jump, and since most electrons are jumping from a ground state to an allowed excited state, the spectrum is simple with few signals. Solvation of the molecule tends to broaden the absorption bands, and changing the solvent can often affect the wavelength of maximum absorption. The detection can either be conducted in a scanning mode or as a fixed wavelength detector (common in HPLC). The diode array detector allows simultaneous acquisition of the entire spectrum.

Atoms can also participate in absorption events. A common procedure is to put the atoms into a gaseous state by burning the compound in a hydrogen or acetylene flame, then pass light of a particular frequency through the flame to see if the intensity of the light is decreased through absorption due to the presence of a particular element. These signals are quite sharp. The experiment is most often conducted in the set wavelength mode. The flame photometric detector (FPD) for phosphorus and sulfur in GC and the atomic absorption (FLAA and GFAA) metals analyzers operate on this principle.

Emission events are normally limited to atoms, because molecules do not tend to remain intact under the excitation conditions. Some elements are easily excited and exhibit lines in the visible range. This is the basis of the flame test where some of the sample is burned in a bunsen burner. A magenta-violet color indicates the presence of potassium, crimson - lithium or strontium, yellow - sodium, green - barium or copper, and blue - calcium. Altogether these explain why driftwood from the sea coast has such appeal as a fuel in fireplaces. In the more general case analytes are introduced into an atomic plasma created from either helium or argon, which has temperatures of 8000 - 10,000 °C. Molecules are instantly destroyed, and the resultant atoms are thermally excited to very high energy levels. As the atoms cool in the outer portions of the plasma the excited electrons drop down to lower energy levels, and the excess energy is given off as photons. The emitted light from the plasma is directed onto a diffraction grating to separate the light by wavelength, which hits a photodetector and registers as an electronic signal. Emission spectra are quite complex, being composed of many lines as a large number of different excited states are populated.

Another application of UV photons is the photoionization detector. The lamps are rated in electron volts (eV). An electron volt is the amount of energy gained by an electron when passed through a one volt potential. It is equal to $1.60 \times 10^{-12}$ ergs or $1.60 \times 10^{-19}$ joules. Lamps of a variety of power outputs are available, but the most useful generate photons of 9 to 10.5 eV.

**Table 3-1. Correlation of photon wavelength to energy content**

| nm | eV |
|---|---|
| 130.0 | 9.5 |
| 129.0 | 9.6 |
| 123.6 | 10.0 |
| 121.6 | 10.2 |
| 116.5 | 10.6 |
| 105.0 | 11.8 |

These are sufficiently strong photons to completely remove an electron from a double or triple bond or an aromatic system in a molecule and create a cation from the molecule. The ionization is performed in a chamber with an applied potential, and the cations neutralize themselves on the negative electrode, registering as a current. The method is non-destructive and the neutralized molecules can be subjected to other detection systems - ELCD (Hall) is a common second detector in the series.

4. IR interactions - IR interactions with molecules exist in the context of heat and temperature. The terms temperature and heat are not synonymous. Temperature refers to the motion of a molecule. The more vigorous the motion, the higher the temperature. Molecules move in three different modes, vibrational, rotational and translational.

**Figure 3-2. Molecular bond motions.**

The atomic bonds that hold molecules together can be pictured as springs that vibrate back and forth and flex from side to side. The movement of the centers of the atoms with respect to each other constitutes the vibrational mode. Molecules exposed to energy at the same level as the frequency of vibration ($E = h\nu$) can absorb the energy, and the vibration becomes more vigorous. This is the idea behind infrared spectroscopy (IR). Infrared radiation (longer wavelength than visible light) has energy content in the same range as molecular bond vibrations and rotations. Mono-atomic substances such as the rare gases have no vibrational energy levels. The rotational modes of movement result from the molecule spinning around its center of mass. The translational mode of motion is when the molecule is moving through space from one location to another.

Heat is the transfer of energy from one molecule to another. It is always a collisional process. It is very possible to have molecules at very high temperatures but there be no heat to speak of. One such area is in the thermosphere; 80 km up in the atmosphere where the average temperature is about 2000 °C, but there are so few molecules that there is essentially no heat.

The IR experiment is most often conducted in the scanning mode as the IR spectrum is extremely useful in the qualitative analysis of unknowns. Many frequency-specific absorptions have been related to particular bondings in molecules. Over 1000 specific interactions have been described in the literature.

**Table 3-2.  Representative IR frequencies**

| Wavenumber cm$^{-1}$ | Functional group | Wavenumber cm$^{-1}$ | Functional group |
|---|---|---|---|
| 3700-3100 (broad) | O—H | 1800 | -C-C(=O)OC- |
| 3049 | C=C—H | 1710 | C-C(=O)-C |
| 2941-2857 | C—H (saturated) | 1690 | $H_2N(C=O)C$ |
| 2273-2000 | -C≡N | 3310 | -C≡C—H |
| 2119 | -C≡C- | 1650 | C=C |

5.  Fluorescence spectroscopy - This is a very simple method of analysis that entails a very complicated explanation. Essentially a molecule or atom is excited with a high energy source, either X-ray or UV photons, and an electron is bumped to a high energy state. The electron migrates to a slightly lower state with a simultaneous release of energy, generally as temperature (rotational, vibrational, or translational energy). After a period of time the electron relaxes to a significantly lower energy level with simultaneous release of a photon of light. Keys to this process are the time delay between excitation and the emission of fluoresence and the lower energy level of the emitted photon *vs.* the excitation photon. This allows a specific detector to be used that is non-responsive to the excitation source and the subsequent increase in sensitivity. The penultimate application of this method is to use an X-ray excitation source and a specific UV detector. The technology obeys Beers Law.

6.  Mass spectrometry - The mass spectrometer consists of three major parts. They are the *ionization source* where analyte molecules are converted by either laser photoionization, collision, or thermal processes into ions. In some systems the ions will further fragment into smaller mass ions, the fragmentation pattern and abundance distribution being a constant phenomenon under the same experimental conditions. The ions and daughter ions are filtered through a variety of different types of *mass filters*, generally operating on the radius of curved movement of the charged ion (smaller radius for lighter ions) in a magnetic field. The ions are then directed onto a *ion detector* to generate an electric signal. Mass spectrometers often are used to generate a mass spectrum of the unknown analyte for identification.

Mass spectrometers have been coupled with a number of separatory and ionization sources including, GC, capillary electrophoresis, ion chromatographs, HPLC and plasma sources.

**Table 3-3. Commonly used detectors for gas chromatography**

| Equipment | Operation |
|---|---|
| Flame ionization detector (FID) | Burns eluting compounds to form positively charged ions detected as a current flow between the burner and a collector, which are held at a high potential. Most sensitive to C-H containing analytes. |
| Electrolytic conductivity detector (ELCD) or Hall detector | Converts organohalogen compounds into the halogen acid, then measures the increase in conductivity of the halogen acid dissolved in a flowing solvent stream. |
| Electron capture detector (ECD) | Functional groups capture electrons from a $^{63}$Ni source and change the ionization level in the detector chamber. Halogen and nitro functions are detected among others. |
| Flame photometric detector (FPD -) | Eluting compounds burned in a hydrogen-rich flame, phosphorus and sulfur atoms emit light, which passes through a narrow band pass filter to a photodetector. |
| Nitrogen-phosphorous detector (NPD) | Similar in construction to a FID, but a heated rubidium salt-covered bead serves as the ionization element rather than a flame. Nitrogen and phosphorous compounds are selectively ionized and detected as current as in the FID. |
| Photo-ionization detector (PID) | A 10.2 eV lamp serves to ionize substances that contain double bonds. An electric potential exists across the ionization cell. The flow of current indicates the presence of ionized molecules. |
| Mass selective detector (MS) | Fragments eluting compounds into ions that are detected by mass/charge as a spectrum. A three-dimensional detector. |
| Infrared detector (IRD) | Absorbed frequencies of IR light are diagnostic for functional group bonds and generate a spectrum. A three-dimensional detector. |
| Atomic emission dectector (AED) | Eluting compounds enter a helium plasma and the emitted photons sorted by a diffration grating and are collected by a photodetector |

Two cases for identification of organic analytes exist. The first is a situation where an analytical standard of the target analyte is available. The second is when a standard is not available. The criteria for claiming an identification are different for the two situations.

When a standard is present the generally accepted identification criteria are that both the standard and the unknown exhibit the exact same properties under two different and independent test conditions. In so far as organic pollutant identifications are concerned, these criteria can be met by the unknown and the standard having the same retention time on two GC columns with different coatings, as embodied in EPA methods 601 and 602. It is incorrect to use identical behavior of the standard and unknown in two dimensional detectors as sufficient criteria for detection.

An example of this misuse is a lab performing 601/602 on a single GC capillary column with the PID and Hall detectors in series. An eluting compound matched the retention time for 1,2-dichlorobenzene, gave responses on both the PID and the Hall, and the lab reported 1,2-dichlorobenzene as present, which was a violation of the client's NPDES permit. The client spent large sums of money trying to track the contamination, but to no avail and the fines kept mounting. Subsequent reanalysis of the discharge water by another laboratory using an analytical GC capillary column and a different polarity confirmation capillary column, as specified in the method, showed the compound to not be 1,2-dichlorobenzene. Further work with GC/MS tentatively identified the compound as 2-chlorotoluene, which was then confirmed by comparison with a standard. The correct compound, 2-chlorotoluene, was not listed on the client's NPDES permit.

A better version of retention time comparison is co-injection of the standard and the unknown, resulting in only one peak on two GC columns with different polarity coatings. However, even this particular test fails for one pair of compounds, piperonyl butoxide and resmethrin, common insecticide ingredients. A more sure identification could depend on identical retention times for the standard and the unknown on a GC column and identical results from a spectral analysis (UV-vis, mass spectra, or IR spectra) for the two compounds. These data are the information obtained from a HPLC-DAD, HPLC/MS, GC/MS or GC/FTIR. These types of instruments provide what is called three dimensional information, *i.e.* retention time of the eluting compound and a spectrum (response *vs.* mass/charge or frequency) of the compound. The former pair of insecticide ingredients can be correctly identified with any of the four combination instruments.

When a standard is not present, any identification must be regarded as tentative. To claim an absolute identification, overwhelming evidence must be presented that leaves no possibility of misidentification. Suitable evidence would include NMR spectra, IR spectra, mass spectra, elemental analysis, etc. and chemical/physical properties, such as melting point, boiling point, chromatographic behavior, and diagnostic reaction results. These tests are well beyond the capabilities of most environmental laboratories. A mass spectral match out of one of the larger libraries such as the NIST or Wiley compilation is insufficient to claim an identification. Compounds identified on the basis of a spectral match alone are termed tentatively identified compounds (TIC). The CLP SOW requires reporting TICs that are greater than 10% of the peak height of the nearest internal standard found in the sample.

There are three common methods of organic analysis used in the EPA protocols[1], with some examples of target analytes performed by the different techniques presented in Appendix A, List of Analytes. The first general method is based on the compounds having a low solubility in the water matrix and a vapor pressure at 20 °C of greater than 1 mm Hg. Compounds having these properties can be stripped from a water solution by purging the sample with helium gas. These compounds are termed "volatile" or "volatile organic compounds (VOC)" and are determined by a purge and trap

---

[1] A complete listing of target analytes by the EPA is available in *List of Lists, A Catalog of Analytes and Methods*, EPA 21W-4005, August, 1991, for the hardcopy. A newer version is for DOS computer systems.

concentrator attached to either a gas chromatograph (GC) or a gas chromatograph/mass spectrometer (GC/MS) by "volatile organic analysis (VOA)." A reverse application of the purge and trap approach is spray extraction[2].

The second group of general methods is based on the compounds being insoluble in the water matrix but soluble in a non-polar organic solvent such as methylene chloride or hexane. The extraction is refined by taking advantage of the acidic or basic nature of the target analytes and adjusting the pH of the water sample accordingly. Further, these compounds must be thermally stable to the conditions encountered in the heated injector and oven (above 270 °C) of the GC and exhibit an appreciable vapor pressure below 270 °C, *i.e.* $>10^{-7}$ mm Hg at 25 °C. Compounds that meet these criteria are termed semivolatile and are determined by extraction from the water matrix with a non-polar solvent (generally methylene chloride), concentrated and assayed by GC, GC/MS, or GC/ FTIR (gas chromatograph/Fourier Transform Infrared). Compounds extracted from the sample when the pH is greater than 12 are called base-neutral extractables (BN). Compounds that are extracted from the sample when acidified to less than pH 2 are termed acid extractables. The combined analysis of base-neutral and acid extractables is termed BNA analysis.

The third general group of target analytes is assayed by high performance liquid chromatography (HPLC). These compounds exhibit a variety of properties such as water solubility, thermal instability, or extremely low vapor pressure, which make them difficult to assay by GC. Samples are either solvent extracted similar to the semivolatiles preparation, or, in some cases, directly injected into the HPLC as a water solution. A variety of detectors are used with HPLC, both two- and three- dimensional. Techniques particular to HPLC are reversed-phase columns that allow chromatography of very polar analytes, ion-pairing chromatography, size-exclusion chromatography, and the related ion chromatography. Ion chromatography is finding many additional applications in the analysis of inorganic anions and cations.

The organic analytical methods are numbered in the 500s for drinking water, 600s and 1600s for surface and wastewaters, and 8000s for groundwater, landfill leachate, hazardous waste characterization, and solids. Other organic methods are found in the Contract Laboratory Program Statement of Work (CLP SOW). None of these methods are identical, although they are very similar. A number of publications have been written comparing and contrasting the methods. One is a special issue of *The Bench Sheet*, Spring, 1992, by Ann Rosencrance, published by the Water Environment Federation. Another is a series of articles by Zoe Grosser titled "EPA Methods Overview" beginning with the September/October 1992 issue of *Environmental Testing & Analysis*. Also available is the *Guide to Environmental Analytical Methods* from Genium Publishing Company, Dept. EAM2B; One Genium Plaza, Schenectady, NY 12304-4690. These three are fairly inexpensive and a useful accessory to the printed methods. Lewis Publishers has a book titled *Compilation of EPAs Sampling and Analysis Methods* by W. Mueller, D.L. Smith, and L. Keith, which is available as either hardcopy or as a computer database, for a stiff fee. None of these materials replace having the methods on hand. They can only give guidance in picking out a method or adjusting a currently used method to another related method.

---

[2]  Baykut, G., and A. Voigt. "Spray Extraction of Volatile Organic Compounds from Aqueous Systems into the Gas Phase for Gas Chromatography/Mass Spectrometry." *Anal. Chem.* 64(6). 1992. pp. 677-681.

Our lab normally runs 8240/8260 for GC-MS volatiles analysis. During completion of a recent WS PE sample there was an ampule for qualitative and quantitative volatile compounds analysis by method 524.2, which is the related GC-MS method for drinking water. The GC-MS technician analyzed the PE sample by the normal 8240/8260 protocol, and we reported our results to EPA. Being a department that seldom if ever misses an analyte, we were quite surprised to have missed bromochloromethane in the PE sample. On examination of the procedure, it was noticed that bromochloromethane is an internal standard in 8240/8260 and a target analyte in 524.2. Naturally since we had added the compound to the sample, we wouldn't report it as a hit. If we had checked one of the available tabular comparisons of the similar methods, we would have probably caught the difference.

# I. VOLATILES

## A. Instrumentation

The basic instrument for volatile organic analysis (VOA) is a gas chromatograph equipped with a purge and trap injector[3] and a variety of detector options. The purge is accomplished by placing the sample in the sparge tube, then passing an inert gas through the sample. The purge can be performed at ambient or elevated temperatures. Purged compounds are retained on the trap, which is filled with one or more absorbents such as Tenax[4], silica gel, activated carbon, or molecular sieves. Purge gas can be passed through the trap after the completion of the sample purging cycle to remove water. The trap is heated to over 200 °C and the valve switched to route the trapped compounds to the gas chromatograph. As gas flows through the chromatographic column, and the oven temperature is raised, the target analytes are transported down the column at a rate depending on their vapor pressure and specific absorption characteristics. The compounds that exit the column (eluants) pass into a detector that tests some chemical or physical characteristic of the compound and sends the results as an electric signal (instrument response) to a processing device. The specific detector used most often constitutes the major hardware difference between the methods.

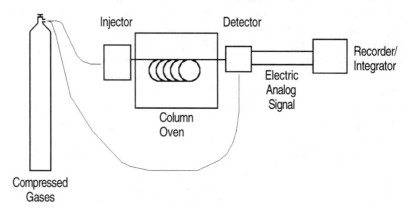

**Figure 3-3. Diagram of a gas chromatograph.**

---

[3] Headspace sampling with GC analysis is a viable technique that has received little EPA attention. For a comparison of headspace to purge and trap see Hewitt *et al., Environ. Sci. Technol.* 1992. 26(10). pp. 1932-1938.

[4] Tradename for a porous polymer made from 2,6-diphenyl-p-phenylene oxide.

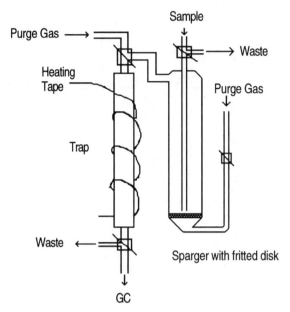

**Figure 3-4. Diagram of a purge and trap for GC.**

The time required for the target analyte to transit the chromatographic column under a set of specified conditions is called the retention time. Known standards of target analytes are subjected to the GC conditions to determine the retention time, which serves as a characteristic piece of information toward establishing the identity of unknowns.

Quantitative analysis of organics is achieved by subjecting aliquots of known concentration standards to the analytical procedure and then preparing a plot of instrument response *vs.* concentration (calibration curve). Depending on the method protocol, a minimum of 3 to 5 different concentration levels of the standard must be analyzed to prepare the calibration curve. Many EPA methods require the addition of a known amount of a known compound as either a check on the efficiency of the sample preparation (surrogate) or as a means of internally calibrating the level of instrument response (internal standard). On rare occasion an added compound can serve both functions.

A key quality control for VOA requires use of analyte-free water for blanks. This water is generated by obtaining deionized water, then boiling it for at least an hour, finally allowing it to cool while vigorously purging the water with analyte free helium or nitrogen. The water is stoppered with glass or Teflon and is generally good for 24 to 48 hours.

## B. Methods

### 501 Trihalomethanes by GC-ECD or ELCD (40 CFR Part 141, Subpart C, Appendix C)

Method 501.1 requires a purge and trap injection system and a packed-column GC with a halogen specific detector to assay the four trihalomethanes. A second column is required for confirmation. Results are reported as total trihalomethanes (TTHM). Method 501.2 is a variation on TTHM determination using a 2.0 mL solvent extraction of a 10.0

mL sample, then direct injection of 3.0 uL of the solvent on the same GC-ECD or ELCD system. The recommended solvent is pentane, however hexane, methylcyclohexane or 2,2,4-trimethyl pentane (isooctane) may be substituted.

**Table 3-4. Target Analytes and MDLs for Method 501**

| Target Analyte | MDL ug/L | Target Analyte | MDL ug/L |
|---|---|---|---|
| Trichloromethane | 0.5 | Dichlorobromomethane | 0.5 |
| Chlorodibromomethane | 0.5 | Tribromomethane | 0.5 |

### 502.1 Volatile halogenated organics in drinking water by purge and trap GC-ECD or ELCD (Reference 27)*

The method uses a purge and trap with packed column GC and Hall electrolytic conductivity to determine halogenated organic target analytes. Five mL sample volumes are purged. Confirmation of identification is required using a second packed column of differing polarity. Calibration by the external standard method requires three-point calibration for a 20-fold concentration range, four-point for a 50-fold range and five-points for a 100-fold range. Internal standard calibration can be performed with either 2-bromo-1-chloropropane or 1,4-dichlorobutane as the internal standard. Daily checking of the calibration curve is required with a laboratory water spike. Further QC measures are daily analysis of a reagent blank and analysis of a laboratory water spike on each work shift.

**Table 3-5. Target Analytes and MDLs for Method 502.1**

| Target Analyte | MDL ug/L | Target Analyte | MDL ug/L |
|---|---|---|---|
| Bromobenzene | - | 1,2-Dichloroethane | 0.002 |
| Bromochloromethane | - | 1,1-Dichloroethene | 0.003 |
| Bromodichloromethane | 0.003 | cis-1,2-Dichloroethene | 0.002 |
| Bromoform | 0.05 | trans-1,2-Dichloroethene | 0.002 |
| Carbon tetrachloride | 0.003 | 1,2-Dichloropropane | - |
| Chlorobenzene | 0.005 | 1,3-Dichloropropane | - |
| Chlorocyclohexane | - | 2,2-Dichloropropane | - |
| 1-Chlorocyclohexene | - | 1,1-Dichloropropene | - |
| Chloroethane | 0.008 | cis-1,3-Dichloropropene | - |
| Chloroform | - | trans-1,3-Dichloropropene | - |
| Chloromethane | 0.01 | Methylene chloride | - |
| 2-Chlorotoluene | - | 1,1,1,2-Tetrachloroethane | - |
| 4-Chlorotoluene | - | 1,1,2,2-Tetrachloroethane | 0.01 |
| Dibromochloromethane | 0.008 | Tetrachloroethene | 0.001 |
| 1,2-Dibromoethane | 0.04 | 1,1,1-Trichloroethane | 0.003 |
| Dibromomethane | - | 1,1,2-Trichloroethane | 0.007 |
| 1,2-Dichlorobenzene | - | Trichloroethene | 0.001 |
| 1,3-Dichlorobenzene | - | Trichlorofluoromethane | - |
| 1,4-Dichlorobenzene | - | 1,2,3-Trichloropropane | - |
| Dichlorodifluoromethane | - | Vinyl chloride | 0.01 |
| 1,1-Dichloroethane | 0.003 | | |

---

* This and other references cited in titles refer to the reference numbers found in Appendix D of this book.

## 502.2 Volatile organics by purge and trap capillary column GC in series with PID and ELCD (Reference 27)

The method uses a purge and trap system to remove volatile organics from a 5.0 mL sample of water. The analysis is performed on a capillary column GC with PID and Hall detectors in series. The recommended operation of the GC is to begin the run at < -10 °C, thus requiring a cryogenically cooled oven. Liquid nitrogen is the most commonly used coolant. Tentative identification of target analytes is performed by matching retention time and by comparing response on the two detectors. GC/MS is recommended as the confirmatory technique. External or internal calibration may be performed. Suggested internal standards are either 1-Chloro-2-fluorobenzene or Fluorobenzene and 2-Bromo-1-chloropropane. A minimum of a three-point calibration is required for a 20-fold calibration range, four-point for a 50-fold range, and five-point for a 100-fold range. Daily checking of the calibration curve is required by analysis of a calibration check standard. During each work shift a water blank and a water blank spike must be analyzed.

**Table 3-6. Target Analytes and MDLs for Method 502.2**

| Target Analyte | MDL ug/L | Target Analyte | MDL ug/L |
|---|---|---|---|
| Bromobenzene | 0.01 | Benzene | 0.01 |
| Bromochloromethane | 0.01 | n-Butylbenzene | 0.02 |
| Bromodichloromethane | 0.02 | sec-Butylbenzene | 0.02 |
| Bromoform | 1.6 | tert-Butylbenzene | 0.06 |
| Bromomethane | 1.1 | Ethylbenzene | 0.01 |
| Carbon tetrachloride | 0.01 | Hexachlorobutadiene | 0.02 |
| Chlorobenzene | 0.01 | Isopropylbenzene | 0.05 |
| Chloroethane | 0.1 | 4-Isopropyltoluene | 0.01 |
| Chloroform | 0.02 | Naphthalene | 0.06 |
| Chloromethane | 0.03 | n-Propylbenzene | 0.01 |
| 2-Chlorotoluene | 0.01 | Styrene | 0.01 |
| 4-Chlorotoluene | 0.01 | Toluene | 0.01 |
| Dibromochloromethane | 0.3 | 1,2,3-Trichlorobenzene | 0.03 |
| 1,2-Dibromo-3-chloropropane | 3.0 | 1,2,4-Trichlorobenzene | 0.02 |
| 1,2-Dibromoethane | 0.8 | 1,2,4-Trimethylbenzene | 0.05 |
| Dibromomethane | 2.2 | 1,3,5-Trimethylbenzene | 0.01 |
| 1,2-Dichlorobenzene | 0.02 | o-Xylene | 0.02 |
| 1,3-Dichlorobenzene | 0.02 | m-Xylene | 0.01 |
| 1,4-Dichlorobenzene | 0.01 | p-Xylene | 0.01 |
| Dichlorodifluoromethane | 0.05 | Methylene chloride | 0.02 |
| 1,1-Dichloroethane | 0.07 | 1,1,1,2-Tetrachloroethane | 0.01 |
| 1,2-Dichloroethane | 0.03 | 1,1,2,2-Tetrachloroethane | 0.01 |
| 1,1-Dichloroethene | 0.07 | Tetrachloroethene | 0.04 |
| cis-1,2-Dichloroethene | 0.01 | 1,1,1-Trichloroethane | 0.03 |
| trans-1,2-Dichloroethene | 0.06 | 1,1,2-Trichloroethane | nd |
| 1,2-Dichloropropane | 0.01 | Trichloroethene | 0.01 |
| 1,3-Dichloropropane | 0.03 | Trichlorofluoromethane | 0.03 |
| 2,2-Dichloropropane | 0.05 | 1,2,3-Trichloropropane | 0.4 |
| 1,1-Dichloropropene | 0.02 | Vinyl chloride | 0.02 |

## 503.1 Volatile aromatic/unsaturated organics by purge and trap GC-PID (Reference 27)

This is a purge and trap method with analysis of target compounds by packed column (5% SP-1200 and 1.75% Bentone 34 on Supelcoport) GC with PID. Compounds are identified by retention time and confirmed by retention times on a second packed column with a different polarity packing (5% 1,2,3-tris(2-cyanoethoxy)propane on Chromosorb W). External standard calibration may be used, however the internal standard method with $\alpha,\alpha,\alpha$-Trifluorotoluene as the internal standard is preferred. The calibration curve must be verified on each working day by analysis of a calibration check standard. Other QC measures include analysis on each work shift of laboratory reagent blanks and laboratory water spiked with the target analytes.

**Table 3-7. Target Analytes and MDLs for Method 503.1**

| Target Analyte | MDL ug/L | Target Analyte | MDL ug/L |
|---|---|---|---|
| Benzene | 0.02 | 4-Isopropyltoluene | 0.009 |
| Bromobenzene | 0.002 | Naphthalene | 0.04 |
| n-Butylbenzene | 0.02 | n-Propylbenzene | 0.009 |
| s-Butylbenzene | 0.02 | Styrene | 0.008 |
| t-Butylbenzene | 0.006 | Tetrachloroethene | 0.01 |
| Chlorobenzene | 0.004 | Toluene | 0.02 |
| 2-Chlorotoluene | 0.008 | 1,2,3-Trichlorobenzene | 0.03 |
| 4-Chlorotoluene | nd | 1,2,4-Trichlorobenzene | 0.03 |
| 1,2-Dichlorobenzene | 0.02 | Trichloroethene | 0.01 |
| 1,3-Dichlorobenzene | 0.006 | 1,2,4-Trimethylbenzene | 0.006 |
| 1,4-Dichlorobenzene | 0.006 | 1,3,5-Trimethylbenzene | 0.003 |
| Ethylbenzene | 0.002 | o-Xylene | 0.004 |
| Hexachlorobutadiene | 0.02 | m-Xylene | 0.004 |
| Isopropylbenzene | 0.005 | p-Xylene | 0.002 |

## 504 1,2-Dibromoethane (EDB) and 1,2-Dibromo-3-chloropropane (DBCP) by GC-ECD (Reference 27)

The method depends on a 2.0 mL hexane extract of 35 mL of sample followed by direct injection of 2 uL of the extract onto a capillary column GC with ECD. A confirmation column is required along with normal quality control. MDL for the two compounds is 0.01 ug/L.

## 524.1 Packed column GC/MS purgeable organics (Reference 27)

The method requires a packed column GC-MS attached to a purge and trap injection system. The packed column is not very efficient for separations, and thus the analyte list is considerably shorter than that of 524.2. Each day of operation the MS must be tuned to 4-Bromofluorobenzene (BFB) acceptance criteria.

**Table 3-8. Daily BFB MS tuning criteria for Method 524.1**

| Mass M/z | BFB Relative Abundance Criteria |
|----------|--------------------------------|
| 50 | 15 to 40% of mass 95 |
| 75 | 30 to 80 % of mass 95 |
| 95 | Base peak, 100% relative abundance |
| 96 | 5 to 9% of mass 95 |
| 173 | <2% of mass 174 |
| 174 | >50% of mass 95 |
| 175 | 5 to 9% of mass 174 |
| 176 | >95% but <101% of mass 174 |
| 177 | 5 to 9% of mass 176 |

The method uses an internal standard (fluorobenzene) for calibration. A minimum of three calibration standards are used for a 20-fold concentration range, four for a 50-fold range and five for a 100-fold range. Calibration may be performed by average response factors (RF), however for each calibrated analyte all individual RFs must be within 20% of the mean for the compound. The other alternative is a second- or third-order regression calibration. The calibrations must be checked at the beginning of each 8-hour shift. Surrogates, BFB and 1,2-dichlorobenzene-$d_4$, are also required. A 25 mL sample, spiked with the surrogates and internal standard, is purged to give the expected MDLs.

**Table 3-9. Target Analytes and MDLs for Method 524.1**

| Target Analyte | MDL ug/L | Target Analyte | MDL ug/L |
|----------------|----------|----------------|----------|
| Benzene | 0.1 | 1,1-Dichloroethene | 0.2 |
| Bromobenzene | 0.1 | trans-1,2-Dichloroethene | 0.2 |
| Bromodichloromethane | 0.5 | 1,2-Dichloropropane | 0.2 |
| Bromoform | 0.7 | 1,3-Dichloropropane | 0.1 |
| Carbon tetrachloride | 0.3 | Methylene chloride | 1.0 |
| Chlorobenzene | 0.1 | Styrene | 0.2 |
| Chloroform | 0.2 | 1,1,2,2-Tetrachloroethane | 0.4 |
| Dibromochloromethane | 0.4 | Tetrachloroethene | 0.3 |
| DBCP | 2.0 | Toluene | 0.1 |
| EDB | 0.4 | 1,1,1-Trichloroethane | 0.3 |
| Dibromomethane | 0.3 | Trichloroethene | 0.4 |
| 1,2-Dichlorobenzene | 1.0 | Trichlorofluoromethane | 0.2 |
| 1,4-Dichlorobenzene | 2.0 | Vinyl chloride | 0.3 |
| Dichlorodifluoromethane | 0.3 | o-Xylene | 0.2 |
| 1,1-Dichloroethane | 0.2 | p-Xylene | 0.3 |
| 1,2-Dichloroethane | 0.2 | | |

## 524.2   Capillary column GC/MS purgeable organics (Reference 27)

This is essentially the exact same method as 524.1 with the exception of the use of a capillary column. The BFB tuning requirements are the same, along with the internal standard and surrogates. The following MDLs were obtained from a wide-bore capillary

(60 m x 0.75 mm VOCOL, 1.5 um film). Use of a narrow-bore capillary (0.32 mm) gives generally better MDLs.

**Table 3-10. Target Analytes and MDLs for Method 524.2**

| Target Analyte | MDL ug/L | Target Analyte | MDL ug/L |
|---|---|---|---|
| Benzene | 0.04 | 1,3-Dichloropropane | 0.04 |
| Bromobenzene | 0.03 | 2,2-Dichloropropane | 0.35 |
| Bromochloromethane | 0.04 | 1,1-Dichloropropene | 0.10 |
| Bromodichloromethane | 0.08 | cis-1,2-Dichloropropene | - |
| Bromoform | 0.12 | trans-1,2-Dichloropropene | - |
| Bromomethane | 0.11 | Ethylbenzene | 0.06 |
| n-Butylbenzene | 0.11 | Hexachlorobutadiene | 0.11 |
| Benzene | 0.04 | 1,3-Dichloropropane | 0.04 |
| tert-Butylbenzene | 0.14 | 4-Isopropyltoluene | 0.12 |
| Carbon tetrachloride | 0.21 | Methylene chloride | 0.03 |
| Chlorobenzene | 0.04 | Naphthalene | 0.04 |
| Chloroethane | 0.10 | n-Propylbenzene | 0.04 |
| Chloroform | 0.03 | Styrene | 0.04 |
| Chloromethane | 0.13 | 1,1,1,2-Tetrachloroethane | 0.05 |
| 2-Chlorotoluene | 0.04 | 1,1,2,2-Tetrachloroethane | 0.04 |
| 4-Chlorotoluene | 0.06 | Tetrachloroethene | 0.14 |
| Dibromochloromethane | 0.05 | Toluene | 0.11 |
| DBCP | 0.26 | 1,2,3-Trichlorobenzene | 0.03 |
| EDB | 0.06 | 1,2,4-Trichlorobenzene | 0.04 |
| Dibromomethane | 0.24 | 1,1,1-Trichloroethane | 0.08 |
| 1,2-Dichlorobenzene | 0.03 | 1,1,2-Trichloroethane | 0.10 |
| 1,3-Dichlorobenzene | 0.12 | Trichloroethene | 0.19 |
| 1,4-Dichlorobenzene | 0.03 | Trichlorofluoromethane | 0.08 |
| Dichlorodifluoromethane | 0.10 | 1,2,3-Trichloropropane | 0.32 |
| 1,1-Dichloroethane | 0.04 | 1,2,4-Trimethylbenzene | 0.13 |
| 1,2-Dichloroethane | 0.06 | 1,3,5-Trimethylbenzene | 0.05 |
| 1,1-Dichloroethene | 0.12 | Vinyl chloride | 0.17 |
| cis-1,2-Dichloroethene | 0.12 | o-Xylene | 0.11 |
| trans-1,2-Dichloroethene | 0.06 | m-Xylene | 0.05 |
| 1,2-Dichloropropane | 0.04 | p-Xylene | 0.13 |

**Table 3-11. Version 4.0 of 524.2 adds the following analytes**

| Target Analyte | MDL ug/L | Target Analyte | MDL ug/L |
|---|---|---|---|
| Acetone | 0.28 | Acrylonitrile | 0.22 |
| Allyl chloride | 0.13 | 2-Butanone | 0.48 |
| Carbon disulfide | 0.093 | Chloroacetonitrile | 0.12 |
| 1-Chlorobutane | 0.18 | trans-1,2-Dichloro-2-butene | 0.36 |
| 1,1-Dichloropropanone | 1.0 | Diethyl ether | 0.28 |
| Ethyl methacrylate | 0.028 | Hexachloroethane | 0.057 |
| 2-Hexanone | 0.39 | Methacrylonitrile | 0.12 |
| Methylacrylate | 0.45 | Methyl iodide | 0.019 |
| Methyl methacrylate | 0.43 | 4-Methyl-2-pentanone | 0.17 |
| Methyl-tert-butyl ether | 0.090 | Nitrobenzene | 1.2 |
| 2-Nitropropane | 0.16 | Pentachloroethane | 0.14 |
| Proprionitrile | 0.14 | Tetrahydrofuran | 1.6 |

## 601   Purgeable halocarbons by GC-ELCD (Reference 42)

The trap is at least 25 cm long and is packed from inlet to exit with 1.0 cm of methyl sili-cone coated packing (3% OV-1), 7.7 cm of 2,6-Diphenylene oxide polymer (Tenax), 7.7 cm of silica gel, and 7.7 cm of coconut charcoal.  An analysis column and confirmation column with Hall electrolytic conductivity detectors are used.  The listed MDLs were ob-tained by EPA on 5.00 mL samples while using a 8-ft x 0.1-in ID GC column packed with 1% SP-1000 on Carbopack B (60-80 mesh).  A confirmation column is required, and the suggested column is a 6-ft x 0.1-in ID column packed with chemically bonded *n*-octane on Porasil-C (100-120 mesh).  All samples are required to be spiked with surrogates and recoveries calculated and maintained.  Suggested surrogates are bromo-chloromethane, 2-bromo-1-chloropropane and 1,4-dichlorobutane.  These can also be used as internal standards.  Samples must be spiked with the target analytes at a minimum rate of 10% of the samples from each sampling site.  Quality control check samples must be analyzed and passed on each working day prior to sample analysis.  Acceptance criteria are included in the method.  Target analytes that fail the daily acceptance criteria must be recalibrated.  This method is most often used in series with method 602 by placing the PID detector first followed by the ELCD.

**Table 3-12.  Target Analytes and MDLs for Method 601**

| Target Analyte | MDL ppb | Target Analyte | MDL ppb |
|---|---|---|---|
| Bromodichloromethane | 0.10 | 1,2-Dichloroethane | 0.03 |
| Bromoform | 0.20 | 1,1-Dichloroethene | 0.13 |
| Bromomethane | 1.18 | *trans*-1,2-Dichloroethene | 0.10 |
| Carbon tetrachloride | 0.12 | 1,2-Dichloropropane | 0.04 |
| Chlorobenzene | 0.25 | *cis*-1,3-Dichloropropene | 0.34 |
| Chloroethane | 0.52 | *trans*-1,3-Dichloropropene | 0.20 |
| 2-Chloroethylvinyl ether | 0.13 | Methylene chloride | 0.25 |
| Chloroform | 0.05 | 1,1,2,2-Tetrachloroethane | 0.03 |
| Chloromethane | 0.08 | Tetrachloroethene | 0.03 |
| Dibromochloromethane | 0.09 | 1,1,1-Trichloroethane | 0.03 |
| 1,2-Dichlorobenzene | 0.15 | 1,1,2-Trichloroethane | 0.02 |
| 1,3-Dichlorobenzene | 0.32 | Trichloroethene | 0.12 |
| 1,4-Dichlorobenzene | 0.24 | Trichlorofluoromethane | nd |
| Dichlorodifluoromethane | 1.81 | Vinyl chloride | 0.18 |
| 1,1-Dichloroethane | 0.07 | | |

## 602   Purgeable aromatics by GC-PID (Reference 42)

This method is often run simultaneously with 601 by placing the PID detector in series before the Hall detector.  If the method is run as a standalone, the trap is packed with 1.0 cm methyl silicone coated support (3% OV-1 on Chromosorb W) and 23 cm of 2,6-Diphenylene oxide polymer (Tenax).  The listed MDLs were obtained by EPA on 5.00 mL samples with a 6-ft x 0.082- in ID GC column packed with 5% SP-1200 and 1.75% Bentone-34 on Supelcoport (100-120 mesh).  The confirmation column was an 8-ft x 0.1-in ID column packed with 5% 1,2,3-Tris(2-cyanoethoxy)propane on Chromosorb W-AW (60-80 mesh).  All samples are required to be spiked with a surrogate and re-coveries calculated and maintained.  The suggested surrogate is $\alpha,\alpha,\alpha$-Trifluorotoluene, which can also be used as an internal standard.  Samples must be spiked with the target analytes at a minimum rate of 10% of the samples from each sampling site.  Quality control check samples must be analyzed and passed on each working day prior to sample analysis. Acceptance criteria are included in the method. Target analytes that fail the daily acceptance criteria must be recalibrated.

**Table 3-13. Target Analytes and MDLs for Method 602**

| Target Analyte | MDL ug/L | Target Analyte | MDL ug/L |
|---|---|---|---|
| Benzene | 0.2 | 1,4-Dichlorobenzene | 0.3 |
| Toluene | 0.2 | 1,3-Dichlorobenzene | 0.4 |
| Ethylbenzene | 0.2 | 1,2-Dichlorobenzene | 0.4 |
| Chlorobenzene | 0.2 | | |

## 624   GC/MS purgeable organics (Reference 42)

The specified trap is packed from the inlet to the exit with 1 cm 3% OV-1 on Chromosorb-W (60/80 mesh), 15 cm Tenax, and 8 cm Grade-15 silica gel (35/60 mesh). The listed MDLs were generated from 5.00 mL samples purged and the volatiles separated on a 6-ft x 0.1-in ID GC column packed with 1% SP-1000 on Carbopack B (60/80 mesh). The target analytes are identified by: 1) matching GC retention time *vs.* that of standards and, by 2) matching the primary peak and at least two secondary peaks in the electron impact mass spectrum obtained at 70 eV with that of the standard. The mass analyzer is tuned daily to meet relative mass abundance criteria for the tuning standard 4-Bromo-1-fluorobenzene (BFB). Calibration is internal standard with a minimum of three points beginning at or slightly higher than the MDL. Individual RFs for each analyte must be within 35% RSD for use of an average RF. Otherwise a plot of RF *vs.* concentration is used. Identified compounds are quantified by the internal standard technique using the area of a key mass fragment in the mass spectrum. Internal standards and surrogates from the suggested list are added to each sample analyzed. Samples at a minimum rate of 5% from each sampling site are spiked with the target analytes. Recoveries are calculated and maintained for each target analyte. Continuing calibration standards containing all target analytes are analyzed on a daily basis to verify the calibration of the instrument. Target analytes not meeting calibration criteria are recalibrated.

**Table 3-14. Internal Standards and Surrogates for Method 624**

| | |
|---|---|
| Benzene-d$_6$ | 1,2-Dichloroethane-d$_4$ |
| Bromochloromethane | Ethylbenzene-d$_5$ |
| 2-Bromo-1-chloropropane | Ethylbenzene-d$_{10}$ |
| 4-Bromofluorobenzene | Fluorobenzene |
| 1,4-Difluorobenzene | Pentafluorobenzene |
| 1,4-Dichlorobutane | |

**Table 3-15. Daily MS tuning requirements for BFB for Method 624**

| Mass M/z | BFB Relative Abundance Criteria |
|---|---|
| 50 | 15 to 40% of mass 95 |
| 75 | 30 to 60 % of mass 95 |
| 95 | Base peak, 100% relative abundance |
| 96 | 5 to 9% of mass 95 |

Continued on next page.

**Table 3-15. Daily MS tuning requirements for BFB for Method 624,** *continued*

| Mass M/z | BFB Relative Abundance Criteria |
|----------|--------------------------------|
| 173 | <2% of mass 174 |
| 174 | >50% of mass 95 |
| 175 | 5 to 9% of mass 174 |
| 176 | >95% but <101% of mass 174 |
| 177 | 5 to 9% of mass 176 |

**Table 3-16. Target Analytes, MDLs, Precision and Accuracy (20 ug/L spike) for Method 624**

| Target Analyte | MDL ppb | %R | RPD |
|----------------|---------|-----|-----|
| Benzene | 4.4 | 37-151 | 0-14 |
| Bromodichloromethane | 2.2 | 35-155 | 0-13 |
| Bromoform | 4.7 | 45-169 | 0-11 |
| Bromomethane | nd | D-242 | 0-36 |
| Carbon tetrachloride | 2.8 | 70-140 | 0-10 |
| Chlorobenzene | 6.0 | 37-160 | 0-13 |
| Chloroethane | nd | 14-230 | 0-23 |
| 2-Chloroethylvinyl ether | nd | D-305 | 0-52 |
| Chloroform | 1.6 | 51-138 | 0-12 |
| Chloromethane | nd | D-273 | 0-40 |
| Dibromochloromethane | 3.1 | 53-149 | 0-12 |
| 1,2-Dichlorobenzene | nd | 18-190 | 0-14 |
| 1,3-Dichlorobenzene | nd | 59-156 | 0-11 |
| 1,4-Dichlorobenzene | nd | 18-190 | 0-14 |
| 1,1-Dichloroethane | 4.7 | 59-155 | 0-10 |
| 1,2-Dichloroethane | 2.8 | 49-155 | 0-12 |
| 1,1-Dichloroethene | 2.8 | D-234 | 0-18 |
| *trans*-1,2-Dichloroethene | 1.6 | 54-156 | 0-11 |
| 1,2-Dichloropropane | 6.0 | D-210 | 0-28 |
| *cis*-1,3-Dichloropropene | 5.0 | D-227 | 0-32 |
| *trans*-1,3-Dichloropropene | nd | 17-183 | 0-21 |
| Ethylbenzene | 7.2 | 37-162 | 0-15 |
| Methylene chloride | 2.8 | D-221 | 0-15 |
| 1,1,2,2-Tetrachloroethane | 6.9 | 46-157 | 0-15 |
| Tetrachloroethene | 4.1 | 64-148 | 0-10 |
| Toluene | 6.0 | 47-150 | 0-10 |
| 1,1,1-Trichloroethane | 3.8 | 52-162 | 0-9 |
| 1,1,2-Trichloroethane | 5.0 | 52-150 | 0-11 |
| Trichloroethene | 1.9 | 71-157 | 0-13 |
| Trichlorofluoromethane | nd | 17-181 | 0-20 |
| Vinyl chloride | nd | D-251 | 0-40 |

## 1624 Volatile organic compounds by isotope dilution GC/MS (Reference 42)

The method uses either deuterium or $^{13}C$ labeled isotopes as surrogates/internal standards. Those compounds lacking a labeled standard are calibrated against bromochloromethane as internal standard. The method requires a five-point calibration either by average RF (individual RFs must deviate less than 35% from the average) or by construction of a calibration curve. Daily tuning requirements for the MS are as listed for a 50 ng sample of BFB.

**Table 3-17. Target Analytes and MDLs for Method 1624**

| Target Analyte | MDL ppb | Target Analyte | MDL ppb |
|---|---|---|---|
| Acetone | 50 | trans-1,2-Dichloroethene | 10 |
| Acrolein | 50 | 1,2-Dichloropropane | 10 |
| Acrylonitrile | 50 | cis-1,3-Dichloropropene | 10 |
| Benzene | 10 | trans-1,3-Dichloropropene | 10 |
| Bromodichloromethane | 10 | Diethyl ether | 50 |
| Bromoform | 10 | p-Dioxane | 10 |
| Bromomethane | 50 | Ethyl benzene | 10 |
| Carbon tetrachloride | 10 | Methylene chloride | 10 |
| Chlorobenzene | 10 | Methyl ethyl ketone | 50 |
| Chloroethane | 50 | 1,1,2,2-Tetrachloroethane | 10 |
| 2-Chloroethylvinylether | 10 | Tetrachloroethene | 10 |
| Chloroform | 10 | Toluene | 10 |
| Chloromethane | 50 | 1,1,1-Trichloroethane | 10 |
| Dibromochloromethane | 10 | 1,1,2-Trichloroethane | 10 |
| 1,1-Dichloroethane | 10 | Trichloroethene | 10 |
| 1,2-Dichloroethane | 10 | Vinyl chloride | 10 |
| 1,1-Dichloroethene | 10 | | |

**Table 3-18. Daily BFB MS tuning requirements for Method 1624**

| Mass M/z | BFB Relative Abundance Criteria |
|---|---|
| 50 | 15 to 40% of mass 95 |
| 75 | 30 to 60 % of mass 95 |
| 95 | Base peak, 100% relative abundance |
| 96 | 5 to 9% of mass 95 |
| 173 | <2% of mass 174 |
| 174 | >50% of mass 95 |
| 175 | 5 to 9% of mass 174 |
| 176 | >95% but <101% of mass 174 |
| 177 | 5 to 9% of mass 176 |

## 8015 Nonhalogenated volatile organics by direct injection or purge and trap GC-FID (Reference 41)

This packed column method forms the basis for the GC petroleum hydrocarbon techniques, commonly refered to as the "California Method" or the GRO method (gasoline range organic) and the DRO method (diesel range organic). Identification of compounds is confirmed using a second packed column of different polarity.

**Table 3-19. Target Analytes and MDLs for Method 8015**

| Target Analyte | MDL ug/L | Target Analyte | MDL ug/L |
|---|---|---|---|
| Diethyl ether | nd | Methyl ethyl ketone | nd |
| Ethanol | nd | Methyl isobutyl ketone | nd |

## 8021 Halogenated and aromatic volatiles by direct injection or purge and trap capillary column GC with ELCD and PID detectors in series (Reference 41)

This is the most common method used by laboratories that lack GC-MS. Identification depends on matching the responses from the two detectors and the retention time with that of standards. This method is only for use in RCRA programs and is not equivalent to a combined 601-602 method for NPDES support, which requires a second column or GC/MS for confirmation. Fluorobenzene and 2-bromo-1-chloropropane are used as internal standards. The surrogates consist of bromochloromethane, 2-bromo-1-chloropropane, 1,4-dichlorobutane and bromochlorobenzene. A minimum of five calibration levels are used.

## 8240 Volatile organic compounds by GC/MS: packed column (Reference 41)

The more pronounced differences between the RCRA methods (8000s) and the drinking water methods (500s) and wastewater methods (600s and 1600s) exist in the easing of the daily calibration checking requirements in the SW-846 methods. A small subset of the target analytes are checked in the matrix spike, and the daily (CCC) has a set number of representative analytes that must meet the acceptance criteria, which means that less time is spent on recalibration and more time on analysis. Daily MS tuning requirements are the same as for 624 and 1624. Calibration is by internal standard RF with a minimum of 5 points. Acceptance criteria for the average RF values requires that CCC all have RF less than 30%. In addition System Performance Check Compounds (SPCC) must have RF greater than listed minimum values. SPCC and CCC must be performed every 12 hours of operation (once a shift). If the SPCC and CCC criteria are met, the overall calibration for the rest of the compounds is accepted as good. The MDL for the target compounds is actually the estimated quantitation limit (EQL) and is the same for groundwater matrix and soil/sediment.

**Table 3-20. Daily MS BFB tuning requirements**

| Mass M/z | BFB Relative Abundance Criteria |
|---|---|
| 50 | 15 to 40% of mass 95 |
| 75 | 30 to 60 % of mass 95 |
| 95 | Base peak, 100% relative abundance |
| 96 | 5 to 9% of mass 95 |
| 173 | <2% of mass 174 |
| 174 | >50% of mass 95 |
| 175 | 5 to 9% of mass 174 |
| 176 | >95% but <101% of mass 174 |
| 177 | 5 to 9% of mass 176 |

### Table 3-21. Daily SPCC criteria for Method 8240

| SPCC | Minimum RF |
|---|---|
| Chloromethane | 0.300 |
| Bromoform | 0.250 |
| Chlorobenzene | 0.300 |

| SPCC | Minimum RF |
|---|---|
| 1,1-Dichloroethane | 0.300 |
| 1,1,2,2-Tetrachloroethane | 0.300 |

### Table 3-22. Target Analytes and MDLs for Method 8240

| Target Analyte | MDL ppb |
|---|---|
| Acetone | 100 |
| Acetonitrile | 100 |
| Allyl chloride | 5 |
| Benzene | 5 |
| Benzyl chloride | 100 |
| Bromodichloromethane | 5 |
| Bromoform | 5 |
| Bromomethane | 10 |
| 2-Butanone | 100 |
| Carbon disulfide | 100 |
| Carbon tetrachloride | 5 |
| Chlorobenzene | 5 |
| Chlorodibromomethane | 5 |
| Chloroethane | 10 |
| 2-Chloroethylvinyl ether | 10 |
| Chloroform | 5 |
| Chloromethane | 10 |
| Chloroprene | 5 |
| 1,2-Dibromo-3-chloropropane | 100 |
| 1,2-Dibromoethane | 5 |
| Dibromomethane | 5 |
| 1,4-Dichloro-2-butene | 100 |
| Dichlorodifluoromethane | 5 |
| 1,1-Dichloroethane | 5 |
| 1,2-Dichloroethane | 5 |
| 1,1-Dichloroethene | 5 |
| trans-1,2-Dichloroethene | 5 |

| Target Analyte | MDL ppb |
|---|---|
| 1,2-Dichloropropane | 5 |
| cis-1,3-Dichloropropene | 5 |
| trans-1,3-Dichloropropene | 5 |
| Ethylbenzene | 5 |
| Ethylmethacrylate | 5 |
| 2-Hexanone | 50 |
| Isobutyl alcohol | 100 |
| Methacrylonitrile | 100 |
| Methylene chloride | 5 |
| Methyl iodide | 5 |
| Methyl methacrylate | 5 |
| 4-Methyl-2-pentanone | 50 |
| Pentachloroethane | 10 |
| Propionitrile | 100 |
| Styrene | 5 |
| 1,1,1,2-Tetrachloroethane | 5 |
| 1,1,2,2-Tetrachloroethane | 5 |
| Tetrachloroethene | 5 |
| Toluene | 5 |
| 1,1,1-Trichloroethane | 5 |
| 1,1,2-Trichloroethane | 5 |
| Trichloroethene | 5 |
| 1,2,3-Trichloropropane | 5 |
| Vinyl acetate | 50 |
| Vinyl chloride | 10 |
| Xylene | 5 |

### Table 3-23. Daily CCC criteria for Method 8240

| CCC | % RSD |
|---|---|
| 1,1-Dichloroethene | <30 |
| 1,2-Dichloropropane | <30 |
| Ethylbenzene | <30 |

| CCC | %RSD |
|---|---|
| Chloroform | <30 |
| Toluene | <30 |
| Vinyl chloride | <30 |

**Table 3-24. Surrogates and Internal Standards for Method 8240**

| |
|---|
| Bromochloromethane (is) |
| 4-Bromofluorobenzene (surr) |
| Chlorobenzene-d$_5$ (is) |
| 1,4-Difluorobenzene (is) |
| 1,2-Dichloroethane-d$_4$ (surr) |
| Toluene-d$_8$ (surr) |

**Table 3-25. Matrix spike compounds for Method 8240**

| |
|---|
| Benzene |
| Chlorobenzene |
| 1,1-Dichloroethene |
| Toluene |
| Trichloroethene |

## 8260 Volatile organic compounds by GC/MS: capillary column (Reference 41)

A variety of capillary columns are suggested for use with 8260, the 60 meter x 0.75 mm ID VOCOL by Supelco with a temperature program from 10 °C to 160 °C being one of them. There are substantial differences between 8240 and 8260 besides the columns. There are different internal standards and target compound lists. Bromochloromethane is an internal standard for 8240 and a target analyte for 8260. Otherwise, the methods are very similar in calibration, tuning, SPCC, CCC and matrix spike requirements. The MDLs listed for the target analytes are based on purging a 25 mL sample, which is somewhat out of the ordinary; a 5 mL sample is normally tested.

**Table 3-26. Daily MS BFB tuning requirements for Method 8260**

| Mass M/z | BFB Relative Abundance Criteria |
|---|---|
| 50 | 15 to 40% of mass 95 |
| 75 | 30 to 60 % of mass 95 |
| 95 | Base peak, 100% relative abundance |
| 96 | 5 to 9% of mass 95 |
| 173 | <2% of mass 174 |
| 174 | >50% of mass 95 |
| 175 | 5 to 9% of mass 174 |
| 176 | >95% but <101% of mass 174 |
| 177 | 5 to 9% of mass 176 |

**Table 3-27. Daily SPCC requirements for Method 8260**

| SPCC | Minimum RF | SPCC | Minimum RF |
|---|---|---|---|
| Chloromethane | 0.300 | 1,1-Dichloroethane | 0.300 |
| Bromoform | 0.250 | 1,1,2,2-Tetrachloroethane | 0.300 |
| Chlorobenzene | 0.300 | | |

### Table 3-28. Daily CCC requirements for Method 8260

| CCC | % RSD |
|---|---|
| 1,1-Dichloroethene | <30 |
| 1,2-Dichloropropane | <30 |
| Ethylbenzene | <30 |

| CCC | %RSD |
|---|---|
| Chloroform | <30 |
| Toluene | <30 |
| Vinyl chloride | <30 |

### Table 3-29. Surrogates and Internal Standards for Method 8260

4-Bromofluorobenzene (surr)
Chlorobenzene-d5 (is)
Dibromofluoromethane (surr)
1,4-Dichlorobenzene-d4 (is)
1,4-Difluorobenzene (is)
Pentafluorobenzene (is)
Toluene-d8 (surr)

### Table 3-30. Matrix spike compounds for Method 8260

Benzene
Chlorobenzene
1,1-Dichloroethene
Toluene
Trichloroethene

### Table 3-31. Target Analytes and MDLs for Method 8260

| Target Analyte | MDL ug/L |
|---|---|
| Dichlorodifluoromethane | 0.10 |
| Chloromethane | 0.13 |
| Vinyl chloride | 0.17 |
| Bromomethane | 0.11 |
| Chloroethane | 0.10 |
| Trichlorofluoromethane | 0.08 |
| 1,1-Dichloroethene | 0.12 |
| Methylene chloride | 0.03 |
| trans-1,2-Dichloroethene | 0.06 |
| 1,1-Dichloroethane | 0.04 |
| 2,2-Dichloropropane | 0.35 |
| cis-1,2-Dichloroethene | 0.12 |
| Chloroform | 0.03 |
| Bromochloromethane | 0.04 |
| 1,1,1-Trichloroethane | 0.08 |
| Carbon tetrachloride | 0.21 |
| 1,1-Dichloropropene | 0.10 |
| Benzene | 0.04 |
| 1,2-Dichloroethane | 0.06 |

| Target Analyte | MDL ug/L |
|---|---|
| 1-Chlorohexane | 0.05 |
| Chlorobenzene | 0.04 |
| 1,1,1,2-Tetrachloroethane | 0.05 |
| Ethylbenzene | 0.06 |
| p-Xylene | 0.13 |
| m-Xylene | 0.05 |
| o-Xylene | 0.11 |
| Styrene | 0.04 |
| Bromoform | 0.12 |
| Isopropylbenzene | 0.15 |
| 1,1,2,2-Tetrachloroethane | 0.04 |
| Bromobenzene | 0.03 |
| 1,2,3-Trichloropropane | 0.32 |
| n-Propylbenzene | 0.04 |
| 2-Chlorotoluene | 0.04 |
| 1,3,5-Trimethylbenzene | 0.05 |
| 4-Chlorotoluene | 0.06 |
| tert-Butylbenzene | 0.14 |
| 1,2,4-Trimethylbenzene | 0.13 |

Continued on next page.

**Table 3-31. Target Analytes and MDLs for Method 8260,** *continued*

| Target Analyte | MDL ug/L |
|---|---|
| Trichloroethene | 0.19 |
| 1,2-Dichloropropane | 0.04 |
| Bromodichloromethane | 0.08 |
| Dibromomethane | 0.24 |
| *trans*-1,3-Dichloropropene | - |
| Toluene | 0.11 |
| *cis*-1,3-Dichloropropene | - |
| 1,1,2-Trichloroethane | 0.10 |
| Tetrachloroethene | 0.14 |
| 1,3-Dichloropropane | 0.04 |
| Dibromochloromethane | 0.05 |
| 1,2-Dibromoethane | 0.06 |

| Target Analyte | MDL ug/L |
|---|---|
| *sec*-Butylbenzene | 0.13 |
| *p*-Isopropyltoluene | 0.12 |
| 1,3-Dichlorobenzene | 0.12 |
| 1,4-Dichlorobenzene | 0.03 |
| *n*-Butylbenzene | 0.11 |
| 1,2-Dichlorobenzene | 0.03 |
| 1,2-Dibromo-3-chloropropane | 0.26 |
| 1,2,4-Trichlorobenzene | 0.04 |
| Hexachlorobutadiene | 0.11 |
| Naphthalene | 0.04 |
| 1,2,3-Trichlorobenzene | 0.03 |

**Table 3-32. Other VOA related procedures listed in SW-846**

| Method # | Title |
|---|---|
| 3810 | Headspace |
| 3820 | Hexadecane extraction and screening of purgeable organics |
| 5030 | Purge and trap |
| 5031 | Water soluble volatile organic compounds by azeotropic distillation |
| 5040 | Analysis of sorbent cartridges from volatile organic sampling train (VOST): GC/MS |
| 5041 | Analysis of sorbent cartridges from VOST: GC/MS capillary column |
| 5100 | Determination of the volatile organic content of waste samples |
| 8010 | Halogenated volatile organics by direct injection or purge and trap GC with a halogen specific detector |
| 8011 | 1,2-Dibromoethane and 1,2-Dibromo-3-chloropropane by microextraction and GC-ECD |
| 8020 | Aromatic volatile organics by direct injection or purge and trap GC-PID with packed column |
| 8030 | Acrolein and acrylonitrile by direct injection or purge and trap packed column GC-FID |
| 8031 | Acrylonitrile by microextraction followed by GC-NPD |

## II. SEMIVOLATILES
## A. Instrumentation

The instruments used in semivolatiles analysis are primarily GC and HPLC for separation and a wide variety of general and selective detectors for analysis. In general-purpose production-oriented labs the instruments on site will be dual capillary column-dual injector GC with dual ECD, single injector capillary column quadrupole GC/MS for semivolatiles, purge and trap equipped single capillary column quadrupole GC/MS for volatiles, and HPLC with post-column derivatization-fluorescence detector and DAD. There may be GC-FID instruments as screening tools or if a lot of petroleum hydrocarbon analysis is being performed.

The quadrupole GC/MS is the workhorse of the lab. Most samples in the volatiles and semivolatiles labs are analyzed by GC/MS. The only reason for having the GC-ECD is because the detection limits required for chlorinated pesticides under the various regulatory programs are so low that the quadrupole GC/MS can't see them. Otherwise the GC-ECD wouldn't be there either. Recent advances by GC/MS manufacturers may bring this about. The quadrupole MS is the preferred instrument because it has the ruggedness to handle the garbage overload present in environmental samples, which the ion trap MS doesn't. This is despite the fact that the ion trap is at least 10 times more sensitive than the quadrupole.

Another reason for the primacy of the GC/MS in the lab is that the MS is a three-dimensional detector and gives analyte identification and confirmation in one run. Most GC instruments have slots for two detectors. If the slots are occupied by a PID and ELCD for volatiles analysis, even though in series, there is room for only one column in the instrument. Thus, to perform 601-602 in compliance with the method, two instruments are required to provide the required confirmation. Most production labs like to operate with a primary instrument and a back-up for the times when the primary is down due to maintenance or repair. This means four GCs are required for the 601-602 samples. On the semivolatiles side, performance of methods 604, 606, 607, 609, 610, 611, 612, 614, 616, 619, 620, 622, and a slew of others would require duplicate GCs equipped with dual ECD, dual FPD, dual NPD, and dual FID; or a single GC/MS with back-up. These considerations plus gas consumption, service contracts, technician salaries, instrument flexibility and GC consumables, such as columns, lead to economics that suggest that the GC/MS is the way to go. Most profitable labs have gone this way.

Balanced against these considerations is the reality of "If I buy an instrument, can I get in enough work to pay for it and still make a profit?" This is the major reason that HPLC/MS has not prospered in the environmental laboratory industry. It's a marvelous instrument. However, until the government regulations are written to require it as a necessary tool to achieve industrial discharge regulatory compliance, there is no profit to be made by paying $200,000 and performing analyses that can be more cheaply performed by a $50,000 HPLC state-of-the-art system, which is presently a marginal investment. The same can be said of capillary electrophoresis and ion chromatography - nice instruments but can the laboratory make a profit?

A diagram of a generic gas chromatography is presented in Figure 3-3. The dual column instruments operate with a single auto-sampler and dual auto-injectors that are attached to the columns. The auto-sampler will place sample X in the front injector turret and then place sample Y in the back turret. The auto-injectors process the samples at the same time and make simultaneous injections onto the columns. The oven program starts, and samples X and Y are analyzed on the two different columns. At the completion of the run, the data for X and Y are processed and stored in the computer. The autosampler next places sample Y in the front turret and sample Z in the back turret. At the completion of the run chromatograms have been generated for sample Y on both the analytical and the confirmation columns.

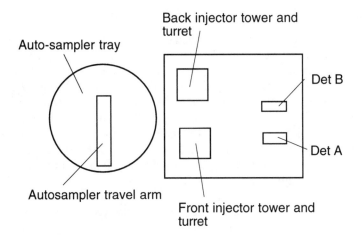

**Figure 3-5. Diagram of dual column GC.**

# B. Methods 500, 600, and 1600 Series

505   Organohalide pesticides & PCBs by GC-ECD (Reference 27)

This is a micro-extraction method that uses 2.0 mL of hexane to extract chlorinated pesticides and PCBs from 35 mL of sample. Two uL of extract are assayed by capillary column (DB-1) GC equipped with an electron capture detector. Use of a confirmation capillary column (OV-17 or Durawax-DX3 are recommended) for identification verification is mandatory. Quantification is external standard with a calibration curve (minimum three-point, recommended five-point). Daily analysis of reagent blanks, calibration check standards and laboratory water spikes are required. At least 10% of the samples must be analyzed as matrix spikes

**Table 3-33. Target Analytes and MDLs for Method 505**

| Target Analyte | MDL ug/L | Target Analyte | MDL ug/L |
|---|---|---|---|
| Aldrin | 0.075 | *cis*-Nonachlor | 0.027 |
| Alachlor | 0.225 | *trans*-Nonachlor | 0.011 |
| Atrazine | 2.4 | Simazine | 6.8 |
| Chlordane | 0.14 | Toxaphene | 1.0 |
| Dieldrin | 0.012 | Aroclor 1016 | 0.08 |
| Endrin | 0.063 | Aroclor 1221 | 15.0 |
| Heptachlor | 0.003 | Aroclor 1232 | 0.48 |
| Heptachlor epoxide | 0.004 | Aroclor 1242 | 0.31 |
| Hexachlorobenzene | 0.002 | Aroclor 1248 | 0.102 |
| Hexachlorocyclopentadiene | 0.13 | Aroclor 1254 | 0.102 |
| Lindane | 0.003 | Aroclor 1260 | 0.189 |
| Methoxychlor | 0.96 | | |

## 506 Phthalate and Adipate esters by GC-PID (Reference 27)

Three isolation/concentration techniques are allowed to be used for sample preparation. The first is a liquid-liquid separatory funnel extraction using 1 L of sample with 50 g sodium chloride added and then extracted 3 x 60 mL $CH_2Cl_2$ and one time with 40 mL hexane. The combined organic layers are dried with sodium sulfate, and concentrated to 1.0 mL using a K-D and nitrogen blowdown. The second technique uses a reversed phase C-18 solid phase cartridge to isolate and concentrate the analytes, then they are eluted with 10 mL $CH_2Cl_2$ followed by drying $(Na_2SO_4)$ and nitrogen blowdown to 1.0 mL. The third procedure uses 47 mm reversed-phase extraction disks to isolate the analytes that are eluted with acetonitrile and methylene chloride. Further cleanup of the sample extract is possible through florisil or alumina columns.

Calibration is external standard with a minimum of three-point calibration. The GC system is calibrated daily. Identification confirmation is required for this method. A GC/MS is the suggested confirmation instrument.

**Table 3-34. Target Analytes and MDLs for Method 506**

| Target Analyte | MDL ug/L | Target Analyte | MDL ug/L |
|---|---|---|---|
| Dimethyl phthalate | 1.14 | Bis(2-ethylhexyl) adipate | 11.82 |
| Diethyl phthalate | 0.84 | Bis (2-ethylhexyl) phthalate | 2.25 |
| Di-n-butyl phthalate | 1.23 | Di-n-octyl phthalate | 6.42 |
| Butyl benzyl phthalate | 2.67 | | |

## 507 N & P pesticides by GC-NPD (Reference 27)

Nitrogen- and phosphorus-containing pesticides are determined by addition of the surrogate (1,3-Dimethyl-2-nitrobenzene) to 1.00 L of sample, buffering to pH 7 with phosphate buffer, extraction with methylene chloride, concentration in a K-D apparatus, solvent transfer to methyl-$t$-butylether (MTBE) and volume adjustment to 5.0 mL. Internal standard is added (Triphenylphosphine) and the sample analyzed by capillary column (DB-5) GC with a Nitrogen Phosphorous detector. Identification is confirmed on a second column (DB-1701). Target analytes are quantified by response factors obtained from calibration curves (three-point minimum, five-point recommended). The calibration curves are checked on each working shift by analysis of a calibration check standard. [Alternately an external standard calibration is allowed.] Matrix spikes are required at a rate of 5% of the samples analyzed. A daily system performance check must be made for sensitivity (Vernolate), chromatographic performance (Bromacil) and column performance (Prometon and Atrazine). Daily analysis of reagent blanks and laboratory water spikes are required.

**Table 3-35. Target Analytes and MDLs for Method 507**

| Target Analyte | MDL ug/L | Target Analyte | MDL ug/L |
|---|---|---|---|
| Alachlor | 0.38 | Methyl paraoxon | 2.5 |
| Ametryn | 2 | Metolachlor | 0.75 |
| Ametraton | 0.6 | Metribuzin | 0.15 |
| Atrazine | 0.13 | Mevinphos | 5 |

Continued on next page.

**Table 3-35. Target Analytes and MDLs for Method 507,** *continued*

| Target Analyte | MDL ug/L | Target Analyte | MDL ug/L |
|---|---|---|---|
| Bromacil | 2.5 | MGK 264 | 0.5 |
| Butachlor | 0.38 | Molinate | 0.15 |
| Butylate | 0.15 | Napropamide | 0.25 |
| Carboxin | 0.6 | Norflurazon | 0.5 |
| Chlorpropham | 0.5 | Pebulate | 0.13 |
| Cycloate | 0.25 | Prometon | 0.3 |
| Diazinon | 0.25 | Prometryn | 0.19 |
| Dichlorvos | 2.5 | Pronamide | 0.76 |
| Diphenamid | 0.6 | Propazine | 0.13 |
| Disulfoton | 0.3 | Simazine | 0.075 |
| Disulfoton sulfone | 3.8 | Simetryn | 0.25 |
| Disulfoton sulfoxide | 0.38 | Stirofos | 0.76 |
| EPTC | 0.25 | Tebuthiuron | 1.3 |
| Ethoprop | 0.19 | Terbacil | 4.5 |
| Fenamiphos | 1 | Terbufos | 0.5 |
| Fenarimol | 0.38 | Terbutryn | 0.25 |
| Fluridone | 3.8 | Triademefon | 0.65 |
| Hexazinone | 0.76 | Tricyclazole | 1 |
| Merphos | 0.25 | Vernolate | 0.13 |

## 508  Chlorinated pesticides by GC-ECD (Reference 27)

Chlorinated pesticides are determined by addition of the surrogate (4,4'-Dichloro-biphenyl) to 1.00 L of sample, buffering to pH 7 with phosphate buffer, extraction with methylene chloride, concentration in a K-D apparatus, solvent transfer to methyl *t*-butyl ether (MTBE) and volume adjustment to 5.0 mL. Internal standard is added (Penta-chloronitrobenzene) and the sample analyzed by capillary column (DB-5) GC with an electron capture detector. Identification is confirmed on a second capillary column (DB-1701). Target analytes are quantified by response factors obtained from calibration curves (three-point minimum, five-point recommended). The calibration curve is veri-fied on each work shift by analysis of a calibration check standard. Daily (or 5% of samples performed daily) analysis of a laboratory water spike is required. System per-formance is checked daily by analysis of a laboratory performance check sample for sensitivity (chlorpyrifos), chromatographic performance (DCPA) and column perfor-mance (chlorothalonil and δ-BHC).

**Table 3-36. Target Analytes and MDLs for Method 508**

| Target Analyte | MDL ug/L | Target Analyte | MDL ug/L |
|---|---|---|---|
| Aldrin | 0.075 | Endrin aldehyde | 0.025 |
| Chlorneb | 0.5 | Etridiazole | 0.025 |
| Chlorobenzilate | 5 | α-BHC | 0.025 |
| Chlordane | 0.0015 | β-BHC | 0.01 |
| Chlorthalonil | 0.025 | δ-BHC | 0.01 |

Continued on next page.

**Table 3-36. Target Analytes and MDLs for Method 508,** *continued*

| Target Analyte | MDL ug/L | Target Analyte | MDL ug/L |
|---|---|---|---|
| DCPA | 0.025 | γ-BHC | 0.015 |
| 4,4'-DDD | 0.0025 | Heptachlor | 0.01 |
| 4,4'-DDE | 0.01 | Heptachlor epoxide | 0.015 |
| 4,4'-DDT | 0.06 | Hexachlorobenzene | 0.0077 |
| Dieldrin | 0.02 | Methoxychlor | 0.05 |
| Endosulfan I | 0.015 | *cis*-Permethrin | 0.5 |
| Endosulfan II | 0.024 | *trans*-Permethrin | 0.5 |
| Endosulfan sulfate | 0.015 | Propachlor | 0.5 |
| Endrin | 0.015 | Trifluralin | 0.025 |

## 508A   PCBs by derivatization and GC-ECD (Reference 27)

This method serves as a pass/fail screening method for detection of PCBs in water with a MDL of 0.5 ppb. The sample (1.0 L) is extracted with methylene chloride; the extract is concentrated in a K-D apparatus; and the solvent exchanged to chloroform. The PCBs are transformed to decachlorobiphenyl by the reaction in Figure 3-6. Antimony pentachloride reacts with the biphenyl in the presence of the iron powder catalyst to perchlorinate the biphenyl in a sealed tube at 205 °C. After cooling the reaction to room temperature 1:1 hydrochloric acid and water destroy the excess $SbCl_5$. The decachlorobiphenyl is extracted into exactly 5.0 mL hexane, and the excess acid is neutralized with sodium bicarbonate followed by analysis on either a packed or capillary column GC with electron capture detector. A five-point calibration curve is required with daily analysis of reagent blanks and analysis of calibration check standards each working shift. Additional QC measures are analysis of laboratory water spikes and matrix spikes at a rate of 5% of the samples determined or at least daily.

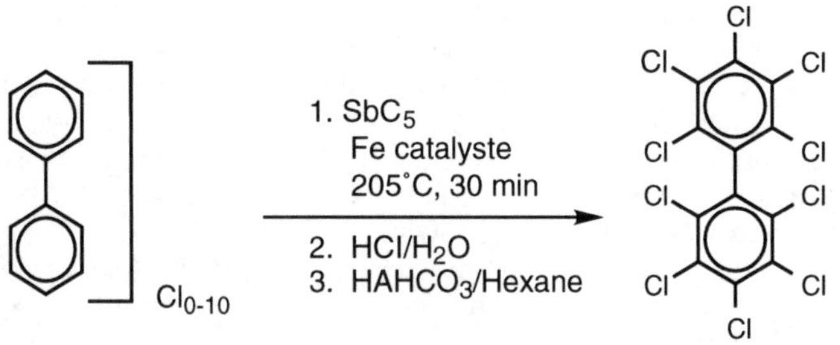

**Figure 3-6. Derivatization of biphenyls to decachlorobiphenyl.**

## 513   2,3,7,8 - TCDD by GC-High Resolution MS (Reference 27)

This is an isotopic dilution method using $^{37}Cl_4$ - TCDD as the surrogate compound and $^{13}C_{12}$-TCDD as the internal standard. One L of sample is extracted with $CH_2Cl_2$, dried and concentrated to 10 uL. (Disk extraction is allowed as an alternate). Further sample cleanup is performed with sequential silica gel and alumina columns. Aliquots of 2.0 uL injections into the GC High Res. MS are made. Calibration is five-point, checked every 12-hours. RFs are allowed to vary to 20% RSD from the average.

## 515.1 Chlorinated acid herbicides by GC-ECD (Reference 27)

The surrogate compound (2,4-Dichlorophenylacetic acid, DCAA) is added to 1.0 L of the sample, the solution made strongly basic (pH 12) with sodium hydroxide and then periodically shaken over 1 hr. This serves to convert any esters or amine salts into the water soluble sodium salt of the acid.

$$RCO_2CH_3 \text{ or } RCO_2^-NR'_4^+ \longrightarrow NaOH \longrightarrow RCO_2Na$$

The sample is washed three times with methylene chloride to remove any base/neutral interferences. The sample is strongly acidified (pH < 2) with sulfuric acid to form the water insoluble free acid,

$$RCO_2Na \longrightarrow H_2SO_4 \longrightarrow RCO_2H$$

which is extracted with ethyl ether ($CH_3CH_2OCH_2CH_3$) and concentrated in a K-D apparatus with solvent exchange to methyl *tert*-butyl ether (MTBE). Methanol is added, and the sample esterified with diazomethane.

$$RCO_2H \longrightarrow CH_2N_2 \longrightarrow RCO_2CH_3$$

Two methods for generation of diazomethane are presented in the method, both beginning with Diazald® (*N*-methyl-*N*-nitroso-*p*-toluenesulfonamide):

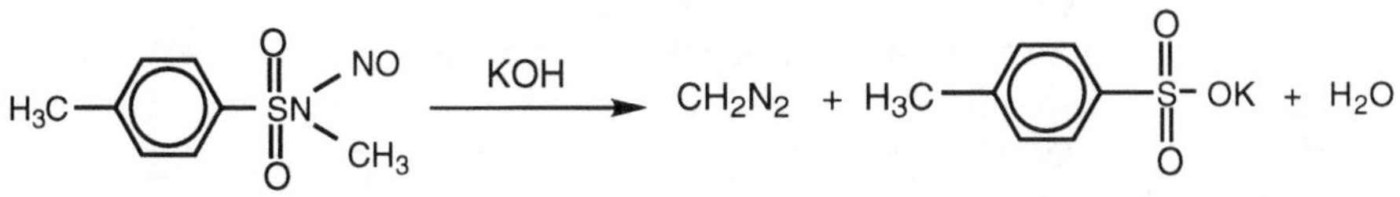

**Figure 3-7. Generation of diazomethane from Diazald®.**

The Diazald reaction can either be performed in bulk with distillation or in a 2-tube microgenerator. The latter procedure can be employed for methylation of up to 30 samples by addition of successive portions of Diazald to the reaction tube. An ether-saturated nitrogen stream is used to sweep the diazomethane from the reaction tube into the sample. Two points of contamination exist in the device: the connectors used to form the joints between the glass tubes and the delivery tube. The EPA methods suggest using rubber tubing for the connections, however a 1/4:1/4 screw fit Teflon® union is a suitable substitution with reduced chance of sample contamination. Use of disposable pipets for the delivery tube, which is changed with every sample, also reduces carry-over. The biggest drawback to this procedure is the continuous venting of diazomethane into the air. Placing the apparatus in a hood with at least 100 cfs draw can lessen the hazard to the operator, however the diazomethane is still around.

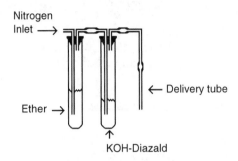

**Figure 3-8. Diazald® microgenerator for diazomethane.**

   A simpler means of generating diazomethane, and potentially less of an explosion hazard, begins with 1-methyl-3-nitro-1-nitrosoguanidine, which is unfortunately a potent mutagen, teratogen, and carcinogen. **DO NOT USE GROUND GLASS VESSELS OR SCRATCHED GLASSWARE WITH ANY DIAZOMETHANE METHOD DUE TO THE VIOLENT EXPLOSIONS THAT ARE TRIGGERED BY CONTACT OF DIAZOMETHANE WITH ROUGH SURFACES.** Dissolve 2.3 g potassium hydroxide (KOH) in 2.3 mL of laboratory water in a 125 Erlenmeyer flask. Add 25 mL of ethyl ether and cool in the freezer. Perform the rest of the steps in a hood. Add 1.5 g 1-methyl-3-nitro-1-nitrosoguanidine in small portions over a period of several minutes to the cold mixture, and agitate the mixture well between additions. A white solid forms with a yellow ether layer. The ether layer contains the diazomethane. Decant the ether into a 40 mL glass vial with a Teflon® faced septum seal. Store in a < 0 °F freezer. Diazomethane can be added to desired reactions by disposable pipet. (Fire polish the end of the pipet first.)

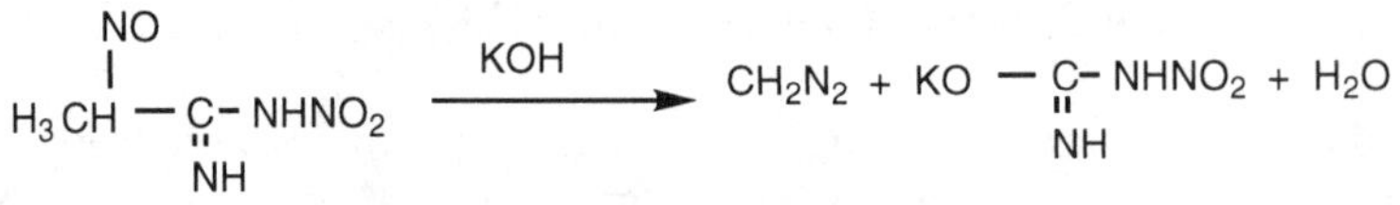

$$H_3CH - \underset{\underset{NH}{\|}}{\underset{\overset{|}{NO}}{C}} - NHNO_2 \quad \xrightarrow{KOH} \quad CH_2N_2 + KO - \underset{\underset{NH}{\|}}{C} - NHNO_2 + H_2O$$

**Figure 3-9. Generation of diazomethane from 1-methyl-3-nitro-1-nitrosoguanidine.**

   An interesting development in the derivatization of organic acids to methyl esters is the use of trimethylsilyldiazomethane (*Yuki Gosei Kagaku Kyokaishi* . 44(2). 1986. pp. 149-159; *Chem Pharm. Bull.* 1981. 29. p. 3249). The material is safe and stable, available commercially as a 2.0 *M* solution in hexanes. It reacts instantly with organic acids at room temperature in methanol to give the methyl esters. Derivatization of phenols requires methanol/acetonitrile solvent and addition of ethyldiisopropylamine as a base. EPA mentioned during a Water Laboratory Certification conference in Chicago (August 29 and 30, 1994) that it is being proposed as a desirable substitute for diazomethane. Unfortunately the cited literature is in Japanese and EPA has as yet to publish any explicit directions for use.

   For the true acids the reaction with diazomethane is almost instantaneous, even at 0 °C. Phenols and other compounds take longer to react. The sample after esterification is chromatographed on Florisil®· Internal standard (4,4'-Dibromooctafluorobiphenyl,

DBOB) is added and the solution analyzed by capillary column (DB-5) GC with electron capture detector. The method requires use of a capillary confirmation column (DB-1701) for identification verification. A minimum of a three-point calibration curve is prepared (five-point is recommended) and checked at least once during every work shift by analysis of a calibration check standard. [An external standard calibration is allowed with a minimum of a three-point calibration curve, which must be verified during each work shift through analysis of at least two different calibration check standards.] Required quality control procedures include daily analysis of a laboratory reagent blank, analysis of a laboratory water spike daily or every 20 samples, and analysis of a sample matrix spike daily or every 10 samples. In addition the instrument system must be checked on a daily basis with a laboratory performance check sample for sensitivity (Dinoseb), chromatographic performance (4-Nitrophenol) and column performance (3,5-Dichlorobenzoic acid and 4-Nitrophenol).

**Table 3-37. Target Analytes and MDLs for Method 515**

| Target Analyte | MDL ug/L | | Target Analyte | MDL ug/L |
|---|---|---|---|---|
| Aciflourfen | 0.096 | | Dichlorprop | 0.26 |
| Bentazon | 0.2 | | Dinoseb | 0.19 |
| Chloramben | 0.093 | | 5-Hydroxydicamba | 0.04 |
| 2,4-D | 0.2 | | 4-Nitrophenol | 0.13 |
| Dalapon | 1.3 | | Pentachlorophenol | 0.076 |
| 2,4-DB | 0.8 | | Picloram | 0.14 |
| DCPA acid metabolites | 0.02 | | 2,4,5-T | 0.08 |
| Dicamba | 0.081 | | 2,4,5-TP | 0.075 |
| 3,5-Dichlorobenzoic acid | 0.061 | | | |

## 515.2 Chlorinated acid herbicides by solid disk extraction and GC-ECD (Reference 27)

Dalapon is dropped from the above analyte list, and the extraction involves saturation of the water sample with sodium sulfate, basification to hydrolyze the herbicides, acidification, then isolation of the target analytes on a polystyrenedivinylbenzene 47 mm disk. Diazomethane is used for derivatization. 2,4-Dichlorophenyl acetic acid is used as surrogate and 4,4'-Dibromooctafluorobiphenyl is the internal standard.

## 525 Semivolatile organics in drinking water by GC-MS (Reference 27)

A 1.0 L sample is acidified to pH 2.0, and internal standards (acenaphthalene-$d_{10}$, phenanthrene-$d_{10}$, and chrysene-$d_{12}$) and surrogate (perylene-$d_{12}$) added. Analytes are isolated on a C-18 reversed-phase cartridge and eluted with 10 mL $CH_2Cl_2$ followed by sodium sulfate drying and nitrogen blowdown to 1.0 mL. Recovery standard (terphenyl-$d_{14}$) is added and 1-2 uL aliquots assayed by GC-MS (ion trap suggested). The MS must be tuned to DFTPP requirements at the start of each 8-hour shift. Calibration is a 6-point calibration. If performed by RF, each RF for an individual compound must be within 30% RSD from the average RF for that compound. A linear, second-, or third-degree regression calibration curve may be prepared and used as an alternative. The calibration is checked at the beginning of each work shift. EPA has published a revision of this method, 525.2 (February, 1994, available from EMSL, Cincinnati) that includes analyte isolation on extraction disks. It also has an interferences note concerning loss of PAH analytes in samples which are not dechlorinated at the time of collection.

**Table 3-38. Target Analytes and MDLs for Method 525**

| Target Analyte | MDL ug/L | Target Analyte | MDL ug/L |
|---|---|---|---|
| Acenaphthalene | 0.1 | Endrin | 0.5 |
| Aldrin | 0.1 | Fluorene | 0.2 |
| Anthracene | 0.04 | Heptachlor | 0.04 |
| Atrazine | 0.1 | Heptachlor epoxide | 0.2 |
| Benzo(a)anthracene | 0.04 | 2,2',3,3',4,4',6-Heptachlorobiphenyl | 0.1 |
| Benzo(b)fluoranthene | - | Hexachlorobenzene | 0.1 |
| Benzo(k)fluoranthene | 0.2 | 2,2',4,4',5,6'-Hexachlorobiphenyl | 0.1 |
| Benzo(a)pyrene | 0.04 | Hexachlorocyclopentadiene | 0.03 |
| Benzo(ghi)perylene | 0.1 | Indeno(123cd)pyrene | 0.1 |
| Butylbenzylphthalate | 0.3 | Lindane | 0.1 |
| a-Chlordane | 0.2 | Methoxychlor | 0.04 |
| g-Chlordane | 0.1 | 2,2',3,3',4,5',6,6'-Octachlorobiphenyl | 0.2 |
| trans-Nonachlor | 0.3 | 2,2',3',4,6-Pentachlorobiphenyl | 0.1 |
| 2-Chlorobiphenyl | 0.1 | Pentachlorophenol | 0.3 |
| Chrysene | 0.04 | Phenanthrene | 0.01 |
| Dibenzo(ah)anthracene | 0.1 | Pyrene | 0.02 |
| Di-n-butylphthalate | 0.3 | Simazine | 0.2 |
| 2,3-Dichlorobiphenyl | 0.1 | 2,2',4,4'-Tetrachlorobiphenyl | 0.1 |
| Diethylphthalate | 0.8 | Toxaphene | - |
| Bis(2-ethylhexyl)phthalate | 0.6 | 2,4,5-Trichlorobiphenyl | 0.06 |
| Bis(2-ethylhexyl)adipate | 0.6 | Alachlor | 1.0 |
| Dimethylphthalate | 0.04 | | |

**Table 3-39. Daily MS DFTPP Tune Requirements for Method 525**

| Mass M/z | DFTPP Relative Abundance Criteria |
|---|---|
| 51 | 10-80% of base peak |
| 68 | <2% of mass 69 |
| 70 | <2% of mass 69 |
| 127 | 10-80% of base peak |
| 197 | <2% of mass 198 |
| 198 | base peak or >50% of 442 |
| 199 | 5-9% of mass 198 |
| 275 | 10-60% of base peak |
| 365 | >1% of base peak |
| 441 | present and < mass 443 |
| 442 | base peak or >50% of 198 |
| 443 | 15-24% of mass 442 |

## 531.1 Measurement of *N*-Methyl carbamates and *N*-Methylcarbamoyl-oximates by direct injection HPLC with post column derivatization (Reference 27)

The HPLC is calibrated using the internal standard procedure (4-Bromo-3,5-dimethyl-phenyl-*N*-methylcarbamate BDMC), with a minimum of a three-point curve. The average RF can be used if the individual RFs for the analyte have <20% RSD, otherwise a calibration curve is prepared. CCV is performed each working shift.

The sample is buffered to pH $3 \pm 0.2$ units with monchloroacetic acid buffer, then filtered through a 0.2 um pore polyester filter. A 0.400 mL sample is injected on the HPLC reverse phase column and chromatographed using a methanol:water linear gradient. The effluent is post-column derivatized (see Method 8318) by hydrolysis and reaction with ortho-phthalaldehyde (OPA). The fluorescent excitation is at 230 nm with detection at >418 nm. Analyte identification requires a confirmation column of different polarity.

**Table 3-40. Target Analytes and MDLs for Method 531.1**

| Target Analyte | MDL ug/L | Target Analyte | MDL ug/L |
|---|---|---|---|
| Aldicarb | 1.0 | Carbofuran | 1.5 |
| Aldicarb sulfone | 2.0 | 3-Hydroxycarbofuran | 2.0 |
| Aldicarb sulfoxide | 2.0 | Methiocarb | 4.0 |
| Baygon | 1.0 | Methomyl | 0.5 |
| Carbaryl | 2.0 | Oxamyl | 2.0 |

## 547 Glyphosate by direct injection HPLC with post-column derivatization and fluorescence detection (Reference 27)

Sample preparation consists of filtration through a 0.45 μm Acrodisc microfilter. A quantity of 0.200 mL of the sample is directly injected on a cation exchange HPLC column at 65 °C with an isocratic mobile phase composed of $KH_2PO_4$ : water : methanol. The eluting material passes through a hypochlorite oxidizing loop followed by reaction with OPA/2-mercaptoethanol in a post-column reactor. The derivatized material is detected by fluorescent excitation at 340 nm and emission detection at >455 nm. Calibration is external standard performed daily with a three-point curve. MDL for the technique runs from 6 to 9 ppb on a 0.200 mL injection. Glyphosate is quite unstable in chlorinated drinking water, which modifies demand for this method.

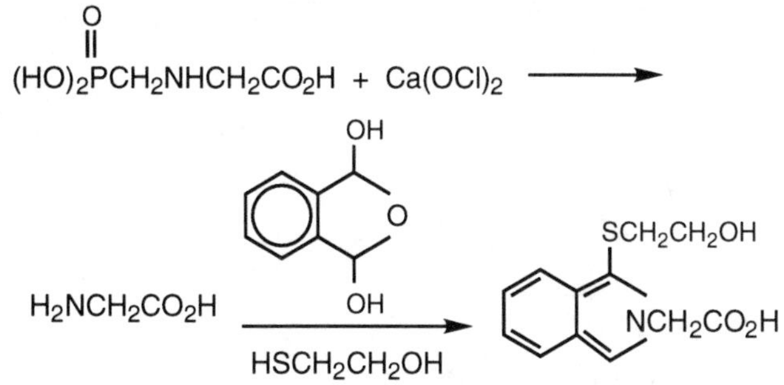

$$(HO)_2PCH_2NHCH_2CO_2H + Ca(OCl)_2 \longrightarrow$$

**Figure 3-10. Post-column derivatization of glyphosate.**

## 548  Endothall by derivatization and GC-ECD (Reference 27)

A 5.0 mL sample is reduced in volume to less than 0.5 mL, then the endothall
derivatized with pentafluorophenylhydrazine in glacial acetic acid with sodium acetate for
90 minutes at 150 °C. The derivative is isolated on a C-18 reversed-phase cartridge then
eluted with 5.0 mL *tert*-butyl methyl ether. Endosulfan I is used as the internal standard.
A four-point calibration curve is prepared and verified daily. Analysis is performed on a
capillary column GC with ECD. Confirmation on a column of different polarity is
required. Directions for preparation and purification of the endothall-PFPH derivative as
a standard are included with the method as an appendix. The MDL is 11.5 µg/L
beginning with the 5.0 mL sample.

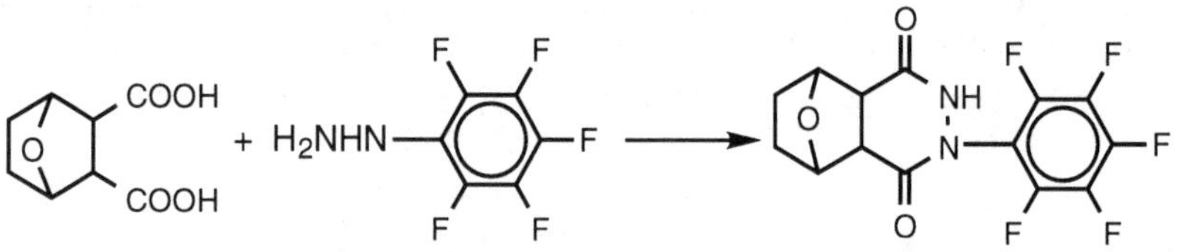

**Figure 3-11.  Derivatization of endothall.**

## 548.1  Endothall by ion-exchange extraction, derivatization and GC-MS

Endothall is isolated on a tertiary amine anion exchange cartridge, then derivatized with
acidic methanol at 50 °C in 30 minutes to the dimethyl ester. Analysis is by either GC-
MS or GC-FID with confirmation column.

## 549  Diquat and paraquat by HPLC with UV detection (Reference 27)

A 250 mL sample is acidified to pH 10.5 ± 0.2 then a C-8 reversed-phase cartridge is
used to isolate the analytes based on an ion-pair mechanism. The analytes are isolated by
elution with phosphoric acid-diethylamine solution. 1-Hexanesulfonic acid solution is
added as an ion-pairing reagent, then the solution assayed by reversed phase HPLC with
phosphoric acid : diethylamine : 1-hexanesulfonic acid eluent with detection at 308 nm
(diquat) and 257 nm (paraquat) using a UV diode array detector. UV spectra are generated by the UV DAD for identification confirmation. Further identification is achieved
by use of 1-heptanesulfonic acid as the ion-pairing reagent and re-running the analysis.
Calibration is three-point external standard with daily checking with two different level
calibration standards. MDL is 0.44 µg/L for diquat and 0.80 for paraquat based on the
250 mL sample processed.

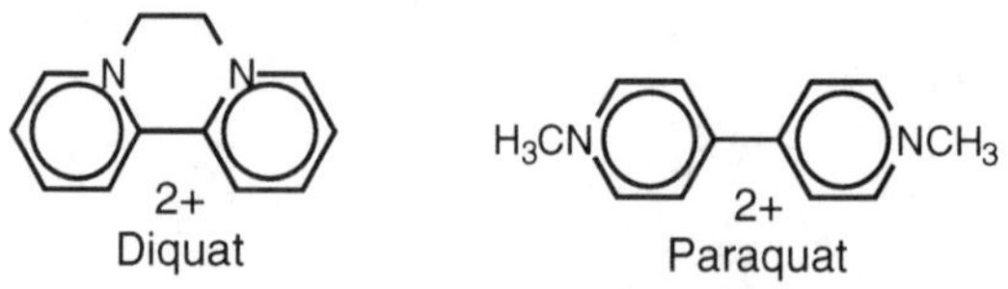

**Figure 3-12.  Diquat and paraquat.**

## 549.1 Diquat and paraquat by ion-pair disk or cartridge and HPLC with DAD (Reference 27)

The methodology of method 549 is extended to include the use of 47mm C-8 reversed-phase extraction disks.

## 550 PAHs by HPLC with UV and fluorescence detection (Reference 27)

A 1.0 L sample is extracted with $CH_2Cl_2$. The extract is dried with sodium sulfate then concentrated and solvent exchanged to acetonitrile. The HPLC is configured for 5 to 100 uL injections with a reversed-phase column and a linear gradient with water : acetonitrile. Detectors are a UV at 254 nm and a fluorescent detector with excitation at 280 nm and detection at >389 nm. Calibration is external standard with a minimum of three-point (recommended five-point) curve, calibrated daily.

Method 550.1 uses a C-18 solid phase disk or cartridge for the analyte isolation with the rest of the method being almost exactly the same. MDLs are slightly lower.

**Table 3-41. Target Analytes and MDLs for Method 550**

| Target Analyte | MDL ug/L | Target Analyte | MDL ug/L |
|---|---|---|---|
| Naphthalene | 3.3 (UV) | Benzo(a)anthracene | 0.002 |
| Acenaphthalene | 2.3 (UV) | Chrysene | 0.063 |
| Acenaphthene | 3.0 (UV) | Benzo(b)fluoranthene | 0.003 |
| Fluorene | 0.25 (UV) | Benzo(k)fluoranthene | 0.002 |
| Phenanthrene | 0.162 | Benzo(a)pyrene | 0.029 |
| Anthracene | 0.079 | Dibenzo(ah)anthracene | 0.019 |
| Fluoranthene | 0.026 | Benzo(ghi)perylene | 0.014 |
| Pyrene | 0.126 | Indeno(123-cd)pyrene | 0.011 |

## 551 Chlorination disinfection by-products by GC-ECD

A 35 mL sample is mixed with 8 g NaCl and extracted with 2 mL of *tert*-butyl methyl ether in a 40 mL VOA vial, then directly injected on a GC with ECD. Calibration is three-point external standard. Identification is confirmed by re-analysis on a GC column of different polarity. This method and method 552 feature prominently in the Information Collection Rule - Disinfection Byproduct (ICR-DBP) program[5] for drinking water systems serving over 100,000 persons, originally set to go into effect October, 1994, but finalized by EPA in 1997.

**Table 3-42. Target Analytes and MDLs for Method 551**

| Target Analyte | MDL ug/L | Target Analyte | MDL ug/L |
|---|---|---|---|
| Bromochloroacetonitrile | 0.011 | 1,2-Dibromoethane | 0.006 |
| Bromodichloromethane | 0.006 | 1,2-Dibromo-3-chloropropane | 0.009 |
| Bromoform | 0.012 | Dichloroacetonitrile | 0.019 |

Continued on next page.

---

[5]   *Federal Register*, Vol 59., No. 28, Thursday, 10 February, 1994.

**Table 3-42. Target Analytes and MDLs for Method 551,** *continued*

| Target Analyte | MDL ug/L | Target Analyte | MDL ug/L |
|---|---|---|---|
| Carbon tetrachloride | 0.004 | 1,1-Dichloropropanone | 0.005 |
| Chloral hydrate | 0.026 | Tetrachloroethene | 0.004 |
| Chloroform | 0.002 | Trichloroacetonitrile | 0.092 |
| Chloropicrin | 0.012 | 1,1,1-Trichloroethane | 0.008 |
| Dibromoacetonitrile | 0.034 | Trichloroethene | 0.002 |
| Dibromochloromethane | 0.012 | 1,1,1-Trichloropropanone | 0.012 |

## 552 Haloacetic acids by GC-ECD (Reference 27)

A 100 mL sample is adjusted to a pH of 11.5 and washed with methyl *tert*-butyl ether (MTBE). After acidification to pH 0.5, the analytes are extracted with MTBE, dried over acidified sodium sulfate and concentrated. Derivatization to the methyl ester is performed with diazomethane (See method 515.1.). 3,5-Dichlorobenzoic acid or 2,3-dichloropropionic acid is used as a surrogate, and 1,2,3-trichloropropane as the internal standard. A minimum of a three-point calibration curve (five recommended) is prepared.

**Table 3-43. Target Analytes and MDLs for Method 552**

| Target Analyte | MDL ug/L | Target Analyte | MDL ug/L |
|---|---|---|---|
| Monochloroacetic acid | 0.052 | Dibromoacetic acid | 0.015 |
| Monobromoacetic acid | 0.0074 | 2-Chlorophenol | 0.14 |
| Dichloroacetic acid | 0.015 | 2,4-Dichlorophenol | 0.32 |
| Trichloroacetic acid | 0.085 | 2,4,6-Trichlorophenol | 0.022 |
| Bromochloroacetic acid | 0.14 | | |

## 604 Phenols by GC-FID and derivatization GC-ECD (Reference 42)

A 1 L sample is pH adjusted with NaOH to pH > 12, then washed with $CH_2Cl_2$. The pH is then adjusted with $H_2SO_4$ to 1 to 2 and the analytes extracted three times with $CH_2Cl_2$. The extracts are dried with sodium sulfate and concentrated with solvent exchange to isopropanol to a volume of 1.0 mL. Calibration of the GC-FID is external standard with a minimum of a three-point calibration. If the RF technique is used each RF must be <10% RSD from the average to assume linearity. Otherwise a calibration curve can be prepared. It is of note that a Hewlett-Packard 5890A GC-FID used by the author resulted in linear calibrations for all the analytes over a $10^4$ calibration range; however, use of another manufacturer's GC-FID system gave calibrations with a pronounced curve for some of the target analytes. Confirmation of identity is by derivatization with pentafluorobenzyl bromide and GC-ECD (See method 8040 for derivatization reaction). The listed MDLs are for the GC-FID method.

**Table 3-44. Target Analytes and MDLs for Method 604**

| Target Analyte | MDL ug/L | Target Analyte | MDL ug/L |
|---|---|---|---|
| 2-Chlorophenol | 0.31 | 4-Chloro-3-methylphenol | 0.36 |
| 2-Nitrophenol | 0.45 | 2,4-Dinitrophenol | 13.0 |
| Phenol | 0.14 | 2-Methyl-4,6-dinitrophenol | 16.0 |
| 2,4-Dimethylphenol | 0.32 | Pentachlorophenol | 7.4 |
| 2,4-Dichlorophenol | 0.39 | 4-Nitrophenol | 2.8 |
| 2,4,6-Trichlorophenol | 0.64 | | |

## 604.1 Hexachlorophene and dichlorophen by HPLC with UV detection (Reference 26)

A 1 L sample is pH adjusted to 4.0 - 4.5 by addition of 50 g $NaH_2PO_4$, then extracted three times with $CH_2Cl_2$. The combined extracts are dried over sodium sulfate and concentrated with solvent exchange to methanol to 2.5 mL. The extract is diluted to 5 mL with water. The HPLC analysis is performed on a reversed-phase column with isocratic acidified acetonitrile : water eluant. The UV detection is at 245 nm. Calibration of the GC-FID is external standard with a minimum of a three-point calibration. If the RF technique is used, each RF must be <10% RSD from the average to assume linearity. Otherwise a calibration curve can be prepared. Daily checking of the calibration curve is required with results within 10% RSD of the curve, otherwise the instrument is recalibrated. Identification is confirmed on a second column. MDLs are 1.0 ug/L for dichlorophen and 1.2 ug/L for hexachlorophene.

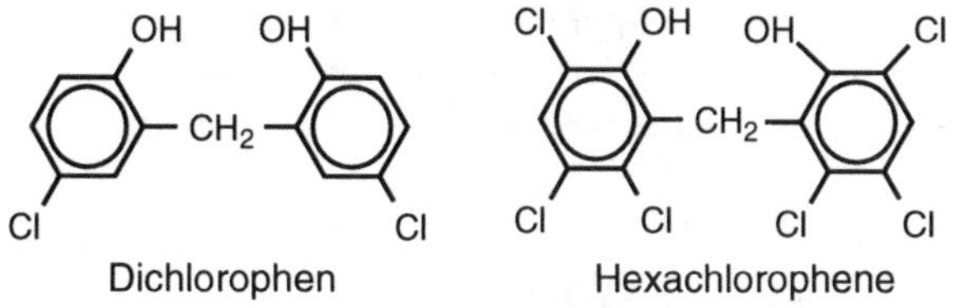

Dichlorophen    Hexachlorophene

**Figure 3-13. Dichlorophen and hexachlorophene.**

## 605 Benzidines by HPLC with electrochemical detection (Reference 26)

A 1 L sample is pH adjusted to 6.5 - 7.5, then extracted three times with $CHCl_3$. The combined $CHCl_3$ extracts are extracted three times with 25 mL of 1.0 $M$ $H_2SO_4$. $Na_3PO_4$ is added to the aqueous acid extracts followed by neutralization to pH 6 to 7 with 5 $N$ NaOH. The neutralized solution is extracted three times with $CHCl_3$ and the combined extracts washed once with water. Methanol is added, and the solution concentrated with a vacuum rotary evaporator. Nitrogen blowdown to 1.0 mL is followed by dilution to 5.0 mL with acetate buffer. The HPLC column is reversed phase with a 1:1 acetonitrile/0.1 $M$ pH 4.7 acetate buffer. Calibration is external standard with a minimum of three points by either RF or calibration curve. The electrochemical detector is run with a potential of +0.8 V; however, if significant interferences are present in the sample, the voltage can be reduced to +0.5 V. The MDLs are 0.08 ug/L for benzidine and 0.13 for 3,3'-dichlorobenzidine at +0.8 V.

## 606 Phthalates by GC-ECD (Reference 42)

A 1 L sample is extracted three times with $CH_2Cl_2$, and the extracts dried over sodium sulfate and concentrated with solvent exchange to hexane to 1.0 mL. Further clean-up with Florisil or alumina is advised in the method. Calibration of the GC-ECD is three-point external standard by either RF (<10% RSD required for linearity) or calibration curve. The calibration curve is verified daily by analysis of one or more calibration standards with a <15% variation in results allowed. Identification is confirmed on a second column of different polarity than the analytical column or GC-MS.

**Table 3-45. Target Analytes and MDLs for Method 606**

| Target Analyte | MDL ug/L | Target Analyte | MDL ug/L |
|----------------|----------|----------------|----------|
| Dimethyl phthalate | 0.29 | Butyl benzyl phthalate | 0.34 |
| Diethyl phthalate | 0.49 | Bis(2-ethylhexyl) phthalate | 2.0 |
| Di-n-butyl phthalate | 0.36 | Di-n-octyl phthalate | 3.0 |

## 607 Nitrosamines by GC-NPD (Reference 42)

A 1 L sample is pH adjusted to 5 to 9 with either NaOH or $H_2SO_4$ as required, then extracted three times with $CH_2Cl_2$. The combined extracts are washed with HCl, then dried with sodium sulfate and concentrated. Clean-up is performed on either Florisil or alumina. Calibration is external standard with a minimum of three standards by either RF (<10% RSD on individual RFs to assume linearity) or calibration curve. The calibration curve is checked daily by analysis of one or more calibration standards. All responses must be <15% from the expected, or the system must be recalibrated. Identification is confirmed on a second column of different polarity than the analytical column. Under the injection port heated conditions, N-nitrosodiphenylamine always degrades to diphenylamine, which is measured.

**Table 3-46. Target Analytes and MDLs for Method 607**

| Target Analyte | MDL ug/L | Target Analyte | MDL ug/L |
|----------------|----------|----------------|----------|
| N-Nitrosodimethylamine | 0.15 | N-Nitrosodiphenylamine | 0.81 |
| N-Nitrosodi-n-propylamine | 0.46 | | |

## 608 Organochlorine pesticides and PCBs by GC-ECD (Reference 42)

A 1 L sample is extracted three times with $CH_2Cl_2$, then the combined extracts dried over sodium sulfate and concentrated with solvent exchange to hexane. Clean-up is on Florisil. Sulfur sometimes interferes and is removed by treatment with either elemental mercury or activated copper powder. Calibration is external standard with a minimum of three standards by either RF (<10% RSD to assume linearity) or calibration curve. The calibration is checked daily with one or more calibration standards. Acceptance criteria is <15% variation from the original calibration, otherwise the system gets recalibrated. Identification must be confirmed on either a second column of differing polarity from the analytical column or GC-MS.

**Table 3-47.  Target Analytes, MDLs, Precision and Accuracy for Method 608**

| Target Analyte | MDL ug/L | Spike Amt | %R | RPD |
|---|---|---|---|---|
| Aldrin | 0.009 | 2.0 | 42-122 | 0-42 |
| α-BHC | 0.003 | 2.0 | 37-134 | 0-48 |
| β-BHC | 0.006 | 2.0 | 17-147 | 0-64 |
| δ-BHC | 0.009 | 2.0 | 19-140 | 0-72 |
| γ-BHC | 0.004 | 2.0 | 32-127 | 0-46 |
| Chlordane | 0.014 | 50 | 45-119 | 0-40 |
| 4,4'-DDD | 0.011 | 10 | 31-141 | 0-56 |
| 4,4'-DDE | 0.004 | 2.0 | 30-145 | 0-55 |
| 4,4'-DDT | 0.012 | 10 | 25-160 | 0-72 |
| Dieldrin | 0.002 | 2.0 | 36-146 | 0-76 |
| Endosulfan I | 0.014 | 2.0 | 45-153 | 0-49 |
| Endosulfan II | 0.004 | 10 | D-202 | 0-122 |
| Endrin aldehyde | 0.023 | - | - | - |
| Endosulfan sulfate | 0.066 | 10 | 26-144 | 0-54 |
| Endrin | 0.006 | 10 | 30-147 | 0-74 |
| Heptachlor | 0.003 | 2.0 | 34-111 | 0-40 |
| Heptachlor epoxide | 0.083 | 2.0 | 37-142 | 0-41 |
| Toxaphene | 0.24 | 50 | 41-126 | 0-51 |
| PCB-1016 | nd | 50 | 50-114 | 0-40 |
| PCB-1221 | nd | 50 | 15-178 | 0-99 |
| PCB-1232 | nd | 50 | 10-215 | 0-71 |
| PCB-1242 | 0.065 | 50 | 39-150 | 0-49 |
| PCB-1248 | nd | 50 | 38-158 | 0-64 |
| PCB-1254 | nd | 50 | 29-131 | 0-55 |
| PCB-1260 | nd | 50 | 8-127 | 0-42 |

## 608.1  Organochlorine pesticides by GC-ECD (Reference 26)

This method was prepared as an addendum to method 608 and adds a number of target analytes.  The sample extraction and clean-up are essentially the same.  A confirmation column is required for identification, although the method also recommends GC/MS as an alternative.

**Table 3-48.  Target Analytes and MDLs for Method 608.1**

| Target Analyte | MDL ug/L | Target Analyte | MDL ug/L |
|---|---|---|---|
| Dibromochloropropane | 0.04 | PCNB | 0.06 |
| Etridiazole | 0.04 | Chloropropylate | 0.2 |
| Chloroneb | 0.04 | Chlorobenzilate | 0.2 |
| Propachlor | 1.0 | | |

## 608.2  Organochlorine pesticides by GC-ECD (Reference 26)

Adds several target analytes to the method 608 list without a significant change in the procedure.  A silica gel column clean-up is included in addition to the Florisil column.

GC/MS is suggested for confirmation of analyte identification, or, alternatively, a confirmation column can be used.

**Table 3-49. Target Analytes and MDLs for Method 608.2**

| Target Analyte | MDL ug/L | Target Analyte | MDL ug/L |
|---|---|---|---|
| Chlorothalonil | 0.001 | Methoxychlor | 0.04 |
| DCPA | 0.003 | cis - Permethrin | 0.2 |
| Dicloran | 0.002 | trans - Permethrin | 0.2 |

### 609  Nitroaromatics and isophorone by GC-FID and GC-ECD (Reference 42)

A 1 L sample is pH adjusted to 5 to 9 with either NaOH or $H_2SO_4$ as required, then extracted three times with $CH_2Cl_2$. The combined extracts are dried over sodium sulfate and concentrated with solvent exchange to hexane. Florisil is used for cleanup. Calibration is external standard with a minimum of three standards by either RF (<10% RSD to assume linearity) or calibration curve. The calibration is checked daily with one or more calibration standards. Acceptance criteria is <15% variation from the original calibration, otherwise the system gets recalibrated. Identification must be confirmed on either a second column of differing polarity from the analytical column or GC-MS. Isophorone and nitrobenzene are analyzed by FID, while the dinitrobenzenes are assayed by ECD.

**Table 3-50. Target Analytes and MDLs for Method 609**

| Target Analyte | MDL ug/L | Target Analyte | MDL ug/L |
|---|---|---|---|
| Isophorone | 5.7 | 2,4-Dinitrobenzene | 0.02 |
| Nitrobenzene | 3.6 | 2,6-Dinitrobenzene | 0.01 |

### 610  PAHs by GC-FID or HPLC with UV and fluorescence detectors (Reference 42)

A 1 L sample is extracted three times with $CH_2Cl_2$, and the combined extracts dried with sodium sulfate and concentrated with solvent exchange to cyclohexane. Clean-up is on silica gel. Analysis by HPLC is on a reversed-phase column with a linear gradient of water/acetonitrile. UV is the preferred detector for naphthalene, acenaphthalene, acenaphthene and fluorene, while fluorescence is used for the rest of the PAHs. HPLC has the advantage over GC as all the PAHs are separated using the technique. GC is complicated by the pairs of compounds anthracene-phenanthrene, chrysene-benzo(a)anthracene, benzo(b)fluoranthene-benzo(k)fluoranthene, and dibenzo(a,h)anthraceneindeno (1,2,3-cd)pyrene being very difficult to separate. Although still not easy, all of these pairs can be successfully resolved on a capillary column if proper attention is paid to GC operating parameters. Calibration is external standard with a minimum of three standards by either RF (<10% RSD to assume linearity) or calibration curve. The calibration is checked daily with one or more calibration standards. Acceptance criteria is <15% variation from the original calibration, otherwise the system gets recalibrated. Identification must be confirmed on either a second column of differing polarity from the analytical column or GC-MS. The following MDLs are from HPLC with the appropriate detectors.

## Table 3-51. Target Analytes and MDLs for Method 610

| Target Analyte | MDL ug/L | Target Analyte | MDL ug/L |
|---|---|---|---|
| Naphthalene | 1.8 (UV) | Benzo(a)anthracene | 0.013 |
| Acenaphthalene | 2.3 (UV) | Chrysene | 0.15 |
| Acenaphthene | 1.8 (UV) | Benzo(b)fluoranthene | 0.018 |
| Fluorene | 0.21 (UV) | Benzo(k)fluoranthene | 0.017 |
| Phenanthrene | 0.64 | Benzo(a)pyrene | 0.023 |
| Anthracene | 0.66 | Dibenzo(a,h)anthracene | 0.030 |
| Fluoranthene | 0.21 | Benzo(ghi)perylene | 0.076 |
| Pyrene | 0.27 | Indeno(1,2,3-cd)pyrene | 0.043 |

## 611 Haloethers by GC-ECD or GC-ELCD (Reference 42)

A 1 L sample is extracted three times with $CH_2Cl_2$, the combined extracts dried with sodium sulfate and then concentrated with solvent exchange to hexane. An optional clean-up with Florisil is included in the method. Calibration is external standard with a minimum of three standards by either RF (<10% RSD to assume linearity) or calibration curve. The calibration is checked daily with one or more calibration standards. Acceptance criteria is <15% variation from the original calibration, otherwise the system gets recalibrated. Identification must be confirmed on either a second column of differing polarity from the analytical column or GC-MS.

## Table 3-52. Target Analytes and MDLs for Method 611

| Target Analyte | MDL ug/L | Target Analyte | MDL ug/L |
|---|---|---|---|
| Bis(2-chloroisopropyl) ether | 0.8 | 4-Chlorophenyl phenyl ether | 3.9 |
| Bis(2-chloroethyl) ether | 0.3 | 4-Bromophenyl phenyl ether | 2.3 |
| Bis(2-chloroethoxy) methane | 0.5 | | |

## 612 Chlorinated hydrocarbons by GC-ECD (Reference 26)

A 1 L sample is extracted three times with $CH_2Cl_2$, the combined extracts dried with sodium sulfate and then concentrated with solvent exchange to hexane. An optional clean-up with Florisil is included in the method. Calibration is external standard with a minimum of three standards by either RF (<10% RSD to assume linearity) or calibration curve. The calibration is checked daily with one or more calibration standards. Acceptance criteria is <15% variation from the original calibration, otherwise the system gets recalibrated. Identification must be confirmed on either a second column of differing polarity from the analytical column or GC-MS.

## Table 3-53. Target Analytes and MDLs for Method 612

| Target Analyte | MDL ug/L | Target Analyte | MDL ug/L |
|---|---|---|---|
| 1,3-Dichlorobenzene | 1.19 | 1,2,4-Trichlorobenzene | 0.05 |
| Hexachloroethane | 0.03 | Hexachlorocyclopentadiene | 0.40 |
| 1,4-Dichlorobenzene | 1.34 | 2-Chloronaphthalene | 0.94 |
| 1,2-Dichlorobenzene | 1.14 | Hexachlorobenzene | 0.05 |
| Hexachlorobutadiene | 0.34 | | |

## 613   2,3,7,8 - TCDD by capillary column GC-MS (Reference 42)

This is an internal standard method using either $^{13}C_{12}$ or $^{37}Cl_4$ 2,3,7,8-TCDD. A 1 L sample with internal standard is extracted three times with $CH_2Cl_2$, and the combined extracts concentrated with solvent exchange to hexane. The hexane solution is washed first with NaOH solution, then with water, at least twice with $H_2SO_4$ solution, and finally twice with water. The extracts are dried with sodium sulfate. Optional clean-ups with either silica gel or alumina  are included in the method. Calibration is internal standard with a minimum of three standards by either RF (<10% RSD to assume linearity) or calibration curve. The calibration is checked daily with one or more calibration standards. Acceptance criteria is <15% variation from the original calibration, otherwise the system gets recalibrated. MDL for dioxin is 0.002 ug/L.

## 614 and 614.1   Organophosphorous pesticides by GC-FPD (614) or NPD (614.1) (Reference 26)

A 1 L sample is extracted three times with 15% $CH_2Cl_2$ - hexane, dried with sodium sulfate and concentrated to 10 mL. An acetonitrile partition is described for fat and oil removal from the sample. A Florisil column clean-up is described in addition to an alumina microcolumn for selective sulfur removal. A silica gel column is used for clean-up of the 614.1 analytes. Calibration is minimum three-point external standard. If the RSD of the calibration factor is <10% over the entire working range, the average calibration factor may be used; otherwise a calibration curve is used. GC/MS or a second confirmation column are required for verification of analyte identification.

**Table 3-54.  Target Analytes and MDLs for Methods 614 and 614.1**

| Target Analyte | MDL ug/L | Target Analyte | MDL ug/L |
|---|---|---|---|
| Diazinon | 0.012 | Ethyl parathion | 0.012 |
| Disulfoton | - | Ethion (614.1) | 0.1 |
| Demeton | - | Malathion | - |
| Methyl parathion | 0.012 | Azinphos methyl | - |
| Terbuphos (614.1) | 0.004 | Dioxathion (614.1) | 0.01 |
| EPN (614.1) | 0.2 | | |

## 615   Chlorinated herbicides by GC-ECD (Reference 26)

A 1 L sample is acidified to pH < 2 with sulfuric acid (1:1) and extracted three times with diethyl ether. The ether extracts are combined in a 250 mL Erlenmeyer flask with a ground glass joint (24/40), 15 mL water and 2 mL 37% KOH added, a Snyder column attached, and the flask heated in a 60-65 °C water bath in the hood for 60 minutes. This hydrolyzes any herbicide esters in the original sample. After cooling the contents of the flask are extracted twice with diethyl ether, and the ether discarded. The aqueous layer is acidified to pH < 2 with sulfuric acid and the free herbicide acids extracted with three portions of ether. The ether extract is dried over acidified sodium sulfate with minimum contact time of 2 hours. After concentration to 0.5 mL, 0.1 mL methanol is added and the acids esterified with diazomethane (see Method 515.1). Silica gel is added (0.1-0.2 g) to destroy excess diazomethane. Calibration is a minimum of three-point external standard. Confirmation of analyte identification is achieved by analysis on a second column or GC/MS.

**Table 3-55. Target Analytes and MDLs for Method 615**

| Target Analyte | MDL ug/L | Target Analyte | MDL ug/L |
|---|---|---|---|
| Dicamba | 0.27 | Dalapon | 5.80 |
| 2,4-D | 1.20 | MCPP | 192 |
| 2,4,5-TP | 0.17 | MCPA | 249 |
| 2,4,5-T | 0.20 | Dichlorprop | 0.65 |
| 2,4-DB | 0.91 | Dinoseb | 0.07 |

# 616  Certain C, H, O pesticides by GC-FID (Reference 26)

A 1 L sample is pH adjusted to 6.8 by the addition of 2 g each of $NaH_2PO_4$ and $Na_2HPO_4$, then solvent extracted three times with methylene chloride. The combined extracts are dried with sodium sulfate and concentrated to about 1-2 mL then solvent exchanged to tert-butyl methyl ether. Sample clean-up is accomplished with deactivated silica gel. Calibration is minimum three-point by the external standard procedure. Analyte identification is confirmed by either a second column or GC/MS.

**Table 3-56. Target Analytes and MDLs for Method 616**

| Target Analyte | MDL ug/L | Target Analyte | MDL ug/L |
|---|---|---|---|
| Cycloprate | 21 | Methoprene | 22 |
| Kinoprene | 18 | Resmethrin | 36 |

# 617  Organochlorine pesticides and PCBs by GC-ECD (Reference 26)

A 1 L sample is extracted three times with 15% methylene chloride:hexane, then concentrated to 1.0 mL and diluted to the final volume of 10 mL. Clean-up is accomplished with acetonitrile partition for removal of fats and oils, Florisil column and mercury removal of sulfur. Calibration is minimum three-point external standard. A second column or GC/MS is required for confirmation of analyte identification.

**Table 3-57. Target Analytes and MDLs for Method 617**

| Target Analyte | MDL ug/L | Target Analyte | MDL ug/L |
|---|---|---|---|
| Aldrin | 0.009 | Endosulfan II | 0.17 |
| α-BHC | 0.004 | Endosulfan sulfate | - |
| β-BHC | - | Endrin | - |
| δ-BHC | - | Endrin aldehyde | - |
| γ-BHC | 0.002 | Heptachlor | 0.004 |
| Captan | - | Heptachlor epoxide | 0.003 |
| Carbophenothion | - | Isodrin | - |
| Chlordane | - | Methoxychlor | 0.176 |
| 4,4'-DDD | 0.012 | Mirex | 0.015 |
| 4,4'-DDE | 0.004 | PCNB | 0.002 |

Continued on next page.

**Table 3-57. Target Analytes and MDLs for Method 617,** *continued*

| Target Analyte | MDL ug/L | Target Analyte | MDL ug/L |
|---|---|---|---|
| 4,4'-DDT | 0.032 | Perthane | - |
| Dichloran | - | Strobane | - |
| Dicofol | - | Toxaphene | - |
| Dieldrin | 0.011 | Trifluralin | 0.013 |
| Endosulfan I | 0.11 | PCBs | - |

## 618   Volatile pesticides by microextraction and GC-ECD (Reference 26)

A 20 mL portion of sample is pH adjusted to the 6 to 8 range, then microextracted with 4 mL cyclohexane. Calibration is by either a minimum three-point external standard or a three-point internal standard with bromoform. Analyte confirmation required by either a second column or GC/MS.

**Table 3-58. Target Analytes and MDLs for Method 618**

| Target Analyte | MDL ug/L | Target Analyte | MDL ug/L |
|---|---|---|---|
| Chloropicrin | 0.8 | EDB | 0.2 |

## 619   Triazine pesticides by GC-NPD (Reference 26)

A 1 L sample is extracted three times with 15% methylene chloride:hexane. The combined extract is dried with sodium sulfate and concentrated with solvent exchange to hexane to 10 mL. A Florisil column clean-up is described. Certain triazines will precipitate from hexane solution. If this occurs the sample is redissolved in methylene chloride and the extract analyzed by FID. Otherwise calibration is a minimum three-point external standard with confirmation required by either a second column or GC/MS.

**Table 3-59. Target Analytes and MDLs for Method 619**

| Target Analyte | MDL ug/L | Target Analyte | MDL ug/L |
|---|---|---|---|
| Prometon | 0.03 | Prometryn | 0.06 |
| Atraton | - | Terbutryn | 0.05 |
| Propazine | 0.03 | Simazine | 0.06 |
| Terbuthylazine | 0.03 | Ametryn | 0.06 |
| Secbumeton | - | Simetryn | 0.07 |
| Atrazine | 0.05 | | |

## 622   Organophosphorous pesticides by GC-NPD or FPD (Reference 26)

A 1 L sample is extracted three times with methylene chloride, the combined extracts are concentrated with solvent exchange to hexane to a final volume of 10 mL. Calibration is by a minimum three-point external standard. Analyte identification is confirmed by use of a second column or by GC/MS.

**Table 3-60. Target Analytes and MDLs for Method 622**

| Target Analyte | MDL ug/L | Target Analyte | MDL ug/L |
|---|---|---|---|
| Demeton | 0.25 | Mevinphos | 0.3 |
| Phorate | 0.15 | Stirophos | 5.0 |
| Disulfonton | 0.20 | Ethoprop | 0.25 |
| Trichloronate | 0.15 | Parathion methyl | 0.3 |
| Fenthion | 0.10 | Ronnel | 0.3 |
| Tokuthion | 0.5 | Chlorpyrifos methyl | 0.3 |
| Bolstar | 0.15 | Chlorpyrifos | 0.3 |
| Fensulfothion | 1.5 | Merphos | 0.25 |
| Azinphos methyl | 1.5 | Diazinon | 0.6 |
| Coumaphos | 1.5 | Naled | 0.1 |
| Dichlorvos | 0.1 | | |

## 622.1  Thiophosphate pesticides by GC-NPD (Reference 26)

A 1 L sample is pH adjusted to the range 6 to 8, then extracted with three portions of methylene chloride. The combined extracts are dried with sodium sulfate and concentrated to 1.0 mL. An optional Florisil column clean-up is described. Calibration is by a minimum three-point external standard.

**Table 3-61. Target Analytes and MDLs for Method 622.1**

| Target Analyte | MDL ug/L | Target Analyte | MDL ug/L |
|---|---|---|---|
| Thionazin | 1 | Fennitrothion | 2 |
| Fonophos | 0.7 | Famphur | 19 |
| Dichlofenthion | 0.7 | Phosmet | 1 |
| Aspon | 0.6 | | |

## 625  GC/MS Base/neutral and acid extractables (BNA) (Reference 42)

The method relies on extraction of the target analytes and acid and base/neutral surrogates from the wastewater with methylene chloride under first basic conditions to isolate the base/neutral fraction, and then acid conditions to remove the acidic fraction. The B/N and A extracts are not combined and through subsequent manipulations and analysis they are kept separate. After concentration the internal standard(s) are added and the solutions analyzed by GC/MS. Retention time match and three peak MS matching is considered to be sufficient evidence for detection of a target analyte. The mass analyzer is operated at 70 eV in the electron impact mode with daily tuning to decafluorotri-phenylphosphine (DFTPP) standards. A minimum of 5% of samples from each sampling site are spiked with the entire complement of target analytes. Spikes that fail the acceptance criteria must immediately be followed with an analysis of a quality control check standard. Quality control check standards with all target analytes are analyzed on a daily basis, with failures being immediately recalibrated. See Method 610 for difficult resolution of PAH pairs. For many wastewater samples there exist significant levels of extractible chromatographic interferences that make this analysis difficult. EPA has published the "pumpkin" manual[5] (so called due to the color of the cover), which gives guidance on resolving analytical problems.

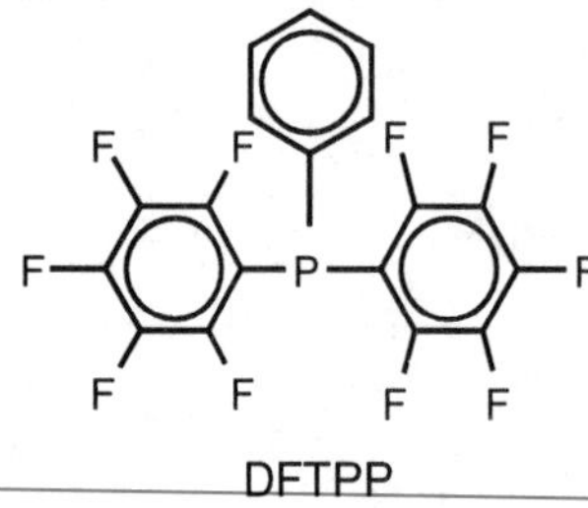

DFTPP

**Figure 3-14. Structure of decafluorotriphenylphosphine (DFTPP).**

**Table 3-62. Daily MS Tune Criteria for DFTPP**

| Mass M/z | DFTPP Relative Abundance Criteria |
|----------|-----------------------------------|
| 51 | 30-60% of base peak |
| 68 | <2% of mass 69 |
| 70 | <2% of mass 69 |
| 127 | 40-60% of mass 198 |
| 197 | <1% of mass 198 |
| 198 | base peak 100% relative abundance |
| 199 | 5-9% of mass 198 |
| 275 | 10-30% of mass 198 |
| 365 | >1% of mass 198 |
| 441 | present and < mass 443 |
| 442 | >40% of mass 198 |
| 443 | 17-23% of mass 442 |

Each operator must demonstrate proficiency in the method by four-fold analysis of a 100 ppb check standard containing each target analyte. The means and standard deviations of the results must meet the published acceptance criteria.

An additional QC procedure involves a daily check of the column performance for benzidine and acids and calculation of the tailing factor. The compound(s) is injected and the resulting peak analyzed. The tailing factor for benzidine must be less than 3.0 and for pentachlorophenol less than 5.0.

---

[5]   Guidance on Evaluation, Resolution and Documentation of Analytical Problems Associated with Compliance Monitoring. USEPA, Office of Water, Engineering and Analysis Division, Washington DC 20460, EPA 821-B-93-001, June 1993.

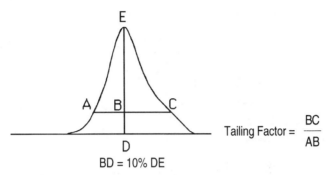

$$\text{Tailing Factor} = \frac{BC}{AB}$$

BD = 10% DE

**Figure 3-15. Tailing factor calculation.**

**Table 3-63. Base/neutral Extractable Target Analytes and MDLs for Method 625**

| Target Analyte | MDL ppb | Target Analyte | MDL ppb |
|---|---|---|---|
| Acenaphthene | 1.9 | Dimethyl phthalate | 1.6 |
| Acenaphthylene | 3.5 | 2,4-Dinitrotoluene | 5.7 |
| Anthracene | 1.9 | 2,6-Dinitrotoluene | 1.9 |
| Aldrin | 1.9 | Di-*n*-octylphthalate | 2.5 |
| Benzo(a)anthracene | 7.8 | Endosulfan sulfate | 5.6 |
| Benzo(b)fluoranthene | 4.8 | Endrin aldehyde | nd |
| Benzo(k)fluoranthene | 2.5 | Fluoranthene | 2.2 |
| Benzo(a)pyrene | 2.5 | Fluorene | 1.9 |
| Benzo(ghi)perylene | 4.1 | Heptachlor | 1.9 |
| β-BHC | 4.2 | Heptachlor epoxide | 2.2 |
| δ-BHC | 3.1 | Hexachlorobenzene | 1.9 |
| Bis(2-chloroethyl) ether | 5.7 | Hexachlorobutadiene | 0.9 |
| Bis(2-chloroethoxy) methane | 5.3 | Hexachloroethane | 1.6 |
| Bis(2-ethylhexyl) phthalate | 2.5 | Indeno(1,2,3-cd)pyrene | 3.7 |
| Bis(2-chloroisopropyl) ether | 5.7 | Isophorone | 2.2 |
| 4-Bromophenyl phenyl ether | 1.9 | Naphthalene | 1.6 |
| Chlordane | nd | Nitrobenzene | 1.9 |
| 2-Chloronaphthalene | 1.9 | N-Nitrosodi-*n*-propylamine | nd |
| 4-Chlorophenyl phenyl ether | 4.2 | PCB-1016 | nd |
| Chrysene | 2.5 | PCB-1221 | 30 |
| 4,4'-DDD | 2.8 | PCB-1232 | nd |
| 4,4'-DDE | 5.6 | PCB-1242 | nd |
| 4,4'-DDT | 4.7 | PCB-1248 | nd |
| Dibenzo(ah)anthracene | 2.5 | PCB-1254 | 36 |
| Di-*n*-butylphthalate | 2.5 | PCB-1260 | nd |
| 1,2-Dichlorobenzene | 1.9 | Phenanthrene | 5.4 |
| 1,3-Dichlorobenzene | 1.9 | Pyrene | 1.9 |
| 1,4-Dichlorobenzene | 4.4 | Toxaphene | nd |
| 3,3'-Dichlorobenzidine | 16.5 | 1,2,4-Trichlorobenzene | 1.9 |
| Dieldrin | 2.5 | Benzyl butyl phthalate | 2.5 |
| Diethyl phthalate | 1.9 | | |

**Table 3-64. Acid Extractable Target Analytes and MDLs for Method 625**

| Target Analyte | MDL ppb |
|---|---|
| 4-Chloro-3-methylphenol | 3.0 |
| 2-Chlorophenol | 3.3 |
| 2,4-Dichlorophenol | 2.7 |
| 2,4-Dimethylphenol | 2.7 |
| 2,4-Dinitrophenol | 42 |
| 2-Methyl-4,6-dinitrophenol | 24 |

| Target Analyte | MDL ppb |
|---|---|
| 2-Nitrophenol | 3.6 |
| 4-Nitrophenol | 2.4 |
| Pentachlorophenol | 3.6 |
| Phenol | 1.5 |
| 2,4,6-Trichlorophenol | 2.7 |

**Table 3-65. Suggested Internal and Surrogate Standards for Method 625**

| Base/Neutral Extractables | | |
|---|---|---|
| Aniline-d$_5$ | Anthracene-d$_{10}$ | 1-Fluoronaphthalene |
| Benzo(a)anthracene-d$_{12}$ | 4,4'-Dibromobiphenyl | 2-Fluoronaphthalene |
| Decafluorobiphenyl | 4,4'-Dibromooctafluorobiphenyl | Naphthalene-d$_8$ |
| 2,2'-Difluorobiphenyl | 4-Fluoroaniline | Nitrobenzene-d$_5$ |
| Phenanthrene-d$_{10}$ | Pyridine-d$_5$ | 2,3,4,5,6-Pentafluorobiphenyl |
| **Acid Extractables** | | |
| 2-Fluorophenol | Pentafluorophenol | |
| Phenol-d$_5$ | 2-Perfluoromethyl phenol | |

# 627  Dinitroaniline pesticides by GC-ECD (Reference 26)

A 1 L sample is extracted with three portions of methylene chloride. The combined extracts are dried with sodium sulfate and concentrated with solvent exchange to hexane to a final volume of 10 mL. Calibration is by a minimum three-point external standard procedure. A second column or GC/MS is required for analyte confirmation. The suggested packed columns are stated to not resolve benfluralin, ethalfluralin and trifluralin, and they are reported together as trifluralin. This resolution problem is not expected to exist if capillary columns are used.

**Table 3-66. Target Analytes and MDLs for Method 627**

| Target Analyte | MDL ug/L |
|---|---|
| Benfluralin | - |
| Ethalfluralin | - |
| Isopropalin | 0.02 |

| Target Analyte | MDL ug/L |
|---|---|
| Profluralin | 0.14 |
| Trifluralin | 0.03 |

# 629  Cyanazine by HPLC with UV detector (Reference 26)

A 1 L sample is extracted three times with $CH_2Cl_2$. The combined extracts are dried with sodium sulfate and concentrated with solvent exchange to methanol. An optional activated Florisil cleanup is described. Analysis is by HPLC with reversed phase column and linear methanol : water gradient. Detection is UV at 245 nm. Calibration is external standard with a minimum of three standards by either RF (<10% RSD to assume linearity) or calibration curve. The calibration is checked daily with one or more calibration standards. Acceptance criteria is <15% variation from the original calibration, otherwise the system gets recalibrated. Identification must be confirmed on a second column of differing polarity from the analytical column. MDL is 6 mg/L.

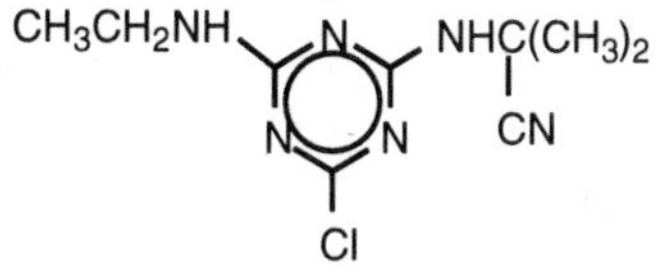

**Figure 3-16. Cyanazine.**

## 630 and 630.1  Dithiocarbamate pesticides by $CS_2$ evolution and UV-Vis colorimetry (630) or GC-ELCD (630.1) (Reference 26)

Dithiocarbamates are hydrolyzed with acid to $CS_2$, which is then measured by either colorimetry or GC-ELCD in the sulfur mode. Both methods are non-discriminate, and results are reported as the analyte Ziram.

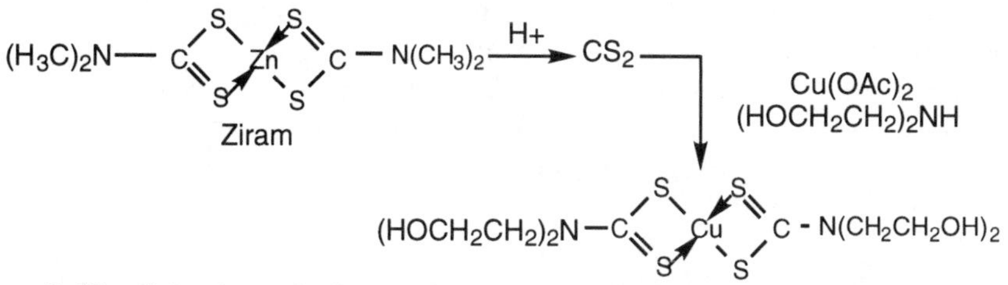

**Figure 3-17. Colorimetric determination of $CS_2$ in Method 630.**

**Table 3-67. Target Analytes and MDLs for Methods 630 and 630.1**

| Target Analyte | MDL ug/L | Target Analyte | MDL ug/L |
|---|---|---|---|
| Amoban | - | Nabam | - |
| AOP | - | Niacide | - |
| Busan 40 | - | Polyram | - |
| Busan 85 | - | Sodium dimethyldithiocarbamate | - |
| Ferbam | - | Thiram | - |
| KN methyl | - | ZAC | - |
| Mancozeb | - | Zineb | - |
| Maneb | 15.3 | Ziram | 1.9 |
| Metham | 3.7 | | |

## 631  Benomyl and carbendazim by HPLC with UV detector (Reference 26)

A 150 mL sample is stirred with 2 mL 50% $H_2SO_4$ for 16 to 24 hours to hydrolyze benomyl to carbendazim. The pH is then adjusted to 6 to 8 and the sample extracted three times with $CH_2Cl_2$. The combined extracts are dried with sodium sulfate and concentrated with solvent exchange to methanol. The HPLC is performed on a reversed phase column with a 1:1 methanol : water isocratic elution. Detection is UV at 254 nm. Calibration is external standard with a minimum of three standards. Confirmation on a second column is required. MDL is 25.0 ug/L for benomyl (as carbendazim) and 8.7 for carbendazim.

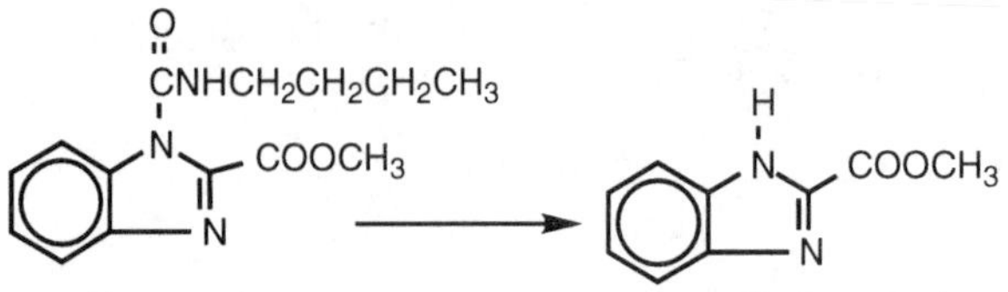

**Figure 3-18. Hydrolysis of benomyl to carbendazim in Method 631.**

## 632  Carbamate and urea pesticides by HPLC with UV detector (Reference 26)

A 1 L sample is extracted three times with $CH_2Cl_2$. The combined extracts are dried with sodium sulfate and concentrated with solvent exchange to methanol or acetonitrile. An optional Florisil cleanup is described. Analysis is by HPLC with reversed-phase column and a variety of solvent systems. Detection is UV at 245 and 280 nm. Calibration is external standard with a minimum of three standards by either RF (<10% RSD to assume linearity) or calibration curve. The calibration is checked daily with one or more calibration standards. Acceptance criteria is <15% variation from the original calibration, otherwise the system gets recalibrated. Identification must be confirmed on a second column of differing polarity from the analytical column.

**Table 3-68.  Target Analytes and MDLs for Method 632**

| Target Analyte | MDL ug/L | Target Analyte | MDL ug/L |
|---|---|---|---|
| Mexacarbate | 0.52 | Neburon | 0.012 |
| Propoxur | 0.11 | Methomyl | 8.9 |
| Monuron | 0.003 | Carbofuran | 3.2 |
| Carbaryl | 0.02 | Fluorometuron | 11.1 |
| Propham | 0.07 | Oxamyl | 9.2 |
| Diuron | 0.009 | Chloropropham | 0.03 |
| Linuron | 0.009 | Barban | 0.05 |
| Methiocarb | 0.02 | | |

## 632.1  Carbamate and amide pesticides by HPLC with UV detection (Reference 26)

A 1 L sample is neutralized to 6.5 to 7.5 pH, 200 g NaCl added and then extracted three times with $CH_2Cl_2$. The combined extracts are dried with sodium sulfate and concentrated with solvent exchange to acetonitrile. An optional Florisil cleanup is described. Analysis is by HPLC with reversed phase column and linear acetonitrile : water gradient. Detection is UV at 245 nm. Calibration is external standard with a minimum of three standards by either RF (<10% RSD to assume linearity) or calibration curve. The calibration is checked daily with one or more calibration standards. Acceptance criteria is <15% variation from the original calibration, otherwise the system gets recalibrated. Identification must be confirmed on a second column of differing polarity from the analytical column.

**Table 3-69. Target Analytes and MDLs for Method 632.1**

| Target Analyte | MDL ug/L | Target Analyte | MDL ug/L |
|---|---|---|---|
| Napropamide | 0.31 | Propanil | 0.85 |
| Vacor | 0.20 | | |

## 633 and 633.1  Organonitrogen pesticides by GC-NPD (Reference 26)

A 1 L sample is extracted three times with $CH_2Cl_2$. The combined extracts are dried with sodium sulfate and concentrated with solvent exchange to acetone. Calibration is external standard with a minimum of three standards by either RF (<10% RSD to assume linearity) or calibration curve. The calibration is checked daily with one or more calibration standards. Acceptance criteria is <15% variation from the original calibration, otherwise the system gets recalibrated. Identification must be confirmed on a second column of differing polarity from the analytical column.

**Table 3-70. Target Analytes and MDLs for Methods 633 and 633.1**

| Target Analyte | MDL ug/L | Target Analyte | MDL ug/L |
|---|---|---|---|
| Terbacil | - | DEET | 3.39 |
| Bromacil | 2.38 | Pronamide (633.1) | 4 |
| Hexazinone | 0.72 | MGK 264 (633.1) | 2 |
| Tricyclazole | - | MGK 326 (633.1) | 6 |
| Metribuzin | 0.46 | Fenarimol | 4 |
| Triadimefon | 0.78 | | |

## 634  Thiocarbamate pesticides by GC-NPD (Reference 26)

A 1 L sample is pH adjusted to the 6 to 8 range with either sodium hydroxide or sulfuric acid then extracted with methylene chloride for 18-24 hours using a continuous liquid-liquid extractor. The extract is dried with sodium sulfate and concentrated to 5.0 mL with solvent exchange to toluene. An optional silica gel clean-up is described. Calibration is either minimum three-point external standard or internal standard using carbazole.

**Table 3-71. Target Analytes and MDLs for Method 634**

| Target Analyte | MDL ug/L | Target Analyte | MDL ug/L |
|---|---|---|---|
| EPTC | 0.9 | Butylate | 0.6 |
| Vernolate | 1.1 | Pebulate | 0.8 |
| Molinate | 0.6 | Cycloate | 1.6 |

## 635  Rotenone by HPLC with UV detector (Reference 26)

A 1 L sample is neutralized to pH 7 then extracted three times with $CH_2Cl_2$. The combined extracts are dried with sodium sulfate and concentrated with solvent exchange to acetonitrile. An optional silica gel cleanup is described. Analysis is by HPLC with reversed phase column and isocratic 60 : 40 acetonitrile : water. Detection is UV at 245 nm. Calibration is external standard with a minimum of three standards by either RF (<10% RSD to assume linearity) or calibration curve. The calibration is checked daily with one or more calibration standards. Acceptance criteria is <15% variation from the original calibration, otherwise the system gets recalibrated. Identification must be confirmed on a second column of differing polarity from the analytical column. MDL is 1.6 ug/L.

## 636  Bensulide by HPLC with UV detector (Reference 26)

A 1 L sample is pH adjusted to 7 then extracted three times with $CH_2Cl_2$. The combined extracts are dried with sodium sulfate and concentrated with solvent exchange to acetonitrile. An optional Florisil cleanup is described. Analysis is by HPLC with reversed-phase column and isocratic 60 : 40 acetonitrile : water elution. Detection is UV at 270 nm. Calibration is external standard with a minimum of three standards by either RF (<10% RSD to assume linearity) or calibration curve. The calibration is checked daily with one or more calibration standards. Acceptance criteria is <15% variation from the original calibration, otherwise the system gets recalibrated. Identification must be confirmed on a second column of differing polarity from the analytical column. MDL is 1.6 ug/L.

## 641  Thiabendazole by direct injection HPLC with fluorescence detector (Reference 26)

The HPLC system is reversed-phase column with 70 : 30 methanol : buffer (triethanol-amine : acetic acid : water) isocratic eluant. The fluorescent detector has excitation at 300 nm and detection at 360 nm. The sample is acidified to pH 1 to 3 and filtered, then 100 uL is injected into the HPLC. Calibration is external standard with a minimum of three standards by either RF (<10% RSD to assume linearity) or calibration curve. The calibration is checked daily with one or more calibration standards. Acceptance criteria is <15% variation from the original calibration, otherwise the system gets recalibrated. Identification must be confirmed on a second column of differing polarity from the analytical column. MDL is 1.7 ug/L.

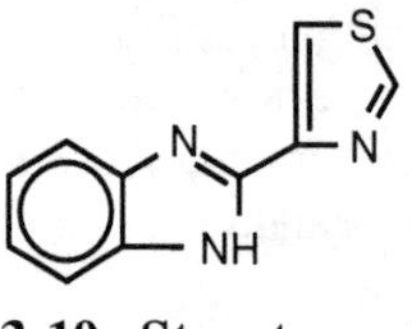

**Figure 3-19.  Structure of thiabendazole.**

## 645  Certain amine pesticides and lethane by GC-NPD (Reference 26)

A 1 L sample is pH adjusted to the 5 to 9 range, then extracted three times with methylene chloride. The extracts are dried over sodium sulfate and concentrated to 10 mL with solvent exchange to hexane. An optional clean-up with deactivated Florisil is described. Calibration is minimum three-point external standard. Analyte confirmation is required by re-analysis on a second column or by GC/MS.

**Table 3-72.  Target Analytes and MDLs for Method 645**

| Target Analyte | MDL ug/L | Target Analyte | MDL ug/L |
|---|---|---|---|
| Alachlor | 0.2 | Fluridone | 0.5 |
| Butachlor | 0.3 | Lethane | 0.1 |
| Diphenamide | 0.2 | Norflurazon | 0.02 |

## 646 Dinitro aromatic pesticides by GC-ECD (Reference 26)

A 1 L sample is pH adjusted to the 5 to 9 range then extracted three times with 15% methylene chloride : hexane. The combined extracts are dried with sodium sulfate and concentrated to 10 mL with solvent exchange to hexane. An optional Florisil clean-up is described. Analyte identification is verified on a second column or by GC/MS. CDN is 1-chloro-2,4-dinitrobenzene.

**Table 3-73. Target Analytes and MDLs for Method 646**

| Target Analyte | MDL ug/L |
|----------------|----------|
| CDN | 0.0005 |
| Dinocap | 0.1 |
| Basalin | 0.0005 |

## 1625 Semivolatile organic compounds by isotope dilution GC/MS (Reference 42)

Isotopically labeled analytes are added to a 1 L sample in a glass beaker and stirred for 1-2 hours. The solution is quantitatively transfered to a continuous liquid-liquid extractor. The sample is pH adjusted to >12 and extracted for 18-24 hours. The extraction solvent is removed, and the pH is adjusted to < 2 after cooling. More methylene chloride is added, and the extraction continued for 18-24 hours. The BN and acid extractables are maintained as separate extracts rather than combining them as in Method 8270. The extracts are dried with sodium sulfate and concentrated to 1.0 mL. Internal standard (2,2'-difluorobiphenyl) is added immediately before GC/MS analysis. Most of the isotopically labeled compounds are perdeuterated; however, a few contain limited numbers of deuterium or are labeled with $^{13}C$. Calibration is either against the labeled analyte or the internal standard with a minimum of a five-point concentration range. The average RF can be used for a compound if each individual value in the calibration is within 10% of the average; otherwise a calibration curve is prepared. At the beginning of each 8-hour shift a calibration standard containing all components at the 100 ug/mL must meet the listed performance criteria in addition to the passing of DFTPP tune criteria. Most of the analytes are the same as those listed in method 625. Of note is the addition of a number of straight-chain saturated hydrocarbons.

**Table 3-74. Daily MS Tune Criteria for DFTPP**

| Mass M/z | DFTPP Relative Abundance Criteria |
|----------|-----------------------------------|
| 51 | 30-60% of base peak |
| 68 | <2% of mass 69 |
| 70 | <2% of mass 69 |
| 127 | 40-60% of mass 198 |
| 197 | <1% of mass 198 |
| 198 | base peak 100% relative abundance |
| 199 | 5-9% of mass 198 |
| 275 | 10-30% of mass 198 |

Continued on next page.

**Table 3-74. Daily MS Tune Criteria for DFTPP,** *continued*

| Mass M/z | DFTPP Relative Abundance Criteria |
|----------|-----------------------------------|
| 365 | >1% of mass 198 |
| 441 | present and < mass 443 |
| 442 | >40% of mass 198 |
| 443 | 17-23% of mass 442 |

## 1656 Organohalide pesticides by GC-ECD or ELCD (Reference 26)

This is the first of the combined methodologies that attempts to meet drinking water, wastewater, RCRA, and CLP protocols. It covers a large number of analytes as shown in Table 3-75. The method describes a number of extraction procedures that are used depending on the solids content of the sample. This is determined by overnight drying of a 5 to 10 g subsample. If the sample is <1% solids, a 1.00 L sample is pH adjusted to 5-9 and continuously extracted with $CH_2Cl_2$ for 18-24 hours. If the sample is 1% to 30% solids, a portion is sonicated with $CH_2Cl_2$ : acetone (1 : 1), then diluted with water to 1% solids and extracted with $CH_2Cl_2$ in a continuous extractor for 18-24 hours. Samples containing >30% solids are mixed with powdered anhydrous sodium sulfate and sonicated three times with 1 : 1 $CH_2Cl_2$ : acetone. Municipal sludges with >30% solids are sonicated two times with acetonitrile and 1 time with $CH_2Cl_2$. The filtered combined extracts are washed three times with 2% sodium sulfate solution. Optional clean-ups include gel permeation chromatography, $C_{18}$ reversed phase extraction cartridge, Florisil column, alumina column, and sulfur removal. The sample extracts are dried over sodium sulfate and concentrated with solvent exchange to hexane. Calibration is external standard with a minimum of three standards by either RF (< 20% coefficient of variation to assume linearity) or calibration curve. The calibration is checked daily with one or more calibration standards. Acceptance criteria is compound specific and must be met, otherwise the system gets recalibrated. Identification must be confirmed on a second column of differing polarity from the analytical column. Surrogate (dibutyl-chlorendate suggested, tetrachloro-*m*-xylene or decachlorobiphenyl are possible if DBC is not available) is added to each sample, and recoveries must be 40-120%.

**Table 3-75. Target Analytes and MDLs for Method 1656**

| Target Analyte | MDL ug/L | Target Analyte | MDL ug/L |
|----------------|----------|----------------|----------|
| Acephate | 2000 | δ-Chlordane | 9 |
| Trifluralin | 50 | Butachlor | 30 |
| Ethalfluralin | 5 | α-Chlordane | 8 |
| Benfluralin | 20 | Endosulfan I | 11 |
| Diallate-A | 45 | 4,4'-DDE | 10 |
| Diallate-B | 32 | Dieldrin | 6 |
| α-BHC | 6 | Captan | 100 |
| PCNB | 6 | Chlorobenzilate | 25 |
| Simazine | 400 | Endrin | 4 |
| Atrazine | 500 | Nitrofen (TOK) | 13 |
| Terbutylazine | 300 | Kepone | 100 |
| δ-BHC | 11 | 4,4'-DDD | 5 |

Continued on next page.

**Table 3-75.  Target Analytes and MDLs for Method 1656,** *continued*

| Target Analyte | MDL ug/L | Target Analyte | MDL ug/L |
|---|---|---|---|
| β-BHC | 7 | Endosulfan II | 8 |
| Heptachlor | 5 | Bromoxynil octanoate | 30 |
| Chlorothalonil | 15 | 4,4'-DDT | 12 |
| Dichlone | 4 | Carbophenothion | 50 |
| Terbacil | 200 | Endrin aldehyde | 11 |
| γ-BHC | 5 | Endosulfan sulfate | 7 |
| Alachlor | 20 | Captafol | 100 |
| Propanil | - | Norfluorazon | 50 |
| Aldrin | 8 | Mirex | 4 |
| DCPA | 3 | Methoxychlor | 30 |
| Metribuzin | 5 | Endrin ketone | 8 |
| Triadimefon | 50 | Fenarimol | 20 |
| Isopropalin | 20 | *cis*-Permethrin | 200 |
| Isodrin | 13 | *trans*-Permethrin | 200 |
| Heptachlor epoxide | 12 | PCBs | 150 |
| Pendamethalin | 30 | Toxaphene | 910 |
| Bromacil | 70 | | |

## 1657  Organophosphorous pesticides by GC-FPD (Reference 26)

This is another of the combined methodologies that attempts to meet drinking water, wastewater, RCRA, and CLP protocols.  It covers a large number of analytes as indicated in Table 3-76.  The method describes a number of extraction procedures that are used depending on the solids content of the sample, which is determined by overnight drying of a 5 to 10 g subsample.  If the sample is <1% solids, a 1.00 L sample is pH adjusted to 5-9 and continuously extracted with $CH_2Cl_2$ for 18-24 hours.  If the sample is 1% to 30% solids, a portion is sonicated with $CH_2Cl_2$ : acetone (1 : 1), then diluted with water to 1% solids and extracted with $CH_2Cl_2$ in a continuous extractor for 18-24 hours.  Samples containing >30% solids are mixed with powdered anhydrous sodium sulfate and sonicated three times with 1 : 1 $CH_2Cl_2$ : acetone.  Municipal sludges with >30% solids are sonicated two times with acetonitrile and one time with $CH_2Cl_2$.  The filtered combined extracts are washed three times with 2% sodium sulfate solution. There is a procedure for extraction and isolation of water soluble pesticides such as methamidophos.  Optional clean-ups include gel permeation chromatography and $C_{18}$ reversed-phase extraction cartridge.  The sample extracts are dried over sodium sulfate and concentrated with solvent exchange to hexane.  Calibration is external standard with a minimum of three standards by either RF (< 20% coefficient of variation to assume linearity) or calibration curve.  The calibration is checked daily with one or more calibration standards.  Acceptance criteria is compound-specific and must be met, otherwise the system gets recalibrated.  Identification must be confirmed on a second column of differing polarity from the analytical column.  Surrogate (tributyl phosphate and triphenylphosphate) is added to each sample, and recoveries must be 40-120%.

**Table 3-76. Target Analytes and MDLs for Method 1657**

| Target Analyte | MDL ug/L | Target Analyte | MDL ug/L |
|---|---|---|---|
| Dichlorvos | 4 | Ronnel | 11 |
| Mevinphos | 74 | Malathion | 11 |
| Acephate | 500 | Fenthion | 22 |
| Trichlorofon | 150 | Parathion | 10 |
| Methamidophos | 100 | Chlorpyrifos | 4 |
| Demeton-A | 19 | Trichloronate | 14 |
| Ethoprop | 7 | Chlorfevinphos | 2 |
| Naled | 18 | Crotoxyphos | 81 |
| Dicrotophos | 81 | Tokuthion | 2 |
| Monocrotophos | 85 | Tetrachlorvinphos | 12 |
| Sulfotepp | 6 | DEF | 50 |
| Phorate | 10 | Merphos-B | 18 |
| Dimethoate | 27 | Fensulfothion | 104 |
| Demeton-B | 21 | Methyl trithion | 10 |
| Dioxathion | 121 | Ethion | 13 |
| Terbufos | 26 | Sulprofos | 6 |
| Phosphamidon-E | 28 | Famphur | 27 |
| Disulfoton | 32 | Phosmet | 14 |
| Diazinon | 38 | EPN | 9 |
| Phosphamidon-Z | 116 | Azinphos methyl | 9 |
| Methyl parathion | 18 | Leptophos | 14 |
| Dichlorofenthion | 6 | Azinphos ethyl | 22 |
| Methylchlorpyrifos | 13 | Coumaphos | 24 |

## 1658 Phenoxy-acid herbicides by derivatization and GC-ECD or ELCD (Reference 26)

This is another of the combined methodologies that attempts to meet drinking water, wastewater, RCRA, and CLP protocols. It covers analytes as indicated in Table 3-77. The method describes a number of extraction procedures used depending on the solids content of the sample, which is determined by overnight drying of a 5 to 10 g subsample. If the sample is <1% solids, a 1.00 L sample is pH adjusted to >12 to hydrolyze compounds, then adjusted to < 2 and continuously extracted with $CH_2Cl_2$ for 18-24 hours. If the sample is 1% to 30% solids, a portion is sonicated with $CH_2Cl_2$ : acetone (1 : 1), then diluted with water to 1% solids and extracted with $CH_2Cl_2$ in a continuous extractor for 18-24 hours. Samples containing >30% solids are mixed with powdered anhydrous sodium sulfate and sonicated three times with 1 : 1 $CH_2Cl_2$ : acetone. Municipal sludges with >30% solids sonicated two times with acetonitrile and one time with $CH_2Cl_2$. The filtered combined extracts are washed three times with 2% sodium sulfate solution. Optional clean-ups include gel permeation chromatography, $C_{18}$ reversed-phase extraction cartridge, and Florisil column. The sample extracts are dried over sodium sulfate and concentrated with solvent exchange to hexane, then esterified with diazomethane. Calibration is external standard with a minimum of three standards by either RF (< 20% coefficient of variation to assume linearity) or calibration curve. The calibration is checked daily with one or more calibration standards. Acceptance criteria is compound- specific and must be met, otherwise the system gets recalibrated. Identification must be confirmed on a second column of differing polarity from the analytical column or GC-MS. Surrogate (2,4-DCPA) is added to each sample, and recoveries must be 40-120%.

**Table 3-77. Target Analytes and MDLs for Method 1658**

| Target Analyte | MDL ug/L |
|---|---|
| 2,4-D | 100 |
| Dinoseb | 50 |
| 2,4,5-T | 50 |
| 2,4,5-TP | 40 |
| Dalapon | 100 |

| Target Analyte | MDL ug/L |
|---|---|
| Dicamba | 110 |
| Dichlorprop | 40 |
| MCPA | 90 |
| MCPP | 56 |
| 2,4-DB | 50 |

## 1659  Dazomet by hydrolysis to methyl isothiocyanate and GC-NPD (Reference 26)

A 50 mL sample is pH adjusted to 10 to 12 and allowed to sit for 3 hours at room temperature. This hydrolyzes the dazomet to methyl isothiocyanate, which is extracted with ethyl acetate and analyzed by GC with an NPD. Calibration is external standard with a minimum of three standards by either RF (<10% RSD to assume linearity) or calibration curve. The calibration is checked daily with one or more calibration standards. Acceptance criteria is < 15% variation from the original calibration, otherwise the system gets recalibrated. Identification must be confirmed on a second column of differing polarity from the analytical column. MDL is 3 ug/L.

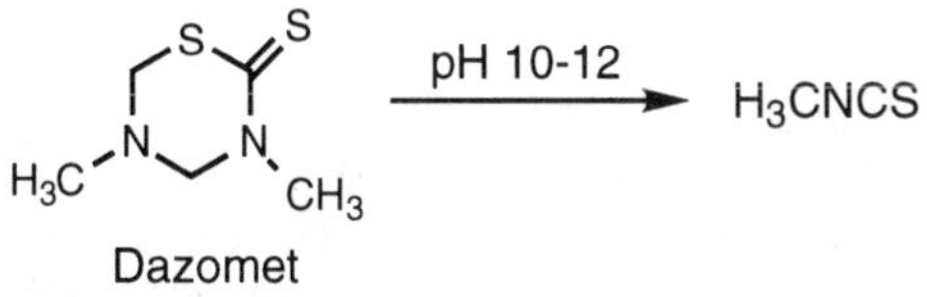

**Figure 3-20. Hydrolysis reaction of dazomet.**

## 1660  Pyrethrins and pyrethroids by HPLC with UV detector (Reference 26)

A 750 mL sample is placed in a 1 L volumetric flask, then 230 g NaCl and 160 mL acetonitrile added. The flask is stirred with a magnetic stir bar for 5 minutes then allowed to sit for 5 minutes. The top layer of acetonitrile is withdrawn (2-5 mL) and 5 mL added. The flask is again stirred. The combined extracts from three extractions are concentrated to 7.5 mL and analyzed by HPLC on a dual-coupled $C_{18}$ reversed-phase columns with a linear gradient elution of 70 : 30 acetonitrile : water to 100% acetonitrile. Detection is by UV at 235 and 245 nm. Identification is assumed if the response of the eluting compound is the same as that of the standard with the same retention time at the two analytical wavelengths. Calibration is multi-point with daily checking of the curve.

**Table 3-78. Target Analytes and MDLs for Method 1660**

| Target Analyte | MDL ug/L |
|---|---|
| Pyrethrin II | 19 |
| Tetramethrin | 16 |
| Allethrin | 16 |
| Pyrethrin I | 22 |
| Cyfluthrin | 22 |

| Target Analyte | MDL ug/L |
|---|---|
| Resmethrin | 22 |
| Fenvalerate | 10 |
| c/t-Permethrin | 20 |
| Sumithrin | 25 |
| t/c-Permethrin | 20 |

## 1661 Bromoxynil by direct injection HPLC with UV detector (Reference 26)

The sample is pH adjusted to 3 to 7 and 40 uL injected on a HPLC with reversed-phase column and detection by UV at 255 and 280 nm. Mobile phase is 50 : 50 methanol : water. The multi-point external standard calibration is checked daily. Identification is assumed if the eluting compound has the same retention time as the standard and equivalent response at the two wavelengths. Bromoxynil is 3,5-dibromo-4-hydroxybenzonitrile, and the MDL is 20 ug/L.

## C. Extraction Techniques

All of the 500, 600, and 1600 series methods are self-contained, covering sample collection, handling, preservation, extraction, clean-up, analysis, and quality control. Only a few of the 8000 series methods (SW-846) are similar in this respect. Most refer the analyst to sections on quality control (Chapter 1 and method 8000), extraction (3500 series methods) and clean-up (3600 series methods). Detailed information on surrogate and matrix spike solutions and use are found in 3500, the introduction section to the extraction methods.

## 3510 Separatory funnel liquid-liquid extraction

This is a method that relies upon partitioning the analytes between the water matrix and an organic phase, most commonly $CH_2Cl_2$. A separatory funnel of 2 L capacity is normally used. Processing of a large number of samples is very labor intensive. In general a fast method, it can become time consuming when emulsion layers form. A BNA extraction may use 300-500 mL of solvent. See method 3650 for information on pH adjustment during the extraction process.

## 3520 Continuous liquid-liquid extraction

This is a method that avoids the problem of emulsions; however, continuous liquid-liquid extraction requires a 18-24 hour extraction period. It is not as labor intensive as separatory funnel extractions. A single technician can set-up and process a very large number of samples on a regular basis. Solvent usage is around 300-500 mL, and either lighter-than-water or heavier-than-water solvents can be used, depending on the exact extractor design. A solvent pool sits at the bottom of the extracting chamber when heavier-than-water solvents such as $CH_2Cl_2$ are used. Extracted analytes are diluted into this solvent pool, then slowly removed by siphon. Modern designs add a stopcock to the siphon tube and a K-D (Kuderna-Danish) Snyder column to the device for extraction, followed by concentration without transferring the sample extract to another set of glassware. The use of the siphon tube allows water to become entrained in the extracting solvent. On solvent removal the major part of the resulting concentrate can be water. A recent technology advance adds a hydrophobic membrane to the bottom of the sample chamber, which allows rapid and efficient separation of the extraction solvent from the water sample and immediate return of the solvent to the concentrator reservoir[6]. The elimination of the solvent pool shortens the extraction time to 4-6 hours, reduces solvent usage to less than 100 mL and makes the technique more time efficient and competitive

---

6    Accelerated One-Step™ Extractor-Concentrator, Corning Glassworks, Corning, NY. One-Step is a registered trademark of Corning Glassworks.

with separatory funnel methods. A further advantage is elimination of water from the sample concentrate without further sample manipulation. See Appendix C for examples of continuous extractors. Method 3650 contains information about use of pH adjustment with continuous liquid-liquid extractors.

## 3540  Soxhlet extraction of solids

This method is considered by EPA to be the exhaustive extraction procedure for solids. It is always the benchmark procedure for comparison when proposed extraction methods are being validated. The solid material is mixed with anhydrous sodium sulfate, then subjected to soxhlet extraction for 16-24 hrs. The method uses up to 300 mL of solvent for the extraction. It can use either lighter-than-water solvents, heavier-than-water solvents or mixtures of the two without modification. When used with heavier-than-water solvents such as Freon or methylene chloride, a glass wool plug is added on top of the sample to avoid particles floating up in the sample cup. A soxhlet extractor is pictured in Appendix C.

## 3541  Automated soxhlet extraction

The sample is dried, powdered, and loaded into an extractor cup, then submersed into 50 mL of the extraction solvent (1:1 Acetone:hexane) and boiled for 1 hour. Afterwards the sample cup is raised to the rinse position, and the solvent is allowed to drain through the cup for an hour. The solvent is then removed by concentration by diverting the solvent return from the condenser. The method is used primarily for PCBs in solids, and a solvent exchange into pure hexane is required prior to analysis.

## 3550  Sonication extraction

A sample is mixed with anhydrous sodium sulfate then extracted three times with one of a variety of solvent mixtures (1:1 acetone : $CH_2Cl_2$). The extraction uses an ultrasonic disrupter horn of at least 300 watts power for agitation of the mixture. See the reference in footnote 8 for an examination of some problems associated with this method.

## 3560  Supercritical fluid extraction

Supercritical fluid extraction (SFE) is a technique that extracts a solid sample under high pressure and elevated temperatures with carbon dioxide (340 atm., 80 °C, 500-1000 mL/min flow). Supercritical fluids exist at any combination of temperature and pressure above the critical point. The supercritical fluid is an excellent solvent for non-polar analytes with the solubilizing ability increasing with increasing density, a function of the pressure. For extraction of more polar analytes, the fluid is modified by addition of methanol, acetonitrile, or a number of other common solvents. Once the pressure is released, the carbon dioxide vaporizes, leaving the concentrated analyte in an appropriate solvent. The instrument has been directly interfaced to both GC and HPLC for automated extraction and analysis. Draft method 3561, SFE of polyaromatic hydrocarbons from soils, is under consideration for inclusion in SW-846. A comparison of SFE and sonication for the removal of amines from soils has been published[7].

---

[7]  Oostdyk, T.S., R.L. Grob, J.L. Snyder and M.E. McNally. "Study of Sonication and Supercritical Fluid Extraction of Primary Aromatic Amines." *Anal. Chem.* 1993. 65(5). pp. 596-600.

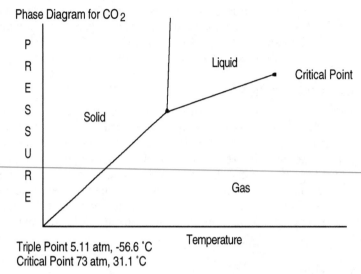

Triple Point 5.11 atm, -56.6 °C
Critical Point 73 atm, 31.1 °C

**Figure 3-21. Phase diagram for supercritical carbon dioxide.**

A recent article reports use of supercritical water for selective extractions of organic analytes[8]. A remarkable selectivity for polar and non-polar target analytes is detailed, which could find extensive use in remediation monitoring.

## 3580  Waste dilution

In this extraction method the non-aqueous sample is diluted with an appropriate organic solvent, often in the ratio of 1 gm sample to 10.0 mL solution.

## D.  Other extraction techniques

### 1.  Liquid-membrane-liquid extraction[9]

These techniques try to perform a simultaneous analyte isolation and introduction of the sample to an analytical instrument similar in idea to the purge and trap - GC interface used in VOC analysis. A relatively large volume (20-100 mL) of the aqueous sample is separated from a small volume (< 5mL) of an organic solvent by a polymer membrane. The organic analytes diffuse across the membrane, become concentrated in the organic solvent, and, after a suitable contact time, are introduced into the GC or HPLC for analysis.

### 2.  Solid phase extraction

This method uses a $C_{18}$ or other chain-length reversed-phase cartridge or disk for isolation and concentration of non-polar organic analytes from water, then elutes the absorbed

---

8    Hawthorne, S.B., Y. Yang, and D.J. Miller. "Extraction of Organic Pollutants from Environmental Solids with Sub- and Supercritical Water." *Analytical Chemistry.* 1994. 66(18). pp. 2912-2920.

9    Melcher, R.G., D.W. Bakke, and G.H. Hughes. "On-line Membrane/Liquid Chromatographic Analyzer for Pentachlorophenol and Other Trace Phenols in Wastewater." *Anal. Chem.* 1992. 64(19). pp. 2258-2262.

compounds with an organic solvent, ready for analysis. Recent introduction of the styrene-divinylbenzene copolymer disks solve many of the breakthrough problems seen with the reversed-phase disks. SPE is also available with ion exchange resins and size-exclusion gels. Current problems include clogging of the disk or cartridge with particulate matter, and incomplete retention of all compounds. The process can be fine tuned for a particular matrix and analysis with superb results. A draft method (method 3535) is proposed for addition into SW-846 covering the solid phase extraction of organochlorine pesticides from aqueous matrices. Many of the newer drinking water and wastewater semivolatiles methods are oriented toward SPE.

### 3. Microwave-assisted liquid extraction from soils

In addition to the metals digestion area, the microwave oven can be used to assist liquid extraction of organic analytes from solid matrices[10]. The extraction was tested in the screw cap sealed Teflon® bomb discussed in the metals digestions in Section 2. The extraction solvent tested was hexane : acetone (1:1) and the optimum time was found to be 10 minutes.

## E. Clean-up

Clean-up methods are directed toward reducing interfering materials in analyte extracts prior to instrument analysis. Environmental samples are unbelievably complex matrices. To achieve the MDLs demanded by government regulators, the samples have to be processed to remove as much garbage as possible. Most MDLs were derived from matrix spikes into purified water, or, in the case of solid samples, the matrix spikes were into purified sand. Sand and DI water are not anything like wastewater from a pulp plant, Georgia red clay, or other real-life samples. A practical reason for clean-up procedures is to extend the useful life of GC and HPLC columns. A five-dollar clean-up often allows use of a $400 column on another day. Method 3600 gives an overview of clean-up methods and a guide to applications.

### 3610 Alumina column

This cleanup method describes various activity grades and pHs of alumina ($Al_2O_3$). Alumina is prepared from $Al(OH)_3$, which is dehydrated and calcined at 900 °C in a carbon dioxide atmosphere. The resulting aluminum oxide particles are coated with a layer of aluminum oxycarbonate $[Al_2(OH)_5]_2CO_3$. This allows for pH adjustment to the acidic, neutral, and basic grades for particular applications. Addition of known quantities of water are used to deactivate the alumina, as it serves as a very active catalytic substance for compound decomposition when anhydrous. Uses are for phthalate esters and nitrosamines.

### 3611 Alumina column clean-up and separation of petroleum wastes

This method is specifically tailored for clean-ups of petroleum wastes and separation into aliphatic, aromatic, and polar fractions for analysis.

---

[10] Lopez-Avila, V., R. Young and W.F. Beckert "Microwave-assisted Extraction of Organic Compounds from Standard Reference Soils and Sediments." *Analytical Chemistry* 1994. 66(7). pp. 1097-1106.

## 3620 Florisil column clean-up

Florisil is an activated form of magnesium silicate. It has more acidic character than alumina or silica gel but is still classified as amphoteric. Commonly used as a clean-up material in pesticide residue analysis, it is considered to be a much milder absorbent than silica gel or alumina with regard to compound decomposition. Specific procedures are given for application to phthalate ester, nitrosamine, nitroaromatic, and chlorinated hydrocarbon target analytes. Florisil is variable in its adsorptive capacity from batch to batch. Determination of the lauric acid value allows Florisil standardization, which is used to calculate the amount of Florisil needed to perform a desired separation. The lauric acid value is determined by measuring the amount of lauric acid adsorbed in milligrams per gram of Florisil from a hexane solution[11]. A standard column for clean-up is determined by dividing the lauric acid value by 110 and multiplying by 20 g (See methods 614 and 617.).

## 3630 Silica gel column clean-up

Silica gel is a precipitated form of silicic acid ($H_2SiO_3$), formed from addition of sulfuric acid to sodium silicate. It forms very strong hydrogen bonds to polar materials and can lead to analyte decomposition. It is somewhat soluble in methanol, which should never be used as an elution solvent. Silica gel will quantitatively remove even slightly polar substances from hexane solutions and serves to isolate the strictly petroleum hydrocarbon analytes from interferences in the DRO and IR-TPH procedures. This procedure presents applications to PCB, PAH and derivatized phenol target analytes.

## 3640 Gel permeation column clean-up

A cross-linked divinylbenzene-styrene copolymer (hydrophobic gel) and organic solvents are used to selectively pass large macromolecules such as proteins, phospholipids, resins, lignins, fulvic and humic acids, etc. from sample extracts while retaining the smaller target analyte molecules in the pores of the gel. The desired analytes are displaced from the gel with a smaller-sized organic solvent, methylene chloride. After preparation the column must be calibrated with a mixture of corn oil, bis(2-ethylhexyl) phthalate, methoxychlor, perylene, and sulfur. Eluants are detected by monitoring flow through a UV detector. Exactly half the sample is lost due to loading the column through an automated injection loop, therefore if GPC is used, the matrix spike and surrogate compounds are added at twice their normal concentration. This problem of losing half the sample can be eliminated by performing a direct injection onto the GPC through a 4-way valve by syringe, or by using an auto-sampler without an injection loop.

---

[11]  "Standardization of Florisil Column by Weight Adjustment Based on Adsorption of Lauric Acid." *ASTM Annual Book of Standards.* 1980. Part 31, D3086, Appendix X3, p. 765.

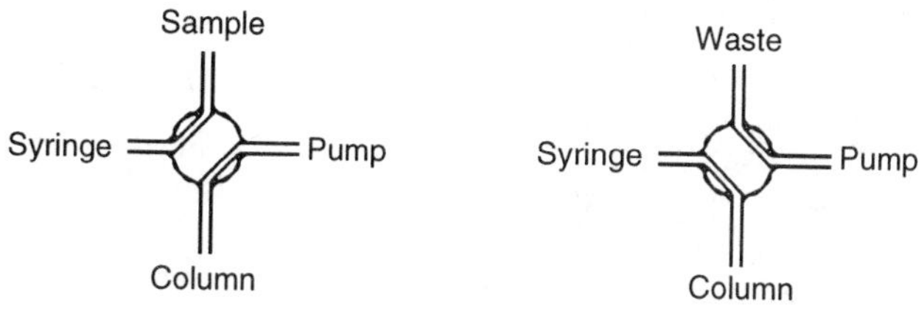

**Figure 3-22. 4-way valve configuration used for manual GPC. The position on the left is for syringe filling and column elution, the position on the right is for injection of sample on the column.**

The styrene-divinyl benzene polymeric packing of the column is not inert toward surface adsorption of organic molecules, particularly those with aromatic rings or electron rich substituents. The effect is not very pronounced with eluting solvents such as methylene chloride or toluene due to the high partition ratio in favor of the solvent. However when less interactive solvents are used such as cyclohexane or ethyl acetate, substantial increases in retention times of PAH and PCB analytes have been noted. This effect has been demonstrated[12] to be a useful tool for clean-up when the target analytes are in a hydrocarbon oil matrix, a very common occurrence.

## 3650  Acid-base partition clean-up

Normally considered a part of the separatory funnel or continuous liquid-liquid extraction, this technique calls for pH adjustment of the water sample with sodium hydroxide to >12 and extraction of all the basic and neutral organics with $CH_2Cl_2$, referred to as the base-neutral (BN) fraction. Then the pH is adjusted to < 2 with sulfuric acid and the sample again extracted to obtain the acid (A) fraction. When used with the continuous extractor, the solution is made acid first, extracted, then pH-adjusted for the base fraction extraction. Some problems in the procedure have been the subject of recent articles[13].

## 3660  Sulfur clean-up

The sample is agitated with either powdered copper, mercury metal, or tetrabutyl-ammonium sulfite to remove elemental sulfur interferences. The latter is the gentlest and suggested for use on organophosphorous and organochlorine pesticide extracts. Sulfur is a common contaminant, and since it is non-polar and easily chromatographs on a GC as a semivolatile, it can dominate an extract. Sulfur is also removed by the GPC.

## 3665  Sulfuric acid/permanganate clean-up

This is a very rigorous oxidative clean-up that will remove most interferents except PCBs, chlorinated benzenes and chlorinated naphthalenes (Halowaxes). A few organochlorine hydrocarbons will survive.

---

[12]  Conrad, E.C., K.P. Kelly and N.L. Schwartz. "GPC and oily solvents." *Environmental Testing and Analysis*, 3(5). 1994. pp. 34-39.

[13]  Chen, P. H., W. A. VanAusdale, and D. F. Roberts. "Oxidation of Phenolic Acid Surrogates and Target Analytes During Acid Extraction of Natural Water Samples for Analysis by GC/MS Using EPA Method 625." *Environmental Science and Technology*. 1991. 25(3). pp. 540-546.

## F. Methods 8000 Series

### 8032 Acrylamide by derivatization then packed column GC-ECD

A 50 mL sample is mixed with 7.5 g KBr, then the solution is pH adjusted with HBr to 1 to 3, bromine water is added, followed by stoppering the flask and storing in the dark at 0 °C for at least an hour. The excess bromine is reduced with sodium thiosulfate. Then sodium sulfate is added, and the mixture extracted two times with ethyl acetate. The combined extracts are dried over sodium sulfate, then dimethyl phthalate internal standard is added, and the volume brought up to 25.0 mL in a low-actinic volumetric flask. An optional Florisil column clean-up is described. Analysis is by packed column GC (free fatty acid polyester FFAP) and ECD. Confirmation of identification is with a second column of differing polarity or GC-MS. Calibration is five-point by either RF or actual curve, checked daily. MDL is 0.032 ug/L of acrylamide monomer.

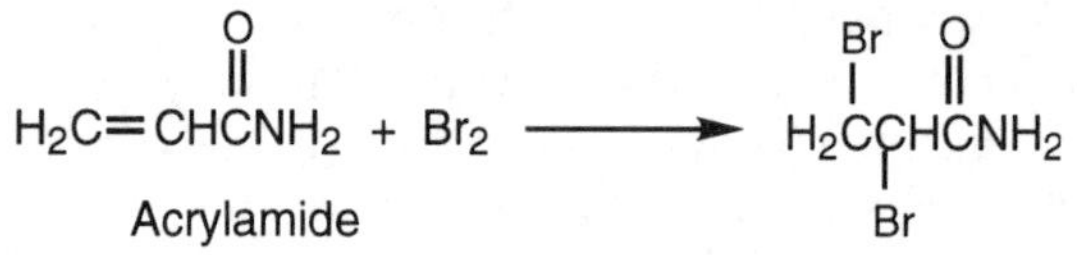

**Figure 3-23. Derivatization reaction of acrylamide.**

### 8040 Phenols by GC FID underivatized; ECD for pentafluorobenzyl-bromide derivatives

Methods 3510, 3520, 3540, 3550 and 3580 are used as appropriate for extraction followed by concentration with solvent exchange to 2-propanol. If the extraction procedure does not have pH adjustment to < 2, then acid-base clean-up (Method 3650) is performed prior to concentration. Use of either or both 2-fluorophenol and 2,4,6-tribromophenol as surrogate compounds is recommended. Calibration is external standard with a five-point calibration and daily checking. Identification of compounds detected using the FID is confirmed by the derivatization GC-ECD procedure. MDLs are listed for the FID; generally higher MDLs are obtained for the derivatization ECD.

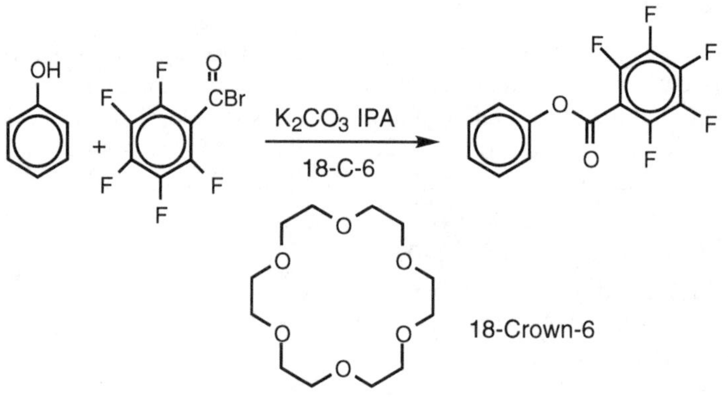

**Figure 3-24. Derivatization reaction of phenols.**

**Table 3-79. Target Analytes and MDLs for Method 8040**

| Target Analyte | MDL ug/L | Target Analyte | MDL ug/L |
|---|---|---|---|
| 2-*sec*-butyl-4,6-dinitrophenol | - | 2-Methyl-4,6-dinitrophenol | 16.0 |
| 4-Chloro-3-methylphenol | 0.36 | 2-Nitrophenol | 0.45 |
| 2-Chlorophenol | 0.31 | 4-Nitrophenol | 2.8 |
| Cresols (methyl phenols) | - | Pentachlorophenol | 7.4 |
| 2-Cyclohexyl-4,6-dinitrophenol | - | Phenol | 0.14 |
| 2,4-Dichlorophenol | 0.39 | Tetrachlorophenols | - |
| 2,6-Dichlorophenol | - | Trichlorophenols | - |
| 2,4-Dimethylphenol | 0.32 | 2,4,6-Trichlorophenol | 0.64 |
| 2,4-Dinitrophenol | 13.0 | | |

## 8061 Phthalate esters by capillary column GC-ECD

Samples (if liquid) are pH adjusted to 5 to 7 and extracted using methods 3510, 3540 or 3550. Method 3520 is not suggested due to loss of analytes by absorption on the glassware. The method includes a description of the use of $C_{18}$ extraction disks for analyte isolation. Samples can be cleaned-up using methods 3610, 3620, 3640 and/or 3660. A modification describing the use of Florisil cartridges for clean-up is included in the method. Extracts are solvent exchanged to hexane or acetonitrile prior to GC analysis. The GC is configured with dual capillary columns and ECDs and a single injector with a Y-splitter. DB-5 and DB-1701 are suggested columns. Calibration is internal standard (butyl benzoate) with a five-point curve either by RF or actual curve, with daily checking.

**Table 3-80. Target Analytes and MDLs for Method 8061**

| Target Analyte | MDL ug/L | Target Analyte | MDL ug/L |
|---|---|---|---|
| Dimethyl phthalate | 0.64 | Butyl benzyl phthalate | 0.042 |
| Diethyl phthalate | 0.25 | Bis(2-*n*-butoxyethyl) phthalate | 0.084 |
| Diisobutyl phthalate | 0.12 | Bis(2-ethylhexyl) phthalate | 0.27 |
| Di-*n*-butyl phthalate | 0.33 | Dicyclohexyl phthalate | 0.022 |
| Bis(4-methyl-2-pentyl) phthalate | 0.37 | Di-*n*-octyl phthalate | 0.049 |
| Bis(2-methoxyethyl) phthalate | 0.51 | Dinonyl phthalate | 0.022 |
| Diamyl phthalate | 0.11 | Diphenyl phthalate (surrogate) | nd |
| Bis(2-ethoxyethyl) phthalate | 0.27 | Diphenyl isophthalate (surrogate) | nd |
| Hexyl-2-ethylhexyl phthalate | 0.13 | Dibenzyl phthalate (surrogate) | nd |
| Dihexyl phthalate | 0.068 | Benzyl benzoate (Internal Standard) | nd |

## 8080 or 8081 Organochlorine pesticides and PCBs by packed column (8080) or capillary column (8081) GC-ECD or ELCD

8081 is an internal standard method using pentachloronitrobenzene as the internal standard, and decachlorobiphenyl and 2,4,5,6-tetrachloro-*m*-xylene as the surrogates. 8080 uses the same surrogates but is an external standard procedure. Each sample is spiked with surrogates, then extracted using Method 3510 or 3520 for liquids or Method 3540, 3541, or 3550 for solids. 1 : 1 hexane : acetone is recommended instead of methylene chloride : acetone in method 3550. When spiking solid samples, they must be mixed with the spike for one to two minutes then allowed to sit for one hour prior to extraction. A variety of clean-ups are suggested based on the exact set of analytes being determined. The pesticides and PCBs can be separated and determined through use of the silica gel fractionation (Method 3630). The pesticide fraction can also be selectively destroyed, leaving only the PCBs by use of the sulfuric acid/permanganate procedure (Method 3665).

DDT and endrin are particularly sensitive to the condition of the GC injector and column. Column condition must be monitored on a daily basis by injecting a mid-level calibration standard containing only DDT and endrin. DDT degrades into DDD and DDE. Endrin degrades into endrin aldehyde and endrin ketone. If breakdown for either exceeds 20%, the system must be corrected. The calculations are shown. Control charts for column condition are a good way to visually monitor the system.

$$\% \text{ DDT breakdown} = \frac{\text{Peak area [DDD + DDE]}}{\text{Peak area [DDD + DDE + DDT]}}$$

$$\% \text{ Endrin breakdown} = \frac{\text{Peak area [aldehyde + ketone]}}{\text{Peak area [endrin + ketone + aldehyde]}}$$

**Figure 3-25. Breakdown equations for monitoring column conditions.**

Calibration is five-point by either RF or calibration curve, verified on a daily basis. Analyte identification is confirmed on a second column of differing polarity from the analytical column. This is most often accomplished by having parallel columns with auto-injectors and ECDs on a dedicated instrument.

**Table 3-81. Target Analytes and MDLs for Method 8081**

| Target Analyte | MDL ug/L | Target Analyte | MDL ug/L |
|---|---|---|---|
| Aldrin | 0.034 | Endosulfan I | 0.030 |
| α-BHC | 0.035 | Endosulfan II | 0.040 |
| β-BHC | 0.023 | Endosulfan sulfate | 0.035 |
| δ-BHC | 0.024 | Endrin | 0.039 |
| γ-BHC | 0.025 | Endrin aldehyde | 0.050 |
| α-Chlordane | - | Heptachlor | 0.040 |
| γ-Chlordane | 0.037 | Heptachlor epoxide | 0.032 |
| 4,4'-DDD | 0.050 | 4,4'-Methoxychlor | 0.086 |
| 4,4'-DDE | 0.058 | Toxaphene | - |
| 4,4'-DDT | 0.081 | Aroclor 1016 | 0.054 |
| Dieldrin | 0.044 | Aroclor 1260 | 0.90 |

The identification of the multi-peaked analytes such as chlordane, toxaphene and the PCBs can be performed by a combination of pattern recognition and retention time. The different PCBs are normally identified by retention time windows such as those illustrated. Quantitation is based upon indicator peaks that are generally present in more than one PCB, mixture. Six peaks are chosen for each PCB and each peak is calibrated to represent the PCB, resulting in separate calibration files for PCBs 1016, 1221, 1232, 1242, 1248, 1254 and 1260. The chromatogram of the sample is then processed against each calibration file. If the six peaks in the calibration file all give approximately the same value, then the PCB is fairly well assured of being a single mixture instead of a mixture of mixtures. This works in most cases for PCBs because they were not subject to variation in the congener distribution in the manufacturing process (although there are two slightly different 1254 standards available[14]), not subject to substantial weathering, and the sulfuric acid/permanganate cleanup reduces interferences. This is not to say that biological modification of the PCB isomer distribution does not occur, because it does, and this quantitation method does not work as well for tissue samples. Chlordane and toxaphene are subject to weathering, and measuring the total area of the elution envelope results in better quantitation for most samples.

---

[14] Dale Chappelow, Analytical Services, Atlanta; GA.

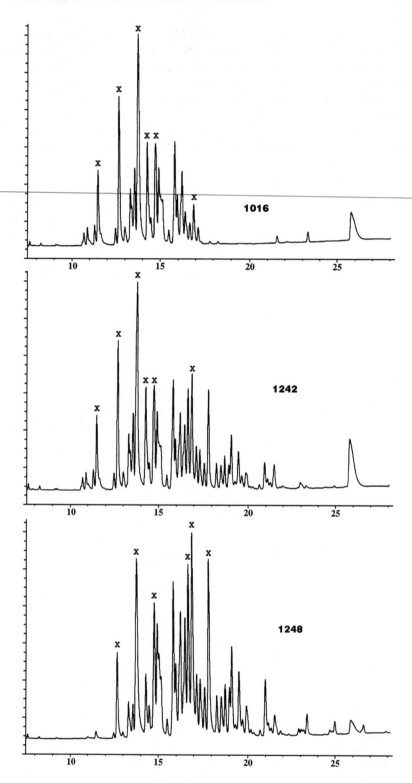

**Figure 3-26. PCBs 1016, 1242 and 1248.**

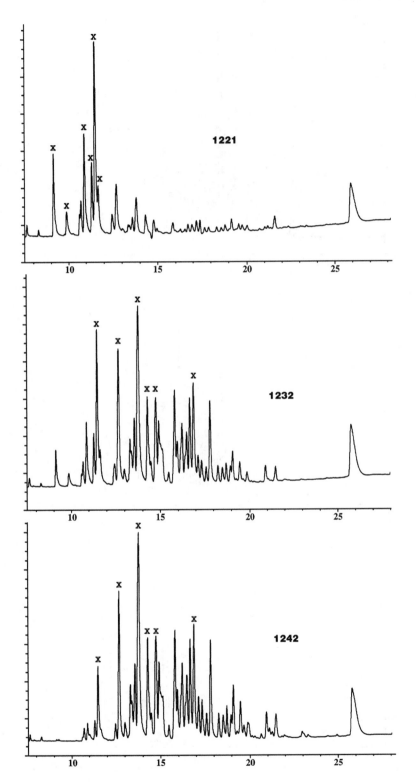

**Figure 3-27. PCBs 1221, 1232 and 1242.**

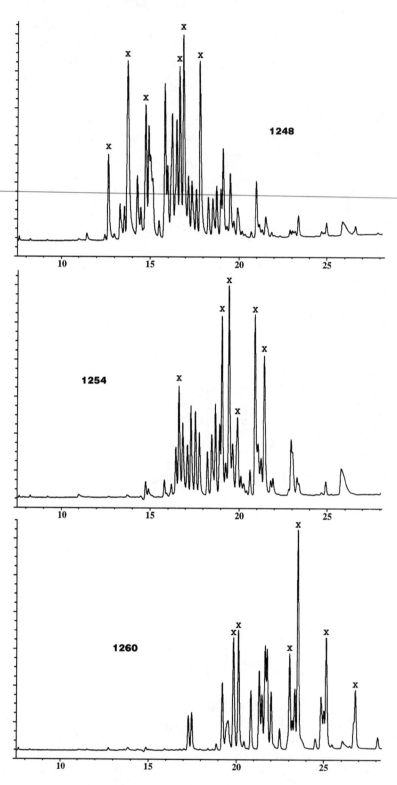

**Figure 3-28. PCBs 1248, 1254 and 1260.**

## 8120 and 8121 Chlorinated hydrocarbons by packed column (8120) or capillary column (8121) GC-ECD

Suggested surrogates are $\alpha$,2,6-Trichlorotoluene, 1,4-dichloronaphthalene and 2,3,4,5,6-pentachlorotoluene. Suggested internal standards are 2,5-dibromotoluene, 1,3,5-tribromobenzene, and $\alpha$, $\alpha'$-dibromo-$m$-xylene. Initial sample extraction is with methylene chloride, followed by drying with sodium sulfate and concentration with solvent exchange to hexane. Methods 3620, 3640, and 3660 are recommended clean-ups.

**Table 3-82. Target Analytes and MDLs for Method 8121**

| Target Analyte | MDL ug/L | Target Analyte | MDL ug/L |
|---|---|---|---|
| Benzal chloride | 2-5 | $\gamma$-BHC | 23 |
| Benzotrichloride | 6.0 | $\delta$-BHC | 20 |
| Benzyl chloride | 180 | Hexachlorocyclopentadiene | 240 |
| 2-Chloronaphthalene | 1300 | Hexachloroethane | 1.6 |
| 1,2-Dichlorobenzene | 270 | Pentachlorobenzene | 38 |
| 1,3-Dichlorobenzene | 250 | 1,2,3,4-Tetrachlorobenzene | 11 |
| 1,4-Dichlorobenzene | 890 | 1,2,4,5-Tetrachlorobenzene | 9.5 |
| Hexachlorobenzene | 5.6 | 1,2,3,5-Tetrachlorobenzene | 8.1 |
| Hexachlorobutadiene | 1.4 | 1,2,4-Trichlorobenzene | 130 |
| $\alpha$-BHC | 11 | 1,2,3-Trichlorobenzene | 39 |
| $\beta$-BHC | 31 | 1,3,5-Trichlorobenzene | 12 |

## 8150 and 8151 Chlorinated herbicides by packed column (8150) or capillary column (8151) GC (derivatization with diazomethane and ECD or Hall)

An internal standard (4,4'-dibromooctafluorobiphenyl) and surrogate (2,4-dichloro-phenylacetic acid) method that uses prior derivatization with either diazomethane (See method 515.1) or pentafluorobenzyl bromide before GC-ECD analysis. Calibration is five-point, checked daily. All detected compounds must be confirmed on a second column of different polarity. The method includes the extraction technique.

A 1 L sample is mixed with 250 g NaCl, then the pH is adjusted to >12 with 6 $N$ NaOH and allowed to sit for one hour with occasional shaking. The solution is extracted three times with $CH_2Cl_2$, which is discarded. The pH is adjusted to < 2 with $H_2SO_4$ and extracted three times with diethyl ether. The combined extracts are dried over sodium sulfate for a minimum of two hours or better, overnight. The dried extracts are concentrated without allowing the extract to go dry. Isooctane and methanol are added if the sample is to be methylated; acetone if derivatized with pentafluorobenzylbromide.

**Table 3-83. Target Analytes and MDLs for Method 8151**

| Target Analyte | MDL ug/L | Target Analyte | MDL ug/L |
|---|---|---|---|
| Acifluorfen | 0.096 | Dinoseb | 0.19 |
| Bentazon | 0.2 | 5-Hydroxydicamba | 0.04 |
| Chloramben | 0.093 | MCPP | 0.09 |
| 2,4-D | 0.2 | MCPA | 0.056 |
| Dalapon` | 1.3 | 4-Nitrophenol | 0.13 |

Continued on next page.

**Table 3-83. Target Analytes and MDLs for Method 8151,** *continued*

| Target Analyte | MDL ug/L |
|---|---|
| 2,4-DB | 0.8 |
| DCPA diacid | 0.02 |
| Dicamba | 0.081 |
| 3,5-Dichlorobenzoic acid | 0.061 |
| Dichloroprop | 0.26 |

| Target Analyte | MDL ug/L |
|---|---|
| Pentachlorophenol | 0.076 |
| Picloram | 0.14 |
| 2,4,5-T | 0.08 |
| 2,4,5-TP | 0.075 |

## 8250 Semivolatile organic compounds by GC/MS: packed column

The target analytes under 8250/8270 are grouped into phenols (acids), phthalate esters, nitrosamines, nitroaromatics and cyclic ketones, polynuclear aromatic hydrocarbons (PAHs), haloethers, organochlorine pesticides and PCBs, chlorinated hydrocarbons, organophosphorous pesticides, and miscellaneous. All the target analytes, other than the phenols, are Base Neutrals (BN). Every one of these groups has a separate method, and the organochlorine pesticides and PCBs are not normally analyzed by GC-MS, as method 8080/8081 using an ECD is much more sensitive. The MS is required to meet DFTPP tune parameters during each 12-hour shift and to pass SPCC and CCC criteria. Calibration is five-point internal standard by RF. A variety of sample extractions are applicable to this method.

**Table 3-84. SPCC for Method 8250**

| SPCC | Minimum RF |
|---|---|
| *N*-Nitroso-di-*n*-propylamine | 0.050 |
| 2,4-Dinitrophenol | 0.050 |

| SPCC | Minimum RF |
|---|---|
| Hexachlorocyclopentadiene | 0.050 |
| 4-Nitrophenol | 0.050 |

**Table 3-85. Daily MS DFTPP Tune Criteria for Method 8250**

| Mass M/z | DFTPP Relative Abundance Criteria |
|---|---|
| 51 | 30-60% of base peak |
| 68 | <2% of mass 69 |
| 70 | <2% of mass 69 |
| 127 | 40-60% of mass 198 |
| 197 | <1% of mass 198 |
| 198 | base peak 100% relative abundance |
| 199 | 5-9% of mass 198 |
| 275 | 10-30% of mass 198 |
| 365 | >1% of mass 198 |
| 441 | present and < mass 443 |
| 442 | >40% of mass 198 |
| 443 | 17-23% of mass 442 |

**Table 3-86.  Calibration Check Compounds (CCC) for Method 8250**

| | |
|---|---|
| Acenaphthene | 2,4-Dichlorophenol |
| *N*-Nitroso-di-*n*-phenylamine | Pentachlorophenol |
| 4-Chloro-3-methylphenol | Hexachlorobutadiene |
| Phenol | Benzo(a)pyrene |
| 1,4-Dichlorobenzene | 2-Nitrophenol |
| Di-*n*-octyl phthalate | 2,4,6-Trichlorophenol |

**Table 3-87.  Internal Standards and Surrogates for Method 8250**

| Internal Standards | Surrogates |
|---|---|
| 1,4-Dichlorobenzene-$d_4$ | Phenol-$d_6$ |
| Acenaphthene-$d_{10}$ | 2,4,6-Tribromophenol |
| Chrysene-$d_{12}$ | 2-Fluorobiphenyl |
| Naphthalene-$d_8$ | 2-Fluorophenol |
| Phenanthrene-$d_{10}$ | Nitrobenzene-$d_5$ |
| Perylene-$d_{12}$ | *p*-Terphenyl-$d_{14}$ |

**Table 3-88.  Matrix Spike Compounds for Method 8250**

| | |
|---|---|
| 1,2,4-Trichlorobenzene | Pyrene |
| Pentachlorophenol | 4-Chloro-3-methylphenol |
| Acenaphthene | *N*-Nitroso-di-*n*-propylamine |
| Phenol | 4-Nitrophenol |
| 2,4-Dinitrotoluene | 1,4-Dichlorobenzene |
| 2-Chlorophenol | |

**Table 3-89.  Target Analytes and MDLs for Method 8250**

| Target Analyte | MDL ug/L | Target Analyte | MDL ug/L |
|---|---|---|---|
| Acenaphthene | 1.9 | 4,6-Dinitro-2-methylphenol | 24 |
| Acenaphthalene | 3.5 | 2,4-Dinitrophenol | 42 |
| Acetophenone | - | 2,6-Dinitrotoluene | 1.9 |
| Aldrin | 1.9 | Diphenylamine | - |
| 4-Aminobiphenyl | - | 1,2-Diphenylhydrazine | - |
| Aniline | - | Di-*n*-octyl phthalate | 2.5 |
| Anthracene | 1.9 | Endosulfan I | - |
| PCBs | 30-36 | Endosulfan II | - |
| Benzidine | 44 | Endosulfan sulfate | 5.6 |
| Benzoic acid | - | Endrin | - |
| Benzo(a)anthracene | 7.8 | Endrin aldehyde | - |
| Benzo(b)fluoranthene | 4.8 | Endrin ketone | - |
| Benzo(k)fluoranthene | 2.5 | Ethyl methanesulfonate | - |

Continued on next page.

**Table 3-89. Target Analytes and MDLs for Method 8250,** *continued*

| Target Analyte | MDL ug/L | Target Analyte | MDL ug/L |
|---|---|---|---|
| Benzo(g,h,i)perylene | 4.1 | Fluoranthene | 2.2 |
| Benzo(a)pyrene | 2.5 | Fluorene | 1.9 |
| Benzyl alcohol | - | Heptachlor | 1.9 |
| α-BHC | - | Heptachlor epoxide | 2.2 |
| β-BHC | 4.2 | Hexachlorobenzene | 1.9 |
| δ-BHC | 3.1 | Hexachlorobutadiene | 0.9 |
| γ-BHC | - | Hexachlorocyclopentadiene | - |
| Bis(2-chloroethoxy)methane | 5.3 | Hexachloroethane | 1.6 |
| Bis(2-chloroethyl)ether | 5.7 | Indeno(1,2,3-cd)pyrene | 3.7 |
| Bis(2-Chloroisopropyl)ether | 5.7 | Isophorone | 2.2 |
| Bis(2-ethylhexyl)phthalate | 2.5 | Methoxychlor | - |
| 4-Bromophenyl phenyl ether | 1.9 | 3-Methylcholanthrene | - |
| Butyl benzyl phthalate | 2.5 | Methyl methanesulfonate | - |
| Chlordane | - | 2-Methylnaphthalene | - |
| 4-Chloroaniline | - | 2-Methylphenol | - |
| 1-Chloronaphthalene | - | 4-Methylphenol | - |
| 2-Chloronaphthalene | 1.9 | Naphthalene | 1.6 |
| 4-Chloro-3-methylphenol | 3.0 | 1-Naphthylamine | - |
| 2-Chlorophenol | 3.3 | 2-Naphthylamine | - |
| 4-Chlorophenyl phenyl ether | 4.2 | 2-Nitroaniline | - |
| Chrysene | 2.5 | 3-Nitroaniline | - |
| 4,4'-DDD | 2.8 | 4-Nitroaniline | - |
| 4,4'-DDT | 4.7 | Nitrobenzene | 1.9 |
| Dibenz(a,j)acridine | - | 2-Nitrophenol | 3.6 |
| Dibenz(a,h)anthracene | 2.5 | 4-Nitrophenol | 2.4 |
| Dibenzofuran | - | N-Nitroso-di-n-butylamine | - |
| Di-n-butyl phthalate | 2.5 | N-Nitrosodimethylamine | - |
| 1,2-Dichlorobenzene | 1.9 | N-Nitrosodiphenylamine | 1.9 |
| 1,3-Dichlorobenzene | 1.9 | N-Nitroso-di-n-propylamine | - |
| 1,4-Dichlorobenzene | 4.4 | N-Nitrosopiperidine | - |
| 3,3'-Dichlorobenzidine | 16.5 | Pentachlorobenzene | - |
| 2,4-Dichlorophenol | 2.7 | Pentachloronitrobenzene | - |
| 2,6-Dichlorophenol | - | Pentachlorophenol | 3.6 |
| Dieldrin | 2.5 | Phenacetin | - |
| Diethyl phthalate | 1.9 | Phenanthrene | 5.4 |
| p-Dimethylaminoazobenzene | - | Phenol | 1.5 |
| 7,12-Dimethylbenz(a)anthracene | - | 2-Picoline | - |
| a,a-Dimethylphenethylamine | - | Pronamide | - |
| 2,4-Dimethylphenol | 2.7 | Pyrene | 1.9 |
| Dimethyl phthalate | 1.6 | 1,2,4,5-Tetrachlorobenzene | - |
| 2,3,4,6-Tetrachlorophenol | - | Toxaphene | - |
| 1,2,4-Trichlorobenzene | 1.9 | 2,4,5-Trichlorophenol | - |
| 2,4,6-Trichlorophenol | 2.7 | 2,4-Dinitrotoluene | 5.7 |

## 8270 Semivolatile organic compounds by GC/MS: capillary column

The increased efficiency of the capillary column over that of the packed column allows 8270 to have a vastly increased target analyte list as compared to 8250. Otherwise these are very similar methods as far as sample preparation and clean-up, MS tuning, SPCC, CCC (one compound added), surrogates, internal standards, and matrix spikes are concerned. Calibration is still five-point internal standard by either average RF or by a regression on RF. Earlier versions of 8270 had acceptance criteria for the average RF of less than 30% RSD, however in 8270B (September 1994) the acceptance criteria dropped to 15% or less. The Estimated Quantitation Limits (EQL) listed are for groundwater. Soil/sediment EQLs run 330 to 660 times higher. A recent trend in state regulatory agencies has been to demand that groundwater be analyzed by method 8270 with MDLs appropriate for drinking water.

**Table 3-90. Daily MS DFTPP tune criteria for Method 8270**

| Mass M/z | DFTPP Relative Abundance Criteria |
|----------|-----------------------------------|
| 51 | 30-60% of base peak |
| 68 | < 2% of mass 69 |
| 70 | < 2% of mass 69 |
| 127 | 40-60% of mass 198 |
| 197 | <1% of mass 198 |
| 198 | base peak 100% relative abundance |
| 199 | 5-9% of mass 198 |
| 275 | 10-30% of mass 198 |
| 365 | >1% of mass 198 |
| 441 | present and < mass 443 |
| 442 | >40% of mass 198 |
| 443 | 17-23% of mass 442 |

**Table 3-91. SPCC for Method 8270**

| SPCC | Minimum RF | SPCC | Minimum RF |
|------|------------|------|------------|
| N-Nitroso-di-n-propylamine | 0.050 | Hexachlorocyclopentadiene | 0.050 |
| 2,4-Dinitrophenol | 0.050 | 4-Nitrophenol | 0.050 |

**Table 3-92. Calibration Check Compounds (CCC) for Method 8270**

| | |
|---|---|
| Acenaphthene | N-Nitroso-di-n-phenylamine |
| 4-Chloro-3-methylphenol | Phenol |
| 1,4-Dichlorobenzene | Di-n-octyl phthalate |
| 2,4-Dichlorophenol | Pentachlorophenol |
| Hexachlorobutadiene | Benzo(a)pyrene |
| 2-Nitrophenol | 2,4,6-Trichlorophenol |
| Fluoranthene | |

## Table 3-93. Internal standards and surrogates for Method 8270

| Internal Standards | Surrogates |
|---|---|
| 1,4-Dichlorobenzene-$d_4$ | Phenol-$d_6$ |
| Acenaphthene-$d_{10}$ | 2,4,6-Tribromophenol |
| Chrysene-$d_{12}$ | 2-Fluorobiphenyl |
| Naphthalene-$d_8$ | 2-Fluorophenol |
| Phenanthrene-$d_{10}$ | Nitrobenzene-$d_5$ |
| Perylene-$d_{12}$ | $p$-Terphenyl-$d_{14}$ |

## Table 3-94. Matrix spike compounds for Method 8270

| | |
|---|---|
| 1,2,4-Trichlorobenzene | Pyrene |
| Pentachlorophenol | 4-Chloro-3-methylphenol |
| Acenaphthene | $N$-Nitroso-di-$n$-propylamine |
| Phenol | 4-Nitrophenol |
| 2,4-Dinitrotoluene | 1,4-Dichlorobenzene |
| 2-Chlorophenol | |

## Table 3-95. Target Analytes and EQLs for Method 8270

| Target Analyte | EQL ug/L | Target Analyte | EQL ug/L |
|---|---|---|---|
| Acenaphthene | 10 | Hexachlorobenzene | 10 |
| Acenaphthalene | 10 | Hexachlorobutadiene | 10 |
| Acetophenone | 10 | Hexachlorocyclopentadiene | 10 |
| 2-Acetylaminofluorene | 20 | Hexachloroethane | 10 |
| 1-Acetyl-2-thiourea | 1000 | Hexachlorophene | 50 |
| 2-Aminoanthraquinone | 20 | Hexachloropropene | 10 |
| Aminoazobenzene | 10 | Hexamethyl phosphoramide | 20 |
| 4-Aminobiphenyl | 20 | Hydroquinone | - |
| Anilazine | 100 | Indeno(1,2,3-cd)pyrene | 10 |
| $o$-Anisidine | 10 | Isodrin | 20 |
| Anthracene | 10 | Isophorone | 10 |
| Aramite | 20 | Isosafrole | 10 |
| Azinphos-methyl | 100 | Kepone | 20 |
| Barban | 200 | Leptophos | 10 |
| Benz(a)anthracene | 10 | Malathion | 50 |
| Benzo(b)fluoranthene | 10 | Maleic anhydride | - |
| Benzo(k)fluoranthene | 10 | Mestranol | 20 |
| Benzoic acid | 50 | Methapyrilene | 100 |
| Benzo(g,h,i)perylene | 10 | Methoxychlor | 10 |
| Benzo(a)pyrene | 10 | 3-Methylcholanthrene | 10 |
| $p$-Benzoquinone | 10 | 4,4'-Methylenebis(2-chloroaniline) | - |
| Benzyl alcohol | 20 | Methyl methanesulfonate | 10 |
| Bis(2-chloroethoxy)methane | 10 | 2-Methylnaphthalene | 10 |
| Bis(2-chloroethyl)ether | 10 | Methyl parathion | 10 |
| Bis(2-chloroisopropyl)ether | 10 | 2-Methylphenol | 10 |
| 4-Bromophenyl phenyl ether | 10 | 3-Methylphenol | 10 |
| Bromoxynil | 10 | 4-Methylphenol | 10 |

Continued on next page.

## Table 3-95.  Target Analytes and EQLs for Method 8270, *continued*

| Target Analyte | EQL ug/L | Target Analyte | EQL ug/L |
|---|---|---|---|
| Butyl benzyl phthalate | 10 | Mevinphos | 10 |
| Captafol | 20 | Mexacarbate | 20 |
| Captan | 50 | Mirex | 10 |
| Carbaryl | 10 | Monocrotophos | 40 |
| Carbofuran | 10 | Naled | 20 |
| Carbophenothion | 10 | Naphthalene | 10 |
| Chlorfenvinphos | 20 | 1,4-Naphthoquinone | 10 |
| 4-Chloroaniline | 20 | 1-Naphthylamine | 10 |
| Chlorobenzilate | 10 | 2-Naphthylamine | 10 |
| 5-Chloro-2-methylaniline | 10 | Nicotine | 20 |
| 4-Chloro-3-methylphenol | 20 | 5-Nitroacenaphthene | 10 |
| 3-(Chloromethyl)pyridine | 100 | 2-Nitroaniline | 50 |
| 2-Chloronaphthalene | 10 | 3-Nitroaniline | 50 |
| 2-Chlorophenol | 10 | 4-Nitroaniline | 20 |
| 4-Chlorophenyl phenyl ether | 10 | 5-Nitro-*o*-anisidine | 10 |
| Chrysene | 10 | Nitrobenzene | 10 |
| Coumaphos | 40 | 4-Nitrobiphenyl | 10 |
| *p*-Cresidine | 10 | Nitrofen | 20 |
| Crotoxyphos | 20 | 2-Nitrophenol | 10 |
| 2-Cyclohexyl-4,6-dinitrophenol | 100 | 4-Nitrophenol | 50 |
| Demeton-O | 10 | 5-Nitro-*o*-toluidine | 10 |
| Demeton-S | 10 | 4-Nitroquinoline-1-oxide | 40 |
| Diallate (*cis* or *trans*) | 10 | *N*-Nitrosodibutylamine | 10 |
| Diallate (*trans* or *cis*) | 10 | *N*-Nitrosodiethylamine | 20 |
| 2,4-Diaminotoluene | 20 | *N*-Nitrosodiphenylamine | 10 |
| Dibenz(a,j)acridine | 10 | *N*-Nitroso-di-*n*-propylamine | 10 |
| Dibenz(a,h)anthracene | 10 | *N*-Nitrosopiperidine | 20 |
| Dibenzofuran | 10 | *N*-Nitrosopyrrolidine | 40 |
| Dibenzo(a,e)pyrene | 10 | Octamethyl pyrophosphoramide | 200 |
| Di-*n*-butyl phthalate | 10 | 4,4'-Oxydianiline | 20 |
| Dichlone | - | Parathion | 10 |
| 1,2-Dichlorobenzene | 10 | Pentachlorobenzene | 10 |
| 1,3-Dichlorobenzene | 10 | Pentachloronitrobenzene | 20 |
| 1,4-Dichlorobenzene | 10 | Pentachlorophenol | 50 |
| 3,3'-Dichlorobenzidine | 20 | Phenacetin | 20 |
| 2,4-Dichlorophenol | 10 | Phenanthrene | 10 |
| 2,6-Dichlorophenol | 10 | Phenobarbital | 10 |
| Dichlorovos | 10 | Phenol | 10 |
| Dicrotophos | 10 | 1,4-Phenylenediamine | 10 |
| Diethyl phthalate | 10 | Phorate | 10 |
| Diethylstilbestrol | 20 | Phosalone | 100 |
| Diethyl sulfate | 100 | Phosmet | 40 |
| Dimethoate | 20 | Phosphamidon | 100 |
| 3,3'-Dimethoxybenzidine | 100 | Phthalic anhydride | 100 |
| Dimethylaminoazobenzene | 10 | 2-Picoline | - |
| 7,12-Dimethylbenz(a)anthracene | 10 | Piperonyl sulfoxide | 100 |
| 3,3'-Dimethylbenzidine | 10 | Pronamide | 10 |
| *a,a*-Dimethylphenethylamine | - | Propylthiouracil | 100 |
| 2,4-Dimethylphenol | 10 | Pyrene | 10 |

Continued on next page.

**Table 3-95.  Target Analytes and EQLs for Method 8270,** *continued*

| Target Analyte | EQL ug/L | Target Analyte | EQL ug/L |
|---|---|---|---|
| Dimethyl phthalate | 10 | Pyridine | - |
| 1,2-Dinitrobenzene | 40 | Resorcinol | 100 |
| 1,3-Dinitrobenzene | 20 | Safrole | 10 |
| 1,4-Dinitrobenzene | 40 | Strychnine | 40 |
| 4,6-Dinitro-2-methylphenol | 50 | Sulfallate | 10 |
| 2,4-Dinitrophenol | 50 | Terbufos | 20 |
| 2,4-Dinitrotoluene | 10 | 1,2,4,5-Tetrachlorobenzene | 10 |
| 2,6-Dinitrotoluene | 10 | 2,3,4,6-Tetrachlorophenol | 10 |
| Dinocap | 100 | Tetrachlorvinphos | 20 |
| Dinoseb | 20 | Tetraethyl pyrophosphate | 40 |
| 5,5-Diphenylhydantoin | 20 | Thionazine | 20 |
| Di-*n*-octyl phthalate | 10 | Thiophenol | 20 |
| Disulfoton | 10 | Toluene diisocyanate | 100 |
| EPN | 10 | *o*-Toluidine | 10 |
| Ethion | 10 | 1,2,4-Trichlorobenzene | 10 |
| Ethyl carbamate | 50 | 2,4,5-Trichlorophenol | 10 |
| Bis(2-ethylhexyl)phthalate | 10 | 2,4,6-Trichlorophenol | 10 |
| Ethyl methanesulfonate | 20 | Trifluralin | 10 |
| Famphur | 20 | 2,4,5-Trimethylaniline | 10 |
| Fensulfothion | 40 | Trimethylphosphate | 10 |
| Fenthion | 10 | 1,3,5-Trinitrobenzene | 10 |
| Fluchloralin | 20 | Tris(2,3-dibromopropyl)phosphate | 200 |
| Fluoranthene | 10 | Tri-*p*-tolyl phosphate | 10 |
| Fluorene | 10 | O,O,O-Triethylphosphorothioate | - |

## 8275  Semivolatile organic compounds by thermal chromatography/MS

This is a fast screening method for solid or waste samples using a pyrolysis cell temperature-programmed to 260 °C for sample introduction.  Direct interface to an FID is used to obtain a rough idea of the amount of analyte in the sample, then the test is repeated with a capillary column and MS for quantitation and identification.  Calibration is five-point internal standard with 1,4-dichlorobenzene-$d_4$, naphthalene-$d_8$, acenaphthene-$d_{10}$, phenanthrene-$d_{10}$, chrysene-$d_{12}$, and perylene-$d_{12}$.  Sample size is limited to about 0.10 g, which implies that sample representativeness may be a problem and multiple assays of a solid may be warranted.

**Table 3-96.  Target Analytes and % Recovery for Method 8275**

| Target Analyte | % Recovery | Target Analyte | % Recovery |
|---|---|---|---|
| 2-Chlorophenol | 18 | Hexachlorobenzene | 71 |
| 4-Methylphenol | 31 | Dibenzothiophene | 35 |
| 2,4-Dichlorophenol | 23 | Phenanthrene | 24 |
| Naphthalene | 87 | Carbazole | 7 |
| 4-Chloro-3-methylphenol | 10 | Aldrin | 12 |
| 1-Chloronaphthalene | 90 | Pyrene | 15 |
| 2,4-Dinitrotoluene | 9 | Benzo(k)fluoranthene | 8 |
| Fluorene | 18 | Benzo(a)pyrene | 8 |
| Diphenylamine | 6 | | |

## 8290  Polychlorinated dibenzodioxins (PCDDs) and polychlorinated dibenzofurans (PCDFs) by high-resolution gas chromatography/ high-resolution mass spectrometry (HRGC/HRMS)

This method requires use of a high resolution magnetic sector MS for the analysis. The sample is spiked with the labeled internal standards in Table 3-97, then extracted and cleaned-up. The extraction is with toluene in a Soxhlet-Dean Starke for solids and methylene chloride separatory funnel for liquids. Clean-up consists of acid-base washing followed by Biosil, alumina and a mixed Celite 545/AX-21 carbon column fractionations. Recovery standards ($^{13}C_{12}$-1,2,3,4-TCDD and $^{13}C_{12}$-1,2,3,7,8,9-HxCDD) are added immediately prior to GC/MS analysis.

**Table 3-97.  Internal standards of Method 8290**

| $^{13}C_{12}$-2,3,7,8-TCDD | $^{13}C_{12}$-2,3,7,8-TCDF | $^{13}C_{12}$-1,2,3,7,8-PeCDD |
|---|---|---|
| $^{13}C_{12}$-1,2,3,7,8-PeCDF | $^{13}C_{12}$-1,2,3,6,7,8-HxCDD | $^{13}C_{12}$-1,2,3,4,7,8-HxCDF |
| $^{13}C_{12}$-1,2,3,4,6,7,8-HpCDD | $^{13}C_{12}$-1,2,3,4,6,7,8-HpCDF | $^{13}C_{12}$-OCDD |

Surrogate and alternate standards (below) can be added to the sample extract prior to any clean-up and fractionation. Good recovery of these compounds indicates that there was no problem with the sample processing and that any poor internal standard recoveries are strictly due to matrix effects of the original sample. Poor recovery of surrogate/ alternate standards indicates problems with the extraction/clean-up.

**Table 3-98.  Surrogate and alternate standards of Method 8290**

| $^{37}Cl_4$-2,3,7,8-TCDD | $^{13}C_{12}$-2,3,4,7,8-PeCDF | $^{13}C_{12}$-1,2,3,4,7,8-HxCDD |
|---|---|---|
| $^{13}C_{12}$-1,2,3,4,7,8-HxCDF | $^{13}C_{12}$-1,2,3,4,7,8,9-HpCDF | $^{13}C_{12}$-1,2,3,7,8,9-HxCDF |
| $^{13}C_{12}$-2,3,4,6,7,8-HxCDF | | |

The guidelines for acceptable internal, surrogate and alternate[15] standard recoveries is 40-135% for the tetra- through hexa-substituted compounds and 25-135% for the higher hepta- and octa- homologues. Mass tuning of the mass spectrometer is achieved by leak of perfluoro kerosene into the ionization chamber during analysis of each sample. Mass lock is achieved at 354.9792 for $C_9F_{13}$, 430.9728 for $C_9F_{17}$ and 442.9278 for $C_{10}F_{17}$.

Compound identification for the dioxins is based on analysis on the DB-5 column with exact retention time within 0.005 units from the calibration if a labeled analog is used as a standard and the simultaneous detection of the two most abundant ions in the molecular ion area in the correct ratio. Furans are not adequately resolved on DB-5 and if detected are re-analyzed on a DB-225 column for identification and quantitation.

---

[15]  Alternate and surrogate standards are used for the same purpose in analysis of water and solid samples. The distinction lies in analysis of PUF samples of air. These surrogate standards are added to the PUF prior to air sampling. Internal standards are added to the PUF prior to extraction and alternate standards are added to the sample extract prior to clean-up and fractionation.

**Table 3-99. Target analytes and minimum calibration levels of Method 8290**

| Target analytes | Water ppq | Solids ppt |
|---|---|---|
| 2,3,7,8-TCDD | 10 | 1 |
| 1,2,3,7,8-PeCDD | 50 | 5 |
| 1,2,3,4,7,8-HxCDD | 50 | 5 |
| 1,2,3,6,7,8-HxCDD | 50 | 5 |
| 1,2,3,7,8,9-HxCDD | 50 | 5 |
| 1,2,3,4,7,8,9-HpCDD | 50 | 5 |
| 1,2,3,4,6,7,8,9-OCDD | 100 | 10 |
| 2,3,7,8-TCDF | 10 | 1 |
| 1,2,3,7,8-PeCDF | 50 | 5 |
| 2,3,4,7,8-PeCDF | 50 | 5 |
| 1,2,3,4,7,8-HxCDF | 50 | 5 |
| 1,2,3,6,7,8-HxCDF | 50 | 5 |
| 2,3,4,6,7,8-HxCDF | 50 | 5 |
| 1,2,3,7,8,9-HxCDF | 50 | 5 |
| 1,2,3,4,6,7,8-HpCDF | 50 | 5 |
| 1,2,3,4,7,8,9-HpCDF | 50 | 5 |
| 1,2,3,4,6,7,8,9-OCDF | 100 | 10 |
| Total TCDD | 10 | 1 |
| Total PeCDD | 50 | 5 |
| Total HxCDD | 50 | 5 |
| Total HpCDD | 50 | 5 |
| Total TCDF | 10 | 1 |
| Total PeCDF | 50 | 5 |
| Total HxCDF | 50 | 5 |
| Total HpCDF | 50 | 5 |

The minimum calibration levels are listed in Table 3-99. Detection limits are variable for each sample depending on the complexity of the background, the initial size of the sample, the solids content of the sample and the judgement of the operator. Many times they are reported as less than the lowest calibration standard. Partly due to the very complex nature of the mixture of dioxins present in a sample and co-occuring PCBs, many interferences are frequently present in the chromatogram from overlapping signals with the analyte peaks. Quantitation of the target analyte is often reported as the Estimated Maximum Possible Concentration (EMPC) when interferences are suspected.

The distinction between surrogate and alternate standards is noticeable when air samples are analyzed. Alternate standards are added to the air sampler media prior to any sampling, while surrogate standards are added during the normal initiation of the clean-up process.

**Table 3-100. Acceptance ranges for molecular ion ratios**

| Number of Cl atoms | Ion type | Acceptance range |
|---|---|---|
| 4 | M/M+2 | 0.65-0.89 |
| 5 | M+2/M+4 | 1.32-1.78 |
| 6 | M+2/M+4 | 1.05-1.43 |

Continued on next page.

**Table 3-100. Acceptance ranges for molecular ion ratios,** *continued*

| Number of Cl atoms | Ion type | Acceptance range |
|---|---|---|
| 6[16] | M/M+2 | 0.43-0.59 |
| 7 | M+2/M+4 | 0.88-1.20 |
| 7[17] | M/M+2 | 0.37-0.51 |
| 8 | M+2/M+4 | 0.76-1.02 |

Methods 513 and 1613 are similar to 8290 in requiring use of a HRMS. Although the CLP-SOW for dioxins does not specify a HRMS, the SOW is almost identical to method 8290. Other dioxin methods are based upon GC-MS using a low resolution mass spectrometer. The mass spectrometer is tuned to DFTPP standards as in 8270 and 625. These methods include 8280, 40 CFR 261 Appendix X, 40 CFR 60 Appendix A Method 23, method 613, and in the BIF methods manual (40 CFR 266 Appendix IX) method 3.4.

## 8310 Polynuclear aromatic hydrocarbons (PAH) by HPLC with UV and fluorescence detection

This is very similar to method 610 (same target analytes and HPLC instrument and operation) with the additional requirements for five-point external standard calibration and decafluorobiphenyl as surrogate. Sample extraction is by Methods 3510 or 3520 at pH 7 for liquids and either 3540 or 3550 for solids. Clean-up by silica gel column (Method 3630) is an option.

## 8315 Formaldehyde and acetaldehyde by HPLC UV detection

Formaldehyde and/or acetaldehyde are isolated by toxic characteristic leaching procedure or TCLP extraction (Method 1311) from solids. The leachate or aqueous sample is buffered to pH $5.0 \pm 0.5$ with acetate buffer and derivatized with 2,4-dinitrophenylhydrazine. The hydrazone derivative is isolated by either solid phase extraction using a $C_{18}$ cartridge or $CH_2Cl_2$ liquid-liquid extraction. Analysis is by isocratic HPLC (3:1 methanol : water) on a reversed-phase column with UV detection at 360 nm. Calibration is external standard with a minimum five-point curve. MDL is 7.2 ug/L for formaldehyde and 171 for acetaldehyde. Confirmation of identity can be by GC-MS or use of another analytical column of different polarity. (The author has performed many of these analyses for aldehydes and found that the hydrazones are GC stable. Preparation of the hydrazone from any of a variety of aldehydes leads to a suitable internal standard; pivalaldehyde has been used with success.)

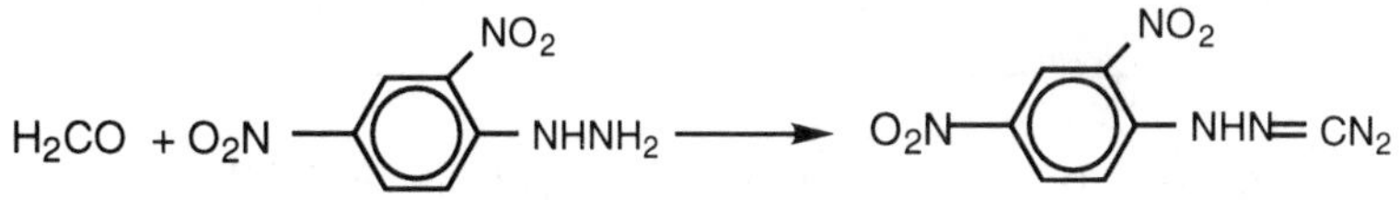

**Figure 3-29. Reaction of formaldehyde with 2,4-DNP.**

---

[16] $^{13}C_{12}$-HxCDF only

[17] $^{13}C_{12}$-HpCDF only

## 8316  Acrylamide, acrylonitrile, and acrolein by HPLC

This is a direct injection technique into the HPLC with a $C_{18}$ reversed-phase column and water-mobile phase with UV detection at 195 nm.  Calibration is five-point external standard.  MDLs are 10 ug/L for acrylamide, 20 for acrylonitrile and 30 for acrolein.

## 8318  *N*-Methyl carbamates by HPLC

Aqueous samples are extracted with $CH_2Cl_2$ and solid samples with acetonitrile.  The extract is then concentrated with solvent exchange to ethylene glycol.  The concentrated extracts are diluted with methanol followed by clean-up with a $C_{18}$ reversed-phase cartridge.  Calibration is five-point external standard.  The HPLC is equipped with a post-column derivatization unit with excitation at 340 nm and emission detection at >418 nm.  The separation is performed on a reversed-phased column with a binary non-linear gradient formed from acidified water and 1:1 methanol : acetonitrile.

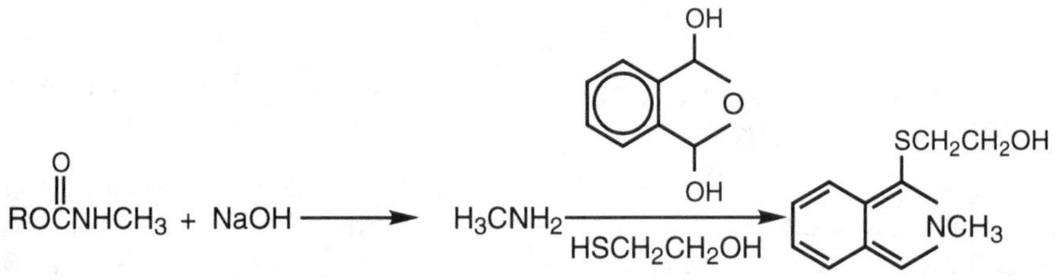

**Figure 3-30.  Post-column derivatization/fluorescence detection of**
***N*-methyl carbamates.**

Thiofluor, the reagent combination used by Pickering Labs replaces the mercaptoethanol with $(CH_3)_2NCH_2CH_2SH$ HCl.

**Table 3-101.  Target Analytes and MDLs for Method 8318**

| Target Analyte | MDL aqueous ug/L | MDL soil ug/Kg |
|---|---|---|
| Aldicarb sulfone | 1.9 | 44 |
| Methomyl | 1.7 | 12 |
| 3-Hydroxycarbofuran | 2.6 | 10 |
| Dioxacarb | 2.2 | >50 |
| Aldicarb | 9.4 | 12 |
| Propoxur | 2.4 | 17 |
| Carbofuran | 2.0 | 22 |
| Carbaryl | 1.7 | 31 |
| Methiocarb | 3.1 | 32 |
| Promecarb | 2.5 | 17 |

## 8321  Non-volatile solvent extractable compounds by HPLC/Thermospray MS

Samples are extracted using 3510 or 3520 for aqueous matrices and 3540 or 3550 for solids.  The calibration is five-point external standard.  Surrogates are suggested, but none are listed.  MS tuning is with polyethylene glycol (PEG-400, 600 or 800).

**Table 3-102. MS Tune Criteria Using PEG 400 for Method 8321**

| Calibration Mass PEG 400 | % Relative Abundance |
|---|---|
| 18.0 | 32.3 |
| 35.06 | 13.5 |
| 36.04 | 40.5 |
| 50.06 | 94.6 |
| 77.04 | 27.0 |
| 168.12 | 5.5 |
| 212.14 | 10.3 |
| 256.17 | 17.6 |
| 300.20 | 27.0 |
| 344.22 | 45.9 |
| 388.25 | 64.9 |
| 432.28 | 100.0 |
| 476.30 | 94.6 |
| 520.33 | 81.1 |
| 564.35 | 67.6 |
| 608.38 | 32.4 |
| 652.41 | 16.2 |
| 653.41 | 4.1 |
| 696.43 | 8.1 |
| 697.44 | 2.7 |

Compound classes that have been analyzed by HPLC-MS include disperse azo dyes, methine dyes, arylmethane dyes, coumarin dyes, anthraquinone dyes, xanthene dyes, flame retardants, alkaloids, aromatic ureas, amides, amino acids, organophosphorous compounds, and chlorinated phenoxyacid herbicides.

# III. MISCELLANEOUS ORGANIC INFORMATION

## A. Mass Spectrometer Tuning

EPA mass analyzer tuning standards 4-bromofluorobenzene (BFB) and decafluorotriphenylphosphine (DFTPP) are required to be met on every 12-hour working shift. Quadrupole electron impact mass analyzers (Hewlett-Packard 5970 and 5971), which autotune results from perfluorotributylamine (PFTBA, FC-43) are generally insufficient to meet the tuning requirements. Recent tuning software updates allow user-defined target abundance ranges for PFTBA. The PFTBA target ranges[18] are listed in Table 3-103 with peak widths at half height 0.48 ± 0.02 for hitting DFTPP.

**Table 3-103. PFTBA Target Tune for DFTPP**

| Mass M/z | Target Relative Abundance |
|---|---|
| 50 | 1.5 ± 0.5 |
| 69 | 100 |

Continued on next page.

---

[18] Neal, Barney. Hewlett-Packard Analytical Education Center. Atlanta, GA. 1992.

**Table 3-103. PFTBA Target Tune for DFTPP,** *continued*

| Mass M/z | Target Relative Abundance |
|----------|---------------------------|
| 131 | 40 ± 15 |
| 219 | 40 ±15 |
| 414 | 1.5 ± 0.5 |
| 502 | 1.0 ± 0.5 |

**Table 3-104. Ideal Results for PFTBA with Peak Widths of 0.50**

| Mass M/z | Ideal Relative Abundance |
|----------|--------------------------|
| 50 | 1-2 |
| 69 | 100 |
| 131 | 35 |
| 219 | 30 |
| 414 | 1-2 |
| 502 | 0.8 |

General guidelines from the PFTBA autotune results for other models of mass analyzers are:

BFB - mass 69 (100%), 131 (25%), 219 (20%)

DFTPP - mass 131 = mass 219

## B. Freons

Freon nomenclature[19]

E     D     X     Y     Z     iiiii

E   indicates the molecule is an ether

D   indicates the number of multiple bonds in the molecule (a 2 in this position can indicate either a triple bond or two double bonds)

X   is one less than the number of carbons in the molecule

Y   is one more than the number of hydrogens in the molecule

Z   is the number of fluorines in the molecule

iiiii   represents isomeric structures when small case letters; when capital B followed by digits, i represents the number of bromines in the molecule

Frequently the code numbers will be prefixed with an "R." This stands for "refrigerant." A prefix of "C" indicates the molecule is cyclic.

Add "90" to the code number. That gives as the first digit the number of carbons, the second digit, the number of hydrogens and the last digit the number of fluorines[20].

---

19   Number Designation and Safety Classification of Refrigerants, ASHRAE standard, ANSI/ASHRAE 34-1992, American Society of Heating, Refrigerating, and Air-Conditioning Engineers, 1791 Tullie Circle, Atlanta, GA 30329, 1992.

20   Bruno, T.J. *Handbook for the Analysis and Identification of Alternate Refrigerants.* CRC Press, Boca Raton, FL. ISBN 0-8493-3926-X. 1995.

## Table 3-105. Freons

| Freon ID | + 90 | Formula | CAS | Structure |
|----------|------|---------|-----|-----------|
| 11 | 101 | $CFCl_3$ | 75-69-4 | $CFCl_3$ |
| 12 | 102 | $CF_2Cl_2$ | 75-71-8 | $CF_2Cl_2$ |
| 12B2 | 102 | $CF_2Br_2$ | 75-61-6 | $CF_2Br_2$ |
| 13 | 103 | $CF_3Cl$ | 75-72-9 | $CF_3Cl$ |
| 13B1 | 103 | $CF_3Br$ | – | $CF_3Br$ |
| 13I1 | 103 | $CF_3I$ | – | $CF_3I$ |
| 14 | 104 | $CF_4$ | 75-73-0 | $CF_4$ |
| 21 | 111 | $CHFCl_2$ | 75-43-4 | $CHFCl_2$ |
| 22 | 112 | $CHF_2Cl$ | 75-45-6 | $CHF_2Cl$ |
| 22B1 | 112 | $CHF_2Br$ | – | $CHF_2Br$ |
| 23 | 113 | $CHF_3$ | 75-46-7 | $CHF_3$ |
| 31 | 121 | $CH_2ClF$ | – | $CH_2ClF$ |
| 31B1 | 121 | $CH_2BrF$ | – | $CH_2BrF$ |
| 32 | 122 | $CH_2F_2$ | 75-10-5 | $CH_2F_2$ |
| 40 | 130 | $ClCH_3$ | 74-87-3 | $ClCH_3$ |
| 41 | 131 | $CH_3F$ | 593-53-3 | $CH_3F$ |
| 112 | 202 | $C_2Cl_4F_2$ | 76-12-0 | $CCl_2FCCl_2F$ |
| 112a | 202 | $C_2Cl_4F_2$ | 76-11-9 | $CClF_2CCl_4$ |
| 113 | 203 | $C_2F_3Cl_3$ | 76-13-1 | $CF_2ClCFCl_2$ |
| 113a | 203 | $C_2F_3Cl_3$ | 354-58-5 | $CCl_3CF_3$ |
| 114 | 204 | $C_2F_4Cl_2$ | 76-14-2 | $CF_2ClCF_2Cl$ |
| 114a | 204 | $C_2F_4Cl_2$ | 374-07-2 | $CCl_2FCF_3$ |
| 115 | 205 | $C_2ClF_5$ | 76-15-3 | $CClF_2CF_3$ |
| 115I1 | 205 | $C_2F_5I$ | – | $C_2F_5I$ |
| 116 | 206 | $C_2F_6$ | 76-16-4 | $CF_3CF_3$ |
| 121 | 211 | $C_2Cl_4FH$ | 354-14-3 | $CCl_2FCCl_2H$ |
| 122 | 212 | $C_2Cl_3F_2H$ | 354-21-2 | $CClF_2CCl_2H$ |
| 123 | 213 | $C_2HF_3Cl_2$ | 306-83-2 | $CF_3CHCl_2$ |
| 123a | 213 | $C_2HF_3Cl_2$ | 354-23-4 | $CClF_2CClFH$ |
| 124 | 214 | $C_2HF_4Cl$ | 2837-89-0 | $CF_3CHFCl$ |
| 124a | 214 | $C_2HF_4Cl$ | – | $CF_2ClCHF_2$ |
| 125 | 215 | $C_2HF_5$ | 354-33-6 | $CF_3CHF_2$ |
| 131 | 221 | $C_2Cl_3FH_2$ | – | $CCl_2HCClFH$ |
| 131a | 221 | $C_2Cl_3FH_2$ | 811-95-0 | $CCl_2FCClH_2$ |
| 132b | 222 | $C_2Cl_2F_2H_2$ | 1649-08-7 | $CClF_2CClH_2$ |
| 133a | 223 | $C_2ClF_3H_2$ | 75-88-7 | $CF_3CClH_2$ |
| 134 | 224 | $C_2H_2F_4$ | 359-35-3 | $CF_2HCF_2H$ |
| 134a | 224 | $C_2H_2F_4$ | 811-97-2 | $CF_3CH_2F$ |
| 141 | 231 | $C_2Cl_2FH_3$ | 25167-88-8 | $CClFHCClH_2$ |
| 141b | 231 | $C_2H_3FCl_2$ | 1717-00-6 | $CFCl_2CH_3$ |
| 142b | 232 | $C_2H_3F_2Cl$ | 75-68-3 | $CClF_2CH_3$ |
| 143 | 233 | $C_2H_3F_3$ | 430-66-0 | $CF_2HCFH_2$ |
| 143a | 233 | $C_2H_3F_3$ | 420-46-2 | $CF_3CH_3$ |
| 150 | 240 | $C_2H_4Cl_2$ | 107-06-2 | $CClH_2CClH_2$ |
| 152 | 242 | $C_2H_4F_2$ | 624-72-6 | $CFH_2CFH_2$ |
| 152a | 242 | $C_2H_4F_2$ | 75-37-6 | $CH_3CHF_2$ |
| 160 | 250 | $C_2H_5Cl$ | 75-00-3 | $CH_3CH_2Cl$ |
| 161 | 251 | $C_2H_5F$ | 353-36-6 | $CFH_2CH_3$ |
| 113B2ab | 203 | $C_2Br_2ClF_3$ | 354-51-8 | $CBrF_2CBrClF$ |

Continued on next page.

## Table 3-105. Freons, *continued*

| Freon ID | + 90 | Formula | CAS | Structure |
|---|---|---|---|---|
| 113B2 | 203 | $C_2Br_2ClF_3$ | 754-17-6 | $CBr_2ClCF_3$ |
| 114B1 | 204 | $C_2BrClF_4$ | 354-53-0 | $CBrF_2CClF_2$ |
| 114B2 | 204 | $C_2BrClF_4$ | 25497-30-7 | $CBrF_2CBrF_2$ |
| 123B1 | 213 | $C_2HBrClF_3$ | 151-67-7 | $CF_3CBrClH$ |
| 123B2 | 213 | $C_2HBr_2F_3$ | 354-04-1 | $CBrF_2CBrFH$ |
| 123aB1a | 213 | $C_2HBrClF_3$ | 354-06-3 | $CBrF_2CClFH$ |
| 132bB2 | 222 | $C_2H_2Br_2F_2$ | 75-82-1 | $CBrF_2CBrH_2$ |
| 133aB1 | 223 | $C_2H_2BrF_3$ | 421-06-7 | $CBrH_2CF_3$ |
| 142B1 | 232 | $C_2H_3BrF_2$ | 359-07-9 | $CF_2HCBrH_2$ |
| 151B1 | 241 | $C_2H_4BrF$ | 762-49-2 | $CBrH_2CFH_2$ |
| 160B1 | 250 | $C_2H_5Br$ | 74-96-4 | $CH_3CH_2Br$ |
| 1110 | 1200 | $C_2Cl_4$ | 127-18-4 | $Cl_2C=CCl_2$ |
| 1111 | 1201 | $C_2Cl_3F$ | 359-29-5 | $Cl_2C=CClF$ |
| 1112 | 1202 | $C_2Cl_2F_2$ | 27156-03-2 | $ClFC=CClF$ |
| 1112a | 1202 | $C_2Cl_2F_2$ | 79-35-6 | $Cl_2C=CF_2$ |
| 1112c | 1202 | $C_2Cl_2F_2$ | – | *cis* $ClFC=CFCl$ |
| 1112t | 1202 | $C_2Cl_2F_2$ | – | *trans* $ClFC=CFCl$ |
| 1113 | 1203 | $C_2ClF_3$ | 79-38-9 | $ClFC=CF_2$ |
| 1114 | 1204 | $C_2F_4$ | 116-14-3 | $F_2C=CF_2$ |
| 1120 | 1210 | $C_2HCl_3$ | 79-01-6 | $Cl_2C=CClH$ |
| 1121c | 1211 | $C_2HCl_2F$ | 430-58-0 | *cis* $ClFC=CClH$ |
| 1121t | 1211 | $C_2HCl_2F$ | – | *trans* $ClFC=CClH$ |
| 1122 | 1212 | $C_2HClF_2$ | 359-10-4 | $F_2C=CClH$ |
| 1123 | 1213 | $C_2HF_3$ | 359-11-5 | $F_2C=CFH$ |
| 1130 | 1220 | $C_2H_2Cl_2$ | 540-59-0 | $ClHC=CClH$ |
| 1130a | 1220 | $C_2H_2Cl_2$ | 75-35-4 | $Cl_2C=CH_2$ |
| 1131a | 1221 | $C_2H_2ClF$ | 2317-91-1 | $ClFC=CH_2$ |
| 1132a | 1222 | $C_2H_2F_2$ | 75-38-7 | $F_2C=CH_2$ |
| 1141 | 1231 | $C_2H_3F$ | 75-02-5 | $FHC=CH_2$ |
| 1112aB2 | 1202 | $C_2Br_2F_2$ | 430-85-3 | $Br_2C=CF_2$ |
| 1113B1 | 1203 | $C_2BrF_3$ | 598-73-2 | $BrFC=CF_2$ |
| 1122B1 | 1212 | $C_2HBrF_2$ | – | $BrHC=CF_2$ |
| 1140B1 | 1230 | $C_2H_3Br$ | 593-60-2 | $H_2C=CBrH$ |
| 215aa | 305 | $C_3Cl_3F_5$ | – | $CClF_2CCl_2CF_3$ |
| 215ba | 305 | $C_3Cl_3F_5$ | 76-17-5 | $CClF_2CClFCClF_2$ |
| 216ba | 306 | $C_3Cl_2F_6$ | 661-97-2 | $CClF_2CClFCF_3$ |
| 217ba | 307 | $C_3ClF_7$ | 76-18-6 | $CF_3CClFCF_3$ |
| 225ca | 315 | $C_3HCl_2F_5$ | 422-56-0 | $CF_3CF_2CCl_2H$ |
| 225cb | 315 | $C_3HCl_2F_5$ | 507-55-1 | $CClF_2CF_2CClFH$ |
| 227ca | 317 | $C_3HF_7$ | – | $CF_3CF_2CHF_2$ |
| 227ea | 317 | $C_3HF_7$ | 431-89-0 | $CF_3CFHCF_3$ |
| 236ea | 326 | $C_3H_2F_6$ | 431-63-0 | $CF_3CFHCF_2H$ |
| 236fa | 326 | $C_3H_2F_6$ | – | $CF_3CH_2CF_3$ |
| 243db | 333 | $C_3H_3Cl_2F_3$ | 338-75-0 | $CF_3CClHCClH_2$ |
| 245ca | 335 | $C_3H_3F_5$ | – | $CHF_2CF_2CH_2F$ |
| 245cb | 335 | $C_3H_3F_5$ | – | $CF_3CF_2CH_3$ |
| 245fa | 335 | $C_3H_3F_5$ | – | $CF_3CH_2CHF_2$ |
| 253fb | 343 | $C_3H_4ClF_3$ | 460-35-5 | $CF_3CH_2CClH_2$ |
| 254cb | 344 | $C_3H_4F_4$ | – | $CHF_2CF_2CH_3$ |
| 262da | 352 | $C_3H_5ClF_2$ | – | $CFH_2CClHCFH_2$ |

Continued on next page.

**Table 3-105. Freons,** *continued*

| Freon ID | + 90 | Formula | CAS | Structure |
|---|---|---|---|---|
| 263fb | 353 | $C_3H_5F_3$ | 421-07-8 | $CF_3CH_2CH_3$ |
| 270aa | 360 | $C_3H_6Cl_2$ | 594-20-7 | $CH_3CCl_2CH_3$ |
| 270fa | 360 | $C_3H_6Cl_2$ | 142-28-9 | $CClH_2CH_2CClH_2$ |
| 270da | 360 | $C_3H_6Cl_2$ | 78-87-5 | $CClH_2CClHCH_3$ |
| 270fb | 360 | $C_3H_6Cl_2$ | 78-99-9 | $CCl_2HCH_2CH_3$ |
| 280da | 370 | $C_3H_7Cl$ | 75-29-6 | $CH_3CClHCH_3$ |
| 280fa | 370 | $C_3H_7Cl$ | 540-54-5 | $CH_3CH_2CH_2Cl$ |
| 216B2 | 306 | $C_3Br_2F_6$ | 661-95-0 | $CBrF_2CBrFCF_3$ |
| 217caB1 | 307 | $C_3BrF_7$ | 422-85-5 | $CF_3CF_2CF_2Br$ |
| 217I1 | 307 | $C_3IF_7$ | – | $CF_3CF_2CF_2I$ |
| 280B1a | 370 | $C_3H_7Br$ | 106-94-5 | $CH_3CH_2CH_2Br$ |
| 280B1 | 370 | $C_3H_7Br$ | 75-26-3 | $CH_3CBrHCH_3$ |
| 1243b | 1333 | $C_3H_3F_3$ | 677-21-4 | $H_2C=CHCF_3$ |
| 1250 | 1340 | $C_3H_4Cl_2$ | 542-75-6 | $ClHC=CHCClH_2$ |
| 1250a | 1340 | $C_3H_4Cl_2$ | 78-88-6 | $H_2C=CClCClH_2$ |
| 1250b | 1340 | $C_3H_4Cl_2$ | 563-58-6 | $Cl_2C=CHCH_3$ |
| 1260 | 1350 | $C_3H_5Cl$ | 107-05-1 | $H_2C=CHCClH_2$ |
| 1260B1 | 1350 | $C_3H_5Cl$ | 106-95-6 | $H_2C=CHCBrH_2$ |
| 2240 | 2330 | $C_3H_3Cl$ | 624-65-7 | $HC\dot{|}CCClH_2$ |
| C318 | 408 | $C_4F_8$ | – | $Cyclo\text{-}C_4F_8$ |
| CE216 | 306 | $C_3F_6O$ | – | $\begin{array}{c} F_2C-CF_2 \\ \vert\ \ \ \ \vert \\ F_2C-O \end{array}$ |
| E125 | 215 | $C_2HF_5O$ | – | $CF_3OCHF_2$ |
| E134 | 224 | $C_2H_2F_4O$ | 1691-17-4 | $HF_2COCHF_2$ |
| E143a | 233 | $C_2H_3F_3O$ | – | $CH_3OCF_3$ |
| E150a | 240 | $C_2H_4Cl_2O$ | 4885-02-3 | $Cl_2HCOCH_3$ |
| E160 | 250 | $C_2H_5ClO$ | 107-30-2 | $ClH_2COCH_3$ |
| E235ca2 | 325 | $C_3H_2F_5ClO$ | – | $CHF_2CClFOCHF_2$ |
| E235da1 | 325 | $C_3H_2F_5ClO$ | – | $CF_3CHClOCHF_2$ |
| E236ea1 | 326 | $C_3H_2F_6$ | – | $CF_3CHFOCF_2H$ |
| E245fa1 | 335 | $C_3H_3F_5O$ | – | $CF_3CH_2OCHF_2$ |
| E263fb1 | 353 | $C_3H_5F_3O$ | – | $CF_3CH_2OCH_3$ |
| E270b | 360 | $C_3H_6Cl_2O$ | 34862-07-2 | $CCl_2HCH_2OCH_3$ |
| E280 | 370 | $C_3H_7ClO$ | 627-42-9 | $CClH_2CH_2OCH_3$ |
| E280a | 370 | $C_3H_7ClO$ | 3188-13-4 | $CClH_2OCH_2CH_3$ |
| E347 | 437 | $C_4H_3F_7O$ | – | $CH_2FOC(CF_3)_2$ |

Analysis of freons is very similar if not exactly the same as analysis of most volatile halocarbons. Most of the compounds are either permanent gases or liquids with high vapor pressures[22]. The standard EPA methods using GC-MS (624 and 8260) can be used effectively for identification and quantitation. Specialized gas chromatographic columns such as PLOT columns[23] and graphitized carbon black[24] have been proven useful for separation of the many isomers of freons.

---

[22] Heiskel, E. *Aerosol Rep.* 1983. 22. pp. 403-415.

[23] de Zeeuw, J., D. Zwiep and J.W. Marinissen, "Separation of Chlorofluorocarbons Using High-Resolution PLOT Columns." *American Laboratory*, March, 1996. 24C-24H.

[24] Bruno, T.J., K.H. Wetz and M. Caciari, 1996. Kovats retention Indices of Halocarbons on a Hexafluoropropylene Epoxide-Modified Graphitized Carbon Black." *Anal. Chem.* 68(8). pp. 1347-1359.

## C. Dyes and Pigments

Dyes and pigments are named in the Colour Index (C.I.)[25] based on first, their chemical properties or preparation, and second, their use in the industry. Most of the C.I. named dyes also have traditional names in addition to the proper scientific name (Table 3-106). Dyes are retained in the substrate material by a variety of mechanisms such as hydrogen-bonding, covalent-bonding, insolubility (precipitation), Van der Waals attraction, and electrostatic attractions[26]. Dye structures are generally complex unsaturated systems with many different conjugated structures represented (Table 3-109). Any single dye or pigment may contain more than one characteristic functionallity and be listed in several fashions. For example Fluorescent Brightener 28 can be listed as both a stilbene and a triazine dye.

EPA reviewed dyes and pigments in a study in 1985[27] and concluded that the dye groups listed in Table 3-108 offered significant potential as health hazards. Most of the compounds are suspected mutagens or carcinogens and should be handled with due respect.

Dyes are mostly water insoluble and when introduced into water systems, accummulate in the bottom sediments where they may be found as either the original dye molecule or transformed to degradation products. The azo linkage is particularly prone to reductive cleavage in the anoxic sediments, releasing hazardous aromatic amines to the water[28]. Sodium dithionite ($Na_2S_2O_4$) in methanol was found to be a facile chemical way to reductively cleave the azo linkages in azo dyes, mimicking the environmental reduction of the compounds.

**Table 3-106. Some common and cross-named dyes within the C.I.**

| Synonymous CI Names | | Common name |
|---|---|---|
| Solvent yellow 77 | Disperse yellow 3 | - |
| Solvent orange 52 | Disperse orange 13 | - |
| Solvent orange 53 | Disperse yellow 9 | - |
| Solvent red 47 | Acid red 93 | - |
| Solvent red 48 | Acid red 92 | Phloxine B |
| Solvent red 43 | Acid red 87 | Eosin Y |
| Solvent red 49 | Basic violet 10 | Rhodamine B |
| Solvent red 111 | Disperse red 9 | - |
| Solvent violet 8 | Basic violet 1 | Methyl Violet B |
| Solvent violet 10 | Acid violet 9 | Violamine R |
| Solvent violet 26 | Disperse red 1 | - |
| Solvent blue 4 | Basic blue 26 | Victoria Blue B |
| Solvent blue 5 | Basic blue 7 | Victoria Pure Blue BO |
| Solvent blue 6 | Basic blue 11 | Victoria Blue R |

Continued on next page.

[25] Society of Dyers and Colorists (SDC). Colour Index, Yorkshire, England; and other monograph and periodic publications of the Society.

[26] Shenai, V.A. 1973. *Chemistry of Dyes and Principles of Dyeing.* Bombay India, Skuak Publications.

[27] *Textile dyes and dyeing equipment classification, properties and environmental aspects.* EPA-600/2-85-010, February, 1995, PB85-173771.

[28] Weber, E.J. and R.L. Adams, Chemical and Sediment Mediated Reduction of The Azo Dye Disperse Blue." 79, 1995. *Environ. Sci. Technol.* 29(5). pp. 1163-1170.

**Table 3-106.  Some common and cross-named dyes within the C.I.,** *continued*

| Synonymous CI Names | | Common name |
|---|---|---|
| Solvent blue 8 | Basic blue 9 | Methylene Blue |
| Solvent blue 68 | Disperse blue 19 | - |
| Solvent blue 69 | Disperse blue 7 | - |
| Solvent blue 36 | Disperse blue 134 | - |
| Solvent green 1 | Basic green 4 | Malachite Green |
| Solvent green 7 | Acid green 9 | - |
| Solvent green 15 | Acid green 7 | - |
| Developer 14 | Oxidation Base 20 | - |

**Table 3-107.  Functional groups found in dyes and representative examples**

| Functional group | Examples |
|---|---|
| triarylmethane | Basic Violet 3, Solvent Blue 4 |
| xanthene | Basic Red 1, Pigment Red 60, Solvent Red 43 |
| anthraquinone | Acid Blue 40, Disperse Blue 3, Disperse Blue 14, Reactive Blue 4, Reactive Blue 19, Mordant Red 11, Vat Blue 6, Vat Brown 1 |
| azo | Acid Orange 60, Acid Black 5 |
| disazo | Direct Red 81, Mordant Orange 6 |
| stilbene | Direct Yellow 4, Fluorescent Brightener 28 |
| pyrazoline | Pigment Orange 34 |
| coumarin | Fluorescent Brightener 61 |
| triazine | Fluorescent Brightener 28, Reactive Yellow 2 |
| phthalocyanine | Direct Blue 86, Pigment Blue 15 |
| quinacridone | Pigment Violet 19 |
| methine | Basic Yellow 2 |

**Table 3-108.  Classes of dyes that present potential environmental/health hazards**

| Dye type | Properties/Use |
|---|---|
| Acid | Water soluble dyes that are applied under acidic conditions.  Further classified as to leveling dyes (uniformity of color coverage), milling dyes (water fast properties which hold in the fibers when wool is converted to felt), super milling dyes (applied from neutral solutions) and metal complex dyes (addition of metal ions forms an insoluble complex).  Sulfonic acid groups generally present on the dye molecules |
| Direct (Substantive) | Water soluble ionic materials that are applied without any mordant pre-dyes.  Bond through hydrogen bonding and electrostatic attraction to the surface of the textile fibers.  Salt and heat are used to transfer dye from the solution to the fiber.  Chemical structure is more linear when compared to the compact acid dyes |
| Azoic Diazo and Azoic Coupling Component | Two-component dyes that react in the fiber to form a high molecular weight insoluble colored molecule. |

Continued on next page.

**Table 3-108. Classes of dyes that present potential environmental/health hazards,**
*continued*

| Dye type | Properties/Use |
|---|---|
| Disperse | Suspensions of low water soluble dyes that preferentially dissolve in hydrophobic fibers. Heat and pressure along with a number of chemical additives, such as anionic surfactants, organic solvent carriers and antifoaming agents, are used to enhance contact with the receiving fibers. |
| Sulfur | Poorly characterized dyes obtained from reaction of complex heterocyclic molecules with either molten sulfur or sodium polysulfide. Typical substrates have been amino and nitrobenzenes, nitro- and aminobiphenyls, phenols, naphthalenes, condensed aromatics, indophenols and various azine, oxazine and thiazone containing molecules. Generally applied by soaking dye recipient in a reduced water-soluble solution of the dye, then oxidizing the dye to an insoluble form. |
| Fiber reactive | Dye molecules with reactive groups attached for forming covalent bonds with nitrogen or oxygen atoms on the fiber. Common reactive groups are dichlorotriazine, dichloroquinoxaline, vinyl sulfone, monochlorotriazine, chloropyrimidine, sulfatoethyl sulfonamide, acrylamide, and N-methylol ureas. |
| Basic | Water soluble quarternary ammonium dyes that are basified to the free base form to precipitate inside the fibers. |
| Oxidation Base | Precursors are water soluble salts of small molecules such as aniline, phenylene diamines, p-aminophenyl sulfamic acid, aminophenols, o-toluidine, dianisidine, xylidene, p-amino-diphenylamine, and 1,4-naphthalenediamine After penetration of the fiber, treatment with inorganic oxidizers create reactive imines that couple and precipitate. Many oxidation bases are also developers. |
| Mordant (chrome) | Dye molecules that are complexed in the fiber to chromium or other metal ions to form large stable molecular groups. |
| Developed (developers) | Small molecular weight aromatic amines that are used to treat the fiber, followed by reaction with nitrite to form reactive diazo- groups that can couple with other added amines, phenols or naphthalenes to produce dye molecules similar to the direct dyes. |
| Vat | Dye is initially reduced to the hydroquinoid and solubilized in caustic to form the leuco vat dye. After the fiber is treated with the leuco vat dye, oxidation with air or inorganic chemicals is used to reform the quinoid dye and precipitate it in the fiber. |
| Pigment | High molecular weight insoluble inorganic and organic materials with no inate attraction for textile fibers. Must be compounded with natural or synthetic resins for application and retention. |
| Optical/Fluorescent brightners | Frequently refered to as fluorescent whitening agents (FWA) they are used to enhance the whiteness of fabrics. The intense blue fluorescence when bound to laundered fabrics offsets the slight yellow cast of the cotton. Common classes are anionic, cationic and nonionic materials of a variety of chemical forms. |
| Solvent | Oil-soluble dyes used for coloration of plastics and non-aqueous products such as brake fluid and gasoline. |

## Table 3-109. Structures of common dyes and pigments

| C.I. name | CAS No. | Structure |
|---|---|---|
| Acid black 52 (Palatine Fast Black WAN) | 5610-64-0 | |
| Acid blue 40 | 6424-85-7 | |
| Acid orange 60 | – | |
| Acid red 266 | – | |
| Acid yellow 151 | – | |
| Azoic diazo component 1 (Fast Bordeaux) | 96-96-8 | |
| Azoic diazo component 2 (Fast Orange GC) | 108-42-9 | |
| Azoic diazo component 10 (Fast Red RC) | 95-03-4 | |

Continued on next page.

**Table 3-109. Structures of common dyes and pigments,** *continued*

| C.I. name | CAS No. | Structure |
|---|---|---|
| Azoic diazo component 13 (Fast Scarlet R) | 99-59-2 | (structure: benzene ring with $NH_2$, $H_3CO$, $NO_2$) |
| Azoic diazo component 28 (Fast Red PDC) | 80-22-8 | (structure: benzene ring with $NH_2$, $H_3CO$, $SO_2NHC_4H_9$) |
| Azoic diazo component 48 (Fast Blue B) | 14263-94-6 | (structure: biphenyl with $H_3CO$, $OCH_3$, $H_2N$, $NH_2$) |
| Basic orange 2 (Chrysoidin) | 532-82-1 | (structure: phenyl—N=N—ring—$NH_2 \cdot HCl$, $H_2N$) |
| Basic red 1 (Rhodamine 6G) | 989-38-8 | (structure: EtHN, O, $\overset{+}{N}HEt$ $Cl^-$, $H_3C$, $CH_3$, $CO_2Et$) |
| Basic violet 3 (Crystal Violet) | 548-62-9 | (structure: $+N(CH_3)_2$, $Cl^-$, $(CH_3)_2N$, $N(CH_3)_2$) |
| Basic yellow 2 (Auramine O) | 2465-27-2 | (structure: NH·HCL, $(CH_3)_2N$, $N(CH_3)_2$) |
| Basic yellow 11 | 4208-80-4 | (structure: indolenine with $Cl^-$, $N^+$, $CH_3$, $CH=CH-HN$, $OCH_3$, $H_3CO$) |
| Coupling component 2 (Naphtol AS) | 92-77-3 | (structure: naphthalene with OH, CONH—phenyl) |

Continued on next page.

**Table 3-109. Structures of common dyes and pigments,** *continued*

| C.I. name | CAS No. | Structure |
|---|---|---|
| Coupling component 7 (Naphtol AS-SW) | 135-64-8 | |
| Coupling component 11 (Naphtol AS-RL) | – | |
| Coupling component 12 (Naphtol AS-ITR) | – | |
| Developer 1 | – | |
| Developer 5 | 135-19-3 | |
| Developer 8 | 92-70-6 | |
| Developer 13 | 106-50-3 | |
| Developer 14 (Oxidation base 20) | 95-80-7 | |
| Developer 17 | 100-01-6 | |

Continued on next page.

**Table 3-109. Structures of common dyes and pigments,** *continued*

| C.I. name | CAS No. | Structure |
|-----------|---------|-----------|
| Direct black 22 | 6473-13-8 | |
| Direct blue 53 (Evans Blue) | 314-13-6 | |
| Direct blue 86 | 1330-38-7 | |
| Direct brown 154 | – | |

Continued on next page.

**Table 3-109.  Structures of common dyes and pigments,** *continued*

| C.I. name | CAS No. | Structure |
|-----------|---------|-----------|
| Direct red 81 | 2610-11-9 | |
| Direct yellow 4 (Brilliant Yellow) | 3051-11-4 | |
| Disperse blue 3 | 2475-46-9 | |
| Disperse blue 14 | 2475-44-7 | |
| Disperse brown 1 | 17464-91-4 | |
| Disperse orange 3 | 730-40-5 | |

Continued on next page.

**Table 3-109. Structures of common dyes and pigments,** *continued*

| C.I. name | CAS No. | Structure |
|---|---|---|
| Disperse orange 30 | 5261-31-4 | |
| Disperse red 1 | 2872-52-8 | |
| Disperse red 13 | 2832-40-8 | |
| Disperse yellow 3 | 2832-40-8 | |
| Disperse yellow 5 | 6439-53-8 | |
| Disperse yellow 54 | – | |
| Fluorescent brightener 28 | 4404-43-7 | |

Continued on next page.

**Table 3-109. Structures of common dyes and pigments,** *continued*

| C.I. name | CAS No. | Structure |
|-----------|---------|-----------|
| Fluorescent brightener 61 (Coumarin 1) | 91-44-1 | |
| Mordant black 11 (Eriochrome Black T) | 1787-61-7 | |
| Mordant brown 1 | 3564-15-6 | |
| Mordant orange 6 | 3564-27-0 | |
| Mordant red 11 (Alizarin) | 72-48-0 | |
| Pigment blue 15 (Copper phthalocyanine) | 147-14-8 | |

Continued on next page.

**Table 3-109. Structures of common dyes and pigments,** *continued*

| C.I. name | CAS No. | Structure |
|---|---|---|
| Pigment orange 34 | – | |
| Pigment red 90 | – | |
| Pigment violet 19 | – | |
| Pigment yellow 1 (Hansa Yellow) | – | |
| Reactive Blue 4 | 13324-20-4 | |

Continued on next page.

**Table 3-109. Structures of common dyes and pigments,** *continued*

| C.I. name | CAS No. | Structure |
|-----------|---------|-----------|
| Reactive Blue 19 (Remazol Brilliant Blue R) | 2580-78-1 | |
| Reactive Yellow 2 (Cibacron Brilliant Yellow 3G-P | 50662-99-2 | |
| Solvent blue 4 | – | |
| Solvent blue 36 | – | |
| Solvent green 3 | 128-80-3 | |

Continued on next page.

**Table 3-109. Structures of common dyes and pigments,** *continued*

| C.I. name | CAS No. | Structure |
|---|---|---|
| Solvent red 3 (Fat Brown B) | 6535-42-8 | |
| Solvent red 23 (Sudan III) | 85-86-9 | |
| Solvent red 24 (Sudan IV) | 85-83-6 | |
| Solvent red 43 (Eosin Y) | 15086-94-9 | |
| Vat blue 6 | – | |
| Vat brown 1 | – | |
| Vat red 1 | – | |

The analysis of environmental samples for residues of dyes, pigments and their degradation products can be quite challenging. Many papers have been published concerning analysis of dyes and pigments[29], and several books have included chapters on the subject[30]. Although thin layer chromatography can be used as a screening tool prior to analysis, instrumental methods are needed for accurate qualitative and quantitative determinations. Some of the materials, particularly the azoic diazo components and some of the developers are standard target analytes under the semivolatile GC-MS procedures (EPA Methods 625 and 8270). Other dyes and pigments are specifically listed as target analytes by LC-MS (EPA Methods 8321 and 8325). Most of the potential targets are large molecules that are not amenable to gas chromatographic techniques and require HPLC for separation. Given the literally thousands of potential compounds to be identified, three dimensional detectors (FTIR, PDA-UV, or MS) are an absolute necessity.

# D. Hydrocarbon Solvents and Fuels

Most hydrocarbon solvents and fuels are obtained from petroleum. Petroleum hydrocarbons are multi-component analytes consisting of four major structural types:
- straight and branched chain aliphatic hydrocarbons (parafins)
- straight and branched chain aliphatic hydrocarbons with various degrees of unsaturation (olefins)
- cyclic aliphatic hydrocarbons (termed naphthalenes in the petroleum industry)
- mono- and polycyclic aromatic hydrocarbons (termed aromatics).

Petroleum hydrocarbons are widely used as industrial solvents and fuels. Classification of petroleum hydrocarbons is by boiling point range and PONA (parafin, olefin, naphthalene, aromatic) content. For example aircraft turbine fuels are differentiated from fuel oils even though they have about the same distillation range, because the turbine fuels have essentially no aromatic compound content while the fuel oils can have substantial percentages of aromatics. Some commercial products are listed in Table 3-110. Greases and lubrication oils are not listed as they generally are above the temperature range analyzed by GC. Many of the solvents and fuels have common names, for example mineral spirits are frequently called Stoddard solvents.

**Table 3-110.  Common industrial hydrocarbon solvents and fuels encountered in GC analysis**

| Solvent/fuel | Standard | Boiling point range °C |
|---|---|---|
| Petroleum ether | ACS reagent | 30-60 |
| Petroleum benzin (naphtha) | - | 35-80 |
| Lacquer thinner | - | 93-115 |
| Hexanes | ASTM D1836 | 63-71 |
| VM&P[31] naphtha (ligroin) | ASTM D3735 | |

Continued on next page.

---

[29]  Poiger, T., J.A. Field, T.M. Field and W. Giger, 1996. "Occurrence of Fluorescent Whiting Agents in Sewage and River Water Determined by Solid-Phase Extraction and High-Performance Liquid Chromatography." *Environ. Sci. Technol.* 30(7). pp. 2220-2226; Kramer, J.B., S. Canonica, J. Hoigne, and J. Kaschig, 1996. "Degradation of Fluorescent Whitening Agents in Sunlit Natural Waters." *Environ. Sci. Technol.* 30(7). pp. 2227-2234.

[30]  Reife, A. and H.S. Freeman, 1996. *Environmental Chemistry of Dyes and Pigments.* John Wiley & Sons, New York, NY.

[31]  Varnish Makers' and Painters' naphtha

---

### Table 3-110. Common industrial hydrocarbon solvents and fuels encountered in GC analysis

| Solvent/fuel | Standard | Boiling point range °C |
|---|---|---|
| Type I - regular | | 120-150 |
| Type II - high flash | | 140-175 |
| Type III - odorless | | 120-150 |
| Mineral spirits | ASTM D235 | |
| Type I - regular[32] | | 149-213 |
| Type II - high flash point | | 177-213 |
| Type III - odorless | | 149-213 |
| Type IV - low dry point | | 149-185 |
| Kerosine | ASTM D3699 | 205-300 |
| Kerosene | non-standard | 175-325 |
| Aromatic naphtha | ASTM D3734 | |
| Type I - aromatic 100 | | 150-175 |
| Type II - aromatic 150 | | 180-215 |
| Fuel oils | ASTM D396 | |
| Grade 1 - light distillate | | 215-288 |
| Grade 2 - heavy distillate | | up to 338 |
| Grade 4 - residual/distillate mix | | - |
| Grade 5 - residual | | - |
| Grade 6 - residual (Bunker C) | | - |
| Naval distillate fuel (military) | MIL-F-16884H | end point 385 |
| Aviation gasolines | ASTM D910 | 75-170 |
| Diesel fuel oils[33] | ASTM D975 | |
| Low sulfur No. 1 | | up to 288 |
| Low sulfur No. 2 | | 282-338 |
| Grade 1 - light distillate | | up to 288 |
| Grade 2 - heavier distillate | | 282-338 |
| Grade 4 - distillate/residual mix | | - |
| Diesel fuel oil (military) | VV-800-D | |
| DF-A - Arctic grade | | up to 300 |
| DF-1 | | up to 330 |
| DF-2 | | up to 370 |
| Aviation turbine fuels | ASTM D1655 | |
| Jet A | | 205-300 |
| Jet A-1 - low freezing point | | 205-300 |
| Jet B - wide distillation range kerosine | | <145 to >245 |
| Aviation turbine fuels (military) | MIL-T-5624P | |
| JP-4 | | 145-270 |
| JP-5 | | 205-300 |
| JP-5/JP-8ST (worst case test mixture) | | 205-300 |
| JP-8 | MIL-T-83133D | 205-300 |
| HIgh-boiling hydrocarbon solvent for wood preservative carrier | ASTM 2604 | up to 307 |
| Low-boiling hydrocarbon solvent for wood preservative carrier | ASTM 3225 | up to 213 |
| Gas turbine fuel oils | ASTM 2880 | |
| Grade 0-GT - mixture of Jet B + naptha | | - |
| Grade 1-GT - distillate | | up to 288 |
| Grade 2-GT - distillate | | up to 338 |
| Grade 3-GT - distillate/residual mix | | - |
| Grade 4-GT - residuals + topped crude | | - |

---

[32] Also called Stoddard solvent, Texsolve S, and Varsol 1.
[33] Grades 1, 2 and 4 are required to contain a visible amount of blue dye, 1,4-dialkylamino-anthraquinone.

Genium Publishing Corporation

Many of the fuel blends also contain non-hydrocarbon additives. In domestic automobile gasoline a variety of oxygenate additives are found. Common oxygentates and other additives are listed in Table 3-111.

**Table 3-111. Common additives in hydrocarbon fuels**

| Additive | Function |
|---|---|
| Ethanol | Gasoline oxygenate |
| Methyl *tert*-butyl ether (MTBE) | Gasoline oxygenate |
| Methyl *tert*-amyl ether (TAME) | Gasoline oxygenate |
| Ethyl *tert*-butyl ether (ETBE) | Gasoline oxygenate |
| Isopropyl alcohol | Fuel system icing inhibitor |
| Ethylene glycol monomethyl ether | Fuel system icing inhibitor |
| 1,4-Dialkylamino-anthraquinone | Blue dye |
| p-Diethylaminoazobenzene | Yellow dye |
| 2,4-bis(alkylphenylazo)-1,3-benzenediol | Yellow dye |
| Alkylazobenzene-4-azo-2-naphthol | Red dye |
| Tetraethyl lead - Ethylene dibromide | Anti-knock mixture |
| *N,N*-diisopropyl-p-phenylenediamine | Antioxidant |
| *N,N*-di-sec-butyl-p-phenylenediamine | Antioxidant |
| 2,4-dimethyl-4-t-butylphenol | Antioxidant |
| 2,6-di-t-butyl-4-methylphenol | Antioxidant |
| 2,6-di-t-butylphenol | Antioxidant |
| Tri-t-butylphenols | Antioxidant |
| Di- and tri-isopropylphenols | Antioxidant |
| *N,N*-disalicylidene-1,2-propanediamine | Metal deactivator |
| Amyl nitrate | Cetane improver |
| Isopropyl nitrate | Cetane improver |
| Hexyl nitrate | Cetane improver |
| Cyclohexyl nitrate | Cetane improver |
| 2-Ethylhexyl nitrate | Cetane improver |
| Octyl nitrate | Cetane improver |

In addition to the petroleum hydrocarbons as sources of hydrocarbon solvents, there is considerable use of terpene solvents in industry. These are loosely classified as turpentines of which there are several in general use.

- Gum turpentine or gum spirits consist of mainly α-pinene with some β-pinene and other hydrocabons, obtained from distillation of gum or resin from living pine trees, boiling point range 154-170 °C
- Steam distilled wood turpentine is mainly α-pinene with traces of dipentene and other hydrocarbon terpenes, obtained through steam distillation of pine chips, BP 150-170 °C
- Sulfate wood turpentine is recovered from the Kraft paper making procedure and is mainly α- and β-pinene
- Dipentene is obtained from continued distillation of the pine resin, BP 170-190 °C
- Pine oil is isolated during the processing of the turpentines and consists of terpene alcohols, BP 200-225° C.

A solvent of increasing industrial and domestic use is d-limonene, BP 176 °C which is refined from the oil of citrus.

## 418.1 and 9073. Total Petroleum Hydrocarbons by IR (Reference 20 and 41)

Method 9073 is a draft method that was eliminated from inclusion in SW-846 due to the reduction of Freon 113 usage and eventual discontinuation. However, the method, which is very similar to 418.1, has been specified by many states as the preferred method for TPH analysis. If the sample is aqueous, 1 L is acidified to pH <2 with HCl, and extracted three times with 30 mL portions of Freon 113. The solvent is drained through filter paper containing sodium sulfate into a 100 mL volumetric flask. The flask is brought to volume with Freon, then several mL discarded. Three grams silica gel is added, and the mixture stirred with a magnetic stir bar for several minutes. The silica gel removes the polar co-extractants such as fatty acids, although several portions of silica gel may be required for complete removal. The sample is read with an IR spectrophotometer at 2950 cm$^{-1}$ against a standard curve. Standards are prepared from an oil mixture consisting of 15.0 mL n-hexadecane, 15.0 mL isooctane and 10.0 mL chlorobenzene.

This standard mixture was chosen to approximate the number and type of carbon-hydrogen bonds found in petroleum products that are a mixture of straight and branched chain aliphatic hydrocarbons and aromatic hydrocarbons. The IR method effectively quantitates the number of C-H bonds in the sample. Falsely high values can result when pure oils, such as hexadecane are analyzed. The number of C-H bonds in the standard is approximated by the percent mass of hydrogen in the calibration mix. It can be calculated as follows:

| Compound | Hexadecane | Chlorobenzene | Isooctane | Total |
|---|---|---|---|---|
| Formula | $C_{16}H_{34}$ | $C_6H_5Cl$ | $C_8H_{18}$ | |
| Molecular wt | 226.43 | 112.55 | 114.22 | |
| % Hydrogen | 15.13 | 4.48 | 15.88 | |
| Density | 0.773 | 1.107 | 0.692 | |
| mL | 15.0 | 10.0 | 15.0 | |
| Mass in Cal mix | 11.595 | 11.070 | 10.380 | 33.045 |
| Weight % | 35.09 | 33.50 | 31.41 | 100 |
| Weight %H | 5.3091 | 1.5008 | 4.9882 | 11.7981 |

For a pure hydrocarbon sample such as hexadecane the weight % hydrogen is 15.13. Analysis of pure hexadecane using the above calibration solution would give:

$$\frac{15.13}{11.7981} = 1,280,000 \text{ mg/kg.}$$

Lighter hydrocarbons will give higher values, while heavier hydrocarbons will give lower maximum results.

Variations on the method use soxhlet extraction, ultrasonic horn extraction, sonication bath or a simple vigorous hand-shaking for two minutes with a Freon 113 extracting solvent for solids. The soxhlet procedure is generally regarded as the most rigorous; however, some clients insist on the open-beaker ultrasonic-horn extraction, which almost always results in lower values. Continuous liquid-liquid extraction with Freon 113 has been used. A novel procedure is required by Missouri where a weighed amount of solid is mixed with sodium sulfate to dry the sample, then packed into a chromatography column and extracted in one pass with 100 mL Freon 113. The eluted Freon 113 is then treated as above with silica gel.

As more and more surcharges and restrictions are placed by the government on Freon 113, these methods will disappear or be modified to use other solvents. Carbon disulfide is used as the solvent in a California method, however it presents its own problems of smell and toxicity. A draft SW-846 method for supercritical carbon dioxide extraction of solids (Method 3560) has been presented. The extraction eluant is transferred to tetra-chloroethene, then read by IR at 2950 cm$^{-1}$ in draft method 8440. Although tetrachloro-ethene possesses toxic properties, it is non-ozone depleting. See the discussion in Section 2 on Oil & Grease for information on draft method 1664 and other performance-based modifications.

## BTEX and GRO by GC

BTEX and GRO are determined by either headspace or purge & trap attached to a GC-FID-PID (modified 8020) or a GC/MS (method 8240 or 8260), or by methanol or hexa-decane microextraction followed by purge & trap or direct injection into the GC or GC/MS. For BTEX the individual benzene, toluene, ethylbenzene and xylenes peaks are summed for the result. For GRO there are several approaches used by the various states. One is to sum the largest 10 peaks in the gasoline envelope. Another is to sum all peaks eluting in the same envelope as a standard gasoline (2-methyl pentane to 1,2,4-trimethyl-benzene). Tennessee suggests the gasoline standard as API PS-6 (American Petroleum Institute) or other appropriate certified standard. Calibration is most commonly five-point external standard.

## DRO by GC

Diesel range organics are determined with a GC-FID. Diesel fuel is normally considered to consist of the hydrocarbon compounds that will elute between decane and pentacosane $C_{10}$ - $C_{25}$. A variety of extraction methods and solvents are used. The California method calls for Freon 113. Other methods use methylene chloride, carbon disulfide, or hexane. Separatory funnels and continuous liquid-liquid extractors are common for water sam-ples. Soxhlet extractors, ultrasonic cell disruptors, sonication baths and simple hand shaking are also used. Calibration and quantitation are variously based on the total enve-lope between decane to penta- or octacosane or on the ten indicator compounds which are the even straight chain saturated hydrocarbons from decane to octacosane, but generally require a five-point curve. Surrogates of pentacosane and $o$-terphenyl have been used and an internal standard, 5-$\alpha$-androstane, is suggested in the Tennessee method.

A very utilitarian procedure is to add 1.00 mg/L (1.00 mL of a 1000 ug/mL solution of the surrogates in methanol) of the surrogates $n$-nonane and $n$-pentacosane to 1 L of aqueous sample in a hydrophobic membrane continuous liquid-liquid extractor/concen-trator such as the Accelerated One-Step® by Corning, Incorporated. The sample is acid-ified to pH < 2 with 1:1 $H_2SO_4$ : water, extracted for 4 hrs (1 hr gives quantitative results) with 100 mL methylene chloride and concentrated to about 2 mL. After transfer to a 2.00 mL volumetric tube (which has been calibrated at 1.00 mL), the sample is reduced in volume to exactly 1.00 mL with a gentle nitrogen stream and mild heating in a 40 °C waterbath. Final transfer to an autosampler vial finishes the sample preparation for liquid samples. Surrogate recoveries from the Accelerated One-Step range from 60-80% for the nonane to 80-100% for the pentacosane, which are directly related to the DRO recovery.

Solid samples are processed in a soxhlet extraction apparatus using 30 g of sample well mixed with 30 g of anhydrous sodium sulfate (dried and baked in a 550 ± 50 °C fur-nace for 4 hours in a quartz pan) and glasswool plugs (solvent extracted with methylene chloride for 18 hrs in a continuous liquid-liquid extractor) at the top and bottom of the sample. 1.00 mL of the above surrogate solution is added and the sample extracted for 4 hours using methylene chloride (about 4-6 cycles per hour). The extract is dried over anhydrous sodium sulfate (furnace dried) and concentrated with either a K-D apparatus or a TurboVap® (Zymark) apparatus to no less than 2 mL. After transfer to a 2.00 mL volumetric tube (which has been calibrated at 1.00 mL), the sample is reduced in volume to exactly 1.00 mL with a gentle nitrogen stream and mild heating in a 40 °C waterbath. Final transfer to an autosampler vial finishes the sample preparation.

Analysis is performed by FID-GC with a 30m x 0.32mm id capillary column with a 95:5 methyl:phenyl silicone stationary phase. The position of the DRO envelope as compared to the surrogates serves to identify the analyte as kerosene, diesel #2, mineral spirits, JP-4, *etc*. Figures 3-31 through 3-36 illustrate chromatograms of a various fuel types.

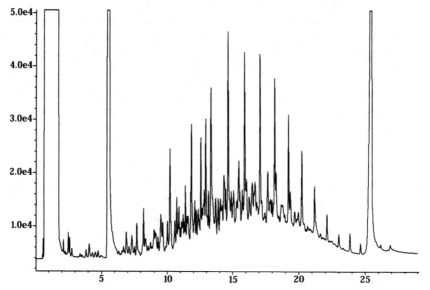

**Figure 3-31. Gas chromatogram of diesel fuel bracketed by the surrogates *n*-nonane and *n*-pentacosane**

Quantitation of the target analyte is by area of the whole envelope above the baseline, against a 5-point calibration curve. QC is assessed by having minimum acceptable recoveries of the surrogates of 45% for nonane and 75% for the pentacosane. The analysis is critically sensitive to volume. Never allow the volume of the sample extract to fall below 1.00 mL, and the final volume of the extract for analysis must be 1.00 mL. Allowing the volume of the extract to fall to as little as 0.75 mL will result in 0-6% recovery of nonane and 10-30% recovery of pentacosane with comparable recoveries of the target analytes.

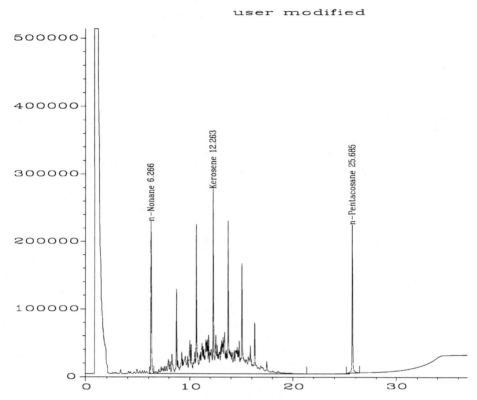

**Figure 3-32. Kerosene by GC-FID.**

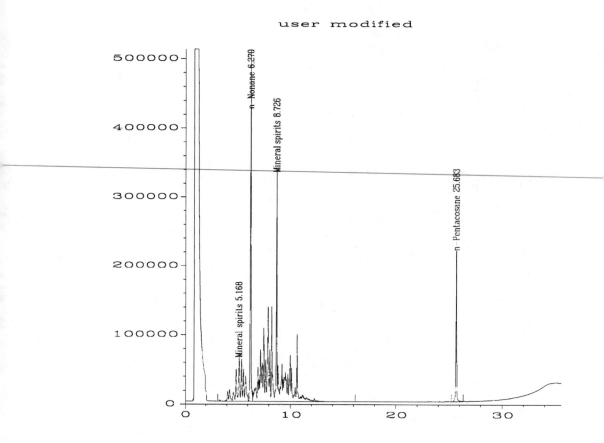

**Figure 3-33. Mineral Spirits by GC-FID.**

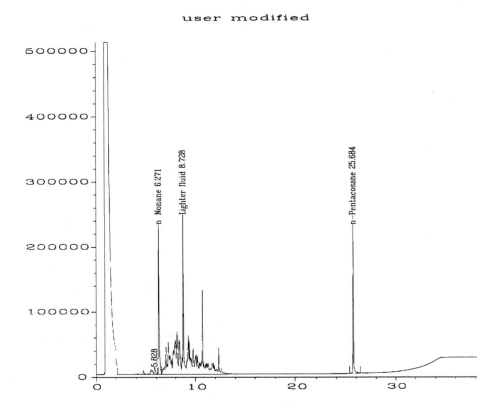

**Figure 3-34. Charcoal lighter fluid by GC-FID.**

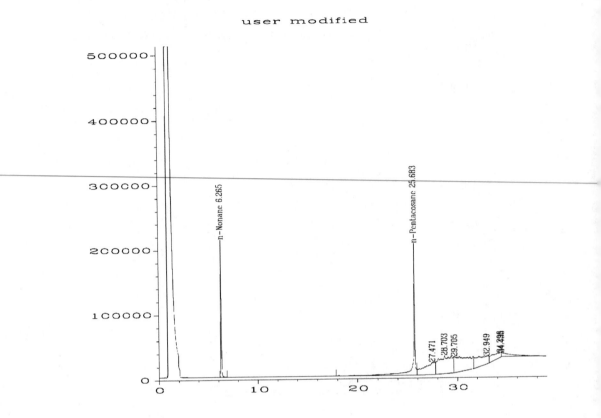

**Figure 3-35. SAE 30 weight oil by GC-FID.**

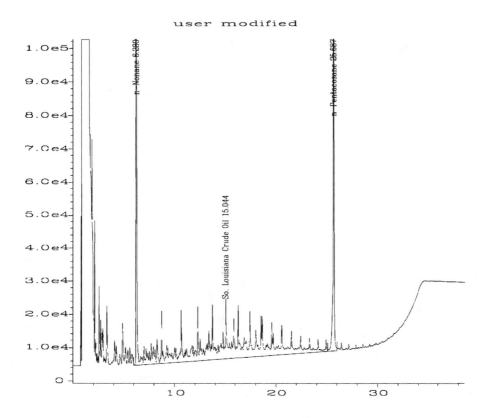

**Figure 3-36. Louisiana crude oil by GC-FID.**

Most petroleum based fuels, solvents and oils can be determined and identified by GC-FID. The key to the identification is frequently determining the boiling point or distillation range. The saturated straight chain hydrocarbons can serve as the calibration standard for boiling points. Table 3-112 lists the boiling points of most of the commonly available hydrocarbon standards.

**Table 3-112. Boiling points of common hydrocarbon standards**

| Hydrocarbon | Carbon number | BP °C |
|---|---|---|
| Propane | 3 | -42.1 |
| n-Butane | 4 | -0.5 |
| n-Pentane | 5 | 35-36 |
| n-Hexane | 6 | 69 |
| Cyclohexane | 6 | 80.7 |
| Benzene | 6 | 80 |
| n-Heptane | 7 | 98 |
| Methylcyclohexane | 7 | 101 |
| Toluene | 7 | 111 |
| n-Octane | 8 | 125-127 |
| Ethylbenzene | 8 | 136 |
| p-Xylene | 8 | 138 |
| n-Nonane | 9 | 151 |
| n-Decane | 10 | 174 |
| Decalin (c + t) | 10 | 189-193 |
| Naphthalene | 10 | 218 |
| n-Undecane | 11 | 196 |
| n-Dodecane | 12 | 216 |
| n-Tridecane | 13 | 234 |
| n-Tetradecane | 14 | 252-254 |
| Anthracene | 14 | 342 |
| n-Pentadecane | 15 | 270 |
| n-Hexadecane | 16 | 284 |
| n-Heptadecane | 17 | 302 |
| n-Octadecane | 18 | 317 |
| n-Nonadecane | 19 | 330 |
| n-Eicosane | 20 | 343 |
| n-Heneicosane | 21 | 356 |
| n-Docosane | 22 | 369 |
| n-Tricosane | 23 | 380 |
| n-Tetracosane | 24 | 391 |
| n-Pentacosane | 25 | 402 |
| n-Hexacosane | 26 | 412 |
| n-Heptacosane | 27 | 422 |
| n-Octacosane | 28 | 432 |
| n-Nonacosane | 29 | 441 |
| n-Triacontane | 30 | 450 |
| n-Hentriacontane | 31 | 458 |

## E. Explosives and chemical warfare residues

In most contract work for the military, samples will eventually arrive that require analysis of explosives and/or chemical warfare residues. Methods for determination of these analytes generally were developed at the USACE Cold Regions Research and

Engineering Laboratory in New Hampshire, although there are other contributors. EPA has adopted many of these methods in either draft or finalized form into SW-846.

Although the standards may pose a small risk of explosion, in general this type of work is no more hazardous than other procedures performed in the semivolatile extractions laboratory. Most of the materials are now commercially available as solutions for calibration and check samples. There are many different types of explosives as illustrated in Table 3-113. Most residues determined in the laboratory are derived from highly nitrated organic structures.

**Table 3-113. Common military explosives and residues**

| Name | CAS | Structure |
|------|-----|-----------|
| 246TNT<br>2,4,6-Trinitrotoluene | 118-96-7 | (structure of 2,4,6-trinitrotoluene with CH₃ at top, O₂N and NO₂ on ring, NO₂ at bottom) |
| RDX<br>Research Dept. Explosive<br>Royal Demolition Explosive<br>Hexahydro-1,3,5-trinitro-1,3,5-triazine | 121-82-4 | (structure of RDX triazine ring with three NO₂ groups) |
| HMX<br>High Melting Explosive<br>Octahydro-1,3,5,7-tetranitro-1,3,5,7-tetrazocine | 2691-41-0 | (structure of HMX tetrazocine ring with four NO₂ groups) |
| ADN<br>Ammonium dinitramide | - | $NH_4N(NO_2)_2$ |
| AP<br>Ammonium perchlorate | 7790-98-9 | $NH_4ClO_4$ |
| TNAZ<br>Trinitroazetidine | - | (structure of trinitroazetidine ring with three NO₂ groups) |
| KDN-AN<br>Potassium dinitramide - ammonium nitrate co-crystal | - | $KN(NO_2)_2 \cdot NH_4NO_3$ |
| Tetryl<br>N-Methyl-N,2,4,6-tetranitrobenzamine | 479-45-8 | (structure of tetryl with H₃C-N-NO₂, O₂N and NO₂ on ring, NO₂ at bottom) |

Continued on next page.

**Table 3-113. Common military explosives and residues,** *continued*

| Name | CAS | Structure |
|------|-----|-----------|
| 135TNB<br>1,3,5-Trinitrobenzene | 99-35-4 | |
| 13DNB<br>1,3-Dinitrobenzene | 99-65-0 | |
| 2-ADNT | 355-72-78-2 | |
| 4-ADNT | 1946-51-0 | |
| 2,6-DNT | 606-20-2 | |
| 2,4-DNT | 121-14-2 | |
| 2NT | 88-72-2 | |
| 3NT | 99-08-1 | |
| 4NT | 99-99-0 | |

Continued on next page.

**Table 3-113.** **Common military explosives and residues,** *continued*

| Name | CAS | Structure |
|------|-----|-----------|
| NG<br>Nitroglycerine | 55-63-0 | $CH_2ONO_2$<br>$CHONO_2$<br>$CH_2ONO_2$ |
| Tetrazine | 31330-63-9 | N—N<br>$\parallel$ C- N= NNHNHCNH$_2$<br>N—N $\parallel$<br>$H_2O$ NH |

## 8330 Nitroaromatics and nitramines by HPLC[34]

Although it is possible to determine these analytes when they are present in high concentration by direct injection of the aqueous sample diluted 1:1 with acetonitrile, the normal procedure uses a salting-out process to isolate and concentrate the target analytes[35]. The sample is saturated with sodium sulfate, and acetonitrile is added. Most of the acetonitrile remains dissolved in the aqueous layer. However, a small portion separates as a layer, and the organic target analytes are concentrated in this layer, which is removed. After repeating the isolation, the combined acetonitrile extracts are back-extracted with a sodium chloride solution, then filtered and analyzed by reverse phase HPLC on a C-18 column with 1:1 methanol:water eluant. Confirmation is achieved on a CN reversed-phase column. Solid samples are prepared by extended sonication (18 hrs in an ultrasonic bath) of the solid with acetonitrile. The extract is treated with calcium chloride solution, then analyzed by reversed-phase HPLC as above.

Recent developments for sample preparation have used solid phase extraction disks and cartridges for isolation of the target analytes from aqueous solutions[36]. Both styrene-divinylbenzene and the more traditional C-18 disks were evaluated. Detection levels were 5 to 10 times lower than the values listed in Table 3-114. An Army publication compares the disk and cartridge solid-phase extractions to the salting-out procedure[37].

**Table 3-114.** **Target Analytes of Method 8330**

| Target Analyte | CAS Number | Water EQL ug/L | Soil EQL mg/kg |
|----------------|------------|----------------|----------------|
| HMX | 2691-41-0 | - | 2.2 |
| RDX | 121-82-4 | 0.84 | 1.0 |
| 1,3,5-Trinitrobenzene | 99-35-4 | 0.26 | 0.25 |
| 1,3-Dinitrobenzene | 99-65-0 | 0.11 | 0.25 |

Continued on next page.

---

34 Developed from U.S. Army methods SM01 and SM02.
35 Leggett, D.C, T.F. Jenkins and P.H. Miyares, "Salting-Out Solvent Extraction for Preconcentration of Neutral Polar Organic Solutes from Water." *Analytical Chemistry.* 1990. 62(13). pp. 1355-1356; T.F. Jenkins, and P.H. Miyares, "Nonevaporative Preconcentration Technique for Volatile and Semi-volatile Solutes in Certain Polar Solvents." *Analytical Chemistry.* 1991. 63(13). pp. 1341-1343.
36 Le Brun, G., "A Solid-Phase Extraction Disk Method for the Extraction of Explosives from Water." *Proceedings of the Fifteenth Annual EPA Conference on Analysis of Pollutants in the Environment.* 1992. pp. 143-175.
37 Jenkins, T.F., P.H. Miyares, K.F. Myers, E.F. McCormick, and A.B. Strong. "Comparison of Cartridge and Membrane Solid-Phase Extraction with Salting-Out Solvent Extraction for Preconcentration of Nitroaromatic and Nitramine Explosives from Water." U.S. Army CRREL Special Report 92-25. 1992.

**Table 3-114. Target Analytes of Method 8330,** *continued*

| Target Analyte | CAS Number | Water EQL ug/L | Soil EQL mg/kg |
|---|---|---|---|
| Tetryl | 479-45-8 | - | 0.65 |
| Nitrobenzene | 98-95-3 | - | 0.26 |
| TNT | 118-96-7 | 0.11 | 0.25 |
| 4-Amino-2,6-dinitrotoluene | 1946-51-0 | 0.060 | - |
| 2-Amino-4,6-dinitrotoluene | 35572-78-2 | 0.035 | - |
| 2,4-Dinitrotoluene | 121-14-2 | 0.31 | 0.26 |
| 2,6-Dinitrotoluene | 606-20-2 | 0.020 | 0.25 |
| 2-Nitrotoluene | 88-72-2 | - | 0.25 |
| 3-Nitrotoluene | 99-08-1 | - | 0.25 |
| 4-Nitrotoluene | 99-99-0 | - | 0.25 |

## 8331 Tetrazene by RP-HPLC

This is a direct injection technique that uses ion pair C-18 reversed phase HPLC for analysis. The ion pairing reagent is 1-decanesulfonic acid, and the eluent is 2:3 methanol:water with acetic acid. Solids are shaken for 5 hrs at 2000 rpm on a platform shaker with a 0.1M solution of 1-decanesulfonic acid in 55:45 methanol:water. Then, the extract is filtered and analyzed. The EPA method is based on research at the USACE Cold Regions Research and Engineering Laboratory[38].

## 8332 Nitroglycerine by HPLC

The presence of nitroglycerine in the sample is determined by thin layer chromatography on silica gel with 20% dichloroethane in carbon tetrachloride as the developing solvent. The spots are visualized with either a 5% diphenylamine in ethanol spray followed by UV light exposure or an alternate Greiss reagent (sulfanilic acid and alpha-naphthylamine in an acetic acid alcoholic KOH mixture) spray followed by heating. Quantitation is by CN reversed-phase HPLC with 60:40 acetonitrile:water mobile phase.

## USATHAMA Method (KN01) for White Phosphorous in Soil or Sediment

This method is under consideration by the EPA for inclusion in SW-846. White phosphorous is the tetrahedral form of elemental phosphorous. It is highly combustible in the presence of oxygen and used by the military in incendiary devices, where it is referred to by the slang term "willy pete." The material is stored under water and can safely be manipulated under a pure nitrogen atmosphere in either a glove bag or box. The analyte is extracted from soil by mixing with isooctane and degassed water for 18 hrs on a platform shaker. Aliquots of the isooctane extract are injected into a GC equipped with a 15 m x 0.53 mm DB-1 capillary column and nitrogen-phosphorous detector. Quantitation is by external standard calibration.

---

[38] Walsh, M.E, and T.F. Jenkins. *Analytical Method for Determining Tetrazine in Water*, Special Report 87-25, 1987, USATHAMA AMXTH-TE-CR-87139; *Analytical Method for Determining Tetrazine in Soil*, 1988. Special Report 88-15, USATHAMA AMXTH-TE--CR-88019.

## Chemical warfare residues

Nerve gases (various organophosphates) and blister agents (nitrogen-or sulfur-based mustards) are the more common chemical warfare compounds that result in requests for residue analysis inside the US. The various residues arise during both the manufacturing process and during decontamination procedures. The residue analytes are listed in Table 3-115 along with the referenced USATHAMA methodology. Possible routes to the residues from the materials used by the US military in munitions are indicated in Figure 3-37.

**Table 3-115. Chemical warfare agent residues**

| Residue | Abbreviation | Method Number | CAS Number |
|---|---|---|---|
| Isopropylmethylphosphonic acid | IMPA | UT03 (aqueous), LT03 (soils) | – |
| Methylphosphonic acid | MPA | UT03 (aqueous) LT03 (soils) | 993-13-5 |
| Fluoroacetic acid | FC2A | UT03 (aqueous) LT03 (soils) | 62-74-8 |
| Chloroacetic acid | CIC2A | UT03 (aqueous), LT03 (soils) LW18(soil) | 79-11-8 |
| Ethylmethylphosphonic acid[39] | EMPA | UT03 (aqueous), LT03 (soils) | – |
| Thiodiglycol | TDGCL | LW18 (soil), UW22 (aqueous) | 111-48-8 |
| Thiodiglycolic acid | TDGCLA | UW22 (aqueous) | 123-93-3 |
| Diisopropylmethylphosphonate | DIMP | UK08 (aqueous), TT9 (soils) | 1445-75-6 |
| Dimethylmethylphosphonate | DMMP | UK08 (aqueous), TT9 (soils) | 756-79-6 |

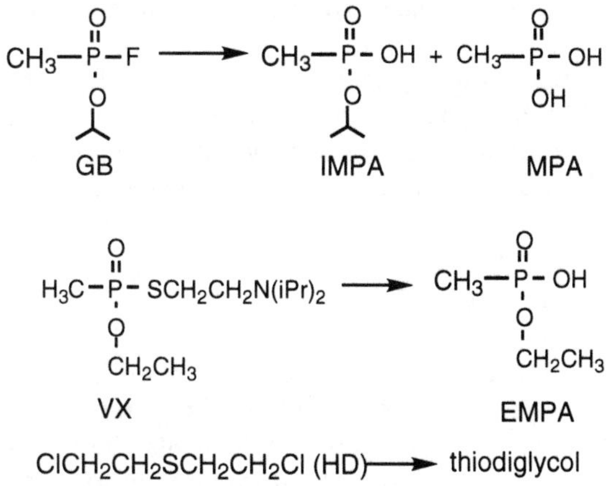

**Figure 3-37. Breakdown products from common military chemical agents.**

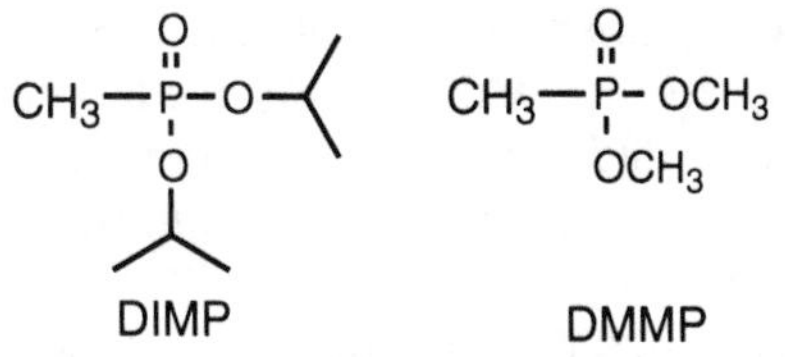

**Figure 3-38. Alkaline/alcohol decontamination products from common military nerve agents.**

[39] Due to co-elution, quantitated as MPA.

**Table 3-116.  Holding times, preservatives and sample containers for chemical warfare residue samples**

| Method | Container and sample size | Preservative | Holding time |
|---|---|---|---|
| UT03 | Amber glass jar with Teflon lid liner 60 mL | 4 °C, minimum headspace | 40 days |
| LT03 | Amber glass with Teflon lid liner, 100 g | 4 °C, minimum headspace | 7 days to extraction, 40 days to analysis |
| LW18 | Amber glass jars with Teflon lid liner, 1.2 L capacity or polybutyrate core tubes | 4 °C | 7 days to extraction, 40 days to analysis |
| UW22 | Amber glass jar with Teflon lid liner, 1.2 L | 4 °C | 7 days to extraction, 40 days to analysis |
| UK08 | Amber glass jar with Teflon lid liner, 1L | 4 °C | 7 days to extraction, 40 days to analysis |
| TT9 | Glass with Teflon lid liner, | 4 °C | 7 days to extraction, 40 days to analysis |

Method UT03 uses a gradient elution ion chromatograph with a conductivity detector for direct analysis of filtered samples.  A silver-form cation exchange resin is used to reduce chloride interference.  Method LT03 requires a DI water extraction of the soil, then is similar to UT03.

Method LW18 requires extraction of the target analytes from soil in alkaline methanol, filtration and concentration, then dilution with acidification and water.  Analysis is performed by HPLC with a reversed-phase C18 column and a buffered phosphate eluant.  Detection is by UV at 215 nm.  Method UW22 concentrates a 500 mL aliquot to 50 mL by boiling, purifies the concentrate by passage through a XAD-7 resin column, further reduces the volume to 5 mL, then dilutes the sample to 10 mL with buffered water.  Analysis is identical to LW18.

Method UK08 uses a continuous liquid-liquid extractor to isolate the target analytes from 1 L of sample with methylene chloride.  The extract is concentrated to 5 mL and analyzed on a FPD-GC with a 5% SP-1000 on Supelcoport 100/120 2 mm glass column.  Method TT9 extracts the soil with DI water then directly injects the water solution on the FID-GC specified in method UK08.

## F.  Plasticizers, anti-oxidants and other additives

Plasticizers, anti-oxidants, UV-inhibitors and flame retardants are frequent contaminants found during forward library searches for non-target compounds (TICs) in GC-MS analyses.  Although these can be environmental pollutants, they may also be present as laboratory contamination.  Anti-oxidants are added to plastic formulations to trap or destroy radicals and peroxides that occur during the initiation of polymer breakdown through oxidation.  Radical traps are commonly hindered phenols and secondary arylamines.  A frequently encountered anti-oxidant of this type is BHT, used to protect processed or preserved foods from oxidation/discoloration.  Compounds used to destroy radicals are phosphites, esters of thiodipropionic acid and other sulfur-containing materials such as thioureas.  Both anti-oxidant functions can be designed into the same compound , for example thiobis (di-sec-amylphenol).

Organic flame retardants commonly contain chlorine, bromine or phosphorus and may be mixed with metal species such as antimony trioxide, antimony pentoxide or sodium antimonate.  Examples of organic flame retardants include deca- and octa-bromodiphenyloxide, tetrabromo phthalic anhydride and phthalate esters, tris (2,3-dibromopropyl) phosphate, tris (2-chloroethyl) phosphate, tetrabromobisphenol-A, and dibromoneopentyl glycol. The compounds may simply be mixed into the bulk plastic or fiber or they may be incorporated as monomers in the polymerization reaction to form the plastic.

Lubricants are used in the plastics industry to ease handling of the materials during molding and fabrication. These additives include many fatty acids and esters, fatty alcohols, and bis-amides. Examples are glycerol monostearate, olelyl alchol, and ethylene bis-stearamide, to name just a very few.

When the base polymer is pure polyvinyl chloride, a very rigid, hard plastic results. To make the formulation flexible and more useable, many different classes of compounds are added to the material as plasticizers. Included as part of this group are the lubricants, although the compounds may serve more important functions than simply lubrication. Tygon tubing is an excellent example. It contains up to 40% by weight bis-(2-ethylhexyl) phthalate as a plasticizer. Compounds frequently found in these applications include monoesters (abietates, lactates, myristates, palmitates, ricinoleates, stearates and tallates), diesters (adipates, azelates, itacontates, maleates, phthalates, terephthalates, sebacates, succinates, and tartrates), triesters (citrates, glycolate-phthalates, phosphates, and trimellitates), glycol esters, glycerol esters, amides, toluenesulfonamides, and tin diesters.

A final group of chemical additives are the UV-stabilizers. These additives are termed hindered amine light stabilizers (HALS). They function by trapping free-radicals, generated in the polymer by UV-light, forming nitroxyl groups that are efficient traps for other radicals. The UV-stabilizers are particularly useful in protecting pigment molecules from UV light bleaching. The HALS are known by tradenames such as Tinuvin, Chimassorb, Maxxim, Cyasorb, Good-rite, Topanex, Lupersol and Sanduvor.

Sometimes the chemical names for these compounds are quite long and the compound is listed in the mass spectral library by a tradename. An example is "octicizer", found in the Wiley MS collection. Some materials are listed in Table 3-117. The research literature contains some reports of analysis of environmental samples for these compounds as target analytes[40], however there have been no regulatory methods written specifically for them.

**Table 3-117. Plasticizers, anti-oxidants, flame retardants and other additives**

| Name | CAS | Structure |
|------|-----|-----------|
| 2.6-Bis(1,1-dimethylethyl)-4-methyl phenol; butylated hydroxytoluene (BHT) | 38222-83-2 | $H_3C$ — ring — OH, with $C(CH_3)_3$ groups top and bottom |
| Butlyated hydroxyanisole (BHA) | 489-01-0 | $H_3CO$ — ring — OH, with $C(CH_3)_3$ groups top and bottom |

Continued on next page.

---

40 Wright, S.J., M.J. Dale, P.R.R. Langridge-Smith, Q. Zhan, and R. Zenobi. "Selective in Situ Detection of Polymer Additives Using Laser Mass Spectrometry." *Anal. Chem.* 1996. 68(20). pp. 3585-3594.

**Table 3-117. Plasticizers, anti-oxidants, flame retardants and other additives,** *continued*

| Name | CAS | Structure |
|------|-----|-----------|
| Trioctyl trimellitate | 3319-31-1 | |
| Tris(2-chloroethyl) phosphate | 115-96-8 | $OP(OCH_2CH_2Cl)_3$ |
| Dimethylitacontate | 617-52-7 | $CH_3O_2CCH_2C(=CH)_2CO_2CH_3$ |
| Octicizer | 1241-94-7 | |
| Irganox 1076 | | |
| Irgafos 168 | | |
| Santo White | | |
| Tinuvin 327 | | |

## G. Endocrine disruptors

A recent book[41] has brought to public attention the potential environmental role of compounds that either mimic the action or block the synthesis/action of hormones within the endocrine systems of such diverse creatures as alligators, frogs, birds, seals, otters, and possibly humans. These compounds act as endocrine disruptors in nature at substantially lower concentrations than any toxicity-derived safe exposure limit. Many of the endocrine disruptors are suspected to be synergistic with each other. Certain combinations of compounds can result in highly active materials at levels where the individual compounds exhibit little to no effects.

Some of the compounds identified as endocrine disruptors have a long history as regulated environmental pollutants. These include many of the chlorinated hydrocarbon pesticides (chlordane, toxaphene, lindane, kepone, methoxychlor, kelthane, dieldrin, and the DDT family), triazine herbicides (atrazine, prometon, propazine, simazine, etc.), diethylstilbesrol, and some industrial chemicals and by-products (PCBs, dioxins, furans, bis(2-ethylhexyl) phthalate). Other compounds singled out as presenting significant problems, that have not attracted very much regulatory attention to date, include octachlorostyrene, synthetic pyrethroids, nonyl phenol and bisphenol-A. The last two materials are common substances arising from the surfactant (non-ionic surfactants) and plastics (epoxy resins) industries, respectively.

**Table 3-118. Some endocrine disruptors**

| Name | CAS | Structure |
|------|-----|-----------|
| Dicofol (kelthane) | 115-32-2 | |
| Chlordecone (kepone) | 143-50-0 | |
| 4,4'-DDT | 50-29-3 | |
| 4-Nonylphenol | 104-40-5 | |
| Bisphenol-A | 80-05-7 | |
| Diethylstilbestrol (DES) | 6898-97-1 | |

Regardless of the socio-political implications and predictions presented in the book, analytically speaking, determination of these compounds in environmental samples offers a substantial challenge. Although methods are available for analysis of all these materials, the detection capabilities of the techniques are at levels considerably higher

---

[41]   Colborn, T., D. Dumanoski and J.P. Myers. *Our Stolen Future*. 1996. Penguin Books, New York, NY.

than estimated requirements. These needed "safe" levels may range from the sub-part per trillion to sub-part per billion (fg/L to ng/L), over a thousand-fold more sensitivity than is commonly reported from environmental laboratories.

# Hazardous Waste and Remediation Analysis

## I. HAZARDOUS WASTE CHARACTERIZATION

Chemical hazards are everywhere there is industry, and most chemicals present health and environmental dangers. EPA is not concerned with the use of chemicals for manufacturing. A 55 gallon steel drum of 50% sodium cyanide in water solution is not a EPA hazard if it is intended to be used. However once the decision is made by the owner that the drum is not to be used, and he will dispose of it, then EPA becomes involved. The legislated responsibility of EPA is to oversee proper disposal of wastes to insure protection of human health and the environment. Hazardous wastes can be identified by one of two general processes. The first is a list of specific wastes from industrial sources that are designated as hazardous. EPA has four lists that cover these classifications of wastes, the F, K, P and U lists.

Hazardous wastes in the F- series are from generic industrial sources. An example is F007 - Spent cyanide plating bath solutions from electroplating operations.

Hazardous wastes in the K-series are from specific sources. An example is K024 - Distillation bottoms from the production of phthalic anhydride from naphthalene.

Hazardous wastes from commercial chemical products, intermediates and residues are listed in the P-series (acute hazard) and U-series (general hazard). Examples are P057 - 2-Fluoro acetamide (CAS No. 640-19-7) and U202 - Saccharin and salts (CAS No. 81-07-2).

These regulations and lists are presented in 40 CFR 261 and following. Section 268.40 of 40 CFR contains a lengthy table that presents treatment standards (and constituents) for each of the listed wastes. From an analytical standpoint the table contains the target analytes for each waste.

The other method for identifying hazardous wastes is to describe chemical properties or characteristics that the waste will exhibit if it is hazardous, and not be concerned with where the waste came from. Four characteristics of hazardous waste are recognized with specific test methods being listed for each characteristic in Chapter 7, SW-846 (EPA's methods manual for analysis of solid wastes).

## A. Ignitability Characteristic (D001)

A hazardous waste exhibits the characteristic of ignitability if a representative sample of the waste has any of the following properties.

1. The material is a liquid, other than an aqueous solution, containing less than 24% alcohol by volume and exhibits a Flash point <60 °C in a Pensky-Martens

closed cup flash tester under ASTM D-93-79 or D-93-80 (Methods 1010 or 1020).

2. The material is not a liquid and is capable under standard temperature and pressure conditions of causing a fire through friction, absorption of moisture, or spontaneous chemical changes and, when ignited, burns so vigorously and persistently that it creates a hazard.

3. The material is an ignitable compressed gas as defined in 49 CFR 173.300. A compressed gas is defined as any substance that exhibits a pressure of >40 psi at 70 °F in a cylinder or an absolute pressure of >104 psi at 130 °F. The gas is flammable if a mixture of 13% or less with air is flammable at atmospheric pressure and temperature. A gas is also considered to be flammable if it is found to be so with the Bureau of Explosives Flame Projection Apparatus, the Open Drum Apparatus or the Closed Drum Apparatus.

4. The material is an oxidizer as defined in 49 CFR 173.151. An oxidizer is any material that yields oxygen readily to stimulate combustion. Examples are chlorates ($ClO_3^-$), perchlorates ($ClO_4^-$), permanganates ($MnO_4^-$), peroxides (such as $H_2O_2$ or $Na_2O_2$), and nitrates ($NH_4NO_3$).

## B. Corrosivity Characteristic  (D002)

A hazardous waste exhibits the characteristic of corrosivity if a representative sample of the waste has either of the following properties:

1. The material is aqueous and exhibits a pH >12.5 or <2 (Methods 9040 and 9041).

2. The material is a liquid and corrodes SAE 1020 steel at a rate >6.35 mm (0.250 inch) per year at a temperature of 55 °C (Method 1110).

A problem with the first laboratory test is that the pH of alkaline solutions changes drastically with temperature[1]. This is illustrated in Figure 4-1, where the inverse relationship of temperature to pH and $pK_w$ is shown. Alkaline solutions which are considered hazardous under the corrosivity characteristic by virtue of a pH slightly greater than 12.5 at room temperature (20 °C) can pass the characteristic if stored above room temperature (25 °C). This is completely converse to physical reality where increasing the temperature of a solution will always make it more corrosive, as demonstrated in the second test for the characteristic, where an elevated temperature is used to complete the test in a shorter period of time. A standard temperature of 25 °C should always be used for corrosivity characterization by pH; however, this is not expressly included in the test description.

---

[1] Meiggs, T.O. "pH in Alkaline Solutions." *Environmental Testing & Analysis.* 1994. 3(1). pp. 58-61.

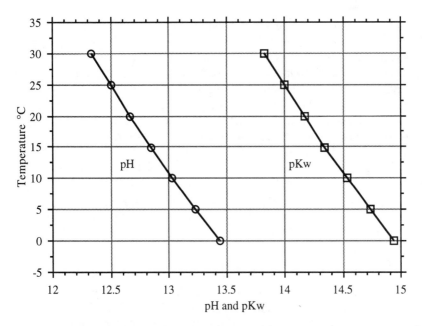

**Figure 4-1.** **Relationship of temperature to pK$_w$ and pH for constant strength alkaline solution.**

## C. Reactivity Characteristic (D003)

A hazardous waste exhibits the characteristic of reactivity if a representative sample of the waste has any of the following properties:

1. The material is normally unstable and readily undergoes violent change without detonating.

2. The material reacts violently with water.

3. The material forms potentially explosive mixtures with water.

4. When mixed with water, the material generates toxic gases or fumes in a quantity hazardous to human health or the environment.

5. The material is a sulfide- or cyanide-containing substance, which, in the pH range 2 to 12.5, can generate H$_2$S or HCN in a quantity hazardous to human health or the environment. (In order to test for this characteristic use Method 7.3.3.2 and 7.3.4.2 for distillation of HCN and H$_2$S from acidified wastes, followed by analysis by Methods 9010 and 9030 respectively).

6. The material will detonate if subjected to a strong initiating source or is heated while confined.

7. The material is capable of detonation or explosive decomposition under standard temperature and pressure conditions.

8. The material is a Class A or Class B explosive as defined in 49 CFR 173.51, 49 CFR 173.53, or 49 CFR 173.88.

## D. Toxicity Characteristic

The TCLP was formalized and revised from the previous EP toxicity test in Federal Register Vol. 55, No. 61, 29 March, 1990, pages 11798-11877. Toxicity consists of a list of specific substances whose presence in a waste above a set level is considered to be toxic. These specific substances are given a D-series code, such as D012 for Endrin. However, the existence of these substances in the waste does not render the waste hazardous as long as they stay in the waste. Occasionally waste is placed in a municipal landfill when it properly belongs in a controlled hazardous waste facility. The biggest difference between the two types of waste facility is that the hazardous waste site is completely isolated from the surrounding environment, while most municipal landfills are in intimate contact with the ground[2]. As rainwater percolates down through the landfill and mixes with the acidic products of organic decomposition, many materials become solubilized and travel down toward the groundwater. The Toxic Characteristic Leaching Procedure (TCLP, Method 1311) is used to mimic the organic acid leaching of hazardous contaminants from municipal landfills.

## E. TCLP (Method 1311, Reference 41[*])

The TCLP is actually a sample processing procedure that precedes any analytical sample preparation. Table 4-1 lists the target analytes under the TCLP. It consists of determination of the percent solids in the waste, determination of the pH, separation of solid from liquid phases, reduction of the particle size of the solid, extraction of the solid with agitation for 18 hours, filtration of the extract, combination of the extract with any original liquid phase, and preservation of the extract for analysis by the required methods (Table 4.2). These procedures are outlined in the flowchart in Figure 4-2. The pH of the sample will determine which of two extraction fluids will be used. For acidic or neutral samples an acetic acid-sodium acetate buffered fluid is used. For basic materials, an acetic acid solution is used. These fluids mimic the acidic "soup" generated in the municipal landfill from the decomposition of organic wastes. A number of the analytes are volatile, and a special extraction-filtration apparatus called a Zero Headspace Extractor (ZHE) is used to process these analytes. Reports of TCLP analyte determinations are based on the level of contaminants in the extraction fluid. They are not corrected to the original waste.

**Table 4-1. Substances listed under TCLP Toxicity Characteristic**

| HW No. | Contaminant | Regulatory Level (mg/L) |
|--------|-------------|-------------------------|
| D004 | Arsenic | 5.0 |
| D005 | Barium | 100.0 |
| D018 | Benzene | 0.5 |
| D006 | Cadmium | 1.0 |
| D019 | Carbon tetrachloride | 0.5 |
| D020 | Chlordane | 0.03 |
| D021 | Chlorobenzene | 100.0 |

Continued on next page.

---

[2] Newer municipal landfills must meet subtitle D regulations, which require liners and leachate collection and treatment capability.

[*] This and other references cited in titles refer to the reference number found in Appendix D of this book

**Table 4-1. Substances listed under TCLP Toxicity Characteristic,** *continued*

| HW No. | Contaminant | Regulatory Level (mg/L) |
|--------|-------------|-------------------------|
| D022 | Chloroform | 6.0 |
| D007 | Chromium | 5.0 |
| D023 | o-Cresol | 200.0 |
| D024 | m-Cresol | 200.0 |
| D025 | p-Cresol | 200.0 |
| D026 | Cresol[3] | 200.0 |
| D016 | 2,4-D | 10.0 |
| D027 | 1,4-Dichlorobenzene | 7.5 |
| D028 | 1,2-Dichloroethane | 0.5 |
| D029 | 1,1-Dichloroethylene | 0.7 |
| D030 | 2,4-Dinitrotoluene | 0.13 |
| D012 | Endrin | 0.02 |
| D031 | Heptachlor (and its epoxide) | 0.008 |
| D032 | Hexachlorobenzene | 0.13 |
| D033 | Hexachlorobutadiene | 0.5 |
| D034 | Hexachloroethane | 3.0 |
| D008 | Lead | 5.0 |
| D013 | Lindane | 0.4 |
| D009 | Mercury | 0.2 |
| D014 | Methoxychlor | 10.0 |
| D035 | Methyl ethyl ketone | 200.0 |
| D036 | Nitrobenzene | 2.0 |
| D037 | Pentachlorophenol | 100.0 |
| D038 | Pyridine | 5.0 |
| D010 | Selenium | 1.0 |
| D011 | Silver | 5.0 |
| D039 | Tetrachloroethylene | 0.7 |
| D015 | Toxaphene | 0.5 |
| D040 | Trichloroethylene | 0.5 |
| D041 | 2,4,5-Trichlorophenol | 400.0 |
| D042 | 2,4,6-Trichlorophenol | 2.0 |
| D017 | 2,4,5-TP (Silvex) | 1.0 |
| D043 | Vinyl chloride | 0.2 |

[3] Total cresol or the separate isomers may be determined. If total cresol is determined, the regulatory level is 200.0 mg/L, while if the individual isomers are determined, each has a regulatory level of 200.0 mg/L.

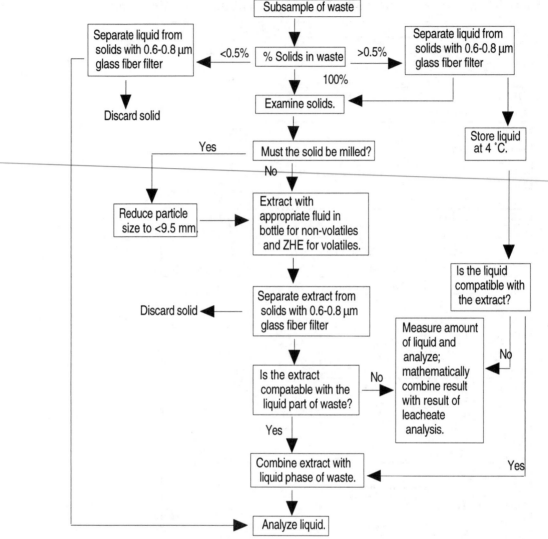

**Figure 4-2. Flowchart of TCLP.**

**Table 4-2. Analytical Methods required under TCLP**

| Volatiles (8260) | Metals (6010) |
|---|---|
| Benzene | Arsenic |
| Carbon tetrachloride | Barium |
| Chlorobenzene | Cadmium |
| Chloroform | Chromium |
| 1,2-Dichloroethane | Lead |
| 1,1-Dichloroethylene | Mercury (7471) |
| Methyl ethyl ketone | Selenium |
| Tetrachloroethylene | Silver |
| Trichloroethylene | |
| Vinyl chloride | |

Continued on next page.

**Table 4-2. Analytical Methods required under TCLP,** *continued*

| Semivolatiles (8270) |
| --- |
| Cresols |
| 1,4-Dichlorobenzene |
| 2,4-Dinitrotoluene |
| Hexachlorobenzene |
| Hexachlorobutadiene |
| Hexachloroethane |
| Nitrobenzene |
| Pentachlorophenol |
| 2,4,5-Trichlorophenol |
| 2,4,6-Trichlorophenol |
| Pyridine |

| Herbicides (8150) |
| --- |
| 2,4-D |
| 2,4,5-TP (Silvex) |

| Pesticides (8080) |
| --- |
| Chlordane |
| Endrin |
| Heptachlor (and epoxide) |
| Lindane |
| Methoxychlor |
| Toxaphene |

## Method 1312:  Synthetic Precipitation Leaching Procedure

This method is designed to mimic the effect of acidic rainfall on wastes and soils. Operationally it is very similar to TCLP except extraction fluid #1 is pH 4.20 $H_2SO_4/HNO_3$ (60/40) for soil samples east of the Mississippi River and all wastes and wastewaters, extraction fluid #2 is pH 5.00 $H_2SO_4/HNO_3$ (60/40) for testing the leachability of soils west of the Mississippi River, and extraction fluid #3 is reagent water for extraction of volatile organics and cyanide.

## II.  GROUNDWATER MONITORING

A topic of increased interest is the monitoring of groundwater contamination by municipal landfill leachate. The EPA has instituted an extensive groundwater monitoring program based on downgradient monitoring wells as landfill checks. Rather than a specific regulatory limit for contaminants, the requirement is to detect a statistically significant increase of contaminants in the downgradient wells over those in the normal background, which is determined by simultaneous monitoring of upgradient wells. The statistically significant increase is determined through use of one of several approved spreadsheet/ statistical programs[4]. The analytes are required to be checked on a regular basis - four times a year being recommended[5]. These are known as the Appendix I analytes (40 CFR Part 258, Appendix I). They were chosen to require only two analytical methods and thereby ease the cost burden on the regulated community. Several states have modified the original intent of the leacheate monitoring program by applying drinking water MCLs as minimum detection levels for the Appendix I analyses. This requires switching from ICP-AES to either GFAA or ICP-MS to meet the detection levels and results in a significant increase in the costs of the monitoring.

---

[4]  GSAS  Intelligent Decision Technologies, Ltd, 3308 Fourth St, Boulder, CO 80304.  GRITS and GRITSTAT version 4.14 USEPA Office of Solid Waste; SAGE  PC Engineering Inc., PO Box 52712, Knoxville, TN 37950-2712. A spreadsheet program for data entry into GRITS.

[5]  "Solid Waste Disposal Facility Criteria; Final Rule." *Federal Register*. October 9, 1991.  pp. 50978-51119.

**Table 4-3. Appendix I Target Analytes for landfill leachate monitoring**

| Inorganic Constituents (Method 6010) | |
|---|---|
| Antimony | Lead |
| Arsenic | Nickel |
| Barium | Selenium |
| Beryllium | Silver |
| Cadmium | Thallium |
| Chromium | Vanadium |
| Cobalt | Zinc |
| Copper | |

| Organic Constituents (Method 8260) | |
|---|---|
| Acetone | *trans*-1,3-Dichloropropene |
| Acrylonitrile | Ethylbenzene |
| Benzene | 2-Hexanone |
| Bromodichloromethane | Methyl chloride |
| Bromoform | Methylene bromide |
| Carbon disulfide | Methylene chloride |
| Carbon tetrachloride | Methyl ethyl ketone |
| Chlorobenzene | Methyl iodide |
| Chloroethane | 4-Methyl-2-pentanone |
| Chloroform | Styrene |
| Dibromochloromethane | 1,1,1,2-Tetrachloroethane |
| 1,2-Dibromo-3-chloropropane | 1,1,2,2-Tetrachloroethane |
| 1,2-Dibromoethane | Tetrachloroethene |
| 1,2-Dichlorobenzene | Toluene |
| 1,4-Dichlorobenzene | 1,1,1-Trichloroethane |
| *trans*-1,4-Dichloro-2-butene | 1,1,2-Trichloroethane |
| 1,1-Dichloroethane | Trichloroethene |
| 1,2-Dichloroethane | Trichlorofluoromethane |
| 1,1-Dichloroethene | 1,2,3-Trichloropropane |
| *cis*-1,2-Dichloroethene | Vinyl acetate |
| *trans*-1,2-Dichloroethene | Vinyl chloride |
| 1,2-Dichloropropane | Xylenes |
| *cis*-1,3-Dichloropropene | |

If any of the Appendix I analytes are detected during the periodic monitoring, assessment monitoring with the Appendix II analytes begins. Appendix II contains many target analytes, covering a number of methods, as illustrated in the Tables.

**Table 4-4.   Analyte Groups in 40 CFR Part 258, Appendix II**

| Analyte Group | Number of Analytes | Test Method |
|---|---|---|
| Chlorinated Acid Herbicides | 4 | 8150 |
| Chlorinated Pesticides | 19 | 8080 |
| PCBs | 6 | 8080 |
| Semivolatile Organics | 112 | 8270 |
| Volatile Organics | 61 | 8260 |
| Metals | 16 | 6010 |
| Cyanide | 1 | 9010 |
| Sulfide | 1 | 9030 |
| Mercury | 1 | 7470 |

**Table 4-5. Semivolatile Organic Target Analytes from Appendix II by Method 8270**

| Target Analyte | PQL ug/L | Target Analyte | PQL ug/L |
|---|---|---|---|
| Acenaphthene | 10 | Acenaphthylene | 10 |
| Acetonphenone | 10 | 2-Acetylaminofluorene | 20 |
| 4-Aminobiphenyl | 20 | Anthracene | 10 |
| Benzo(a)anthracene | 10 | Benzo(b)fluoranthene | 10 |
| Benzo(k)fluoranthene | 10 | Benzo(ghi)perylene | 10 |
| Benzo(a)pyrene | 10 | Benzyl alcohol | 20 |
| Bis(2-chloroethoxy)methane | 10 | Bis(2-chloroethyl)ether | 10 |
| Bis(2-chloroisopropyl)ether | 10 | Bis(2-ethylhexyl)phthalate | 20 |
| 4-Bromophenyl phenyl ether | 10 | Butyl benzyl phthalate | 10 |
| p-Chloroaniline | 20 | 4-Chloro-3-methylphenol | 20 |
| Chlorobenzilate | 10 | 2-Chloronaphthalene | 10 |
| 2-Chlorophenol | 10 | 4-Chlorophenyl phenyl ether | 10 |
| Chrysene | 10 | m-Cresol | 10 |
| o-Cresol | 10 | p-Cresol | 10 |
| Diallate | 10 | Dibenz(a,h)anthracene | 10 |
| Dibenzofuran | 10 | Di-n-butyl phthalate | 10 |
| 1,2-Dichlorobenzene | 10 | 1,3-Dichlorobenzene | 10 |
| 1,4-Dichlorobenzene | 10 | 3,3'-Dichlorobenzidine | 20 |
| 2,4-Dichlorophenol | 10 | 2,6-Dichlorophenol | 10 |
| Diethyl phthalete | 10 | Thionazin | 20 |
| Dimethoate | 20 | p-(Dimethylamino)azobenzene | 10 |
| 7,12-Dimethylbenz(a)anthracene | 10 | 3,3'-Dimethylbenzidine | 10 |
| 2,4-Dimethylphenol | 10 | Dimethyl phthalate | 10 |
| m-Dinitrobenzene | 20 | 4,6-Dinitro-2-methylphenol | 50 |
| 2,4-Dinitrophenol | 50 | 2,4-Dinitrotoluene | 10 |
| 2,6-Dinitrotoluene | 10 | Di-n-octyl phthalate | 10 |
| Diphenylamine | 10 | Disulfoton | 10 |
| Ethyl methansulfonate | 20 | Famphur | 20 |
| Fluoranthene | 10 | Fluorene | 10 |
| Hexachlorobenzene | 10 | Hexachlorobutadiene | 10 |
| Hexachlorocyclopentadiene | 10 | Hexachloroethane | 10 |
| Hexachloropropene | 10 | Indeno(1,2,3-cd)pyrene | 10 |
| Isodrin | 20 | Isophorone | 10 |
| Isosafrole | 10 | Kepone | 20 |
| Methapyrilene | 100 | 3-Methylcholanthrene | 10 |
| Methyl methanesulfonate | 10 | 2-Methylnaphthalene | 10 |
| Methyl parathion | 10 | Naphthalene | 10 |
| 1,4-Naphthoquinone | 10 | 1-Naphthylamine | 10 |
| 2-Naphthylamine | 10 | 2-Nitroaniline | 50 |
| 3-Nitroaniline | 50 | 4-Nitroaniline | 20 |
| Nitrobenzene | 10 | 2-Nitrophenol | 10 |
| 4-Nitrophenol | 50 | N-Nitrosodi-n-butylamine | 10 |
| N-Nitrosodiethylamine | 20 | N-Nitrosodimethylamine | 10 |
| N-Nitrosodiphenylamine | 10 | N-Nitrosodipropylamine | 10 |
| N-Nitrosomethylethylamine | 10 | N-Nitrosopiperidine | 20 |
| N-Nitrosopyrrolidine | 40 | 5-Nitro-o-toluidine | 10 |
| Parathion | 10 | Pentachlorobenzene | 10 |
| Pentachloronitrobenzene | 20 | Pentachlorophenol | 50 |

Continued on next page.

**Table 4-5. Semivolatile Organic Target Analytes from Appendix II by Method 8270,** *continued*

| Target Analyte | PQL ug/L | Target Analyte | PQL ug/L |
|---|---|---|---|
| Phenacetin | 20 | Phenanthrene | 10 |
| Phenol | 100 | p-Phenylenediamine | 10 |
| Phorate | 10 | Pronamide | 200 |
| Pyrene | 10 | Safrole | 10 |
| 1,2,4,5-Tetrachlorobenzene | 10 | 2,3,4,6-Tetrachlorophenol | 10 |
| o-Toluidine | 10 | 1,2,4-Trichlorobenzene | 10 |
| 2,4,5-Trichlorophenol | 10 | 2,4,6-Trichlorophenol | 10 |
| O,O,O-Triethyl phosphorothiolate | 10 | 1,3,5-Trinitrobenzene | 10 |

**Table 4-6. Volatile Organic Target Analytes from Appendix II by Method 8260**

| Target Analyte | PQL ug/L | Target Analyte | PQL ug/L |
|---|---|---|---|
| Acetone | 100 | Acetonitrile | - |
| Acrolein | 100 | Acrylonitrile | 200 |
| Allyl chloride | 10 | Benzene | 5 |
| Bromochloromethane | 5 | Bromodichloromethane | 5 |
| Bromoform | 5 | Carbon disulfide | 100 |
| Carbon tetrachloride | 10 | Chlorobenzene | 5 |
| Chloroethane | 10 | Chloroform | 5 |
| Chloroprene | 20 | Dibromochloromethane | 5 |
| 1,2-Dibromo-3-chloropropane | 25 | 1,2-Dibromoethane | 5 |
| 1,2-Dichlorobenzene | 5 | 1,3-Dichlorobenzene | 5 |
| 1,4-Dichlorobenzene | 5 | trans-1,4-Dichloro-2-butene | 100 |
| Dichlorodifluoromethane | 5 | 1,1-Dichloroethane | 5 |
| 1,2-Dichloroethane | 5 | 1,1-Dichloroethene | 5 |
| cis-1,2-Dichloroethene | 5 | trans-1,2-Dichloroethene | 5 |
| 1,2-Dichloropropane | 5 | 1,3-Dichloropropane | 5 |
| 2,2-Dichloropropane | 15 | 1,1-Dichloropropene | 5 |
| cis-1,3-Dichloropropene | 10 | trans-1,3-Dichloropropene | 10 |
| Ethylbenzene | 5 | Ethyl methacrylate | 10 |
| 2-Hexanone | 50 | iso-Butyl alcohol | 100 |
| Methacrylonitrile | 100 | Bromomethane | 10 |
| Chloromethane | 10 | Methyl ethyl ketone | 100 |
| Iodomethane | 10 | Methylmethacrylate | 30 |
| Methyl isobutyl ketone | 100 | Methylene bromide | 10 |
| Methylene chloride | 10 | Naphthalene | 5 |
| Priopronitrile | 150 | Styrene | 10 |
| 1,1,1,2-Tetrachloroethane | 5 | 1,1,2,2-Tetrachloroethane | 5 |
| Tetrachloroethene | 5 | Toluene | 5 |
| 1,1,1-Trichloroethane | 5 | 1,1,2-Trichloroethane | 5 |
| Trichloroethene | 5 | Trichlorofluoromethane | 5 |
| Vinyl acetate | 50 | Vinyl chloride | 10 |
| Xylene | 5 | | |

**Table 4-7.** **Organochlorine Pesticide Target Analytes from Appendix II by Method 8080**

| Target Analyte | PQL ug/L | Target Analyte | PQL ug/L |
|---|---|---|---|
| Aldrin | 0.05 | α-BHC | 0.05 |
| β-BHC | 0.05 | δ-BHC | 0.1 |
| γ-BHC | 0.05 | Chlordane | 0.1 |
| 4,4'-DDD | 0.1 | 4,4'-DDE | 0.05 |
| 4,4'-DDT | 0.1 | Dieldrin | 0.05 |
| Endosulfan I | 0.1 | Endosulfan II | 0.05 |
| Endosulfan sulfate | 0.5 | Endrin | 0.1 |
| Endrin aldehyde | 0.2 | Heptachlor | 0.05 |
| Heptachlor epoxide | 1 | Methoxychlor | 2 |
| PCBs | 50 | Toxaphene | 2 |

**Table 4-8.** **Metal Elements Target Analytes from Appendix II by Method 6010**

| Target Analyte | PQL ug/L | Target Analyte | PQL ug/L |
|---|---|---|---|
| Antimony | 300 | Arsenic | 500 |
| Barium | 20 | Beryllium | 3 |
| Cadmium | 40 | Chromium | 70 |
| Cobalt | 70 | Copper | 60 |
| Lead | 400 | Nickel | 150 |
| Selenium | 750 | Silver | 70 |
| Thalium | 400 | Tin | 40 |
| Vanadium | 80 | Zinc | 20 |

**Table 4-9.** **Chlorinated Acid Herbicide Target Analytes from Appendix II by Method 8150**

| Target Analyte | PQL ug/L | Target Analyte | PQL ug/L |
|---|---|---|---|
| 2,4-D | 10 | Dinoseb | 1 |
| 2,4,5-TP | 2 | 2,4,5-T | 2 |

**Table 4-10.** **Miscellaneous Target Analytes from Appendix II**

| Target Analyte | PQL ug/L | Target Analyte | PQL ug/L |
|---|---|---|---|
| Cyanide | 200 | Mercury | 2 |
| Sulfide | 4000 | | |

# III. UNDERGROUND STORAGE TANKS

There are a tremendous number of underground storage tanks (UST) used for a wide variety of purposes in the United States. The most common purpose is the storage of refined petroleum products for fuel at gas stations and other facilities. Many of these are leaking. The EPA oversees, and the states implement remediation of, the leaking underground storage tanks (LUST). There are a wide variety of analytical methods that are used to support these programs, almost as many as there are states.

The analytical challenge is two-fold. First, the petroleum analyte must be removed from the solid or water matrix and second, a qualitative and quantitative determination of the analyte is performed. Often the first is predetermined by the choice of the second.

The common methods for determination of the petroleum products are gas chromatography (GC) with a variety of detectors and infrared spectrophotometry (IR). Other far less common methods are gravimetric, immunoassay, and colorimetric. Traditional gas chromatographic analysis within the petroleum industry has concentrated upon characterization of the oil as to the boiling range (simulated distillation) and PONA (parafins, olefins, naphthalenes and aromatics). Environmental qualitative determinations of petroleum range from characterization as oil & grease to geographic location of the origin of the petroleum. Total petroleum hydrocarbons (TPH), total benzene, toluene, ethylbenzene and xylene (BTEX), gasoline range organics; (GRO) and diesel range organics (DRO) are the most common requested determinations, although further classification as to gasoline, diesel, kerosene, aviation fuel, mineral spirits, *etc.* is sometimes requested. Additionally, the determination of oxygenates in the fuel is becoming more commonplace. These are ethanol, methyl *tert*-butyl ether (MTBE), methyl *tert*-amyl ether (TAME), or ethyl *tert*-butyl ether (ETBE). Other than ethanol, the oxygenates can be calibrated and run as target analytes using purge and trap GC or GC-MS. Ethanol is miscible with water and can most effectively be determined by direct injection into a GC-FID with either a Pora-Pac Q packed -column or a PLOT capillary column

The common extraction methods are liquid-liquid separatory funnel, continuous liquid-liquid extractor, soxhlet extractor, ultrasonic horn, ultrasonic bath, purge & trap, and headspace. Listed in Table 4-11 are some of the variety of analytical methods required for similar parameters from a random selection of State UST programs.

### Table 4-11. Analytical Methods required for UST Characterizations from a random selection of State programs

| State | Parameter | Approved Methods[6] |
|---|---|---|
| Missouri [7] | BTEX | 8020 or 8240 |
| | TRPH | 418.1 modified to mix sample with anh. $Na_2SO_4$, pack into a column and elute in a single pass with 100 mL Freon-113 |
| | Heavy metals | 1311 (TCLP extraction)/6010 |
| Mississippi[8] | BTEX | 602, 624, 8020, 8240 or 8260 |
| | TPH | 418.1 or SM 503E |
| Texas[9] | BTEX + MTBE | 5030/8020 |
| | TPH (water) | 418.1 or ASTM D-3328-78, method B (capillary column FID-GC) with samples and standard oil prepared as in 418.1 |
| | TPH (soil) | Extraction by 3540 or 3550 with Freon, analysis as for water. |
| | TDS [10] | 160.1 |

Continued on next page.

---

[6]  All methods EPA unless otherwise indicated.

[7]  Underground Storage Tank Closure Guidance Document, January 1992, Missouri Department of Natural Resources, Division of Environmental Quality, Water Pollution Control Program, P.O. Box 176 Jefferson City MO 65102.

[8]  State of Mississippi Underground Storage Tank Program Sampling Policy for Petroleum Tank Closures, October, 1991, Mississippi Department of Environmental Quality, Office of Pollution Control P.O. Box 10385, Jackson, MS 39289-0385.

[9]  *Guidance Manual for LPST Cleanups in Texas*, January 1990, Texas Water Commission, Petroleum Storage Tank Division, P.O. Box 13087, Austin, TX 78701.

[10]  Remediation goal levels for benzene, BTEX and TPH depend on initial TDS values for the groundwater.

**Table 4-11.  Analytical Methods required for UST Characterizations from a random selection of State programs,** *continued*

| State | Parameter | Approved Methods[11] |
|---|---|---|
| Illinois[12] | BTEX | any appropriate method from SW-846 |
| | PAH | any appropriate method from SW-846 |
| | Metals | TCLP plus any appropriate method from SW-846 |
| | BNA | any appropriate method from SW-846 |
| | Pesticides | any appropriate method from SW-846 |
| South Carolina[13,14] | BTEX + MTBE | 602 or 5030/8020 for water, 5030/8020 for soil |
| | TPH gasoline | 5030/FID-GC |
| | TPH diesel | 3510/FID-GC for water, 3550/FID-GC for soil |
| | TPH waste oil | 9070 with silica gel clean-up for water, 9071 with silica gel clean-up for soil. |
| | PAH (water) | 610, 625, 3510/8100, 8270 or 8310 |
| | PAH (soil) | 3550/8100, 8270 or 8310 |
| | Mercury (water) | 245.1, 245.2, 7470 or 7471 |
| | Mercury (soil) | 7470 or 7471 |
| | Metals | digestion followed by FLAA, GFAA or ICP |
| California[15] | TPH (TRPH) | SCL 418[16] for waters and 418 with Freon hand shake extraction of soil/sodium sulfate mixture |
| | TPH as gasoline (GRO) and BTEX | Headspace/FID-GC (SCL 818) or purge & trap/FID-GC (SCL 815) (methanol extraction of soils) |
| | TPH as diesel (DRO) | SCL 816, waters are extracted with Freon, soils are mixed with sodium sulfate and shaken with carbon disulfide, methylene choride or Freon, then analyzed by direct injection FID-GC |
| | Organolead | Extract with xylene then react with Aliquat336[17]/MIBK and $I_2$/benzene and analyze by FLAA for lead. |

Continued on next page.

Continued on next page.

---

[11]  All methods EPA unless otherwise indicated.

[12]  *Leaking Underground Storage Tank Soil Sampling Requirements*, February 1993, Illinois Environmental Protection Agency, Bureau of Land, 2200 Churchill Road, Springfield, IL 62794-9276.

[13]  *Petroleum Hydrocarbon Analytical Methology for Ground-water and Soil Assessment*, January, 21, 1992, South Carolina Department of Health and Environmental Control, Laboratory Certification Section, P.O. Box 72, State Park, SC 29147.

[14]  "The laboratory may use an alternate analytical technique that has at least equivalent detection limits, precision, and accuracy as the referenced method, if approval is obtained from the GWPD prior to use.  Use of alternate columns and gas chromatographic operating conditions is encouraged to obtain better sensitivity and quantitation of the contaminants of interest.  Laboratories are also encouraged to develop new analytical techniques for identifying the type of contamination as well as the extent of contamination...EPA method 418.1 will not be used for TPH analyses conducted for groundwater and soil assessment."

[15]  *Guidelines for Choosing the Proper Analytical Methods for TPH Analysis*, Rev. No. 1, February 3, 1992, State of California Department of Health Services, California Leaking Underground Fuel Tank Task Force, 2151 Berkeley Way, Berkeley, CA 94704-1011.

[16]  Southern California Laboratory modification of EPA method 418.1.

[17]  Tricapryl methyl ammonium chloride.

**Table 4-11. Analytical Methods required for UST characterizations from a random selection of state programs, *continued***

| State | Parameter | Approved Methods [18] |
|---|---|---|
| Tennessee [19] | GRO + BTEX | Purge & trap FID-GC or PID/FID-GC, high level soils extracted with methanol then a portion of the methanol is added to water and purged. Standards, calibration and surrogates are specific in the TN method. |
| | DRO | Waters are extracted by separatory funnel or continuous liquid-liquid extraction and soils by sonication, both with methylene chloride, analysis by FID-GC. Standards, calibration and surrogates are specific in the TN method. |
| Wisconsin [20] | GRO | Wisconsin modified GRO, all soils preserved in methanol, purge and trap FID-GC or PID/FID-GC |
| | DRO | Wisconsin modified DRO, soils extracted in VOA vial by sonication, waters extracted by 3010 or 3020, analysis by FID-GC |
| | VOC | 5030/8021 or 8260 |
| | PVOC | 5030/8020, 8021 or 8260 |
| | PAH | 8310, 3540/8270, or 3550/8270 |
| | PCB | 3540 or 3550/8080 or 3510 or 3520/8080 |
| | Lead | 3020 or 3050/7420, 7421 or 6010 |
| | Cadmium | 3020 or 3050/7130, 7131 or 6010 |
| | Cyanide | 7.3.3.2 of SW-846 |
| | Sulfide | 7.3.4.2 of SW-846 |
| | Free liquids | 9095 |
| | % moisture | 7.3.3.1.5 of SW-846 |
| | Oil & grease | 413.1 |
| | TSS | 160.2 |
| Florida [21] | BTEX | 602, or 5030/8020 |
| | 1,2-Dichloroethane | 601 or 5030/8010 |
| | Total volatile aromatics | 602 or 5030/8020 |
| | Volatile halocarbons | 601 or 5030/8010 |
| | TPH | 418.1 or 9073 |
| | PAH | 610, 625, 8100, 8250, 8270 |

Continued on next page.

---

[18] All methods EPA unless otherwise indicated.

[19] State of Tennessee Department of Environment and Conservation, Division of Underground Storage Tanks, 4th Floor L & C Tower, 401 Church St, Nashville, TN 37243-1541.

[20] *Leaking Underground Storage Tank (LUST) and Petroleum Analytical and Quality Assurance Guide,* July 1993, PUBL-SW-13093, Wisconsin Department of Natural Resources, P.O. Box 7921 Madison, WI 53707.

[21] Florida FAC Rule 17.770, 1993.

**Table 4-11.** **Analytical Methods required for UST Characterizations from a random selection of State programs,** *continued*

| State | Parameter | Approved Methods[22] |
|-------|-----------|---------------------|
| New Mexico[23] | Gasoline | Field analysis of headspace in a 500 mL jar half full of soil with a PID or FID OVA. |
| | | Laboratory analysis by 8240 |
| | TPH | 418.1 or prior approved equivalent method |
| Washington[24] | Identification | WTPH-HCID GC direct injection of methylene chloride extract of soils or water to identify petroleum fraction |
| | GRO | WTPH-G methanol extract of soil or direct water sample is purged into FID-GC. Trifluorotoluene and bromofluorobenzene surrogates, total envelope to dodecane quantitated |
| | DRO | WTPH-D 3510 for water and either 3540 or 3550 extraction for soils with methylene chloride followed by FID-GC. 2-Fluorobiphenyl and *o*- or *p*-terphenyl surrogates used and total envelope dodecane to tetracosane quantitated. |
| | TPH | WTPH-418.1 for heavy petroleum oils other than DRO or GRO. 3510 for water and either 3540 or 3550 with freon for soils |
| Arizona[25] | TPH-IR | Method BLS-181, 20 g soils are extracted by shaking 30 min with freon in a 40 mL VOA vial with sodium sulfate and silica gel. Aqueous samples are extracted with freon. 418.1 analysis at 2930 cm$^{-1}$. |
| | BTEX | Method BLS-191, 193, Soil is extracted with methanol (40 mL VOA vial), then extract or aqueous sample 5030/8015. Peak height quantitation. Surrogates are benzotrifluoride and bromochloropropane |
| | DRO | Method BLS-191, Freon or methylene chloride extraction of soil (40 mL VOA vial with sodium sulfate and silica gel) 10 mL extract conc. to 1.0 mL then 8015. All peaks C10 to C22 above baseline are integrated. |
| Alaska[26] | GRO | Method AK101.0 Purge and trap GC-FID or PID/FID or water samples or methanol extracts of soil samples, baseline integration of C6 to C10 |
| | DRO | Method AK102.0 GC-FID analysis of methylene chloride extracts, baseline integration of C10 to C25 |
| | Residual Range Organics RRO | Method AK103.0 GC-FID analysis of methylene chloride extracts, baseline integration from C25 to C45 |

# IV. EPA CONTRACT LABORATORY PROGRAM

CLP and CLP deliverables are the magic buzz words among sales and promotion persons in the environmental business, despite there being very few CLP laboratories in the industry. The contract laboratory program exists so that the government and EPA will have sufficient laboratory capability to monitor the Superfund remediation projects authorized under CERCLA. The CLP is not a laboratory certification program. The only CLP laboratories are those holding current contracts with the EPA under the most

---

[22] All methods EPA unless otherwise indicated.
[23] Underground Storage Tank Regulations, EIB/USTR State of New Mexico, amended 1990.
[24] Total Petroleum Hydrocarbons Analytical Methods for Soil and Water, Washington State Department of Ecology, April, 1992.
[25] Arizona Department of Health Services, State Laboratory Services.
[26] Alaska Department of Environmental Conservation, AS44.46.03.100(a)(17), December 1993.

recent bid and accepted Statement of Work (SOW). Copies of the most recent CLP SOW are available from NTIS. Contact with the program is through the CLP technical project officer (TPO) at each of the EPA regional headquarters. Having an EPA contract under the CLP is predicated upon having the required number and types of instruments and technicians to perform the work as specified in the SOW, passing a set of PE samples related to the SOW, passing an on-site audit by the EPA, being able to produce all the required forms and documents related to the analysis as specified in the SOW in both hardcopy and electronic media (the deliverables), and finally being one of the low bidders for the current contract period.

The Statements of Work are not so much written toward producing the best data possible, but rather producing comparable data from a variety of laboratories of known quality that is legally defensible. Further there is distinct slant in the methods toward identification of what is possibly on the site, rather than rigorous quantitation of a select set of regulated analytes. Work undertaken by the EPA under CERCLA and supported by CLP laboratories is totally oriented toward litigation against the offending parties, thus all laboratory results must be ready for court challenge.

Two general SOWs are bid – the organic and the inorganic - and both exist in low-concentration, multi-concentration, and high-concentration versions. A SOW for dioxins is available. A SOW for air analysis exists in draft form, as does a Quick Turn-around SOW. The organic SOW contains methods and specifications for volatiles, semivolatiles, and pesticides/aroclors modeled after methods 8260, 8270 and 8080 respectfully. The inorganic multi-concentration SOW covers specifications for 22 metals, mercury, and cyanide, while the high-concentration version adds pH and conductivity to the analytes. The organic analytes are specified in the Target Compound List (TCL), while the inorganic analytes are specified in the Target Analyte List (TAL).

In addition to the TCL compounds the organic SOW requires reporting of tentatively identified compounds (TIC). These are components that are at least 10% of the response of the nearest internal standard and are searched against the mass spectral library for possible matches. The contractor must examine the 30 largest peaks in the volatile run for TIC and the 30 largest peaks in each extractable run that fit the criteria. If no match is found in the library, the peak is reported as unknown.

**Table 4-12. CLP[27] Inorganic Target Analyte List (TAL) for metals**

| Analyte | Method[28] | CRQL[29] ug/L |
|---|---|---|
| Aluminum | 200.7 | 200 |
| Antimony | 200.7, 204.2 | 60 |
| Arsenic | 200.7, 206.2 | 10 |
| Barium | 200.7 | 200 |
| Beryllium | 200.7, 210.2 | 5 |
| Cadmium | 200.7, 213.2 | 5 |
| Calcium | 200.7, 215.1 | 5000 |
| Chromium | 200.7, 218.2 | 10 |
| Cobalt | 200.7 | 50 |
| Copper | 200.7 | 25 |

Continued on next page.

---

[27] CLP-SOW ILM03

[28] All of these methods are modified for the CLP-SOW and are found in Exhibit D, ILM03.0.

[29] The CRDLs are the instrument detection limits obtained in pure water that must be met using the procedure in Exhibit E, ILM03.0. The detection limits for samples may be considerably higher, depending on the sample matrix.

**Table 4-12.  CLP[30] Inorganic Target Analyte List (TAL) for metals,** *continued*

| Analyte | Method[31] | CRQL[32] ug/L |
|---|---|---|
| Iron | 200.7 | 100 |
| Lead | 200.7, 239.2 | 3 |
| Magnesium | 200.7, 242.1 | 5000 |
| Manganese | 200.7 | 15 |
| Mercury | 245.1, 245.2, 245.5 | 0.2 |
| Nickel | 200.7 | 40 |
| Potassium | 200.7, 258.1 | 5000 |
| Selenium | 200.7, 270.2 | 5 |
| Silver | 200.7, 272.2 | 10 |
| Sodium | 200.7, 273.1 | 5000 |
| Thallium | 200.7, 279.2 | 10 |
| Vanadium | 200.7 | 50 |
| Zinc | 200.7 | 20 |
| Cyanide | 335.2 | 10 |

**Table 4-13.  CLP Forms included as deliverables with each sample for metals**

| Form | Title |
|---|---|
| I-IN | Inorganic Analysis Data Sheet |
| II(Part 1)-IN | Initial and Continuing Calibration Verification |
| II(Part 2)-IN | CRDL Standard for AA and ICP |
| III-IN | Blanks |
| IV-IN | ICP Interference Check Sample |
| V(Part 1)-IN | Spike Sample Recovery |
| V(Part 2)-IN | Post Digest Spike Sample Recovery |
| VI-IN | Duplicates |
| VII-IN | Laboratory Control Sample |
| VIII-IN | Standard Addition Results |
| IX-IN | ICP Serial Dilutions |
| X-IN | Instrument Detection Limits (Quarterly) |
| XI(Part 1)-IN | ICP Interelement Correction Factors (Annually) |
| XI(Part 2)-IN | ICP Interelement Correction Factors (Annually) |
| XII-IN | ICP Linear Ranges (Quarterly) |
| XIII-IN | Preparation Log |
| XIV-IN | Analysis Run Log |

---

[30]  CLP-SOW ILM03
[31]  All of these methods are modified for the CLP-SOW and are found in Exhibit D, ILM03.0.
[32]  The CRDLs are the instrument detection limits obtained in pure water that must be met using the procedure in Exhibit E, ILM03.0.  The detection limits for samples may be considerably higher, depending on the sample matrix.

## Table 4-14. CLP VOA Target Compound List (TCL)[33]

| Analyte | CAS | CRQL Water ug/L | CRQL Soil ug/kg |
|---|---|---|---|
| Chloromethane | 74-87-3 | 10 | 10 |
| Bromomethane | 74-83-9 | 10 | 10 |
| Vinyl chloride | 75-01-4 | 10 | 10 |
| Chloroethane | 75-00-3 | 10 | 10 |
| Methylene chloride | 75-09-2 | 10 | 10 |
| Acetone | 67-64-1 | 10 | 10 |
| Carbon disulfide | 75-15-0 | 10 | 10 |
| 1,1-Dichloroethene | 75-35-4 | 10 | 10 |
| 1,1-Dichloroethane | 75-34-3 | 10 | 10 |
| 1,2-Dichloroethene | 540-59-0 | 10 | 10 |
| Chloroform | 67-66-3 | 10 | 10 |
| 1,2-Dichloroethane | 107-06-2 | 10 | 10 |
| 2-Butanone | 78-93-3 | 10 | 10 |
| 1,1,1-Trichloroethane | 71-55-6 | 10 | 10 |
| Carbon tetrachloride | 56-23-5 | 10 | 10 |
| Bromodichloromethane | 75-27-4 | 10 | 10 |
| 1,2-Dichloropropane | 78-87-5 | 10 | 10 |
| cis-1,3-Dichloropropane | 10061-01-5 | 10 | 10 |
| Trichloroethene | 79-01-6 | 10 | 10 |
| Dibromochloromethane | 124-48-1 | 10 | 10 |
| 1,1,2-Trichloroethane | 79-00-5 | 10 | 10 |
| Benzene | 71-43-2 | 10 | 10 |
| trans-1,3-Dichloropropene | 10061-02-6 | 10 | 10 |
| Bromoform | 75-25-2 | 10 | 10 |
| 4-Methyl-2-pentanone | 108-10-1 | 10 | 10 |
| 2-Hexanone | 591-78-6 | 10 | 10 |
| Tetrachloroethene | 127-18-4 | 10 | 10 |
| 1,1,2,2-Tetrachloroethane | 79-34-5 | 10 | 10 |
| Toluene | 108-88-3 | 10 | 10 |
| Chlorobenzene | 108-90-7 | 10 | 10 |
| Ethylbenzene | 100-41-4 | 10 | 10 |
| Styrene | 100-42-5 | 10 | 10 |
| Xylenes (total) | 1330-20-7 | 10 | 10 |

---

[33] CLP-SOW OLM02.1, 1993.

## Table 4-15. CLP Forms included as deliverables with each sample for VOA

| Form | Title |
|---|---|
| I VOA | Volatile Organics Analysis Data Sheet |
| I VOA-TIC | Volatile Organics Analysis Data Sheet Tentatively Identified Compounds |
| II VOA-1 | Water Volatile System Monitoring Compound Recovery |
| II VOA-2 | Soil Volatile System Monitoring Compound Recovery |
| III VOA-1 | Water Volatile Matrix Spike/Matrix Spike Duplicate Recovery |
| III VOA-2 | Soil Volatile Matrix Spike/Matrix Spike Duplicate Recovery |
| IV VOA | Volatile Method Blank Summary |
| V VOA | Volatile Organic Instrument Performance Check Bromofluorobenzene (BFB) |
| VI VOA | Volatile Organics Initial Calibration Data |
| VII VOA | Volatile Continuing Calibration Check |
| VIII VOA | Volatile Internal Standard Area and RT Summary |

## Table 4-16. CLP Target Analyte List (TCL) for Semivolatile Organic Compounds[34]

| Analyte | CAS | CRQL Water ug/L | CRQL Soil ug/kg |
|---|---|---|---|
| Phenol | 108-95-2 | 10 | 330 |
| Bis(2-Chloroethyl)ether | 111-44-4 | 10 | 330 |
| 2-Chlorophenol | 95-57-8 | 10 | 330 |
| 1,3-Dichlorobenzene | 541-73-1 | 10 | 330 |
| 1,4-Dichlorobenzene | 106-46-7 | 10 | 330 |
| 1,2-Dichlorobenzene | 95-50-1 | 10 | 330 |
| 2-Methylphenol | 95-48-7 | 10 | 330 |
| 2,2'-oxybis(1-Chloropropane) | 108-60-1 | 10 | 330 |
| 4-Methylphenol | 106-44-5 | 10 | 330 |
| N-Nitroso-di-n-propylamine | 621-64-7 | 10 | 330 |
| Hexachloroethane | 67-72-1 | 10 | 330 |
| Nitrobenzene | 98-95-3 | 10 | 330 |
| Isophorone | 78-59-1 | 10 | 330 |
| 2-Nitrophenol | 88-75-5 | 10 | 330 |
| 2,4-Dimethylphenol | 105-67-9 | 10 | 330 |
| Bis(2-Chloroethoxy)methane | 111-91-1 | 10 | 330 |
| 2,4-Dichlorophenol | 120-83-2 | 10 | 330 |
| 1,2,4-Trichlorobenzene | 120-82-1 | 10 | 330 |
| Naphthalene | 91-20-3 | 10 | 330 |
| 4-Chloroaniline | 106-47-8 | 10 | 330 |
| Hexachlorobutadiene | 87-68-3 | 10 | 330 |
| 4-Chloro-3-methylphenol | 59-50-7 | 10 | 330 |
| 2-Methylnaphthalene | 91-57-6 | 10 | 330 |
| Hexachlorocyclopentadiene | 77-47-4 | 10 | 330 |
| 2,4,6-Trichlorophenol | 88-06-2 | 10 | 330 |
| 2,4,5-Trichlorophenol | 95-95-4 | 25 | 830 |
| 2-Chloronaphthalene | 91-58-7 | 10 | 330 |
| 2-Nitroaniline | 88-74-4 | 25 | 830 |
| Dimethylphthalate | 131-11-3 | 10 | 330 |

Continued on next page.

---

[34] CLP-SOW OLM02.1, 1993

**Table 4-16.  CLP Target Analyte List (TCL) for Semivolatile Organic Compounds[35], *continued***

| Analyte | CAS | CRQL Water ug/L | CRQL Soil ug/kg |
|---|---|---|---|
| Acenaphthylene | 208-96-8 | 10 | 330 |
| 2,6-Dinitrotoluene | 606-20-2 | 10 | 330 |
| 3-Nitroaniline | 99-09-2 | 25 | 830 |
| Acenaphthene | 83-32-9 | 10 | 330 |
| 2,4-Dinitrophenol | 51-28-5 | 25 | 830 |
| 4-Nitrophenol | 100-02-7 | 25 | 830 |
| Dibenzofuran | 132-64-9 | 10 | 330 |
| 2,4-Dinitrotoluene | 121-14-2 | 10 | 330 |
| Diethylphthalate | 84-66-2 | 10 | 330 |
| 4-Chlorophenylphenylether | 7005-72-3 | 10 | 330 |
| Fluorene | 86-73-7 | 10 | 330 |
| 4-Nitroaniline | 100-01-6 | 25 | 830 |
| 4,6-Dinitro-2-methylphenol | 534-52-1 | 25 | 830 |
| N-Nitroso-diphenylamine | 86-30-6 | 10 | 330 |
| 4-Bromophenylphenylether | 101-55-3 | 10 | 330 |
| Hexachlorobenzene | 118-74-1 | 10 | 330 |
| Pentachlorophenol | 87-86-5 | 25 | 830 |
| Phenanthrene | 85-01-8 | 10 | 330 |
| Anthracene | 120-12-7 | 10 | 330 |
| Carbazole | 86-74-8 | 10 | 330 |
| Di-n-butylphthalate | 84-74-2 | 10 | 330 |
| Fluoranthene | 206-44-0 | 10 | 330 |
| Pyrene | 129-00-0 | 10 | 330 |
| Butylbenzylphthalate | 85-68-7 | 10 | 330 |
| 3,3'-Dichlorobenzidine | 91-94-1 | 10 | 330 |
| Benzo(a)anthracene | 56-55-3 | 10 | 330 |
| Chrysene | 218-01-9 | 10 | 330 |
| Bis(2-Ethylhexyl)phthalate | 117-81-7 | 10 | 330 |
| Di-n-octylphthalate | 117-84-0 | 10 | 330 |
| Benzo(b)fluoranthene | 205-99-2 | 10 | 330 |
| Benzo(k)fluoranthene | 207-08-9 | 10 | 330 |
| Benzo(a)pyrene | 50-32-8 | 10 | 330 |
| Indeno(1,2,3-cd)pyrene | 193-39-5 | 10 | 330 |
| Dibenzo(a,h)anthracene | 53-70-3 | 10 | 330 |
| Benzo(g,h,i)perylene | 191-24-2 | 10 | 330 |

**Table 4-17.  CLP Forms included as deliverables with each sample for Semivolatile Organic Compounds**

| Form | Title |
|---|---|
| I SV-1 | Semivolatiles Organics Analysis Data Sheet |
| I SV-2 | Semivolatiles Organics Analysis Data Sheet (page 2) |
| I SV-TIC | Semivolatile Organics Analysis Data Sheet Tentatively Identified Compounds |
| II SV-1 | Water Semivolatile Surrogate Recovery |
| II SV-2 | Soil Semivolatile Surrogate Recovery |
| III SV-1 | Water Semivolatile Matrix Spike/Matrix Spike Duplicate Recovery |

Continued on next page.

---

[35]  CLP-SOW OLM02.1, 1993

**Table 4-17. CLP Forms included as deliverables with each sample for Semivolatile Organic Compounds,** *continued*

| Form | Title |
|------|-------|
| III SV-2 | Soil Semivolatile Matrix Spike/Matrix Spike Duplicate Recovery |
| IV SV | Semivolatile Method Blank Summary |
| V SV | Semivolatile Organic Instrument Performance Check Decafluorotriphenylphosphine (DFTPP) |
| VI SV-1 & 2 | Semivolatile Organics Initial Calibration Data |
| VII SV-1 & 2 | Semivolatile Continuing Calibration Check |
| VIII SV-1 & 2 | Semivolatile Internal Standard Area and RT Summary |

**Table 4-18. CLP Pesticide/Aroclor Target Compound List (TCL)[36]**

| Analyte | CAS | CRQL Water ug/L | CRQL Soil ug/kg |
|---------|-----|-----------------|-----------------|
| α-BHC | 319-84-6 | 0.050 | 1.7 |
| β-BHC | 319-85-7 | 0.050 | 1.7 |
| δ-BHC | 319-86-8 | 0.050 | 1.7 |
| γ-BHC (Lindane) | 58-89-9 | 0.050 | 1.7 |
| Heptachlor | 76-44-8 | 0.050 | 1.7 |
| Aldrin | 309-00-2 | 0.050 | 1.7 |
| Heptachlor epoxide | 111024-57-3 | 0.050 | 1.7 |
| Endosulfan I | 959-98-8 | 0.050 | 1.7 |
| Dieldrin | 60-57-1 | 0.10 | 3.3 |
| 4,4'-DDE | 72-55-9 | 0.10 | 3.3 |
| Endrin | 72-20-8 | 0.10 | 3.3 |
| Endosulfan II | 33213-65-9 | 0.10 | 3.3 |
| 4,4'-DDD | 72-54-8 | 0.10 | 3.3 |
| Endosulfan sulfate | 1031-07-8 | 0.10 | 3.3 |
| 4,4'-DDT | 50-29-3 | 0.10 | 3.3 |
| Methoxychlor | 72-43-5 | 0.50 | 17 |
| Endrin ketone | 53494-70-5 | 0.10 | 3.3 |
| Endrin aldehyde | 7421-93-4 | 0.10 | 3.3 |
| α-Chlordane | 5103-71-9 | 0.050 | 1.7 |
| γ-Chlordane | 5103-74-2 | 0.050 | 1.7 |
| Toxaphene | 8001-35-2 | 5.0 | 170 |
| Aroclor-1016 | 12674-11-2 | 1.0 | 33 |
| Aroclor-1221 | 11104-28-2 | 2.0 | 67 |
| Aroclor-1232 | 11141-16-5 | 1.0 | 33 |
| Aroclor-1242 | 53469-21-9 | 1.0 | 33 |
| Aroclor-1248 | 12672-29-6 | 1.0 | 33 |
| Aroclor-1254 | 11097-69-1 | 1.0 | 33 |
| Aroclor-1260 | 11096-82-5 | 1.0 | 33 |

---

[36] CLP-SOW OLM02.1, 1993

**Table 4-19. CLP Forms included as deliverables with each sample for Pesticide/Aroclor**

| Form | Title |
|------|-------|
| I PEST | Pesticide Organics Analysis Data Sheet |
| II PEST-1 | Water Pesticide Surrogate Recovery |
| II PEST-2 | Soil Pesticide Surrogate Recovery |
| III PEST-1 | Water Pesticide Matrix Spike/Matrix Spike Duplicate Recovery |
| III PEST-2 | Soil Pesticide Matrix Spike/Matrix Spike Duplicate Recovery |
| IV PEST | Pesticide Method Blank Summary |
| VI PEST-1 | Pesticide Initial Calibration of Single Component Analytes (RT Data) |
| VI PEST-2 | Pesticide Initial Calibration of Single Component Analytes (Calibration Factor Data) |
| VI PEST-3 | Pesticide Initial Calibration of Multicomponent Analytes |
| VI PEST-4 | Pesticide Analyte Resolution Summary |
| VI PEST-5 | Performance Evaluation Mixture |
| VI PEST-6 | Individual Standard Mixture A |
| VI PEST-7 | Individual Standard Mixture B |
| VII PEST-1 | Pesticide Calibration Verification Summary (Breakdown Summary) |
| VII PEST-2 | Pesticide Calibration Verification Summary (Mixtures A & B Summary) |
| VIII PEST | Pesticide Analytical Sequence |
| IX PEST-1 | Pesticide Florisil Cartridge Check |
| IX PEST-2 | Pesticide GPC Calibration |
| X PEST-1 | Pesticide Identification Summary for Single Component Analytes |
| X PEST-2 | Pesticide Identification Summary for Multicomponent Analytes |

The CLP deliverables for each sample for organics analysis consist of CLP Form DC-1 (Sample Log-in Sheet), DC-2-1 through DC-2-5 (Organics Complete SDG File [CSF] Inventory Sheet), SDG Case Narrative, SDG Cover Sheet/Traffic Report and the specific forms in Tables 4-15, 4-17, and 4-19, depending on the type of sample and exact analysis required. Additional information in the deliverable package for VOA includes the reconstructed ion chromatogram (RIC) for the sample, raw spectra and background-subtracted mass spectra of target compounds identified, quantitation reports, mass spectra of all reported TICs with three best library matches, RICs and Quan reports for all standards for both initial and continuing calibrations, and finally raw QC data for BFB, blanks, and MS/MSD. Semivolatile data packages consist of the same material required for VOA samples with the substitution of DFTPP tune data for BFB tune data and the addition of GPC calibration data-UV detector traces, raw GPC data and GPC chromatograms. Pesticide analyses have copies of the chromatograms from the primary and secondary columns, GC integration report or data system printout, manual work sheets, calibration chromatograms and data system printouts, calibration printouts of retention times and corresponding peak areas or peak heights, GPC calibration data-UV detector traces, and raw QC data concerning blanks, MS/MSD, GPC and Florisil clean-up. If the pesticide/ PCB is confirmed by GC/MS, copies of raw spectra and copies of background-subtracted mass spectra of target compounds (samples and standards) must be included. Miscellaneous data in the sample package include copies of preparation and analysis logbook pages, internal sample and sample extract transfer chain-of-custody records, screening records, all instrument output from screening activities, airbills, chain-of-custody records, sample tags, sample log-in sheet, other shipping/receiving records, internal lab sample transfer records and tracking sheets, and telephone communication log.

Data in the organic reports are qualified by data flags. These are commonly used throughout the remediation business and have the following meanings as described in Tables 4-20 through 4-23.

**Table 4-20. Laboratory flags for organic data**

| Flag | Use |
|------|-----|
| U | Compound was a target analyte but was not detected. |
| J | Reported value is estimated. This could arise because the compound is a TIC and was not calibrated or the compound was detected at a level less than the CRQL. |
| N | Applied to all TICs when a definitive compound is reported. Not used for generic descriptions of TICs such as "chlorinated hydrocarbon". |
| NJ | Applied to TICs when an estimated amount has been determined for a definitive compound. |
| P | Used for Pesticide/PCB target analytes when more than 25% difference in quantitation exists between the two columns. The lower of the 2 values is reported and flagged. |
| C | Used for Pesticide/PCB target analytes when the presence is confirmed by GC-MS. |
| B | Used when the reported target analyte or TIC is also found in the blank. |
| E | Used for target analytes when the reported value exceeds the upper limit of the calibration curve. |
| D | Used to indicate that the value for the analyte was obtained from a diluted re-analysis. Separate Form I are used for original analysis and diluted re-analysis. All results on the diluted Form I will be flagged with a D. |
| A | Used to indicate that the reported TIC is a suspected aldol condensation product. |
| X, Y, Z | Laboratory defined flags. |

**Table 4-21. Data Reviewer flags for organic data**

| Flag | Use |
|------|-----|
| U | Compound was a target analyte but was not detected. |
| J | Reported value is estimated. This could arise because the compound is a TIC and was not calibrated or the compound was detected at a level less than the CRQL. |
| N | Applied to all TICs when a definitive compound is reported. Not used for generic descriptions of TICs such as "chlorinated hydrocarbon". |
| NJ | Applied to TICs when an estimated amount has been determined for a definitive compound. |
| R | Sample results are rejected due to a serious deficiency in the ability to analyze the sample and meet quality control criteria. The presence or absence of the target analyte can not be verified. |
| UJ | The analyte was not detected at the stated quantitation limit, however the value is an estimate and may be inaccurate or imprecise. |

**Table 4-22. Laboratory flags for inorganic data. The fields are Concentration (C), Qualifier (Q) and Method (M)**

| Field | Flag | Use |
|-------|------|-----|
| C | B | The reported value was obtained from a reading that was less than the CRDL but greater than or equal to the IDL. |
| | U | Target analyte was not detected. |
| Q | E | Estimated value |
| | M | Duplicate injection precision was not met. |
| | N | Spiked sample recovery was not within control limits. |
| | S | Reported value determined by method of standard additions (MSA). |
| | W | Post digestion spike for graphite furnace AA analysis is out of control limits and sample absorbance is less than 50% of spike absorbance. |
| | * | Duplicate analysis is not within control limits. |
| | + | Correlation coefficient for MSA is less than 0.995. |
| M | P | ICP-AES |
| | A | Flame AA |
| | F | Furnace AA |
| | M | Microwave digestion. |
| | CV | Manual cold vapor AA |
| | AV | Automated cold vapor AA |
| | CA | Midi-distillation spectrophotometric |
| | AS | Semi-automated spectrophotometric |
| | C | Manual spectrophotometric |
| | T | Titrimetric |
| | NR | Analyte is not required to be analyzed. |

**Table 4-23. Data Reviewer flags for inorganic data**

| Flag | Use |
|------|-----|
| U | Compound was a target analyte but was not detected. |
| J | Reported value is estimated. This could arise because the compound was detected at a level less than the CRQL. |
| R | Sample results are rejected due to a serious deficiency in the ability to analyze the sample and meet quality control criteria. The presence or absence of the target analyte cannot be verified. |
| UJ | The analyte was not detected at the stated quantitation limit, however the value is an estimate and may be inaccuracte or imprecise. |

The CLP deliverables for inorganic sample analysis consist of Form DC-2 (Full Inorganics Complete SDG File [CSF] Inventory Sheet), a cover page and the complete set of Inorganics forms listed in Table 4-13. In addition, ICP raw data, GFAA raw data, mercury raw data, cyanide raw data, preparation logs raw data, percent solids determination log, traffic report, shipping/receiving documents (airbill, chain-of-custody records, sample tags, lab and DCI sample log-in sheets, and SDG cover sheet), internal lab sample transfer records and tracking sheets, internal original sample prep and analysis records (prep records, analysis records, and others), telephone communication log, and any other miscellaneous documents must be included.

Evaluation of the data provided by the contract laboratory is guided by two EPA documents. The first is *USEPA Contract Laboratory Program National Functional Guidelines for Inorganic Data Review* (EPA-540/R-94/013, PB94-963502), and the second is *USEPA Contract Laboratory National Functional Guidelines for Organic Data Review* (EPA-540/R-94/012, PB94-963501). Both of these are available from NTIS. These guides are very well written and embody a considerable amount of common sense. They can be used for evaluation of any data and should be part of the reference material of any QA department.

A laboratory that submits a bid under a CLP SOW does so for a set maximum number of samples during a specified time period. Each type of sample has contract-specified maximum holding times before the sample preparation and the sample analysis parts of the procedure are accomplished. CLP laboratories tend to have cyclical business; when they have a contract they feast, otherwise it's famine with high overhead. Where laboratories get into trouble is giving in to the temptation of bidding at the maximum sample capacity of the laboratory based on a required minimum number of instruments in the lab. Murphy's Law always holds (Unexpected difficulties always arise at the most inopportune times.), and the laboratory is suddenly faced with too many samples and not enough people or instrument time to meet the holding times. Rather than give the samples back to the agency and not win the next contract, some laboratories have submitted backdated results to appear to meet holding times. When the deception is discovered by the EPA during the next audit, the responsible persons have been prosecuted and awarded jail time instead of the next contract.

## V. Other Government Contract Agencies

Other government agencies, besides the EPA, contract out analytical work. These include the Department of Energy (DOE) Hazardous Wastes Remediation Actions Program (HAZWRAP, administered by Lockheed-Martin), the Department of Defense (DOD), the U.S. Army Corps of Engineers (USACE), the U.S. Army Environmental Center Agency (USAEC formerly USATHAMA), the U.S. Navy Environmental Energy Support Activity (NEESA), the U.S. Air Force Center for Environmental Excellence (AFCEE), and NASA to name but a few. All of these organizations have just as strict laboratory validation requirements as the EPA CLP, but none have the glamour...or the notoriety.

Direct access to these government contracts is limited to engineering firms (often referred to as "prime contractor" or simply "primes") that submit bids for remediation services. Candidate laboratories are nominated/sponsored by the engineering firm as a subcontractor for analytical services. The laboratories are certified/validated by the government contractor based on an evaluation of the QA manual, performance of PE samples, and, finally, an on-site visit.

The Corps of Engineers has the most developed laboratory validation program of the Department of Defense agencies. The program is detailed in *Validation of Analytical Chemistry Laboratories*, publication EM-200-1-1, 1 July, 1994.

Examples of the TCL and TAL for U.S. Army Corps of Engineers contracts are presented in Tables 4-24 through 4-27. Although largely based on the related lists from the CLP, there are differences. In the volatile TCL the USACE has added vinyl acetate and 2-chloroethylvinyl ether as analytes while dropping 1,1,2-trichloroethane. In the semi-volatile TCL benzoic acid and benzyl alcohol are added, and carbazole is dropped. In the pesticide/PCB TCL technical chlordane replaces alpha- and gamma-chlordane, and endrin ketone is dropped. USACE also specifies a number of anions (chloride, fluoride, bromide, nitrate, nitrite, phosphate and sulfate) on the inorganic TAL, which are performed by either ion chromatography (EPA Method 300.0) or standard wet chemical methods. Other contracted analyses of USACE include dioxins, explosives residues, chemical warfare agent residues, and chlorinated acid herbicides. Required detection levels for the various analytes and matrices are often job specific but in general water analyses, especially groundwater samples, require drinking water detection limits.

**Table 4-24. USACE VOA Target Compound List (TCL)[37]**

| | | |
|---|---|---|
| Chloromethane | Bromomethane | Vinyl chloride |
| Chloroethane | Methylene chloride | Acetone |
| Carbon disulfide | 1,1-Dichloroethene | 1,1-Dichloroethane |
| 1,2-Dichloroethene | Chloroform | 1,2-Dichloroethane |
| 2-Butanone | 1,1,1-Trichloroethane | Carbon tetrachloride |
| Vinyl acetate | Bromodichloromethane | 1,2-Dichloropropane |
| cis-1,3-Dichloropropene | Trichloroethene | Dibromochloromethane |
| Benzene | trans-1,3-Dichloropropene | Bromoform |
| 2-Chloroethylvinylether | 4-Methyl-2-pentanone | 2-Hexanone |
| Tetrachloroethene | Toluene | 1,1,2,2-Tetrachloroethane |
| Chlorobenzene | Ethyl benzene | Styrene |
| Xylenes (total) | | |

**Table 4-25. USACE BNA Semi-volatile Target Compound List (TCL)[38]**

| | | |
|---|---|---|
| Phenol | Bis(2-chloroethyl)ether | 2-Chlorophenol |
| 1,3-Dichlorobenzene | 1,4-Dichlorobenzene | Benzyl alcohol |
| 1,2-Dichlorobenzene | 2-Methylphenol | Bis(2-chloroisopropyl)ether |
| 4-Methylphenol | N-Nitroso-di-n-propylamine | Hexachloroethane |
| Nitrobenzene | Isophorone | 2-Nitrophenol |
| 2,4-Dimethylphenol | Benzoic acid | Bis(2-chloroethoxy)methane |
| 2,4-Dichlorophenol | 1,2,4-Trichlorobenzene | Naphthalene |
| 4-Chloroaniline | Hexachlorobutadiene | 4-Chloro-3-methylphenol |
| 2-Methylnaphthalene | Hexachlorocyclopentadiene | 2,4,6-Trichlorophenol |
| 2,4,5-Trichlorophenol | 2-Chloronaphthalene | 2-Nitroaniline |
| Dimethylphthalate | Acenaphthylene | 2,6-Dinitrotoluene |
| 3-Nitroaniline | Acenaphthene | 2,4-Dinitrophenol |
| 4-Nitrophenol | Dibenzofuran | 2,4-Dinitrotoluene |
| Diethylphthalate | 4-Chlorophenylphenyl ether | Fluorene |
| 4-Nitroaniline | 4,6-Dinitro-2-methylphenol | N-Nitrosodiphenylamine |
| 4-Bromophenylphenyl ether | Hexachlorobenzene | Pentachlorophenol |
| Phenanthrene | Anthracene | Di-n-butylphthalate |
| Fluoranthene | Pyrene | Butylbenzylphthalate |
| 3,3'-Dichlorobenzidine | Benzo(a)anthracene | Chrysene |
| Bis(2-ethylhexyl)phthalate | Di-n-octylphthalate | Benzo(b)fluoranthene |
| Benzo(k)fluoranthene | Benzo(a)pyrene | Indeno(123cd)pyrene |
| Dibenzo(ah)anthracene | Benzo(ghi)perylene | |

---

[37] Table D-4, USACE ER 1110-1-263.
[38] Table D-5, USACE ER 1110-1-263.

## Table 4-26. USACE Pesticide/PCB Target Compound List (TCL)[39]

| | | |
|---|---|---|
| Aldrin | alpha-BHC | beta-BHC |
| delta-BHC | gamma-BHC (Lindane) | Chlordane |
| 4,4'-DDD | 4,4'-DDE | 4,4'-DDT |
| Dieldrin | Endosulfan I | Endosulfan II |
| Endosulfan sulfate | Endrin | Endrin aldehyde |
| Heptachlor | Heptachlor epoxide | Methoxychlor |
| Toxaphene | Aroclor-1016 | Aroclor-1221 |
| Aroclor-1232 | Aroclor-1242 | Aroclor-1248 |
| Aroclor-1254 | Aroclor-1260 | |

## Table 4-27. Target Analyte List (TAL) for metals under USACE[40]

| Metal | Technique[41] | Soil/Sediment | Groundwater[42] | Surface Water |
|---|---|---|---|---|
| Antimony | DA | CLP[43]//7040 | 3005/7040 | 204.1 |
| | GF | CLP/7041 | 3020/7041 | 204.2 |
| | ICP | CLP/6010 | 3005/6010 | 200.7 |
| Arsenic | GF | 3050/7060 | 7060 | 206.2 |
| | H | 7061 | 7061 | 206.3 |
| Barium | DA | 3050/7080 | 3005/7080 | 208.1 |
| | GF | 3050/7081 | 3020/7081 | 208.2 |
| | ICP | 3050/6010 | 3005/6010 | 200.7 |
| Beryllium | DA | 3050/7090 | 3005/7090 | 210.1 |
| | GF | 3050/7091 | 3020/7091 | 210.2 |
| | ICP | 3050/6010 | 3005/6010 | 200.7 |
| Cadmium | DA | 3050/7130 | 3005/7130 | 213.1 |
| | GF | 3050/7131 | 3020/7131 | 213.2 |
| | ICP | 3050/6010 | 3005/6010 | 200.7 |
| Calcium | DA | 3050/7140 | 3005/7140 | 215.1 |
| | ICP | 3050/6010 | 3005/6010 | 200.7 |
| Chromium | DA | 3050/7190 | 3005/7190 | 218.1 |
| | GF | 3050/7191 | 3020/7191 | 218.2 |
| | ICP | 3050/6010 | 3005/6010 | 200.7 |
| Copper | DA | 3050/7210 | 3005/7210 | 220.1 |
| | GF | 3050/7211 | 3020/7211 | 220.2 |
| | ICP | 3050/6010 | 3005/6010 | 200.7 |
| Iron | DA | 3050/7380 | 3005/7380 | 236.1 |
| | GF | 3050/7381 | 3020/7381 | 236.2 |
| | ICP | 3050/6010 | 3005/6010 | 200.7 |

Continued on next page.

[39] Table D-6, USACE ER 1110-1-263.

[40] Table D-2, USACE ER 1110-1-263, 1 Oct 90. Engineering and Design Chemical Data Quality Management for Hazardous Waste Remediation Activities.

[41] DA = Direct Aspiration; GF = Graphite Furnace; H = Hydride; CV = Cold Vapor; ICP = Inductively Coupled Plasma

[42] Any water sample may be analyzed by the groundwater techniques. Groundwater samples must be analyzed by these techniques. Surface water and other water samples may be analyzed by the 200-series or SW-846 methods.

[43] Follow CLP sample preparation guidance. Existing data in SW-846 is inadequate.

**Table 4-27. Target Analyte List (TAL) for metals under USACE[44], *continued***

| Metal | Technique[45] | Soil/Sediment | Groundwater[46] | Surface Water |
|-------|-----------|---------------|-------------|---------------|
| Lead | DA | 3050/7420 | 3005/7420 | 239.1 |
| | GF | 3050/7421 | 3020/7421 | 239.2 |
| | ICP | 3050/6010 | 3005/6010 | 200.7 |
| Manganese | DA | 3050/7460 | 3005/7460 | 243.1 |
| | GF | 3050/7461 | 3020/7461 | 243.2 |
| | ICP | 3050/6010 | 3005/6010 | 200.7 |
| Mercury | CV | 7471 | 7470 | 245.1 |
| Nickel | DA | 3050/7520 | 3005/7520 | 249.1 |
| | GF | - | - | 249.2 |
| | ICP | 3050/6010 | 3005/6010 | 200.7 |
| Selenium | GF | 3050/7740 | 7740 | 270.2 |
| | H | 7741 | 7741 | 270.3 |
| Silver | DA | 3050/7760 | 7760 | 272.1 |
| | GF | 3050/7761 | 7761 | 272.2 |
| | ICP | 3050/6010 | 3005/6010 | 200.7 |
| Sodium | DA | 3050/7770 | 3005/7770 | 273.1 |
| | GF | - | - | 273.2 |
| | ICP | 3050/6010 | 3005/6010 | 200.7 |
| Thallium | DA | 3050/7840 | 3005/7840 | 279.1 |
| | GF | 3050/7841 | 3020/7841 | 279.2 |
| | ICP | 3050/6010 | 3005/6010 | 200.7 |
| Zinc | DA | 3050/7950 | 3005/7950 | 289.1 |
| | GF | 3050/7951 | 3020/7951 | 289.2 |
| | ICP | 3050/6010 | 3005/6010 | 200.7 |

Beginning with USACE PE samples in 1994, aluminum, cobalt, magnesium, potassium, and vanadium were included as target analytes. With the addition of these TAL metals the USACE list is identical to that of the most recent CLP-SOW for inorganics.(ILM03).

Other government programs defer specifically to the CLP methods, analyte lists and reporting forms. The HAZWRAP is somewhat unique in having 5 different reporting and methodology levels, depending on the exact project.

**Level A** - Qualitative or semiquantitative analysis, indicator parameters, immediate response in the field. Requires no formal final report; the only deliverables are sample results. The daily single point calibration must be kept on file.

---

[44] Table D-2, USACE ER 1110-1-263, 1 Oct 90. Engineering and Design Chemical Data Quality Management for Hazardous Waste Remediation Activities.

[45] DA = Direct Aspiration; GF = Graphite Furnace; H = Hydride; CV = Cold Vapor; ICP = Inductively Coupled Plasma

[46] Any water sample may be analyzed by the groundwater techniques. Groundwater samples must be analyzed by these techniques. Surface water and other water samples may be analyzed by the 200-series or SW-846 methods.

**Level B** - Semiquantitative or quantitative analysis, compound specific, rapid turnaround in the field. Deliverables include sample results, method blanks, three-point calibration, and continuing calibration checks.

**Level C** - Quantitative analysis with technically defensible data on major remediation sites or site near populated areas. See Table 4-28 for deliverables.

**Level D** - Quantitative analysis with legally defensible data from sites on the National Priorities List or sites near populated areas that are likely to be litigated. A full CLP data package is required. Deliverables include the summary package and remainder of the data package, including initial and continuing calibration, matrix spikes, matrix spike duplicates, blanks, duplicates, surrogate recoveries, chromatograms, mass spectra, and absorbance data. For methods not defined by the CLP, calibration information, method blanks, blank/spikes, chromatograms, absorbance, matrix spikes, and matrix spike duplicates are reported. Plotted control charts associated with the LCS are presented with the data.

**Level E** - Qualitative to quantitative analysis that is non-standard method specific to unique matrices (pure waste, air, biota, explosives, etc.). May involve method development along with determination of precision and accuracy. The minimum information to be submitted includes: sample results, method blank data, initial and continuing calibration data, and control charts from the LCS data. Exact deliverables will be stated in the work plan.

**Table 4-28. HAZWRAP Level C deliverables**

| Analyte Group | Method requirements | Deliverables[47] |
|---|---|---|
| All methods | Holding times information and method requested | Signed chain-of-custody forms |
| | Discussion of lab problems | Case narrative |
| | LCS with results on control charts run with each batch of samples | Control chart copies |
| Organics | Sample results | CLP form 1 |
| | Surrogate recoveries | CLP form 2 |
| | Matrix spike/Matrix spike duplicate | CLP form 3 |
| | Method blank | CLP form 4 |
| | GC/MS tune | CLP form 5 |
| | GC/MS initial calibration | CLP form 6 |
| | GC initial and continuing calibration | CLP form 8D and 9 |
| | GC/MS continuing calibration | CLP form 7 |
| | GC/MS internal standard area | CLP form 8 |
| | Second column confirmation | CLP form 10 and copies of chromatograms |

Continued on next page.

---

[47] If alternate forms are used, copies must be submitted to HAZWRAP Project Manager for approval prior to initiating work.

**Table 4-28. HAZWRAP Level C deliverables,** *continued*

| Analyte Group | Method requirements | Deliverables[48] |
|---|---|---|
| Metals | Sample results | CLP form 1 |
| | Initial and continuing calibration | CLP form 2 |
| | Method blank | CLP form 3 |
| | ICP interference check | CLP form 4 |
| | Spike sample recovery | CLP form 5A |
| | PDS spike recovery for ICP | CLP form 5B |
| | PDS for GFAA | Recovery noted on raw data |
| | Duplicates | CLP form 6 |
| | LCS | CLP form 7 |
| | Standard addition | CLP form 8 |
| | Holding times | CLP form 10 |
| Wet chemistry | LCS | Control chart copy |
| | Method blank | Report result |
| | Sample results | Report result |
| | Spike/spike duplicate and/or calibration | Report result |
| | Calibration check | Report RPD |

Under HAZWRAP, SW-846, CLP, or other EPA methods are used for most analyses in Levels C and E; however, all semivolatile and volatile organic analyses by GC/MS are to be performed by the most recent CLP-SOW. On the other hand, the AFCEE requirements allow SW-846 methods and analyte lists for the most part, but specify PQL for water and soil samples. These are presented in Tables 4-29 and 4-30.

A number of documents are available as either hardcopy or as downloads from the Internet related to AFCEE. These include:

1. *Handbook to Support the Installation Restoration Program (IRP) Statement of Work for Remedial Investigation/Feasibility Studies (RI/FS)* May, 1987 (Version 1.2), April, 1988 (version 2.0), and May, 1989 (version 3.0)

2. *Handbook to Support the Installation Restoration Program (IRP) Statement of Work, Volume 1 Remedial Investigation/Feasibility Studies,* 5/91.

3. *Handbook for the Installation Restoration Program (IRP) Remedial Investigations and Feasibility Studies (RI/FS),* published by AFCEE September, 1993

4. *Quality Assurance Project Plan (QAPP),* version 1.1, February, 1996

5. *Guidance for AFCEE Quality Assurance/Quality Control (QA/QC) Audits of Installation Restoration Program Contact Laboratories,* October, 1991

---

[48] If alternate forms are used, copies must be submitted to HAZWRAP Project Manager for approval prior to initiating work.

The Internet address for AFCEE is http://www.afcee.brooks.af.mil.  A more complete discussion of AFCEE is presented in a recent book[49].

**Table 4-29.  AFCEE Inorganic Target Analyte List[50]**

| Parameter/Method | Analyte | Water PQL mg/L | Soil PQL mg/kg |
|---|---|---|---|
| Alkalinity A2320 | Carbonate | 10 | - |
| | Bicarbonate | 10 | - |
| | Hydroxide | 10 | - |
| Radioactivity SW9310 | Gross alpha & gross beta | 4 pCi/L | Establish before analysis |
| SW9315 | Radium 226 | 1 pCi/L | Establish before analysis |
| SW 9320 | Radium 228 | 3 pCi/L | Establish before analysis |
| Filterable residue E160.1 | TDS | 10 | - |
| Nonfilterable residue E160.2 | TSS | 5 | - |
| Common Anions SW9056 | Chloride | 0.2 | - |
| | Fluoride | 0.2 | - |
| | Sulfate | 0.2 | - |
| | Nitrate | 0.1 | - |
| | ortho Phosphate | 0.1 | - |
| Nitrate-Nitrate (N) E353.1 E353.2 | Nitrate + nitrite | 0.1 | - |
| SW3020/3050/7041 | Antimony | 0.005 | 0.5 |
| SW7060 | Arsenic | 0.005 | 0.5 |
| SW3020/3050/7131 | Cadmium | 0.001 | 0.1 |
| SW3020/3050/7191 | Chromium | 0.005 | 0.5 |
| SW3020/3050/7421 | Lead | 0.005 | 0.5 |
| SW7470/7471 | Mercury | 0.001 | 0.1 |
| SW7740 | Selenium | 0.005 | 0.5 |
| SW3020/3050/7841 | Thallium | 0.001 | 0.1 |
| SW3020/3050/7911 | Vanadium | 0.004 | 0.4 |
| ICP Metals SW3005/3050/6010 | Aluminum | 0.5 | 50 |
| | Antimony | 0.4 | 40 |
| | Arsenic | 0.6 | 60 |
| | Barium | 0.02 | 2 |
| | Beryllium | 0.003 | 0.3 |
| | Cadmium | 0.04 | 4 |
| | Calcium | 0.1 | 10 |
| | Chromium | 0.07 | 7 |
| | Cobalt | 0.07 | 7 |
| | Copper | 0.06 | 6 |
| | Iron | 0.07 | 7 |
| | Lead | 0.5 | 50 |
| | Magnesium | 0.3 | 30 |

Continued on next page.

---

[49]  Berger, W., H. McCarty and R.-K. Smith, 1996.  *Environmental Laboratory Data Evaluation*, Genium Publishing, Schenectady, NY 12304.

[50]  *HQ AFCEE Handbook for the Installation Restoration Program (IRP) Remedial Investigations and Feasibility Studies (RI/FS)*, September, 1993.

**Table 4-29. AFCEE Inorganic Target Analyte List[51], *continued***

| Parameter/Method | Analyte | Water PQL mg/L | Soil PQL mg/kg |
|---|---|---|---|
| ICP Metals SW3005/3050/6010, *continued* | Manganese | 0.02 | 2 |
| | Molybdenum | 0.08 | 8 |
| | Nickel | 0.15 | 15 |
| | Potassium | 5 | 500 |
| | Selenium | 0.8 | 80 |
| | Silver | 0.07 | 7 |
| | Sodium | 0.3 | 30 |
| | Thallium | 0.4 | 40 |
| | Vanadium | 0.08 | 8 |
| | Zinc | 0.02 | 2 |
| SW9010/9012 | Total cyanide | 0.02 | - |

**Table 4-30. AFCEE Organic Target Compound List[52]**

| Parameter/Method | Analyte | Water PQL ug/L | Soil PQL mg/kg |
|---|---|---|---|
| Petroleum hydrocarbons E418.1  SW3550/E418.1 | AFCEE permission required for use | 1 mg/L | 30 |
| SW5030/8015 mod | Gasoline | 0.1 mg/L | 1 |
| SW3550/8015 mod | Diesel, jet fuel | 1 mg/L | 10 |
| Purgeable halocarbons SW5030/8010 | Bromobenzene | 5 | 0.05 |
| | Bromodichloromethane | 1 | 0.005 |
| | Bromoform | 2 | 0.05 |
| | Bromomethane | 10 | 0.01 |
| | Carbon tetrachloride | 1 | 0.005 |
| | Chlorobenzene | 2.5 | 0.005 |
| | Chloroethane | 5 | 0.005 |
| | Chloroform | 0.5 | 0.005 |
| | 1-Chlorohexane | 5 | 0.005 |
| | 2-Chloroethylvinylether | 10 | 0.01 |
| | Chloromethane | 1 | 0.005 |
| | Dibromochloromethane | 1 | 0.005 |
| | Dibromomethane | 5 | 0.005 |
| | 1,2-Dichlorobenzene | 2 | 0.005 |
| | 1,3-Dichlorobenzene | 3 | 0.005 |
| | 1,4-Dichlorobenzene | 2 | 0.005 |
| | 1,1-Dichloroethane | 1 | 0.005 |
| | 1,2-Dichloroethane | 1 | 0.005 |
| | 1,1-Dichloroethene | 1 | 0.005 |
| | *cis*-1,2-Dichloroethene | 1 | 0.005 |
| | *trans*-1,2-Dichloroethene | 1 | 0.005 |
| | *cis*-1,3-Dichloropropene | 5 | 0.005 |
| | 1,2-Dichloropropane | 1 | 0.005 |
| | *trans*-1,3-Dichloropropene | 3 | 0.005 |
| | Methylene chloride | 2 | 0.005 |
| | 1,1,1,2-Tetrachloroethane | 5 | 0.005 |
| | 1,1,2,2-Tetrachloroethane | 1 | 0.005 |

Continued on next page.

---

[51]  *HQ AFCEE Handbook for the Installation Restoration Program (IRP) Remedial Investigations and Feasibility Studies (RI/FS)*, September, 1993.

[52]  *HQ AFCEE Handbook for the Installation Restoration Program (IRP) Remedial Investigations and Feasibility Studies (RI/FS)*, September, 1993.

**Table 4-30. AFCEE Organic Target Compound List[53]**, *continued*

| Parameter/Method | Analyte | Water PQL ug/L | Soil PQL mg/kg |
|---|---|---|---|
| Purgeable halocarbons SW5030/8010, *continued* | Tetrachloroethene | 1 | 0.005 |
| | 1,1,1-Trichloroethane | 1 | 0.005 |
| | 1,1,2-Trichloroethane | 1 | 0.005 |
| | Trichloroethene | 1 | 0.005 |
| | Trichlorofluoromethane | 1 | 0.005 |
| | Trichloropropane | 10 | 0.01 |
| | Vinyl chloride | 2 | 0.005 |
| Nonhalogenated volatile organics SW5030/8015 | Diethyl ether | 50 | Establish PQL prior to analysis |
| | Methyl ethyl ketone | 50 | Establish PQL prior to analysis |
| | Methyl isobutyl ketone | 50 | Establish PQL prior to analysis |
| Purgeable aromatic volatiles SW5030/8020 | Benzene | 2 | 0.002 |
| | Chlorobenzene | 2 | 0.002 |
| | 1,2-Dichlorobenzene | 4 | 0.004 |
| | 1,3-Dichlorobenzene | 4 | 0.004 |
| | 1,4-Dichlorobenzene | 3 | 0.003 |
| | Ethylbenzene | 2 | 0.002 |
| | Toluene | 2 | 0.002 |
| | Xylenes | 2 | 0.002 |
| Organochlorine pesticides & PCBs SW3510/3550/8080 | Aldrin | 0.04 | 0.003 |
| | $\alpha$-BHC | 0.03 | 0.002 |
| | $\beta$-BHC | 0.06 | 0.004 |
| | $\delta$-BHC | 0.09 | 0.006 |
| | $\gamma$-BHC | 0.04 | 0.003 |
| | Chlordane | 0.14 | 0.009 |
| | 4,4'-DDD | 0.11 | 0.007 |
| | 4,4'-DDE | 0.04 | 0.003 |
| | 4,4'-DDT | 0.12 | 0.008 |
| | Dieldrin | 0.02 | 0.01 |
| | Endosulfan I | 0.14 | 0.009 |
| | Endosulfan II | 0.04 | 0.003 |
| | Endosulfan sulfate | 0.66 | 0.04 |
| | Endrin | 0.06 | 0.004 |
| | Endrin aldehyde | 0.23 | 0.02 |
| | Heptachlor | 0.03 | 0.002 |
| | Heptachlor epoxide | 0.83 | 0.06 |
| | Methoxychlor | 1.76 | 0.1 |
| | Toxaphene | 2.4 | 0.2 |
| | PCB-1016 | 1 | 1 |
| | PCB-1221 | 1 | 1 |
| | PCB-1232 | 1 | 1 |
| | PCB-1242 | 1 | 1 |
| | PCB-1248 | 1 | 1 |
| | PCB-1254 | 1 | 1 |
| | PCB-1260 | 1 | 1 |

Continued on next page.

---

[53] *HQ AFCEE Handbook for the Installation Restoration Program (IRP) Remedial Investigations and Feasibility Studies (RI/FS)*, September, 1993.

### Table 4-30. AFCEE Organic Target Compound List[54], *continued*

| Parameter/Method | Analyte | Water PQL ug/L | Soil PQL mg/kg |
|---|---|---|---|
| Organophosphorous pesticides SW3510/3550/8140 | Azinphos methyl | 15 | 1 |
| | Bolstar | 1.5 | 0.1 |
| | Clorpyrifos | 3 | 0.2 |
| | Coumaphos | 15 | 1 |
| | Demeton-O | 2.5 | 0.2 |
| | Demeton-S | 2.5 | 0.2 |
| | Diazinon | 6 | 0.4 |
| | Dichlorovos | 10 | 0.7 |
| | Disulfoton | 2 | 0.1 |
| | Ethoprop | 2.5 | 0.2 |
| | Fensulfothion | 1.5 | 1 |
| | Fenthion | 1 | 0.1 |
| | Merphos | 2.5 | 0.2 |
| | Mevinphos | 3 | 0.2 |
| | Naled | 1 | 0.1 |
| | Parathion methyl | 0.3 | 0.02 |
| | Phorate | 1.5 | 0.1 |
| | Ronnel | 3 | 0.2 |
| | Stirophos | 50 | 2.4 |
| | Tokuthion | 5 | 0.4 |
| | Trichloronate | 1.5 | 0.1 |
| Chlorinated phenoxy acid herbicides SW8150 | 2,4-D | 12 | 0.8 |
| | 2,4-DB | 9 | 0.6 |
| | 2,4,5-T | 2 | 0.1 |
| | 2,4,5-TP | 1.7 | 0.1 |
| | Dalapon | 60 | 4 |
| | Dicamba | 2.7 | 0.2 |
| | Dichloroprop | 6.5 | 0.5 |
| | Dinoseb | 0.7 | 0.05 |
| | MCPA | 2500 | 170 |
| | MCPP | 1900 | 130 |
| Semivolatile organic compounds SW3510/3550/8270 | **BN Extractibles** | | |
| | Acenapthene | 10 | 0.7 |
| | Acenapthylene | 10 | 0.7 |
| | Benzo(a)anthracene | 10 | 0.7 |
| | Benzo(b)fluoranthene | 10 | 0.7 |
| | Benzo(ghi)perylene | 10 | 0.7 |
| | Benzo(a)pyrene | 10 | 0.7 |
| | Benzyl alcohol | 20 | 1.3 |
| | bis(2-chloroethoxy)methane | 10 | 0.7 |
| | bis(2-chloroethyl)ether | 10 | 0.7 |
| | bis(2-chloroisopropyl)ether | 10 | 0.7 |
| | bis(2-ethylhexyl)phthalate | 10 | 0.7 |
| | 4-Bromophenylphenylether | 10 | 0.7 |
| | Butylbenzylphthalate | 10 | 0.7 |
| | 4-Chloroaniline | 20 | 1.3 |
| | 2-Chloronaphthalene | 10 | 0.7 |
| | 4-Chlorophenylphenylether | 10 | 0.7 |
| | Chrysene | 10 | 0.7 |
| | Dibenz(ah)anthracene | 10 | 0.7 |
| | Dibenzofuran | 10 | 0.7 |

Continued on next page.

---

[54] *HQ AFCEE Handbook for the Installation Restoration Program (IRP) Remedial Investigations and Feasibility Studies (RI/FS)*, September, 1993.

**Table 4-30. AFCEE Organic Target Compound List[55], *continued***

| Parameter/Method | Analyte | Water PQL ug/L | Soil PQL mg/kg |
|---|---|---|---|
| Semivolatile organic compounds SW3510/3550/8270 *continued* | Di-n-butylphthalate | 10 | 0.7 |
| | 1,2-Dichlorobenzene | 10 | 0.7 |
| | 1,3-Dichlorobenzene | 10 | 0.7 |
| | 1,4-Dichlorobenzene | 10 | 0.7 |
| | 3,3'-Dichlorobenzidine | 20 | 1.3 |
| | Diethylphthalate | 10 | 0.7 |
| | Dimethylphthalate | 10 | 0.7 |
| | 2,4-Dinitrotoluene | 10 | 0.7 |
| | 2,6-Dinitrotoluene | 10 | 0.7 |
| | Di-n-octylphthalate | 10 | 0.7 |
| | Fluoranthene | 10 | 0.7 |
| | Fluorene | 10 | 0.7 |
| | Hexachlorobenzene | 10 | 0.7 |
| | Hexachlorobutadiene | 10 | 0.7 |
| | Hexachlorocyclopentadiene | 10 | 0.7 |
| | Hexachloroethane | 10 | 0.7 |
| | Indeno(123cd)pyrene | 10 | 0.7 |
| | Isophorone | 10 | 0.7 |
| | 2-Methylnaphthalene | 10 | 0.7 |
| | Naphthalene | 10 | 0.7 |
| | 2-Nitroaniline | 50 | 3.3 |
| | 3-Nitroaniline | 50 | 3.3 |
| | 4-Nitroaniline | 50 | 3.3 |
| | Nitrobenzene | 10 | 0.7 |
| | *n*-Nitrosodiphenylamine | 10 | 0.7 |
| | *n*-Nitrosodipropylamine | 10 | 0.7 |
| | Phenanthrene | 10 | 0.7 |
| | Pyrene | 10 | 0.7 |
| | 1,2,4-Trichlorobenzene | 10 | 0.7 |
| **Acid extractibles** | | | |
| | Benzoic acid | 50 | 1.6 |
| | 4-Chloro-3-methylphenol | 20 | 1.3 |
| | 2-Chlorophenol | 10 | 0.3 |
| | 2,4-Dichlorophenol | 10 | 0.3 |
| | 2,4-Dimethylphenol | 10 | 0.3 |
| | 4,6-Dinitro-2-methylphenol | 50 | 3.3 |
| | 2,4-Dinitrophenol | 50 | 3.3 |
| | 2-Methylphenol | 10 | 0.3 |
| | 4-Methylphenol | 10 | 0.3 |
| | 2-Nitrophenol | 10 | 0.3 |
| | 4-Nitrophenol | 50 | 1.6 |
| | Pentachlorophenol | 50 | 3.3 |
| | Phenol | 10 | 0.3 |
| | 2,4,5-Trichlorophenol | 50 | 3.3 |
| | 2,4,6-Trichlorophenol | 10 | 0.3 |

Continued on next page.

---

[55] *HQ AFCEE Handbook for the Installation Restoration Program (IRP) Remedial Investigations and Feasibility Studies (RI/FS)*, September, 1993.

**Table 4-30. AFCEE Organic Target Compound List[56], *continued***

| Parameter/Method | Analyte | Water PQL ug/L | Soil PQL mg/kg |
|---|---|---|---|
| Volatile organic compounds[57] SW8260[58] | Dichlorodifluoromethane | 1.0 | .005 |
| | Chloromethane | 1.3 | .007 |
| | Vinyl chloride | 1.1 | .009 |
| | Bromomethane | 1.1 | .005 |
| | Chloroethane | 1 | .005 |
| | Trichlorofluoromethane | 0.8 | .004 |
| | 1,1-Dichloroethene | 1.2 | .006 |
| | Methylene chloride | 0.3 | .002 |
| | *trans*-1,2-Dichloroethene | 0.6 | .003 |
| | 1,1-Dichloroethane | 0.4 | .002 |
| | 2,2-Dichloropropane | 3.5 | .02 |
| | *cis*-1,2-Dichloroethene | 1.2 | .006 |
| | Chloroform | 0.3 | .002 |
| | Bromochloromethane | 0.04 | .002 |
| | 1,1,1-Trichloroethane | 0.8 | .004 |
| | Carbon tetrachloride | 2.1 | .01 |
| | 1,1-Dichloropropene | 1 | .005 |
| | Benzene | 0.4 | .002 |
| | 1,2-Dichloroethane | 0.6 | .003 |
| | Trichloroethene | 1 | .01 |
| | 1,2-Dichloropropane | 0.4 | .002 |
| | Bromodichloromethane | 0.8 | .004 |
| | Dibromomethane | 2.4 | .01 |
| | *trans*-1,3-Dichloropropene | - | - |
| | Toluene | 1.1 | .005 |
| | *cis*-1,3-Dichloropropene | - | - |
| | 1,1,2-Trichloroethane | 1 | .005 |
| | Tetrachloroethene | 1.4 | .007 |
| | 1,3-Dichloropropane | 0.4 | .002 |
| | Dibromochloromethane | 0.5 | .003 |
| | 1,2-Dibromoethane | 0.6 | .003 |
| | 1-Chlorohexane | 0.5 | .003 |
| | Chlorobenzene | 0.4 | .002 |
| | 1,1,1,2-Tetrachloroethane | 0.5 | .003 |
| | Ethylbenzene | 0.6 | .003 |
| | *p*-Xylene | 1.3 | .007 |
| | *m*-Xylene | 0.5 | .003 |
| | *o*-Xylene | 1.1 | .005 |
| | Styrene | 0.4 | .002 |
| | Bromoform | 1.2 | .006 |
| | Isopropylbenzene | 0.5 | .008 |
| | 1,1,2,2-Tetrachloroethane | 0.4 | .002 |
| | Bromobenzene | 0.3 | .002 |
| | 1,2,3-Trichloropropane | 3.2 | .02 |
| | *n*-Propylbenzene | 0.4 | .002 |
| | 2-Chlorotoluene | 0.4 | .002 |

Continued on next page.

[56]  *HQ AFCEE Handbook for the Installation Restoration Program (IRP) Remedial Investigations and Feasibility Studies (RI/FS)*, September, 1993.

[57]  The target PQL for soil and water matrices were incorrect in the 1993 publication. They were corrected to these listed values in AFCEE *Quality Assurance Project Plan (QAPP)*, version 1.1, February, 1996.

[58]  This method may be substituted for SW8240 on a project specific basis.

**Table 4-30. AFCEE Organic Target Compound List[59], *continued***

| Parameter/Method | Analyte | Water PQL ug/L | Soil PQL mg/kg |
|---|---|---|---|
| Volatile organic compounds[60] SW8260[61] | 1,3,5-Trimethylbenzene | 0.5 | .003 |
| | 4-Chlorotoluene | 0.6 | .003 |
| | *tert*-Butylbenzene | 1.4 | .007 |
| | 1,2,4-Trimethylbenzene | 1.3 | .007 |
| | *sec*-Butylbenzene | 1.3 | .007 |
| | *p*-Isopropyltoluene | 1.2 | .006 |
| | 1,3-Dichlorobenzene | 1.2 | .006 |
| | 1,4-Dichlorobenzene | 0.3 | .002 |
| | *n*-Butylbenzene | 1.1 | .005 |
| | 1,2-Dichlorobenzene | 0.3 | .002 |
| | DBCP | 2.6 | .01 |
| | 1,2,4-Trichlorobenzene | 0.4 | .002 |
| | Hexachlorobutadiene | 1.1 | .005 |
| | Naphthalene | 0.4 | .002 |
| | 1,2,3-Trichlorobenzene | 0.3 | .002 |
| Volatile organic compounds SW8240 | Acetone | 100 | 0.1 |
| | Benzene | 5 | 0.005 |
| | Bromodichloromethane | 5 | 0.005 |
| | Bromoform | 5 | 0.005 |
| | Bromomethane | 10 | 0.01 |
| | 2-Butanone | 100 | 0.1 |
| | Carbon disulfide | 5 | 0.005 |
| | Carbon tetrachloride | 5 | 0.005 |
| | Chlorobenzene | 5 | 0.005 |
| | Dibromochloromethane | 5 | 0.005 |
| | Chloroethane | 10 | 0.01 |
| | 2-Chloroethylvinylether | 10 | 0.01 |
| | Chloroform | 5 | 0.005 |
| | Chloromethane | 10 | 0.01 |
| | 1,1-Dichloroethane | 5 | 0.005 |
| | 1,2-Dichloroethane | 5 | 0.005 |
| | 1,1-Dichloroethene | 5 | 0.005 |
| | *cis*-1,2-Dichloroethene | 5 | 0.005 |
| | *trans*-1,2-Dichloroethene | 5 | 0.005 |
| | 1,2-Dichloropropane | 5 | 0.005 |
| | *cis*-1,3-Dichloropropene | 5 | 0.005 |
| | *trans*-1,3-Dichloropropene | 5 | 0.005 |
| | Ethylbenzene | 5 | 0.005 |
| | 2-Hexanone | 50 | 0.05 |
| | Methylene chloride | 5 | 0.005 |
| | 4-Methyl-2-pentanone | 50 | 0.05 |
| | Styrene | 5 | 0.005 |
| | 1,1,2,2-Tetrachloroethane | 5 | 0.005 |
| | Tetrachloroethene | 5 | 0.005 |
| | Toluene | 5 | 0.005 |
| | 1,1,1-Trichloroethane | 5 | 0.005 |

Continued on next page.

---

[59] *HQ AFCEE Handbook for the Installation Restoration Program (IRP) Remedial Investigations and Feasibility Studies (RI/FS)*, September, 1993.

[60] The target PQL for soil and water matrices were incorrect in the 1993 publication. They were corrected to these listed values in AFCEE *Quality Assurance Project Plan* (QAPP), version 1.1, February, 1996.

[61] This method may be substituted for SW8240 on a project specific basis.

**Table 4-30. AFCEE Organic Target Compound List[62], *continued***

| Parameter/Method | Analyte | Water PQL ug/L | Soil PQL mg/kg |
|---|---|---|---|
| Volatile organic compounds SW8240, *continued* | 1,1,2-Trichloroethane | 5 | 0.005 |
| | Trichloroethene | 5 | 0.005 |
| | Vinyl acetate | 50 | 0.05 |
| | Vinyl chloride | 10 | 0.01 |
| | Xylenes (total) | 5 | 0.005 |
| Dioxin & furans | 2,3,7,8-TCDD (SW8280) | 0.44 ng/L | 0.17 ug/kg |
| | 2,3,7,8-TCDD (SW8290) | 0.01 ng/L | 0.001 ug/kg |
| Explosives SW8330 | HMX | 13 | 2.2 |
| | RDX | 14 | 1 |
| | 1,3,5-Trinitrobenzene | 7.3 | 0.25 |
| | 1,3-Dinitrobenzene | 4 | 0.25 |
| | Tetryl | 44 | 0.65 |
| | Nitrobenzene | 7 | 0.26 |
| | 2,4,6-Trinitrotoluene | 6.9 | 0.25 |
| | 2,4-Dinitrotoluene | 5.7 | 0.25 |
| | 2,6-Dinitrotoluene | 9.4 | 0.26 |
| | *o*-Nitrotoluene | 12 | 0.25 |
| | *m*-Nitrotoluene | 7.9 | 0.25 |
| | *p*-Nitrotoluene | 8.5 | 0.25 |
| Polynuclear aromatic hydrocarbons SW3510/3550/8310 | Naphthalene | 18 | 1.2 |
| | Acenaphthylene | 23 | 1.54 |
| | Acenaphthene | 18 | 1.2 |
| | Fluorene | 2.1 | 0.14 |
| | Phenanthrene | 6.4 | 0.42 |
| | Anthracene | 6.6 | 0.44 |
| | Fluoranthene | 2.1 | 0.14 |
| | Pyrene | 2.7 | 0.18 |
| | Benzo(a)anthracene | 0.13 | 0.009 |
| | Chrysene | 1.5 | 0.1 |
| | Benzo(b)fluoranthene | 0.18 | 0.012 |
| | Benzo(k)fluoranthene | 0.17 | 0.011 |
| | Benzo(a)pyrene | 0.23 | 0.015 |
| | Dibenzo(ah)anthracene | 0.3 | 0.02 |
| | Benzo(ghi)perylene | 0.76 | 0.05 |
| | Indeno(123cd)pyrene | 0.43 | 0.03 |
| Total phenols SW9065 | Total phenols | 0.02 | - |

# VI. Mixed Waste

The term "mixed waste" refers to samples that are both hazardous and radioactive. In general the hazardous waste part of the analysis is performed by SW-846 methods that have been modified to protect the instrument and the technician from the radioactive nature of the waste. This may involve performing all or part of the analysis in a hood, a hot cell, or a glove box, depending on the nature and level of the radioactivity. The mixed waste methods have been collected into the DOE analytical procedures database, which is available on-line. The majority of the methods are for measuring the radioactive part of the waste rather than the hazardous part. Contact with the database can be initiated by calling Brian O'Malley at 1-505-667-0089 at Los Alamos National Laboratory and requesting access information and a password. The DOE also published the

---

[62] *HQ AFCEE Handbook for the Installation Restoration Program (IRP) Remedial Investigations and Feasibility Studies (RI/FS), September, 1993.*

*DOE Methods for Evaluating Environmental and Waste Management Samples*, document DOE/EM-0089T, as a guide to mixed waste sampling and analysis. This compilation of methods has become comerciallized and is being updated by Battelle Press. A 1997 edition is available; for information call 1-800-451-3543.

Radioactive materials contain atoms that are unstable and are prone to breakdown accompanied by emission of either particles or energy. The common emission products are alpha particles (2 protons and 2 neutrons with a mass of 4 amu and a charge of +2), beta particles (an electron, 1/2000 of the mass of a proton and a -1 charge), gamma rays (no mass and no charge but high energy) and neutron particles (1 amu mass and no charge). Neutrons are further characterized as thermal (low energy) or fast (high energy).

**Table 4-31. Characteristics of Radioactivity**

| Particle | Range | Bio hazard | Shielding |
|----------|-------|------------|-----------|
| alpha | 1-2 inches in air | external none, internal very hazardous QF = 20 | few cm of air, sheet of paper, layer of dead skin |
| beta | 10 ft in air | external skin and eyes, internal hazardous QF = 1 | plastic, glass, metal foil or safety glasses |
| gamma | several hundred feet in air | external/internal hazard QF = 1 | concrete, lead or steel |
| neutron | several hundred feet in air | external/internal hazard QF varies with energy | water or plastic |

Materials that are radioactive are undergoing active generation of radiation through disintegration, however the effect of the radiation depends on its exact type. Items and people exposed to radiation do not become radioactive. This occurs only if the actual radioactive material is incorporated into the item or ingested/inhaled by the person.

## A. Units of radiation measure

**Roentgen (R)** - amount of gamma rays necessary to produce one electrostatic unit of electric charge in 1 cc of dry air or $2.58 \times 10^{-4}$ coulombs/kilogram air. A coulomb is equal to 1 amp/sec.

**RAD (Radiation absorbed dose)** - energy deposited on a material from a radioactive source: 1 RAD is equal to 100 erg/gram or 0.01 joule/kilogram. A RAD is not a biological measure. The SI unit of measure is the Gray, which is equal to 1 joule/kilogram absorbed energy. 1 Gray is equal to 100 RAD.

**REM (Roentgen equivalent man)** - energy absorbed by a human multiplied by the Quality factor to give an estimated biological effect. 1000 mREM = 1 REM. The SI unit is the Sievert, and 1 Sv is equal to 100 REM.

**Curie (Ci)** - amount of material that emits radioactivity equal to $2.2 \times 10^{12}$ disintegrations per minute (dpm) or $3.7 \times 10^{10}$ disintegrations per second (dps). A microcurie (uCi) is 1/1,000,000 Curies. A Becquerel (Bq) is the SI unit for a disintegration per second.

**Quality Factor (QF)** - a multiplier that converts RAD to REM. The QF depends on the type of radiation and on the energy content. The energy content of neutrons is expressed as mega electron volts (MeV). An electron volt is the energy imparted to an electron when it is accelerated in a 1 volt potential, also equal to $1.60 \times 10^{-19}$ joules. A MeV is then $1.60 \times 10^{-13}$ joules.

## B. Acute Radiation Dosage Results

< 10,000 mREM essentially no effect, average background exposure: comic rays 28 mREM/year, terrestrial radiation 28 mREM/year, internally ingested natural radionuclides ($^{40}K$) 40 mREM/year, medical X-rays 40 mREM/year, nuclear testing atmospheric residues 1 mREM/year, consumer products 10 mREM/year. A maximum dose of 500 mREM over the 9 months of a pregnancy is allowed by NCRP.

| | |
|---|---|
| 10,000 - 50,000 mREM | slight blood changes |
| 100,000 mREM | radiation sickness (nausea, hair loss, delirium, vomiting) in some people |
| >200,000 mREM | general radiation sickness |
| 450,000 mREM | 50% of exposed persons die within 30 days |
| >500,000 mREM | recovery problematic (30 firefighters at Chernobyl received in excess of 800,000 mREM and all died) |

DOE exposure limits for whole body under normal conditions are 5,000 mREM/year, and the administrative control level is 2,000 mREM.

## C. Radiation Quality Factors

As indicated in Table 4-32 the alpha particles are the most biological damaging form of radiation. Radon presents a significant hazard for 3 reasons: (1) it is a gas, which means it readily enters the body; (2) second, it decays rapidly giving off an alpha particle; and (3), the decay products are solids and stick in the lungs, rapidly decaying to generate more alpha particles, as shown in Table 4-33.

**Table 4-32. Quality factors for radiation types**

| Radiation type | Quality Factor |
|---|---|
| X-ray, gamma ray, beta particles and high speed electrons | 1 |
| Alpha particles, multiply charged particles, fission fragments | 20 |
| High-energy protons | 10 |
| Unknown neutrons | 10 |
| $<1 \times 10^{-3}$ MeV neutrons | 2 |
| $1 \times 10^{-2}$ MeV neutrons | 2.5 |
| 0.1 MeV neutrons | 7.5 |
| 0.5 to 1 MeV neutrons | 11 |
| 2.5 MeV neutrons | 9 |
| 5 MeV neutrons | 8 |
| 7 MeV neutrons | 7 |
| 10 MeV neutrons | 6.5 |
| 14 MeV neutrons | 7.5 |
| 20 MeV neutrons | 8 |
| 40 MeV neutrons | 7 |
| 60 MeV neutrons | 5.5 |
| 100 MeV neutrons | 4 |
| >200 MeV neutrons | 3.5 |

**Table 4-33. Uranium decay series**

| Nuclide | Product particle | Nuclide half-life |
|---|---|---|
| Uranium 238<br>↓ *decays to* | alpha | $4.61 \times 10^9$ years |
| Thorium 234<br>↓ *decays to* | beta | 24.1 days |
| Protactinium 234<br>↓ *decays to* | beta | 6.75 hours |
| Uranium 234<br>↓ *decays to* | alpha | $2.48 \times 10^5$ years |
| Thorium 230<br>↓ *decays to* | alpha | $8.0 \times 10^4$ years |
| Radium 226<br>↓ *decays to* | alpha | $1.62 \times 10^3$ years |
| Radon 222<br>↓ *decays to* | alpha | 3.82 days |
| Polonium 218<br>↓ *decays to* | alpha | 3.1 minutes |
| Lead 214<br>↓ *decays to* | beta | 26.8 minutes |
| Bismuth 214<br>↓ *decays to* | beta | 19.7 minutes |
| Polonium 214<br>↓ *decays to* | alpha | $1.6 \times 10^{-4}$ seconds |
| Lead 210<br>↓ *decays to* | beta | 20.4 years |
| Bismuth 210<br>↓ *decays to* | beta | 5.0 days |
| Polonium 210<br>↓ *decays to* | alpha | 138.4 days |
| Lead 210 | | Stable |

## Table 4-34. DOE Methods[63]

| Method | Description |
|---|---|
| **Sampling Methods** | |
| SA010 | Sampling headspace gas for volatile organic compounds within a TRU waste drum with a sampling manifold |
| SA011 | Sampling headspace gas within a TRU waste drum with SUMMA® canisters for volatile organic compounds |
| SD010R | Collecting samples from TRU waste drum containing solid process residues and soils |
| SO010R | Collection of liquid samples for effluent monitoring of operations facilities |
| ST010 | General method for sampling liquids and solids in low-level waste storage tanks |
| ST011R | General method for sampling liquids and solids in high-level waste storage tanks |
| SW010R | Core samples in cement solidified low-level liquid waste |
| **Organic Methods** | |
| OC010R | Preparation and cleanup of hydrocarbon-containing samples for the analysis of volatile organic compounds |
| OG015R | Major nonhalogenated volatile organics in radioactive aqueous liquids analyzed by direct aqueous injection gas chromatography (DAI-GC) |
| OG081R | Analysis of PCBs as Aroclors in solid radioactive mixed wastes, Rev 1 |
| OH100R | Direct analysis of TCLP acidic semivolatile compounds in radioactive liquid wastes or leachates using HPLC and UV |
| OM100R | Analysis of semivolatile organic compounds using capillary gas chromatography with ion trap mass spectrometer detection |
| OM500R | Qualitative analysis of low molecular weight organic acids in mixed hazardous waste samples by thermospray LC-MS |
| OM510R | Determination of chelators and their degradation products in mixed hazardous waste samples by derivatization GC/MS |
| OP010R | Remote purge and trap-gas chromatography of volatile organics in high-level radioactive wastes |
| OP020R | Ultrasonic solvent extraction for volatile organic analysis of solid RMW |
| OP030R | Purge and trap in a glove box |
| OP040R | Reduced-scale zero headspace extraction for TCLP volatiles in shielded or contaminant conditions |
| OP100R | PCBs in aqueous radioactive mixed wastes using solid phase extraction disks and GC-ECD |
| OP120R | Reduced scale liquid-liquid extraction of semivolatile organic compounds |
| OP130R | Analysis of TCLP semivolatiles and pesticides in radioactive mixed waste sludges |
| OP550R | Ultrasonic extraction |
| OS010 | Total organic chlorine in oil, field test kit method |
| OS020 | Immunoassay for polychlorinated biphenyls (PCBs) in soils |
| OS030 | A photoacoustic infrared method for the detection of selected chlorinated volatile organic compounds (VOCs) in water |
| OS040 | Rapid determination of volatile organic contaminants in water and soils by direct purge mass spectrometry |
| OS050 | Supercritical fluid extraction for the analysis of comtaminated soils |
| OS060 | Immunoassay for petroleum fuel hydrocarbons in soil |

Continued on next page.

---

[63] *DOE Methods for Evaluating Environmental and Waste Management Samples*, 1997, Battelle Press, Columbus, OH. E-mail press@battelle.org

## Table 4-34. DOE Methods[64], *continued*

| Method | Description |
|--------|-------------|
| **Inorganic methods** | |
| MB100 | Immunoassay for mercury in soils |
| MM100 | Inductively coupled plasma mass spectrometry for radionuclide analysis |
| MM210 | ICP-MS of 99Tc, 230Th and 234U using flow injection preconcentration |
| MM800 | Ion chromatography and ICP-MS determination of uranium concentration isotopic abundance in groundwater and drinking water |
| MP100R | Solvent extraction of uranium and thorium from radioactive liquid wastes |
| MP110R | Cleanup of transuranic liquid wastes using extraction chromatgraphy |
| MS100R | A reflectometry based instrument for reading colorimetric test strips |
| MS110 | An indicator strip-based colorimetric test for chromate ions ($CrO_4^{2-}$) in aqueous samples |
| MS210 | An indicator strip based colorimetric test for lead ($Pb^{2+}$) in water |
| MS310 | An indicator strip based colorimetric test for nitrate ions ($NO_3$) in water and soil |
| MS410 | An indicator strip-based colorimetric test for nickel ($Ni^{2+}$) in aqueous samples |
| MU012R | Total cyanide by remote microdistillation and argentometric titration |
| MU016 | Alkaline digestion procedure for the extraction of hexavalent chromium |
| **Radiological methods** | |
| RA010 | Method for utilization of alpha track detectors for characterization of gross alpha emission from indoor surfaces |
| RA020 | Method for utilization of Electret ionization chambers for characterization of gross alpha emission from indoor surfaces |
| RI010 | Gamma-ray spectrometry |
| RI100 | Liquid scintillation instrumentation method |
| RP230 | Iodine-129 analysis in aqueous solutions |
| RP280 | Determination of Lead-210 in water using extraction chromatography |
| RP300 | Nickel-59 and nickel-63 determination in aqueous samples |
| RP330 | Separation of niobium for niobium-94 and niobium-93m determination |
| RP450 | Determination of Radium-226 in aqueous samples |
| RP500 | Purification of strontium in water before strontium-89/strontium-90 measurement |
| RP501 | Determination of total radioactive strontium in high-level samples using extraction chromatography |
| RP510 | Determination of strontium-90 in dissolved environmental samples using Chelex-100 |
| RP515 | Rapid determination of Radiostrontium using Empore Strontium RAD Disks |
| RP520 | Determination of strontium-90 in soil, water and filter samples |
| RP530 | Determination of selenium-79 in aqueous samples |
| RP550 | Technetium-99 analysis using extraction chromatography |
| RP570 | Radiochemical determination of thorium isotopes in aqueous samples |
| RP580 | Water distillation from soil and aqueous matrices using a Lachat Microdist™ System for tritium determination |
| RP710 | Laboratory method for gross alpha and beta activity determinations |
| RP720 | Rapid determination of gross alpha, gross beta and gross tritium in water using liquid scintillation counter |
| RP725 | Group actinide screening using extraction chromatography |
| RP730 | Gross gamma screening for environmental matrices |

Continued on next page.

---

[64] *DOE Methods for Evaluating Environmental and Waste Management Samples*, 1997, Battelle Press, Columbus, OH. E-mail  press@battelle.org

**Table 4-34. DOE Methods[65], *continued***

| Method | Description |
|---|---|
| | **Radiological methods, *continued*** |
| RP735 | Determination of total fissile content by neutron activation followed by delayed neutron counting |
| RP800 | Sequential separation of americium and plutonium by extraction chromatography |
| RS100 | In-situ analysis of gamma-ray emitting radionuclides by borehole logging |
| RS551 | Rapid isolation and measurement of Tc-99 using anion exchange filter membranes |

## VII. Field Analytical Methods

The ability of a laboratory to perform tests on the site of a remediation of a spill or hazardous materials dump is a great asset. As the site is being dug, the quick analysis of the excavated material serves to guide the efforts to the most contaminated areas and determine when the work is finished. Several alternatives exist to the laboratory. The first is to place all the normal laboratory equipment in a large van and essentially take the lab to the site. The transportation of GC, GC-MS and metals analytical instruments (GFAA or ICP) is the ultimate in the mobile lab and can be worth the effort in some cases. The data obtained from such a facility can be of any desired level of quality, with even CLP packages being generated. Drawbacks are that the instruments are not designed to be moved and require more frequent maintenance and repair efforts. The power, gas and water consumption can be quite large and limit the siting of the van. Further, the waste disposal problems are identical to those occuring in a fixed-base laboratory.

Another alternative is to purchase portable analytical instruments and place them at the site or very close by in a motel room, small van or outbuilding. The advantage of portable instruments such as GCs is that they are build ruggedly to withstand the constant moving about and can be operated on normal 120 V current and small cylinders of helium, compressed air and hydrogen. The portable laboratory instruments usually generate level 2 to level 3 quality data. The disadvantages of the portable GCs is that they have limited oven temperature ranges and stability and normally only have the capacity for a single column and one or two detectors in series. The use of portable GCs for volatiles analysis is an ideal application, however semivolatile organic compound analysis stretches their capability. The analysis of a single sample by portable GC takes approximately the same amount of time as that required by a full sized instrument (30 to 55 minutes per sample). Also, use of organic solvents for sample extraction, even in the modified forms of microextractions, can be somewhat hard to justify in a motel room.

EPA is preparing a compendium of field analytical methods. This compendium is built upon a publication from September, 1988 (Field Screening Methods Catalog, EPA/540/2-88/005, PB 89134159) that reviewed, without detail, field analysis procedures in use within the Regions. Containing 154 methods, the Field Methods Compendium was made available as a draft in March, 1994. Obtained from the various regional EPA offices, the methods are written in a common format but present a wide range of performance evaluation data, from none to slight modifications of fully validated methods. Some methods in the compendium are simply outdated while others are in need of consolidation, however, taken as a whole the document is extremely useful. The contents of the compendium are presented in Table 4-35.

---

[65] *DOE Methods for Evaluating Environmental and Waste Management Samples*, 1997, Battelle Press, Columbus, OH. E-mail press@battelle.org

**Table 4-35. Contents of EPA Field Methods Compendium (Draft), OERR-9285.2-11, February, 1994**

| Method | Title |
|--------|-------|
| VW-001 | Volatile organics in water by purge and trap |
| -002 | Volatile organics in water by automated headspace - external standard method |
| -003 | Volatile organics in water by automated headspace - internal standard method |
| -004 | Volatile organics in water by manual headspace |
| -005 | VOA water/pentane extraction GC-ECD |
| -006 | VOA water/carbon disulfide extraction GC-FID |
| -007 | VOA water/headspace GC-PID |
| -008 | Field screening of target purgeable volatile organic compounds (aqueous matrix) |
| -009 | Method for field screening of volatile organic compounds in water and soil by headspace analysis using the HNu 301P gas chromatograph |
| -010 | Method for field screening of volatile organic compounds in water and soil by headspace analysis using the Photovac 10S10 gas chromatograph |
| -011 | VOA water, soil, sediment/methanol, water extraction GC-PID/ELCD |
| -012 | Volatile organic compound verification by purge and trap with PID/ELCD detection |
| -013 | Volatile organic screening by heated headspace with FID detection |
| -014 | Analysis of volatile organic compounds in water by purge and trap |
| VS-001 | Volatile organics in soil/sediment by purge and trap |
| -002 | Volatile organics in soil/sediment by automated headspace - external standard method |
| -003 | VOA soil/pentane extraction GC-ECD |
| -004 | VOA soil/carbon disulfide extraction GC-FID |
| -005 | VOA soil/headspace GC-PID |
| -006 | Field screening of target purgeable volatile organic compounds (solid matrix) |
| -007 | Analysis of halogenated and aromatic volatile organic compounds in soil and water by purge and trap gas chromatograph |
| VG-001 | Volatile organics in soil gas - adsorbent tube method |
| -002 | Volatile organics in soil gas using electrolytic conductivity detector - direct analysis |
| -003 | Halogenated volatile organics in soil gas using electron capture detector - direct analysis |
| -004 | VOA soil gas charcoal GC-ECD |
| -005 | VOA soil gas canisters GC-PID |
| -006 | Field screening analysis of volatile contaminants in soil gas matrix |
| -007 | Analysis of halogenated and aromatic volatile compounds in air and soil gas by thermal desorption gas chromatograph |
| -008 | Volatile organics in soil gas |
| -009 | Field method for volatile indicator parameters in soil gas samples using Photovac GC-PID |
| -010 | Sampling and field gas chromatographic analysis for volatile organics in soil gas |
| -011 | Analysis of halogenated and aromatic volatile organics compounds in whole gas samples by purge and trap gas chromatograph |

Continued on next page.

**Table 4-35.    Contents of EPA Field Methods Compendium (Draft), OERR-9285.2-11, February, 1994,** *continued*

| Method | Title |
|---|---|
| VA-001 | Volatile organics in air - adsorbent tube method |
| -002 | Halogenated volatile organics in air using electrolytic coductivity detector - direct analysis |
| -003 | Volatile organics in air - portable direct analysis |
| -004 | Volatile organics in air using electron capture detector - direct analysis |
| -005 | Field screening analysis of ambient air |
| -006 | Manual analysis of ambient air for selected volatile organic compounds by a portable gas chromatograph |
| -007 | Standard operating procedure for the analysis of ambient air for selected volatile organic compounds by a portable gas chromatograph |
| -008 | Automated analysis of ambient air for selected volatile organic compounds by a portable gas chromatograph |
| S-001 | SV water/carbon disulfide extraction GC-FID |
| -002 | Field screening of target semivolatile organic compounds (aqueous matrix) |
| -003 | SV soil/methylene chloride extraction GC-FID |
| -004 | Field screening of target semivolatile organic compounds (solid matrix) |
| P-001 | Chlorinated pesticides in soil |
| -002 | Field screening of organochlorine pesticides (solid matrix) |
| -003 | Chlorinated pesticides in water |
| -004 | Field screening of organochlorine pesticides (aqueous matrix) |
| -005 | Organophosphorous pesticides in water |
| -006 | Organophosphorous pesticides in soil/sediment |
| -007 | Phenoxyherbicides in soil/sediment |
| -008 | Phenoxyherbicides in water |
| -009 | CLP pesticide/PCB analysis by gas chromatograph |
| -010 | Preparation of sediment. soil, and water samples for pesticide analysis |
| -011 | Field extraction and analysis of chlorinated pesticides in soil by ECD |
| PCB-001 | Polychlorinated biphenyls (PCB) in oil |
| -002 | Field screening of polychlorinated biphenyls (PCB) compounds (solid matrix) |
| -003 | Polychlorinated biphenyls (PCB) in water |
| -004 | Field screening of polychlorinated biphenyls (PCB) compounds (aqueous matrix) |
| -005 | PCB/Pesticides soil/hexane extraction GC-ECD |
| -006 | PCB soil/solvent extraction perchlorination GC-ECD |
| -007 | Preparation and analysis of samples for polychlorinated biphenyls |
| -008 | Field analysis of PCBs |
| -009 | Polychlorinated biphenyls (PCBs) in soil |
| PAH-001 | Field gas chromatographic analysis for polynuclear aromatic hydrocarbons (in water and soil) |
| -002 | Polynuclear aromatic hydrocarbons (PAH) water/hexane extraction GC-FID |
| -003 | Polynuclear aromatic hydrocarbons (PAH) soil/hexane extraction GC-FID |
| -004 | Total polynuclear aromatic hydrocarbon screening procedure for sediments |
| -005 | Polycyclic aromatic hydrocarbons in soil/sediment |

Continued on next page.

**Table 4-35.** **Contents of EPA Field Methods Compendium (Draft), OERR-9285.2-11, February, 1994,** *continued*

| Method | Title |
|---|---|
| PAH-006 | Polynuclear aromatic hydrocarbons in water |
| -007 | Polynuclear aromatic hydrocarbons in oil |
| -008 | PAH soil/methanol extraction, sonication UV |
| -009 | Analysis of PAH by gas chromatograph |
| -010 | Preparation of sediment soil and water samples for semivolatile compounds: PAH, phenols |
| -011 | Extraction and analysis of PAH in soil by GC/FID |
| -012 | FASP extraction and analysis of PAH by HPLC |
| O-001 | Pentachlorophenol in soil/sediment |
| -002 | TPH soil/freon extraction IR |
| -003 | TPH-G soil/methanol extraction GC-PID, ELCD |
| -004 | TPH-HCID soil/methylene chloride extraction GC-FID |
| -005 | Analysis of phenols by gas chromatograph |
| -006 | Analysis of total petroleum hydrocarbons by headspace gas chromatography |
| -007 | Low level methane analysis of Summa canister gas sample |
| -008 | Extraction and analysis of pentachlorophenol in soil by electron capture |
| -009 | Field extraction and analysis of TPH in soil by FID |
| I-001 | Selected metals in soil/sediment by X-ray fluorescence |
| -002 | Inorganics soil/acid digestion AA-flame |
| -003 | Hexavalent chromium soil/alkaline digestion spectrophotometer |
| -004 | Inorganics water/acid digestion AA-flame |
| -005 | Mercury analysis by cold vapor atomic absorption spectrometry |
| -006 | FASP mercury cold vapor atomic absorption |
| C-001 | Alkalinity/Water/Titration |
| -002 | Chemical Oxygen Demand/Water/Open Reflux |
| -003 | Chloride, Nitrate, and Sulfate Anions/Water/IC |
| -004 | Hardness/Water/EDTA Colorimetric |
| -005 | Oil and Grease/Water/Gravimetric |
| -006 | Total Dissolved Solids/Water/Dried |
| -007 | Total Organic Carbon/Water/Analyzer |
| -008 | Total Suspended Solids/Water/Dried |
| -009 | 10-Day Chronic Toxicity Test Using *Daphnia Magna or Daphnia Pulex.* |
| -010 | Extractable Organics/Soil/Gravimetric |
| -011 | Moisture/Soil/Drying oven |
| -012 | Paint Filter Test/Soil/Paint Filters |
| -013 | pH/Soil/pH Meter |
| -014 | Specific Gravity/Soil |
| -015 | Total Carbon/Soil/Combustion Train |
| -016 | Total, Fixed, and Volatile Solids/Soil |
| -017 | Water Level Measurement |
| -018 | Controlled Pumping Test |
| -019 | Slug Test |

Continued on next page.

**Table 4-35.** **Contents of EPA Field Methods Compendium (Draft), OERR-9285.2-11, February, 1994,** *continued*

| Method | Title |
|---|---|
| C-020 | General Surface Geophysics |
| -021 | 7-Day Standard Reference Toxicity Test Using *Larval Pimephales Promelas:* |
| -022 | 24-Hour Rangefinding Test Using *Daphnia Magna or Daphnia Pulex:* |
| -023 | 96-Hour Acute Toxicity Test Using *Larval Pimephales Promelas:* |
| -024 | 24-hour Rangefinding Test Using *Larval Pimephales Promelas:* |
| -025 | 48-Hour Acute Toxicity Test Using *Daphnia Magna or Daphnia Pulex:* |
| -026 | 7-Day Renewal Toxicity Test Using *Ceriodaphnia Dubia:* |
| -027 | 7-Day Static Toxicity Test Using *Larval Pimephales Promelas:* |
| -028 | 96-Hour Static Toxicity Test Using *Selenastrum Capricornutum:* |
| K-001 | Hazard Categorization |
| -002 | Compatibility Testing |
| R-001 | Radiological/Quality Control For Sample Preparation, Counting, and Data Handling |
| -002 | Radiological/Determination Of Gross Alpha/Beta In Soil Samples [simplified methods] |
| -003 | Radiological/Soil Sample Preparation |
| -004 | Radiological/Determination Of Gross Alpha/Beta In Water Samples |
| -005 | Radiological/Determination Of Gross Alpha/Beta Activity In Water Samples [dot level] |
| -006 | Radiological/Determination Of Gross Alpha/Gross Beta In Core Samples, Soil, Bottom Sediments, Sludges, And Silts Samples [high organic samples] |
| -007 | Radiological/Determination Of Gross Alpha/Beta In Biota, vegetation/food stuff, [simplified methods] |
| -008 | Determination Of Gross Alpha/Beta In Biota [vegetation/food stuff][extended methods] |
| IA-001 | X-MET 880 Field Portable X-Ray Fluorescence Operating Procedure |
| IM-002 | Operation of the X-MET 880 X-Ray Fluorescence Spectrometer |
| -003 | Field Flame Atomic Absorption Analysis SOP |
| OA-001 | Sentax Scentograph Gas Chromatograph Field Use |
| -002 | GC/MS Analysis of Tenax/CMS Cartridges and Summa Canisters |
| -003 | Photonionization Detector (PID) HNU |
| -004 | Photovac 10A10 Portable Gas Chromatograph Operation |
| -005 | Photovac 10S50, 10S55, and 10S70 Gas Chromatograph Operation |
| -006 | Photovac GC Analysis for Soil, Water, and Air/Soil Gas |
| RA-001 | Radiological/Determination Of Detection Levels For Gross Alpha And Gross Beta Analysis |
| -002 | Radiological/Radiochemical Analysis Efficiency, Background, And Recovery Standards (Counter) Preparation |
| -003 | Radiological Operation Of The LB5100 Gas Proportional Counter |
| -004 | Radiological/Setup And Operation Of The Counter Top Centrifuge |
| SM-001 | Sample Equipment Decontamination |
| SWSS-001 | Surface Water Sampling |
| -002 | Sediment Sampling |
| WS-001 | Drum Sampling |

Continued on next page.

**Table 4-35.** **Contents of EPA Field Methods Compendium (Draft), OERR-9285.2-11, February, 1994,** *continued*

| Method | Title |
|---|---|
| WS-002 | Tank Sampling |
| -003 | Chip, Wipe, and Sweep Sampling |
| -004 | Waste Pile Sampling |
| SS-001 | Soil Sampling |
| -002 | Soil Gas Sampling |
| GWS-001 | Groundwater Well Sampling |
| GS-001 | Collection of Gaseous Samples by Using Tedlar Bags |
| QA-001 | Quality Assurance/Quality Control Samples |

## A. Immunoassay Kits

The recent introduction of immunoassay kits as field screening tests for a variety of analytes is another alternative available to the laboratory. EPA has looked at draft methods for pentachlorophenol (4010), 2,4-D (4015), PCBs (4020), TPH (4030), BTEX (4031), PAH (4035), Toxaphene (4040), Chlordane (4041), DDT (4042), TNT (4050 and 8515), and RDX (4051) by immunoassay, which are in a variety of stages of the acceptance process for inclusion in SW-846. There is also an immunoassay kit for mercury in the inorganic form. The PCB kit (4020) was promulgated on 4 January, 1994. The chemistry of the kits allow them to be very selective and gives the technician the ability to perform many analyses in a relatively short period of time. All consumables are included in the kit, and if the colorimeter is battery powered, there are few limitations as to where the test station can be set up. The basis for the test begins with an enzyme-catalyzed reaction of a substrate to give a colored product. One example is the horseradish peroxidase catalyzed reaction of tetramethylbenzidine with hydrogen peroxide, which forms a blue-colored product from the colorless substrate[66]. The enzyme is modified to chemically attach a portion or all of the target molecule to it, in such a fashion so that the enzyme catalytic ability is not affected. To make the antibodies, a larger molecule such as albumin, hemocyanin or thyroglobulin is derivatized with the analyte molecule and then injected into vertebrate host animals (rabbits or horses) to stimulate the immune response[67]. The antibodies are isolated and purified, then used without further processing in the polyclonal method. The monoclonal antibody method uses hybridoma technology to fuse the antibody-producing cells from the spleen with myeloma cells, then culture the resulting progeny cells to produce large amounts of the antibody[68]. Regardless of the source, the antibodies are used to coat either the insides of small test tubes or wells in a 96 well test plate or covalently bound to small superparamagnetic particles. In the test a diluted extract of the analyte (aqueous DMSO, isopropanol or methanol[69]) is mixed with the antibody, forming the antibody-analyte

[66] Carter, K. "The Performance of Immunoassay-Based Field Methods for Pentachlorophenol and Polychlorinated Biphenyls." *Proceedings of the Fifteenth Annual EPA Conference on Analysis of Pollutants in the Environment.* May 6-7, 1992. pp 389-424.

[67] Friedman, S.B. "Immunoassay Methods for Environmental Field Screening." *Proceedings of the 8th Annual Waste Testing and Quality Assurance Symposium,* July 13-17, 1992. pp 43-57.

[68] Swift, R.P., J.R. Leavell, and C.W. Brandenburg. "Evaluation of the ENSYS PAH-RISc® Test Kit." *Proceedings of the 9th Annual Waste Testing & Quality Assurance Symposium.* July 12-16, 1993. pp 484-499.

[69] Harrison, R.O. and R.E. Carlson. "Analysis of PCB's by Enzyme Immunoassay." *Proceedings of the 8th Annual Waste Testing and Quality Assurance Symposium* July 13-17, 1992. pp. 120-128.

complex. Analyte-modified enzyme (enzyme conjugate) is added, which forms a complex with the rest of the available antibody. The test tube is then washed out with detergent, removing any uncomplexed analyte modified enzyme. The antibody complexes are left immobilized on either the sides of the test tube or on the magnetic particles, which are held by another magnet in the bottom of the tube. Substrate is added and the enzymatic reaction allowed to proceed for a period of time, terminated by addition of a stop solution, such as acid, to denature the enzyme, and then the intensity of the colored product is determined on a colorimeter. A blank is run with the samples to determine the maximum amount of color formed when no target analyte is present. Any target analyte in the sample will decrease the amount of remaining enzyme and decrease the amount of colored product formed from the substrate. The color decrease is calibrated by running standard concentrations of target analyte in each batch.

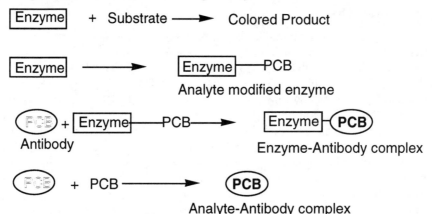

**Figure 4-3.   Interaction of enzyme, substrate, antibody and PCB target analyte.**

The EPA is currently evaluating the immunoassay kits as pass-fail procedures for a regulatory action level, for instance 20 ppm for PCB in soil on remediation sites. Future evaluations may include quantitative abilities. The kits are designed to minimize the number of false negatives (ideally zero), however there can be up to 10% false positives. For fixed laboratory confirmation purposes, EPA recommends confirmation of all positive immunoassay readings and 10% of the negatives.

The validation package for consideration of a new method for inclusion in SW-846 or for adaptation of an existing method for a new matrix consists of the following information[70]:

1.  Cross reactivity with similar analytes
2.  Cross reactivity with dissimilar analytes
3.  False negative/false positive rates
4.  Extraction efficiency for solid matrices
5.  Performance data on spiked samples compared with standard SW-846 lab methods
6.  Performance data on real samples compared with standard SW-846 lab methods.

---

[70]  Lesnik, B. "Immunoassay Methods: the EPA Approach." *Environmental Lab*. June/July, 1994. pp. 37-44.

In addition to the EPA draft methods for immunoassay kits, there are a large number of other assays commercially available. These include atrazine (triazine pesticides), alaclor, cyanazine, metolachlor, benomyl/carbendazim, aldicarb, carbofuran, captan, cyclodienes, methoprene, procymidone, metalaxyl, isoproturon, paraquat, DDT and others. Some kits are almost entirely selective for the target analyte, such as the 2,4-D kits, while others are cross-reactive to a number of related compounds such as general triazine pesticides in the atrazine test, and 4,4'-DDT, 4,4'-DDE and 4,4'-DDD in the DDT kit. Immunoassays for metals have also been reported[71].

## B. Qualitative Screening Tests

At least once a week a client comes to the laboratory with a sample and asks, "What is it?" or "What's in it?" Although it is possible to run a large battery of specific tests on the sample for metals, organics, and inorganic non-metallic parameters, frequently these test results are negative, expensive, and lead to mistaken or no conclusions about the sample. Through judicious choice of a few simple qualitative test procedures, enough information can be obtained to lead directly to a suitable answer[72].

An initial physical examination can often be useful. The smell or lack of smell of the sample may direct you in specific analytical directions. For liquid samples determination of whether the liquid is water or not is easily accomplished by mixing a drop with water and then mixing another drop with methylene chloride. It's going to be soluble in one or the other. An approximation of the density is also obtained by observing whether the drop floats or sinks in the insoluble mixture. Determining the solubility of solid samples is accomplished the same way.

Burning a small portion of the sample on the tip of a stainless steel spatula with a match flame is informative. Most organic materials will rapidly burn while inorganic materials will not. In either case observe the color of the match flame. Green indicates the presence of copper or boron, red is lithium or strontium, orange-red is calcium, yellow is sodium, and violet is potassium. If a copper loop is used to hold the sample while burning, the Bielstein test for halogen is performed. A distinct green color indicates the presence of halogen in the sample. Consult Feigl and Anger for a more complete flame test analysis.

If the sample is a stain or tightly adhered to the surface of a larger item, exposing the sample to the flame of a tightly focused propane torch or placing the item in a 550°C muffle furnace can help determine whether the stain is organic or not.

### Oxidizers

A rapid test for the substatial presence of oxidizers can be performed by testing a small portion of the sample on a potassium iodide-starch paper that has been moistened with acetic acid. An intense blue to black stain on the paper indicates that oxidizers are present. A more sensitive test consists of addition of four drops $0.5M$ KI to four drops of the sample acidified with four drops $3M$ HCl, then shaking with ten drops of

71   Chakrabarti, P., F.M. Hatcher, R.C. Blake, P.A. Ladd and D.A. Blake. "Enzyme Immunoassay to Determine Heavy Metals Using Antibodies to Specific Metal-EDTA Complexes: Optimization and Validation of an Immunoassay for Soluble Indium." *Analytical Biochemistry* 217:70-75; 17th Annual EPA Conference on Analysis of Pollutants in the Environment, May 3-5, 1994, Norfolk VA.

72   Feigl, F., and V. Anger, 1972. *Spot Tests in Inorganic Analysis*, Elsevier; New York, NY; Feigl, F, and V. Anger, *Spot Tests in Organic Analysis*, Elsevier, NY, New York, www.elsevier.com.

chloroform. This extracts any formed $I_2$ as an intense purple color into the chloroform. An alternate is to treat four drops of the sample with two drops of $12M$ HCl, then add four drops of saturated $MnCl_2$ in $12M$ HCl. Heat in boiling water for two minutes then look for the formation of a deep brown to black coloration ($MnCl_3$). The $MnCl_3$ is unstable and may produce a precipitate of $MnO_2$ on standing.

### Reducers

To test for reducing agents, mix a drop of weak iodine-potassium iodide solution (see *Standard Methods* 4500-Cl C.3.h) with the sample. If the brown color of the test solution is bleached, the presence of reducing agents is indicated. Decolorization of the orange color of a weak potassium dichromate solution can also be used to indicate the presence of reducing agents. Permanganate decolorization is also useful. To four drops of the sample add five drops water and six drops $3M$ $H_2SO_4$. Insure that the solution is acidic. Add two drops $0.01M$ $KMnO_4$ solution and observe for decolorization. If the solution is still purple, heat in boiling water for several minutes.

An alternate test for reducing agents is to prepare a test reagent by mixing two drops of $0.1M$ $Fe(NO_3)_3$, two drops of $0.1M$ $K_3Fe(CN)_6$, and four drops of $3M$ $HNO_3$ and dilution to 1 mL with water. Addition of four drops of the test solution will generate a dark blue precipitate of Prussian Blue if reducers are present. Any blue or green coloration to the test reagent after addition of the sample should be viewed as a positive.

### Sodium fusion test

The sodium fusion test has a long history of use in qualitative analysis, and just because it was discovered back in the 1800's doesn't mean it's not useful now. The test consists of carefully heating a small portion (1 g) of the sample with a small piece of sodium in a test tube. After any initial reaction subsides, alcohol is very cautiously added to quench any unreacted sodium. The mixture is then dissolved in water, with heating if necessary. Sulfur in the sample is detected by addition of 5 mL of the water solution to three drops of 10% lead acetate solution in 2 mL of 10% sodium hydroxide. A black precipitate is a positive for sulfur. Nitrogen is detected by heating 2 mL of the water solution, then adding five drops of 10% sodium hydroxide followed by five drops of 10% ferrous sulfate. After the solution returns to room temperature the suspension is just acidified with 10% hydrochloric acid. A blue or green solution or a blue precipitate is a positive for the presence of nitrogen. Chlorine is determined by acidification of 5 mL of the water solution with nitric acid, then addition of several drops of 10% silver nitrate. A white precipitate indicates chlorine presence. Phosphorus is determined by heating 5 mL of the water solution with 3 mL concentrated nitric acid, then addition of 10 mL of 10% ammonium molybdate. The sample is heated to 60 °C for a few minutes, then allowed to sit. A yellow precipitate indicates the presence of phosphorus.

### Cations and anions

Metals in the sample are most economically identified by digesting a portion of the sample in acid and analyzing the digestate by ICP (see Section 2-H). The traditional cation qualitative analysis scheme is not cost effective unless a complete metals identification is necessary, and even then sending the sample off for X-ray diffraction testing is a less expensive means of analysis.

On the other hand, unless one has access to an ion chromatograph or a capillary ion electrophoresis instrument, spot testing for the common anions is very cost effective. Several manufacturers have dip-stick spot tests that can be used to screen samples. Other procedures use addition of one or two drops of a reagent to one or two drops of a sample. Often these tests are the same as the quantitative EPA procedure run in a yes-no manner. Thus if addition of a drop of barium chloride solution results in a white precipitate, this can be indication of the presence of sulfate. Silver nitrate addition can indicate chlorine, bromine or iodine in the sample if a white precipitate is formed. If reaction of a drop of the sample with sulfanillic acid-NED reagent generates a red color, the presence of nitrite is indicated. However, these tests may be subject to interferences unless suitable pre-treatment of the sample has been performed.

For a systematic evaluation of the sample the traditional anion analytical scheme can be very informative and quick[73]. There are four groups of anions in the traditional scheme. They are:

1. *Acid-volatized anions - carbonate, sulfite, thiosulfate, sulfide and nitrite* – Cyanide may be included in this group. A small portion of the sample (six drops) is treated dropwise with four drops $3M$ sulfuric acid and the sample is observed for gas evolution. The sample may be warmed but not heated. The evolved gases could be $CO_2$ from carbonate, $SO_2$ from sulfite or thiosulfate, $H_2S$ from sulfide, HCN from cyanide, or $NO_2$ from nitrite. The creation of a white or yellow precipitate along with gas evolution is probably elemental sulfur from thiosulfate. If the evolved gas is brown, nitrite was probably present. If cyanide is suspected, addition of an iron salt ($Fe[NO_3]_3$) can create ferricyanide and hold it in the sample until Group 3. Addition of hydrogen peroxide to another portion of the sample (to oxidize any sulfite to sulfate) and repeating the acid addition and bubbling the evolved gas into saturated $Ba(OH)_2$ solution will generate a white precipitate in the trap solution if the gas is $CO_2$. If the gas is not $CO_2$, use of a hydrogen peroxide/$Ba(OH)_2$ trap on the gas from the acidified sample can verify $SO_2$ evolution. $H_2S$ can be detected by the smell or darkening of lead acetate paper or solution. Use of zinc acetate or cadmium nitrate solution in a trap will indicate $H_2S$ through formation of a precipitate. HCN can be trapped in NaOH solution and spot tested with pyridine-barbituric acid reagent.

2. *Non-volatized anions precipitated as barium or calcium salts from dilute ammonia solution - sulfate, borate, phosphate, chromate, fluoride, oxalate, arsenite and arsenate* – To the acid treated solution from group 1, add dropwise, $3M$ $NH_3$ solution until basic. Then add three drops of $0.3M$ $Ba(NO_3)_2$. Formation of a precipitate indicates $BaSO_4$, $Ba(BO_2)_2$, $Ba_3(PO_4)_2$, and/or $BaCrO_4$ formation. After complete precipitation, the sample can be centrifuged and the supernatent is treated with three drops $0.5M$ $Ca(NO_3)_2$. Formation of a precipitate indicates $CaF_2$, $CaC_2O_4$, $Ca_3(AsO_3)_2$ and/or $Ca_3(AsO_4)_2$. Addition of 15 drops $3M$ HCl to the barium precipitate will not dissolve $BaSO_4$; the other possibilities are soluble in acid.

3. *Non-volatized anions precipitated as silver salts from dilute nitric acid solution - chloride, bromide, iodide, thiocyanate, ferrocyanide and ferricyanide* – Acidify 6 drops of the sample solution with four drops $3M$ $HNO_3$, then add 2 drops $0.5M$ $AgNO_3$. Any formed precipitate could consist of AgCl, AgBr, AgI, AgSCN, $Ag_4Fe(CN)_6$, and/or $Ag_3Fe(CN)_6$.

---

[73] Margolis, E.J., 1962. *Qualitative Anion-Cation Analysis*, John Wiley & Sons, New York, NY.

4. *Non-volatized anions of the "soluble" group - nitrate* – To test for nitrate, the brown-ring procedure is appropriate. First, nitrite must be removed. To an eight drop portion of the sample add 15 mg powdered urea, then acidify with three drops $3M$ $H_2SO_4$. Add six drops water, then heat in a boiling water bath until gas evolution ceases. Second, other interferring anions must be removed through addition of five drops of a saturated $Ag_2SO_4$ solution. If any precipitate is formed it is removed through centrifuging the sample. To the clear supernatent in a clean test tube add six drops freshly prepared $0.2M$ $FeSO_4$ and stir well. Using a pipet carefully add a one-half inch thick layer of concentrated $H_2SO_4$ to the bottom of the test tube without any mixing into the other solution. Allow the tube to sit undisturbed for several minutes, then look for the formation of an intense brown ring at the interface between the two layers. The brown ring $[Fe(NO)^+]$ confirms the presence of nitrate ion.

Another test for nitrate is to add nitron acetate (1,5-diphenylanilodihydrotriazol acetate), which forms a crystalline precipitate with nitrate[74]. Other anions also form precipitates with nitron, and thus should be absent from the sample.

In the traditional procedure, acetate is included with nitrate as a soluble anion determined by steam distillation of the acidified solution followed by smelling for a vinegar odor. Steam distillation is a fairly good isolation procedure, however modern techniques suggest subsequent determination by direct injection GC-FID. Use of GC would also determine other organic anions such as the phenols and other organic acids.

These tests are performed sequentially on an aqueous sample. Combined with the information obtained with an ICP scan, very fast identification of samples can be performed.

[74] Wolff, J.-C., P.D.P. Taylor and P. de Bievre. "Traceable Values for Nitrate in Water Samples by Isotopic Dilution Analysis using a Small Thermionic Quadrupole Mass Spectrometer." *Anal. Chem.* 68(18). pp. 3231-3237

# Air Pollution and Monitoring

One of the more interesting phone calls an environmental laboratory will receive is from an existing or potential client who says, "We have an odor down here, and we need to know what it is." After an extended game of 20 questions, the Project Manager will forward the client's problem to the technical manager for air analysis and the game will be repeated. The lab's objective is to intelligently guess exactly what is causing the problem, then go to the site and take a sample for an analysis that will confirm the guess.

## I. SAMPLING

The proper method of air sampling depends to a great extent on the desired target analytes, the test method chosen and the tested object. The EPA has published methods for testing outdoor ambient air, indoor air, motor vehicle exhausts, and stationary sources. The latter are point sources of atmospheric effluent for industries, most often referred to as stacks. The EPA also has methods for testing volatile emissions from painted or coated items. Some analytes can be directly quantitated in the gas phase, and transportation of the instrument to the sampling site becomes part of the preferred sampling method. However, most analytes cannot be directly measured and must be trapped on a solid adsorbent or in a liquid before transportation to the laboratory and analysis. In general the analytes directly measured in the field depend on gas phase chemistry, while the solution- or solid-trapped analytes are determined by techniques similar to those already discussed for analysis of water or solid samples.

### A. Filter Cassette

A common and easy form of sampling is the filter cassette. This consists of an appropriate filter of paper, polymer membrane, or glass fibers backed with a support in a holder. The filters can have a range of random pore sizes as in the glass fiber filters or be very consistent with 5.0 um to 0.8 um sizes common in the polymer membranes. The filter may be uncoated, which results in the trapping of particulate matter, or it may be treated chemically for the preferential trapping of selected analytes, which may be in the form of a gas, liquid aerosol, or solid particles. The filter holder can be plastic, either acrylic or polycarbonate, for use at room temperature, or it may be of stainless steel for use at elevated temperature such as 120 °C in stack testing. The cassette works by attaching a metered pump to one side of the cassettes and sucking air through the filter. The open end of the cassette may consist of a small hole or be completely open faced. Intended for sampling tiny particles, cassettes fail miserably when used for sampling large particles such as visible airborne wood, glass, metal, or plastic fibers generated from grinding machines and lathes. The reason may lie in the presence of static charges

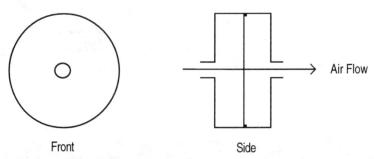

Front    Side

**Figure 5-1.   Diagram of an air sampling filter cassette.**

## B. Annular Denuder

Annular denuders are constructed of metal or plastic concentric tubes coated with an absorbent or reactive chemical layer to trap target analytes from rapid air streams.  Flows on the order of several hundred liters per minute can be handled by the large model denuders with very good trapping efficiencies.

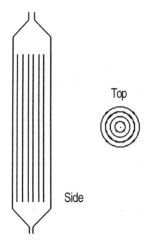

**Figure 5-2.  Diagram of an annular denuder.**

**Table 5-1.   Coating materials used on annular denuders**

| Coating Material | Target Analyte |
|---|---|
| Oxalic acid | $NH_3$, aniline |
| Oleic acid | $SO_3$ |
| $H_3PO_4$ | $NH_3$ |
| $K_2CO_3$ | $SO_2$, $H_2S$ |
| $Na_2CO_3$ | $SO_2$, HCl, $HNO_3$, $HNO_2$ |
| $CuSO_4$ | $NH_3$ |
| $PbO_2$ | $SO_2$, $H_2S$ |

Continued on next page.

**Table 5-1  Coating materials used on annular denuders,** *continued*

| Coating Material | Target Analyte |
|---|---|
| $WO_3$ | $NH_3$, $HNO_3$ |
| MgO | $HNO_3$ |
| NaF | $HNO_3$ |
| NaOH + guaiacol | $NO_2$ |
| $HSO_3^-$ + triethanolamine | $CH_2O$ |
| Nylon | $SO_2$, $HNO_3$ |
| Powdered Tenax | Halocarbons |
| Silica gel | Aniline |
| ICl | $R_4Pb$ |

# C. Impinger

Impingers are used for trapping airborne target analytes into a liquid solution, which is then analyzed. The trapping solution can be one of a wide variety of solvent/derivatization media for both particulates and specific target analytes. Midget impingers can hold up to 20-25 mL of trapping solution, while larger models are available to handle liters of solution. The maximum flow through the midget impingers is 1 to 2 liters per minute limited by blowing the liquid solution out of the device. Larger impingers can handle much higher flows. See Figure 5-5 for an example.

**Table 5-2.  Trapping solutions used in impingers**

| Target Analyte | Trapping Solution |
|---|---|
| Acetaldehyde | Water |
| Acetates | Ethanol |
| Acetic acid | Glycerol/water |
| Acetonitrile | Permanganate solution |
| Acrolein | Hexylresorcinol solution |
| Aldehydes | MBTH solution |
| Amines | HCl/isopropanol |
| Ammonia/aniline | dilute $H_2SO_4$ |
| Butanol | Water |
| Carbon disulfide | Copper salt/diethylamine |
| Chlorine | Methyl Orange solution |
| Formaldehyde | Bisulfite solution |
| Mercaptans | $Hg(OAc)_2$ solution |
| Phenol | NaOH solution |
| $SO_2$ | Tetrachloromercurate solution |

# D. Adsorbent Trap

Adsorbent traps can be as simple as glass tubes filled with Tenax, activated charcoal, $C_{18}$ reversed phase media, silica gel, or cold traps (liquid $N_2$, or solid $CO_2$), etc. for trapping target analytes from air streams. If volatile, the analytes can be thermally desorbed directly into the analytical instrument. Another method uses solvent desorption of the analytes, followed by further sample processing and analysis.

A different type of adsorbent trap is used for semivolatile analytes. These have been found to be effectively trapped by a combination of a piece of polyurethane foam (PUF) backed by an adsorbent Amberlite® resin such as XAD-2. The sampling adsorbents are exhaustively extracted with a 9:1 combination of diethyl ether:hexane in a soxhlet apparatus for at least 16 hours at 4 cycles per hour prior to use. Normally 273 m³ of air are drawn through the device at 6 cubic feet (0.17 m³) per minute.

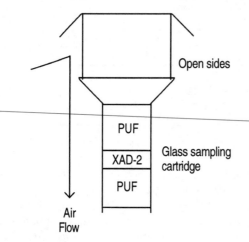

**Figure 5-3. Diagram of a hi-flow semivolatiles sampler.**

## E. Grab Sample

Various types of grab samples for volatile organic analysis can be obtained. They range from an inflatable inert plastic bag called a Tedlar® bag of 0.6- to 10-liter capacity, to an evacuated 1 liter glass flask closed with stopcocks at either end, or a stainless steel 6- or 12-liter capacity ball that is specially polished on the inside with the SUMMA® process. The Tedlar® bag requires a sample pump to fill it, while the SUMMA® canister and the glass flask are filled by simply opening the stopcock or valve and allowing the container to come to atmospheric pressure, then closing the valve or stopcock.

## F. Bulk Sample

Bulk samples are commonly obtained with cyclones, electrostatic precipitators, venturi scrubbers, baghouse filters, dust-fall buckets, etc. These techniques are used on the industrial scale for removal of contaminants from air prior to venting to the atmosphere and often provide massive quantities of material for sampling.

## G. Cascade Impactor

Particulates come in a variety of sizes. The larger sizes captured by a gauze mask are the particles that would normally be trapped by the mucus membranes and hairs in the nasal passages. Of more concern are the very tiny particles on the order of 0.1 to 1.0 um in length that will easily pass through the nasal passages and gauze filters and become lodged deep in the lungs. Particles of this order of size are termed "respirable" and present the greatest health hazard. To test for respirable particles a Cascade impactor is used that allows separation of particulates by size. Impactor plates are often coated with a grease or oil to enhance trapping.

Air Flow

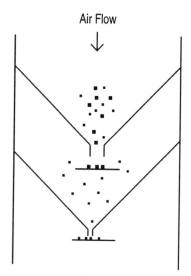

**Figure 5-4. Diagram of a cascade impactor.**

## H. Colorimetric Indicator Tubes

Sampling events are not always planned, particularly in the case of transportation accidents or warehouse fires. Quick information is needed about the presence of hazardous materials in the air surrounding the site, and nothing can really match the use of colorimetric indicator tubes in these cases. Designed for detection of a limited number of analytes in a very short period of time, one or two operators of the calibrated hand pumps with a series of the tubes can rapidly determine what hazards are present and which are not. Two companies supply the tubes, Sensidyne and Dragger. Both provide handbooks on the chemistry of the tubes and kits and procedures for rapid assessment of hazardous sites. The calibrated pumps sold by the two companies are not interchangeable. For general purpose monitoring the EPA has approved the use of colorimetric tubes for $NH_3$, $CO_2$, CO, $Cl_2$, HCN, $H_2S$, and $SO_2$.

## I. Stack Testing

Monitoring industrial effluents from stacks is described in detail in 40 CFR part 60, Appendix A, and requires placing permanent sampling ports (nipples) in the sides of the stack in an area with limited turbulence. Sampling is accomplished at many points over the cross-section of the stack. The number and placement of the points is set by the geometry and size of the stack (Method 1). The air velocity of the stack must be determined, and a pitot tube is used for this purpose (Method 2 - 2D). The gas sample can be routed directly from the pitot tube to an instrument analyzer for direct read-out of target analytes, or it may be directed into a sampling train, that is used for most of the chemical methods with appropriate solutions in the traps.

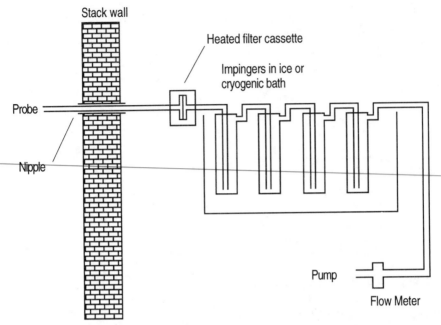

**Figure 5-5. Simplified sampling train for stack testing.**

## II. REPORTING RESULTS

Both ppm and mg/m³ are commonly found in reports, however the ppm value is actually a partial pressure result rather than being similar to the mass/volume or mass/mass units found in soil and water analysis. The partial pressure depends upon the ideal gas relationship, PV = nRT, where R = 0.0821 L x Atm/mol x K if P is measured in atmospheres, V is measured in liters, n is in moles and T is in Kelvin. The trick lies in the number of moles, which depends on the measured mass of analyte and its molecular mass. For example 1.0 mg of chloromethane and 1.0 mg of carbon tetrachloride in a cubic meter of air give very different ppm values, 0.49 and 0.16 respectfully. An equation relating the two units for air analysis is given in Figure 5-6.

$$\text{ppm} = \frac{24.6 \text{ x mg/m}^3}{\text{Mwt}} \quad \text{at STP conditions} \ (T = 0 \ ^\circ C, P = 1.00 \ \text{atm})$$

**Figure 5-6. Relationship between ppm and mg/m³ for reporting air results.**

Safety has not been stressed very much in this handbook; however, all chemists, technicians, and chemical workers should be aware of the Material Safety Data Sheets available for their information and protection in working with chemicals. One of the characterizations on the MSDS is the evaporation rate, which is a relative scale based on the vapor pressure of butyl acetate at 20 °C (10 mm Hg). Although alternate reference materials are cited on some MSDSs, butyl acetate is the most common. Values listed in the MSDS physical characteristics section are derived from the equation in Figure 5-7. Values less than 1.0 indicate that the substance is less volatile than butyl acetate; values greater than 1.0 mean the material is more volatile than butyl acetate.

$$\text{Evaporation rate} = \frac{\text{vapor pressure of cmpd at 20 °C}}{10 \text{ mmHg}}$$

**Figure 5-7. Equation for the evaporation rate.**

## III. SPECIFIC METHODOLOGIES

A natural method for monitoring contaminants in air is infrared spectroscopy. This is because the analysis is most conveniently performed in the gas phase, the infrared analysis region extends from 3700 cm[-1] to 500 cm[-1,] and almost all molecules display a spectrum in that range. Recent advances using folded path lengths, Fourier transform IR (FTIR), and liquid-nitrogen-cooled photodetectors have pushed the detection limits for many field sampled analytes to or below the ppb level[1]. The sun has been used as the light source for monitoring the atmosphere by long-path IR. Other long distance techniques use a mirror to bounce the IR light beam back to the source for measurement at a single station where an interferometer obtains a frequency spectrum of a range of wavelengths at one instant then converts the signal to a wavelength spectrum using Fourier transforms. Measuring target analytes can be both qualitative and quantitative, with the biggest interferences being carbon dioxide and water vapor. The reference lists over 130 specific compounds with MDLs for which methods have been developed.

## A. Carbon Oxides

### 1. $CO_2$ and CO

CO is most easily monitored real-time by Fourier transform long-path IR by detecting absorption at 2165 - 2183 cm[-1]. One set-up uses a path length of 25 m, i.e., the width of a road. $CO_2$ is also monitored by the same system at 2342 cm[-1]. Coupled to a video system this allows spot checking of on-road vehicle emissions[2].

Another instrument for CO monitoring uses non-dispersive IR (NDIR). The instrument relies on lasers, or selective bandwidth filters and/or detectors for isolation of absorption signals rather than prisms or gratings. One device uses a carbon-monoxide-filled cell as a specific detector and measures the decrease in signal between the clean air reference cell and the sample cell. The difference is proportional to CO concentration in the sample cell. Most IR energy absorbed by carbon monoxide is transferred into heat. Measuring the temperature increase in the sample cell compared to the reference cell is another detection method in NDIR. Non-dispersive instruments are target-analyte-specific.

---

[1]  Hanst, P.L. and S.T. Hanst, *Gas Measurement in the Fundamental Infrared Region*, Volume I. Infrared Analysis, Inc., 11629 Deborah Dr., Potomac, MD 20854.  (301) 299-9751.
[2]  Bishop, G. A., and D. F. Stedman. "On-road Carbon Monoxide Emission Measurement Comparisons for the 1988 - 1989 Colorado Oxy-fuels Program." *Environ. Sci. Technol.* 1990. 24(6). pp. 843-847.

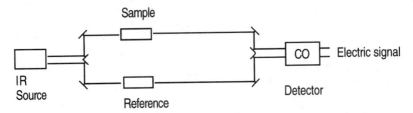

**Figure 5-8. Diagram of a non-dispersive IR instrument for measuring carbon monoxide.**

## 2. Method 10. Carbon Monoxide

Method 10 is for on-site stack testing using a NDIR. Method 10A requires passing the gas through an alkaline permanganate solution to remove sulfur and nitrogen oxides, followed by collection of the sample in a Tedlar® bag. Carbon monoxide is determined by reaction with *p*-sulfaminobenzoic acid and silver nitrate in basic solution followed by colorimetric determination[3]. Method 10B assays the carbon monoxide trapped in the Tedlar® bag from method 10A by gas chromatography followed by catalytic reduction on nickel at 400 °C to methane and then assay of the methane by FID. The method in 40 CFR 50, App. C, is also NDIR as is method IP-3A. Carbon monoxide is determined in method IP-3C with electrochemical oxidation. The detector is an electrochemical cell consisting of a membrane with a sensor and a counter electrode attached to either side. The counter electrode side is filled with deionized water. The CO-containing air contacts the saturated membrane and reacts with the water.

$$CO + H_2O \longrightarrow CO_2 + 2H^+ + 2e^-$$

The hydrogen ions pass through the membrane, and the other cell reaction occurs.

$$2H^+ + 2e^- + 1/2\ O_2 \longrightarrow H_2O$$

The electrons are detected as they pass through the circuit connecting the sensor and counter electrodes. The net reaction is oxidation of CO to $CO_2$.

## 3. Method 6A. Carbon Dioxide

This is a gravimetric method that depends on the absorption of carbon dioxide on Ascarite II, which is a sodium hydroxide coated silica, 8- to 20-mesh size. Method 6B allows substitution of 5 Å molecular sieves. Carbon dioxide can be determined by gas chromatography followed by reduction to methane and passage of the effluent through an FID.

## B. Organic Analytes

Hydrocarbons and other volatile organic compounds can be determined by IR; however, the more common technique is to obtain either a grab sample in a Tedlar® bag or a

---

3   Lambert, J.L. and R.E. Weins. "Induced Colorimetric Method for Carbon Monoxide." *Anal. Chem.* 1974. 46(7). pp. 929-930; Levaggi, D.A. and M. Feldstein, "The Colorimetric Determination of Low Concentrations of Carbon Monoxide." *Industrial Hygiene Jour.* 1964. 25. pp. 64-66. (Jan.-Feb.).

SUMMA® canister for direct introduction into a GC with specific detector or a GC/MS, or to collect an adsorbed sample on Tenax or activated charcoal for thermal or solvent desorption and analysis. Semivolatiles are collected on adsorbents such as XAD-2 or PUF, solvent desorbed, then analyzed by either capillary column GC-FID, GC-ECD or GC/MS, depending on the exact analytes. These techniques have rather high detection limits, but are very flexible in the compounds that can be detected. The air CLP SOW specifies these types of methods. For the lowest detection limits, the sampling and analysis must be restricted to a specific target analyte.

## 1. Method 40 CFR 50, App. E. Hydrocarbons

The air sample is passed into an FID to determine the total hydrocarbon content (THC). A sample is next passed through a stripper column, which removes water, $CO_2$, and hydrocarbons other than methane. Direct introduction of this effluent into a GC separates the carbon monoxide from the methane. Detection is with a catalytic reducer to methane followed by an FID. The difference between the THC and the methane-alone value gives the value for the non-methane hydrocarbons (NMHC). A variation on the procedure gives a measurement method (Method 25) for non-methane organic compounds (NMOC). The whole gas sample is trapped in a dry-ice-cooled condenser, then passed through a gas chromatographic column, which separates carbon monoxide, carbon dioxide, and methane from the gas stream. The residual organic materials are back flushed into an oxidizer made from 19% chromia on alumina pellets at 650 °C, which converts everything to carbon dioxide. The effluent then passes into a reducer packed with nickel at 400 °C, which reduces the carbon dioxide into methane. Final analysis is by FID. Method TO-12 relies on a liquid-argon-cooled (-186 °C) trap to pass methane without retention. Thermal desorption of the trap contents into an FID gives NMOC (CO and $CO_2$ give no FID response.). Method 25A passes the whole trapped sample through a flame ionization analyzer without the GC column to give a total organic value. Method 25B uses a NDIR for determination of total organics.

## 2. MASA 116. Formaldehyde (Reference 18)*

Aldehydes, and formaldehyde in particular, are irreversibly adsorbed to most traps. Most of these compounds present distinct health hazards in low-to-modest air concentrations and must be monitored. The most sensitive determinations of formaldehyde and other aldehydes use specific derivatization processes and colorimetric or instrument analysis of the derivative. The oldest method for formaldehyde is the chromotropic acid procedure. After years of misrepresentation, the reaction mechanism and product have recently been elucidated[4].

---

* This and other references cited in titles refer to the reference number found in Appendix D of this book.

[4] Georghiou, P.E. and C.K. Ho. "The Chemistry of the Chromotropic Acid Method for the Analysis of Formaldehyde." *Can. J. Chem.* 1989. 67. pp. 971-876.

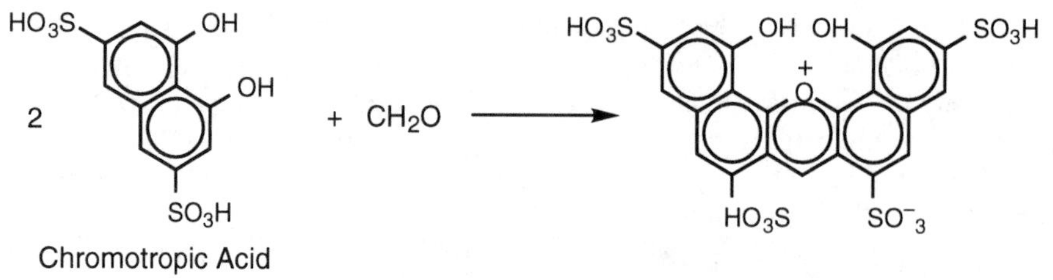

**Figure 5-9. Reaction of chromotropic acid with formaldehyde.**

The reaction with bisulfite and para-Rosaniline, has recently been used for determination of formaldehyde[5]. Method IP-6B uses this chemistry for continuous monitoring of formaldehyde through a 550 nm photodetector.

Formaldehyde, and aldehydes in general, react with 2,4-dinitrophenylhydrazine (DNPH) under mildly acidic conditions in water to form very stable hydrazones. This reaction has been used for over a hundred years to prepare solid derivatives of aldehydes for melting point characterization and identification. These derivatives are very strong UV absorbers and can be determined by direct injection HPLC. A more sensitive analysis results from extraction and concentration of the hydrazones followed by either HPLC or GC analysis. Method TO-5 uses the solvent extraction with HPLC determination. Methods TO-11 and IP-6A use a DNPH-coated solid absorbent for sampling. The hydrazones are eluted with acetonitrile and determined by HPLC. Method IP-6C uses a passive DNPH-loaded sampler followed by elution with acetonitrile and HPLC detection for formaldehyde.

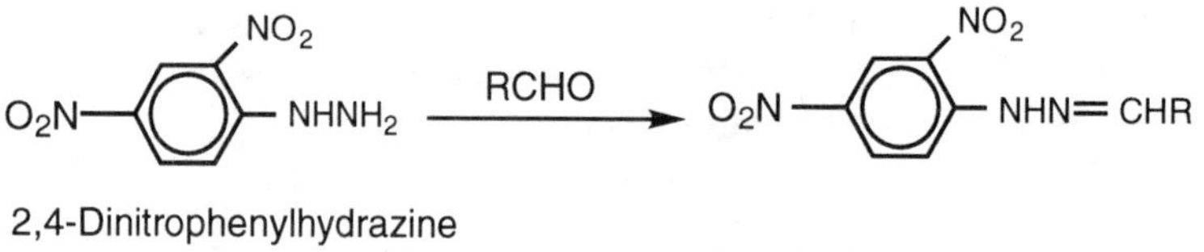

2,4-Dinitrophenylhydrazine

**Figure 5-10. Reaction of DNPH with aldehydes.**

The reaction of formaldehyde with benzothiazolinon hydrazone (MBTH) is very similar to that with DNPH, and the utility of the derivative is similar.

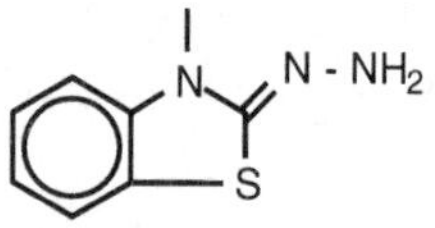

**Figure 5-11. Structure of MBTH.**

Aldehydes in general react with dansylhydrazine to give a hydrazone that is easily analyzed by HPLC with either fluorescent or chemiluminescent detection[6]. Either detec-

5  Groah, W.J., J. Bradfield, G. Gramp, R. Rudzinski and G. Heroux. "Comparative Response of Reconstituted Wood Products to European and North American Test Methods for Determining Formaldehyde Emissions." *Environ. Sci. Technol.* 1991. 25(1). pp. 117-122.

6  Nondek, L. D.R. Rodler and J.W. Birks. "Measurement of Sub-ppbv Concentrations of Aldehydes in a Forest Atmosphere Using a New HPLC Technique." *Environ. Sci. Technol.* 1992. 26(6) pp. 1174-1178.

tion technique can lower the detection limits by a factor of 100 to 10,000 over those seen with UV detection. A follow-up report on the method[7] offers significant improvement in the removal of interferences.

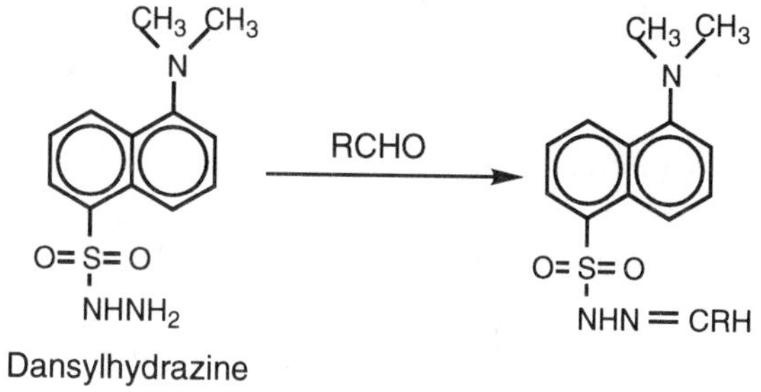

Dansylhydrazine

**Figure 5-12. Reaction of aldehydes with dansylhydrazine.**

## 3. Formic acid

Formic acid ($HCO_2H$) is the next oxidation step from formaldehyde toward carbon dioxide. It is one of the major contributing organic acids to the acidic soup formed in municipal landfills as a product of anaerobic bacterial decomposition of organic materials. Formic acid vapors can be analyzed in-situ by FTIR long-path at 1105 cm-1. Samples collected for laboratory analysis can be obtained on KOH-impregnated 47 mm glass fiber filters in forced air samplers followed by HPLC on size exclusion columns with dilute $H_2SO_4$ eluant and UV detection[8].

## 4. MASA 114. Acrolein (Reference 18)

Acrolein ($CH_2=CHCHO$) is an important industrial monomer aldehyde used for the formation of many polymers. It is highly reactive. It can be analyzed by many of the above methods for aldehydes A highly specific procedure for acrolein begins with collection of an air sample in an impinger containing 1% $NaHSO_3$. The initial bisulfite addition product is reacted with 4-hexyl resorcinol and $HgCl_2$ in a trichloroacetic acid-ethanol solution to form an intense blue product that is read at 605 nm. The product is not well characterized[9].

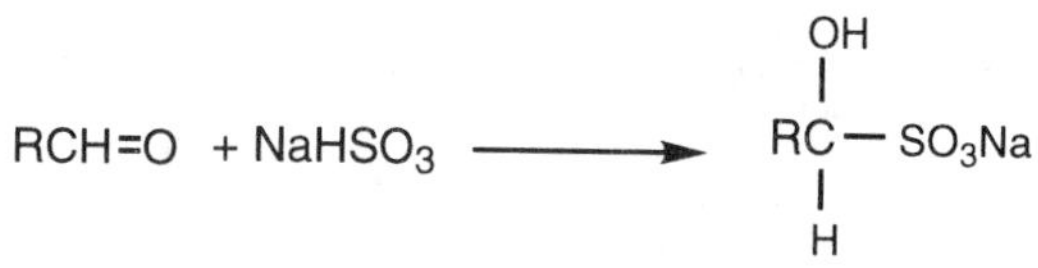

**Figure 5-13. Reaction of aldehydes with bisulfite.**

---

[7] Rodler, D.R., L. Nondek and J.W. Birks. "Evaluation of Ozone and Water Vapor Interferences in the Derivatization of Atmospheric Aldehydes with Dansylhydrazine." *Environ. Sci. Technol.* 1993. 27(13). pp. 2814-2820.

[8] Grosjean, D., E. C. Tuazon and E. Fujita. "Ambient Formic Acid in Southern California Air: A Comparison of Two Methods, Fourier Transform Infrared Spectroscopy and Alkaline Trap-liquid Chromatography with UV Detection." *Environ. Sci. Technol.* 1990. 24(1) pp. 144-146

[9] Cohen, I.R., and A.P. Altshuller. "A New Spectrophotometric Method for the Determination of Acrolein in Combustion Gases and in the Atmosphere." *Analytical Chemistry.* 1961. 33(6) pp. 726-733.

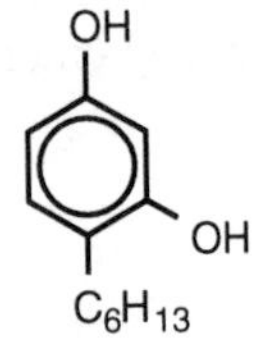

**Figure 5-14. Structure of 4-hexyl-resorcinol.**

## 5. Halocarbons

IR or capillary column GC-ECD or GC-MS are most often used for halocarbon analysis, as appropriate. A portable monitor for halocarbons passes the sample air into a cell containing an AC arc between copper and platinum electrodes. When halide vapors are present, a bright line spectrum of copper appears, the intensity of which is proportional to the halocarbon concentration.

## C. Inorganic Analytes

### 1. MASA 202. Free Atmospheric Chlorine (Reference 18)

Free atmospheric chlorine is a very hazardous, but transient, species, and it is best monitored on site with a colorimetric tube. Being a symmetrical molecule, it is not detected by IR, although it is feasible to determine it by Raman spectroscopy. A wet chemical method involves the instantaneous bleaching of the primary standard methyl orange at pH 3.0. The reduction of methyl orange in the impinger can be measured colorimetrically or by comparison with color standards. The bleaching reaction is highly specific for chlorine.

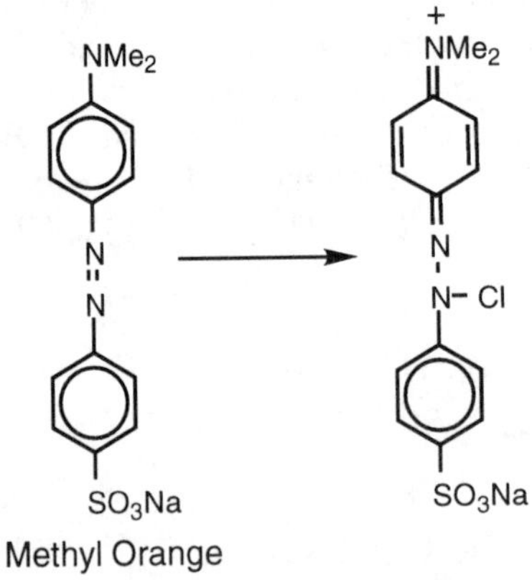

Methyl Orange

**Figure 5-15. Proposed first step for the bleaching reaction of methyl orange with chlorine.**

## 2. Sulfur Compounds

Inorganic sulfur exists in the atmosphere as hydrogen sulfide, carbonyl sulfide (COS), carbon disulfide, sulfur dioxide, and sulfuric acid. Organic sulfur can be present as mercaptans (RSH), thioethers ($R_2S$), sulfoxides ($R_2SO$), sulfones ($R_2SO_2$), and sulfates

($R_2SO_4$). Other more complex forms are dithio ethers, thiophenes, thio acids, dithio acids, and a host of others. All can be monitored by IR. A general method for total sulfur involves chemiluminescent detection of sulfur species[10]. The sulfur compound is combusted to form SO, which reacts with ozone to form an excited sulfur dioxide. Relaxation of the excited species is accompanied by emission of light.

$$\text{"S"} + \text{Hydrogen flame} \longrightarrow \text{SO} - O_3 \longrightarrow SO^*_2 + O_2$$
$$SO^*_2 \longrightarrow SO_2 + h\nu$$

**Figure 5-16. Chemiluminescent detection of sulfur compounds.**

Mercaptans (RSH) can be selectively determined by trapping in an impinger as mercuric sulfide, then treating with DPD and ferric chloride to give a colorimetric reaction. The product is probably similar to methylene blue with the "R" group from the mercaptan still hanging off the sulfur. Hydrogen sulfide can be determined in a similar fashion by trapping as cadmium sulfide then reacting to form methylene blue.

$$RSH + Hg(OAc)_2 - \text{impinger} \longrightarrow HgS$$
$$HgS + DPD + H^+ + FeCl_3 \longrightarrow \text{Lambert-Beers Law red color (500 nm)}$$

**Figure 5-17. Determination of mercaptans.**

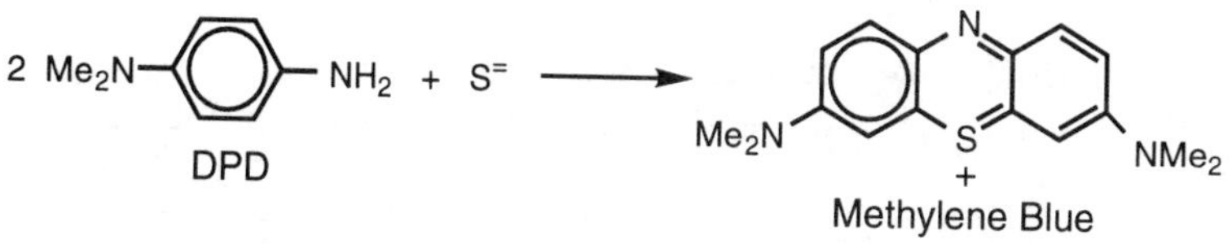

Methylene Blue

**Figure 5-18. Formation of methylene blue from sulfide.**

Hydrogen sulfide is determined in method 11 by trapping in a cadmium sulfate solution at pH 3 to form cadmium sulfide, addition of an excess known amount of iodine solution, then iodometric titration with sodium thiosulfate or PAO and starch indicator to determine the excess iodine.

$$S^{-2} + I_2 \longrightarrow S° + 2I^-$$
$$I_{2(excess)} + 2Na_2S_2O_3 \longrightarrow 2I^- + 2Na^+ + Na_2S_4O_6$$

**Figure 5-19. Iodometric determination of sulfide.**

Hydrogen sulfide, carbonyl sulfide, and carbon disulfide are known as total reduced sulfur (TRS), along with mercaptans, thioethers and dithioethers, and are determined in methods 15 and 16 by gas chromatographic separation of the compounds with an FPD in the sulfur mode. Methods 15A and 16A mix the sampled gas stream with air, remove interfering sulfur dioxide with a citrate buffer scrubber, pass it through an oxidizing combustion chamber at 1100 °C, then trap the produced $SO_2$ in a peroxide impinger where it is oxidized to sulfate. The sulfate is determined by the barium perchlorate -

---

[10] Benner, R. L., and D. H. Stedman. "Field Evaluation of the Sulfur Chemiluminescence Detector." *Environ. Sci. Technol.* 1990. 24(10) pp. 1592-1596.

thorin titration as in method 6. Method 16B is similar in that TRS is oxidized to sulfur dioxide, but the determination is by GC-FPD in the sulfur mode.

## 3. Sulfur Dioxide

Sulfur dioxide is a primary atmospheric contaminant arising from the burning of soft coal and other low-grade fossil fuels. Another source is the production of metals from ores, which are often metal sulfides. A wide variety of detection methods are available. Sulfur dioxide is amenable to IR monitoring at 1361 cm-1 with a 100-meter path length detection limit of 2.0 ppb. Another method uses pulsed fluorescence. Sulfur dioxide irradiated with narrow band (46 nm wide) UV light with a maximum of 216 nm will emit fluorescence over the range 240 - 420 nm, which is detected with a photomultiplier tube. The relationship between emitted intensity and concentration is linear. $SO_2$ can also be determined by its UV absorbance. All these instrumental techniques are allowed in 40 CFR 60, App. A, Method 6C.

There are also a variety of wet chemical methods for $SO_2$. Impinger collection with tetrachloromercurate or formaldehyde results in oxidation to sulfite or bisulfite.

$$SO_2 + K_2HgCl_4 + H_2O \longrightarrow HgCl_2SO_3^{-2} + 2HCl$$

$$SO_2 + CH_2O + H_2O \longrightarrow HOCH_2SO_3H$$

**Figure 5-20. Impinger collection of sulfur dioxide.**

Analysis of the trapped formaldehyde-bisulfite is accomplished by reaction with *p*-rosaniline to form *p*-rosanilinemethylsulfonic acid. This forms the basis for method 40 CFR 50, Appendix A.

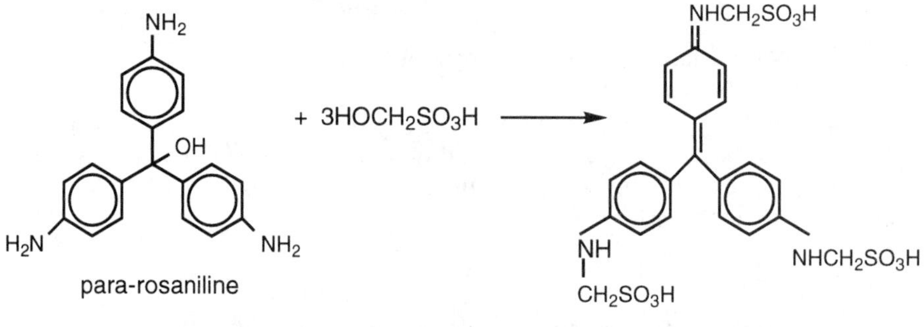

**Figure 5-21. Reaction of formaldehyde-bisulfite with *p*-rosaniline.**

Another method involves impinger collection of $SO_2$ in $H_2O_2$ with resulting oxidation to sulfate followed by analysis for sulfate. Gravimetric analysis with barium is time honored, but not very sensitive. Turbidimetric analysis of barium sulfate is more sensitive.

$$SO_2 + H_2O_2 \longrightarrow H_2SO_4$$

$$SO_4^{-2} + Ba^{+2} \longrightarrow BaSO_4 \text{ (turbidimetric analysis)}$$

**Figure 5-22. Oxidation of sulfur dioxide with peroxide to sulfate.**

Barium methylthymol blue method (MASA 720C) is a variation where a standard solution of barium methylthymol blue dye is mixed with $SO_4^{-2}$ solution. The barium is removed from the dye complex by precipitation as $BaSO_4$. The reduction in dye absorbance is linear with $SO_4^{-2}$ concentration. The barium methylthymol blue has a maximum absorbance at 608 nm. The free MTB has maximum absorbance at 460 nm, so either can be read. This technique lends itself nicely to automation.

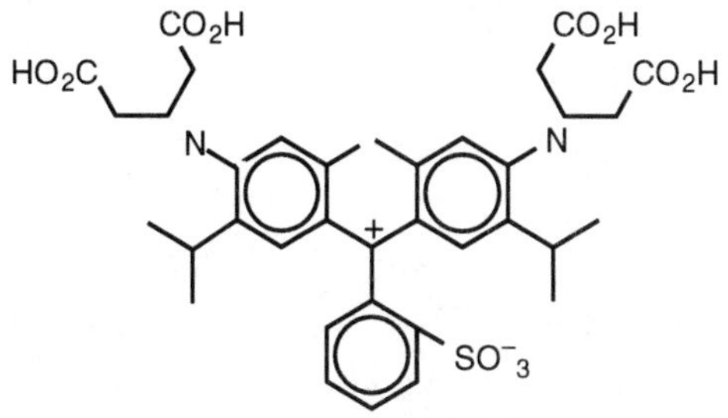

**Figure 5-23. Structure of Methylthymol Blue.**

A titration method using $Ba(ClO_4)_2$ and a thorin indicator is useful for moderate $SO_4^{-2}$ levels (>2.5 ug/mL). The free yellow color of thorin changes to a pink when complexed with $Ba^{+2}$. This is the determinative procedure of 40 CFR 60, App. A, Methods 6, 6A, 6B, and 8.

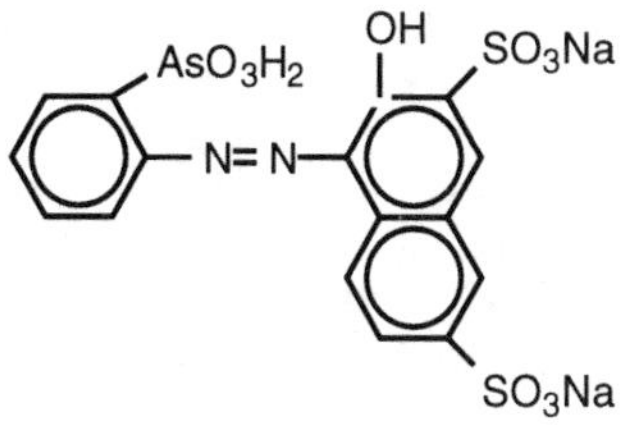

**Figure 5-24. Structure of thorin.**

A spectroscopic method uses barium chloranilate (MASA 720F). Addition to a sample solution containing $SO_4^{-2}$ gives the insoluble $BaSO_4$ and hydrogenchloranilate, which is read at 312 nm.

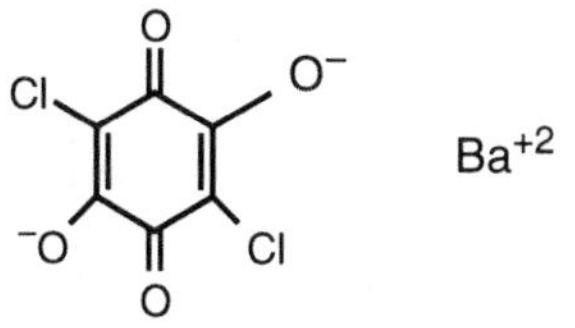

**Figure 5-25. Structure of barium chloranilate.**

## 4. Nitrogen Oxides

**Table 5-3. Nitrogen oxides**

| Compound | Name | Comment |
|---|---|---|
| $N_2O$ | Nitrous oxide | laughing gas |
| NO | Nitric oxide | reacts readily with oxygen |
| $NO_2$ | Nitrogen dioxide | toxic, dimerizes to $N_2O_4$ |
| $N_2O_3$ | Dinitrogen trioxide | decomposes below room temperature |
| $N_2O_4$ | Dinitogen tetroxide | dimer of $NO_2$ |
| $N_2O_5$ | Nitrogen pentoxide | highly reactive |

A large number of nitrogen oxides exist, ranging from nitrous oxide ($N_2O$), the historic laughing gas, to nitrogen dioxide, a brown, choking, toxic gas and an important component of smog. (NO) and nitrogen dioxide are pollutants that arise from the high temperature direct combination of $N_2$ and $O_2$ in internal combustion engines. Nitric oxide is determined by IR at 1920-1870 cm$^{-1}$ with a 4.0 ppb detection limit in a 100 meter path length or by chemiluminescence resulting from reaction with $O_3$. Nitrogen dioxide can be determined in the same instrument by pretreatment reduction to nitric oxide. These techniques are described in 40 CFR 50, Appendix F.

$$NO + O_3 \longrightarrow NO^*_2 + O_2 \; ; \; NO^*_2 \longrightarrow NO_2 + h\nu$$

$$2NO_2 + Mo \; (or \; Carbon) \; - \; 200 \; °C \longrightarrow 2NO$$

**Figure 5-26. Chemiluminescent reaction of nitric oxide with ozone.**

Method 7 and MASA 407 are for the determination of nitrogen oxides. Nitrogen oxides (except $N_2O$) are trapped in an impinger with sulfuric acid-hydrogen peroxide by oxidation to nitric acid. The nitric acid is reacted with phenoldisulfonic acid (formed from phenol and fuming sulfuric acid) to form a product that is determined colorimetrically at 400-415 nm.

Method 7A uses the same trapping solution, with determination by ion chromatography. Method 7B determines the formed nitric acid by UV spectrophotometry.

Methods 7C and 7D use an alkaline-permanganate trapping solution that oxidizes the nitrogen oxides to nitrate ion. Method 7C then reduces the nitrate to nitrite with a cadmium column and determines the nitrite with sulfanilic acid and $N$-naphthyl-ethylenediamine as in Method 352. Method 7D uses ion chromatography for the detection of nitrate.

Method IP-5B traps $NO_2$ on triethanolamine, then determines the nitrite by colorimetric reaction with sulfanilamide and $N$-1-naphthylethylene diamine. Method IP-5C again traps the $NO_2$ on triethanolamine but performs the determination by ion chromatography.

Method IP-5A determines nitrogen dioxide in a continuous mode by reaction with 5-amino-2,3-dihydro-1,4-phthalazine dione (Luminol) in base solution to produce light, which is detected by a photodetector.

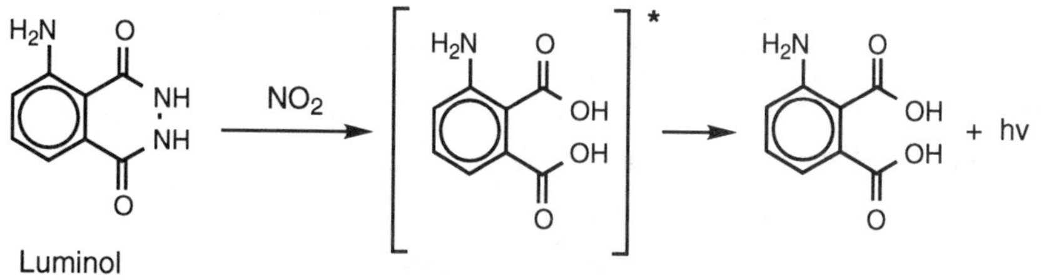

**Figure 5-27. Luminol reaction with nitrogen dioxide.**

## 5. Ozone

Ozone can be measured by IR at 1045 $cm^{-1}$ with a 2.0 ppb detection limit in a 100 meter path length. It is also determined by chemiluminescent reaction with $CH_2=CH_2$ (Method 40 CFR 50, App. D) or nitric oxide. Ozone has a UV absorption at 254 nm, which has been used for analysis.

## 6. Metals

Most metals exist in the atmosphere attached to particulates, although mercury can exist as the elemental vapor. Collection is performed with air sampling cassettes, the filter acid digested, and metals assayed by AA (Method 40 CFR 50, App. G and Method 12 for lead, Method 104 for beryllium, and Method 108 for arsenic) or ICP. Several different types and pore sizes of membrane filters are available. The mixed cellulose ester membrane (MCE) is easily digested overnight in nitric acid at room temperature and preferred for metals analysis. Use of the polyethylene, PVC, or Teflon membranes leaves a gooey mess upon attempted digestion.

Mercury is sampled in acidic iodine monochloride (ICl) solution, then determined by cold vapor AA in methods 101 and 102. Method 101A is similar except the mercury collection is in an acidic permanganate solution.

## 7. Particulates

Gravimetric assay of filter trapable particulates in a cassette from a high-volume forced-air system is the easiest to perform; however, the detection limit is quite high. A more sensitive analysis measures the optical density of transparent filter tape to measure particulate haze.

## 8. Asbestos

Asbestos is a family of silicates with a variety of other minerals that form long flexible fibers. Two general groups are recognized, the serpentine, and amphibole asbestos. The serpentines are acid labile while the amphiboles are acid resistant. Both are fire resistant fibers. Asbestos generally exists as 0.1 to 1.0 um fibers, which are invisible to the eye, and can be suspended in air, which results in their easy inhalation.

The most widely occuring serpentine is chrysotile (White asbestos) $Mg_6(Si_4O_{10})(OH)_8$. Amphiboles are divided into five distinct chemical types. Ascarite is a NaOH-treated asbestos used for $CO_2$ absorption in combustion analysis.

**Table 5-4. Amphibole asbestos**

| |
|---|
| anthophyllite - $(Mg, Fe)_7(Si_8O_{22})(OH)_2$  low iron content |
| amosite - $Fe_5Mg_2(Si_8O_{22})(OH)_2$ |
| actinolite - $Ca_2(Mg, Fe)_5(Si_8O_{22})(OH)_2$ |
| tremolite - $Ca_2Mg_5(Si_8O_{22})(OH)_2$ |
| crocidolite - $Na_2Fe_5(Si_8O_{22})(OH)_2$   (blue asbestos) |

An EPA method for analysis is covered in *Analytical Method for Determination of Asbestos Fibers in Water*, US EPA Environmental Research Laboratory, Athens, GA 30613. September, 1983. EPA 600/4-83-043. It is available from NTIS as publication number PB-83260471. The method requires prior oxidation with ozone and UV light to remove organic materials, filtration with a fine pore membrane (0.1 um pore size) followed by fixing the surface with carbon vacuum deposition and transmission electron microscopic examination. Selected area electron diffraction is used to determine the crystal structure, and element composition is accomplished by energy dispersive X-ray analysis.

Other asbestos analysis methods are found in Title 40 CFR in the TSCA regulations. 40 CFR 763, Subpart E (follows 763.99), Appendix A contains mandatory and non-mandatory transmission electron miscroscopy procedures for analysis of asbestos fibers on air filters. Part 763, Subpart F (follows 763.119), Appendix A, Section 1 contains a polarized light microscopy method for determination of asbestos in bulk insulation samples, while Section 2 contains an X-ray powder diffraction method. Part 763.121, Appendices A and B contain reference EPA/OSHA methods for air sampling and analysis of asbestos fibers by positive phase contrast microscopy. The majority of environmental laboratories subcontract this work to the few labs that specialize in it.

## IV.  EPA Methods

Most of the following methods are available online from the EPA Research Triangle Park service center at ttnwww.rtpnc.epa.gov. The website also contains a large number of downloadable draft and proposed methods that have yet to be finalized. Any of these methods may be usable regardless of promulgation status in light of the *Federal Register* notice of Monday, 24 February, 1997, pp 8314-8328, concerning use of alternate methods as credible evidence in compliance monitoring situations for air programs.

**Table 5-5.  EPA Air Program Methods found in 40 CFR**

| 40 CFR Part | Appendix | Method No. | Method Description |
|---|---|---|---|
| 50 | A | – | Reference method for the determination of sulfur dioxide in the atmosphere (Pararosaniline method) |
| 50 | B | – | Reference method for the determination of suspended particulate matter in the atmosphere (High-Volume method) |
| 50 | C | – | Measurement principle and calibration procedure for the measurement of carbon monoxide in the atmosphere by non-dispersive IR |

Continued on next page.

**Table 5-5. EPA Air Program Methods found in 40 CFR,** *continued*

| 40 CFR Part | Appendix | Method No. | Method Description |
|---|---|---|---|
| 50 | D | – | Measurement principle and calibration procedure for the measurement of ozone in the atmosphere |
| 50 | E | – | Reference method for determination of hydrocarbons corrected for methane |
| 50 | F | – | Measurement principle and calibration procedure for the measurement of nitrogen dioxide in the atmosphere (Gas Phase Chemiluminescence) |
| 50 | G | – | Reference method for the determination of lead in suspended particulate matter collected from ambient air |
| 50 | H | – | Interpretation of National Ambient Air Quality Standards for ozone |
| 50 | J | – | Reference method for the determination of particulate matter as $PM_{10}$ in the atmosphere |
| 51 | M | 201 | Determination of $PM_{10}$ emissions (Exhaust Gas Recycle procedure) |
| 51 | M | 201A | Determination of $PM_{10}$ emissions (Constant Sampling Rate procedure) |
| 51 | M | 202 | Determination of condensible particulate emissions from stationary sources |
| 52 | D | - | Sulfur dioxide emissions from stationary sources by continuous monitors |
| 60.47 | I | - | Determination of sulfur dioxide emissions from fossil fuel fired combustion sources (continuous bubbler method) |
| 60.648 | - | - | Optional procedure for measuring hydrogen sulfide in acid gas -Tutwiler procedure |
| 60 | A | 1 | Sample and velocity transverses for stationary sources |
| 60 | A | 1A | Sample and velocity traverses for stationary sources with small stacks or ducts |
| 60 | A | 2 | Determination of stack gas velocity and volumetric flow (type S pitot tube) |
| 60 | A | 2A | Direct measurement of gas volume through pipes and small ducts |
| 60 | A | 2B | Determination of exhaust gas volume flow from gasoline vapor incinerators |
| 60 | A | 2C | Determination of stack gas velocity and volumetric flow rate in small stacks |
| 60 | A | 2D | Measurement of gas volumetric flows in small pipes |
| 60 | A | 2E | Landfill gas production flow rate |
| 60 | A | 3 | Gas analysis for the determination of dry molecular weight |
| 60 | A | 3A | Determination of oxygen and carbon dioxide concentrations in emissions from stationary sources |
| 60 | A | 3B | Gas analysis for the determination of the emission rate correction factor or excess air |
| 60 | A | 3C | $CO_2$, $CH_4$, $N_2$, $O_2$ by TCD |
| 60 | A | 4 | Determination of moisture content in stack gases |
| 60 | A | 5 | Determination of particulate emissions from stationary sources |
| 60 | A | 5A | Particulate emissions from asphalt |
| 60 | A | 5B | Non-sulfuric acid particulates from stationary sources |

Continued on next page.

**Table 5-5. EPA Air Program Methods found in 40 CFR,** *continued*

| 40 CFR Part | Appendix | Method No. | Method Description |
|---|---|---|---|
| 60 | A | 5D | Particulate emissions from positive pressure fabric filters |
| 60 | A | 5E | Particulate emission from wool fiberglass insulation manufacturing industry |
| 60 | A | 5F | Determination of non-sulfate particulate matter from stationary sources |
| 60 | A | 5G | Particulate emissions from wood heaters from a dilution tunnel sampling location. |
| 60 | A | 5H | Determination of particulate emissions from wood heaters from a stack location |
| 60 | A | 6 | $SO_2$ from stationary sources |
| 60 | A | 6A | $SO_2$, moisture, and $CO_2$ from fossil fuel combustion sources |
| 60 | A | 6B | Determination of sulfur dioxide and carbon dioxide daily average emissions from fossil fuel combustion sources. |
| 60 | A | 6C | Determination of sulfur dioxide emissions from stationary sources (Instrumental Analyzer procedure) |
| 60 | A | 7 | $NO_2$ from stationary sources |
| 60 | A | 7A | Determination of nitrogen oxide emissions from stationary sources - ion chromatography method |
| 60 | A | 7B | Determination of nitrogen oxide emissions from stationary sources (ultraviolet spectrophotometry) |
| 60 | A | 7C | Determination of nitrogen oxide emissions from stationary sources - alkaline-permanganate/colorimetric method |
| 60 | A | 7D | Determination of nitrogen oxide emissions from stationary sources - alkaline-permanganate/ion chromatographic method |
| 60 | A | 7E | Determination of nitrogen oxide emissions from stationary sources (Instrumental Analyzer procedure) |
| 60 | A | 8 | Determination of sulfuric acid mist and $SO_2$ emissions from stationary sources |
| 60 | A | 9 | Visual determination of the opacity of emissions from stationary sources |
| 60 | A | 9 Alternate Method 1 | Determination of the opacity of emissions from stationary sources remotely by LIDAR |
| 60 | A | 10 | Determination of carbon monoxide emissions from stationary sources |
| 60 | A | 10A | Determination of carbon monoxide emissions in certifying continuous emission monitoring systems at petroleum refineries |
| 60 | A | 10B | Determination of carbon monoxide emissions from stationary sources |
| 60 | A | 11 | $H_2S$ of fuel gas streams in petroleum refineries |
| 60 | A | 12 | Inorganic lead emissions from stationary sources |
| 60 | A | 13A | Total fluoride emissions from stationary sources (SPADNS Zirconium Lake method) |
| 60 | A | 13B | Total fluoride emissions from stationary sources (Specific Ion Electrode method) |

Continued on next page.

## Table 5-5. EPA Air Program Methods found in 40 CFR, *continued*

| 40 CFR Part | Appendix | Method No. | Method Description |
|---|---|---|---|
| 60 | A | 14 | Fluoride emissions from potroom roof monitors for aluminum plants |
| - | - | 14A | Total fluoride emissions from selected sources at primary aluminum plants (proposed) |
| 60 | A | 15 | $H_2S$, COS, and $CS_2$ emissions from stationary sources |
| 60 | A | 15A | Determination of total reduced sulfur emissions from sulfur recovery plants in petroleum refineries |
| 60 | A | 16 | Semi-continuous determination of sulfur emissions from stationary sources |
| 60 | A | 16A | Determination of total reduced sulfur emissions from stationary sources (Impinger technique) |
| 60 | A | 16B | Determination of total reduced sulfur emissions from stationary sources |
| 60 | A | 17 | Particulate emissions from stationary sources |
| 60 | A | 18 | Gaseous organic compound emissions by gas chromatography[11] |
| 60 | A | 19 | $SO_2$ removal efficiency and particulate, $SO_2$, and $NO_x$ emission rates |
| 60 | A | 20 | $NO_x$, $SO_2$, and diluent emissions from gas turbines |
| 60 | A | 21 | Determination of volatile organic compound leaks |
| 60 | A | 22 | Visual determination of fugitive emissions from material sources and smoke emissions from flares |
| 60 | A | 23 | Determination of polychlorinated dibenzo-p-dioxins and polychlorinated dibenzofurans from stationary sources |
| 60 | A | 24 | Volatile matter content, water content, density, volume of solids, and weight of solids of surface coatings |
| 60 | A | 24A | Determination of volatile matter content and density of printing inks and related coatings |
| 60 | A | 25 | Total gaseous nonmethane organic emissions as carbon |
| 60 | A | 25A | Determination of total gaseous organic concentration using a flame ionization analyzer |
| 60 | A | 25B | Determination of total gaseous organic concentration using a non-dispersive infrared analyzer |
| 60 | A | 25C | NMOC in landfill gas |
| 60 | A | 25D | Determination of the volatile organic concentration of waste samples[12] |
| 60 | A | 25E | Determination of vapor phase organic concentration in waste samples |
| 60 | A | 26 | Determination of hydrogen halide emissions from stationary sources - midget impinger method[13] |
| 60 | A | 26A | Determination of hydrogen halide and halogen emissions from stationary sources - isokinetic method[14] |

Continued on next page.

---

[11] Modified in *Federal Register*, Volume 59, pp. 19306 to 19401, Friday, 22 April 1994.
[12] *Federal Register*, Friday, 22 April 1994. Volume 59, pp. 19306 to 19323.
[13] Same as footnote 12.
[14] Same as footnote 12.

**Table 5-5. EPA Air Program Methods found in 40 CFR,** *continued*

| 40 CFR Part | Appendix | Method No. | Method Description |
|---|---|---|---|
| 60 | A | 27 | Vapor tightness of gasoline delivery tank using pressure-vacuum test |
| 60 | A | 28 | Certification and auditing of wood heaters |
| 60 | A | 28A | Measurement of air to fuel ratio and minimum achievable burn ratios for wood-fired appliances |
| 60 | A | 29 | Metals emissions from stationary sources |
| 61 | B | 101 | Determination of particulate and gaseous mercury emissions from chlor-alkali plants - air streams |
| 61 | B | 101A | Determination of particulate and gaseous mercury emissions from sewage sludge incinerators |
| 61 | B | 102 | Determination of particulate and gaseous mercury emissions from chlor-alkali plants - hydrogen streams |
| 61 | B | 103 | Beryllium screening method |
| 61 | B | 104 | Determination of beryllium emissions from stationary sources |
| 61 | B | 105 | Determination of mercury in wastewater treatment plant sewage sludge |
| 61 | B | 106 | Determination of vinyl chloride from stationary sources |
| 61 | B | 107 | Determination of vinyl chloride content of in-process wastewater samples and vinyl chloride content of polyvinyl chloride resin, slurry, wet cakes and latex samples |
| 61 | B | 107A | Determination of vinyl chloride content of solvents, resin-solvent solution, polyvinyl chloride resin, resin slurry, wet resin, and latex samples |
| 61 | B | 108 | Determination of particulate and gaseous arsenic emissions |
| 61 | B | 108A | Determination of arsenic content in ore samples from nonferrous smelters |
| 61 | B | 108B | Determination of arsenic content in ore samples from nonferrous smelters |
| 61 | B | 108C | Determination of arsenic content in ore samples from nonferrous smelters |
| 61 | B | 111 | Polonium-210 emissions from stationary sources |
| 61 | B | 114 | Test methods for measuring radionuclide emissions from stationary sources |
| 61 | B | 115 | Monitoring for Radon-222 emissions |
| - | - | 201 | Instack $PM_{10}$ |
| - | - | 201A | Instack $PM_{10}$ CRS |
| - | - | 202 | Condensible particulate matter |
| - | - | 203 | Continuous opacity monitoring for compliance (proposed) |
| - | - | 203A | Time averaged visual opacity (proposed) |
| - | - | 203B | Time-exception visual opacity (proposed) |
| - | - | 203C | Instantaneous limitation visual opacity (proposed) |
| - | - | 204 | Permanent or temporary total enclosure for determining capture efficiency (proposed) |
| - | - | 204A | VOCs in liquid input stream (proposed) |
| - | - | 204B | VOCs in captured stream (proposed) |
| - | - | 204C | VOCs in captured stream dilution technique (proposed) |

Continued on next page.

**Table 5-5. EPA Air Program Methods found in 40 CFR,** *continued*

| 40 CFR Part | Appendix | Method No. | Method Description |
|---|---|---|---|
| - | - | 204D | Fugitive VOCs from temporary total enclosure (proposed) |
| - | - | 204E | Fugitive VOCs from building enclosure (proposed) |
| - | - | 204F | VOCs in liquid input stream distillation (proposed) |
| - | - | 205 | Gas dilution calibration |
| 63 | A | 301 | Field validation of pollutant measurement methods from various waste media |
| - | - | 303 | By-product coke oven batteries |
| - | - | 303A | Nonrecovery coke oven batteries |
| 63 | A | 304 | Method for determination of biodegradation rates of organic compounds[15] |
| - | - | 304A | Vent option biodegradation rates |
| - | - | 304B | Scrubber option biodegradation rates |
| 63 | A | 305 | Method for measurement of individual volatile organics in wastewater[16] |
| - | - | 306 | Chromium emissions |
| - | - | 306A | Chromium emissions (mason jar method) |
| - | - | 306B | Surface tension |
| - | - | 307 | Emissions from solvent vapor cleaners |
| - | - | 308 | Procedure for methanol emissions (proposed) |
| - | - | 310 | Residual solvent in ethylene-propylene (proposed) |
| - | - | 311 | HAPS in paints & coatings |
| - | - | 312 | Residual solvent in latex rubber (proposed) |
| - | - | 313 | Residual toluene and styrene in crumb rubber (proposed) |
| - | - | 315 | PM and MCEM from aluminum production facilities (proposed) |
| - | - | 318 | Extractive FTIR method for measurement of emissions from the mineral wool and wool fiberglass industries (proposed) |
| - | - | 319 | Filtration efficiency for paint overspray arrestors (proposed) |
| 80 | A | | Test for the determination of phosphorous in gasoline |
| 80 | B | 1 | Standard method test for lead in gasoline by atomic absorption spectrometry |
| 80 | B | 2 | Automated method test for lead in gasoline by atomic absorption spectrometry |
| 80 | B | 3 | Test for lead in gasoline by X-ray spectrometry |
| 80 | D | | Sampling procedures for fuel volatility |
| 80 | E | 3 | Test for determining Reid vapor pressure (RVP) of gasoline and gasoline-oxygenate blends. Method 3 - Evacuated chamber method |
| 80 | F | 1 | Test for determining the quantity of alcohol in gasoline. Method 1 - Water extraction method |
| 80 | F | 2 | Test method for determination of $C_1$ to $C_4$ alcohols and MTBE in gasoline by gas chromatography |
| 80 | G | | Sampling procedures for diesel fuel |

[15] *Federal Register*, Thursday, 31 December, 1992. Volume 57, Number 252. pp. 62785-62797. Finalized in Federal Register, Friday, 22 April, 1994. Volume 59, pp. 19402-19625.

[16] Same as footnote 15.

**Table 5-6.** **Methods for compliance with burning hazardous wastes in boilers and industrial furnaces (BIF) regulations**

| 40 CFR Part | Appendix | Method No. | Method Description |
|---|---|---|---|
| 266 | IX | 3.1 | Methodology for the determination of metals emissions in exhaust gases from hazardous waste incineration and similar combustion processes |
| | | 3.2 | Determination of hexavalent chromium emissions from stationary sources (Method $Cr^{+6}$) |
| | | 3.3.1 | Isokinetic $HCl/Cl_2$ emission sampling train (Method 0050) |
| | | 3.3.2 | Midget impinger $HCl/Cl_2$ emission sampling train (Method 0051) |
| | | 3.3.3 | Protocols for analysis of samples from $HCl/Cl_2$ emission sampling train (Method 9057) |
| | | 3.4 | Determination of polychlorinated dibenzo-p-dioxins (PCDDs) and polychlorinated dibenzofurans (PCDF) from stationary sources (Method 23) |
| | | 3.5 | Sampling for aldehyde and ketone emissions from stationary sources (Method 0011) |
| | | 3.6 | Analysis for aldehydes and ketones by HPLC (Method 0011A) |

**Table 5-7.** **Compendium of Methods for the determination of Toxic Organic Compounds in ambient air[17]**

| Method | Description |
|---|---|
| TO1 | Determination of volatile organic compounds in ambient air using Tenax adsorption and gas chromatography (GC-MS) |
| TO2 | Determination of volatile organic compounds in ambient air by carbon molecular sieve adsorption and GC-MS |
| TO3 | Determination of volatile organic compounds in ambient air using cryogenic preconcentration techniques and gas chromatography with FID and ECD |
| TO4A | Determination of organochlorine pesticides and polychlorinated biphenyls in ambient air |
| TO5 | Determination of aldehydes and ketones in ambient air using HPLC |
| TO6 | Determination of phosgene in ambient air using HPLC |
| TO7 | Determination of n-nitrosodimethylamine in ambient air using GC |
| TO8 | Determination of phenol and methylphenols (cresols) in ambient air using HPLC |
| TO9A | Determination of polychlorinated dibenzo-p-dioxins (PCDD) in ambient air using high resolution GC - high resolution MS |
| TO10A | Determination of organochlorine pesticides in ambient air using low-volume polyurethane foam (PUF) sampling with GC/ECD |
| TO11A | Determination of formaldehyde in ambient air using adsorbent cartridge followed by HPLC |
| TO12 | Determination of non-methane organic compounds (NMOC) in ambient air using cryogenic preconcentration and direct flame ionization detection |
| TO13A | Determination of polyaromatic hydrocarbons (PAHs) in ambient air using high volume sampling with GC-MS and high resolution liquid chromatography analysis |
| TO14A | Determination of volatile organic compounds in ambient air using SUMMA polished canister sampling and GC analysis |
| TO15 | SUMMA passivated canister sampling with GC coupled to a MS or ion trap for polar and non-polar VOC |
| TO16 | VOC by real-time monitoring by FTIR |
| TO17 | VOC by real-time or solid adsorbent sampling followed by GC-FID |

[17] Available from the Internet at website http://ttnwww.rtpnc.epa.gov

**Table 5-8.  Compendium of Methods for the determination of Inorganic Compounds in ambient air**[18]

| Method | Description |
|--------|-------------|
| IO-1 | Continuous measurement of suspended particulate matter (SPM) in ambient air |
| IO-1.1 | Continuous monitoring of ambient $PM_{10}$ concentration using the Graseby Anderson $PM_{10}$ Attenuation Monitor |
| IO-1.2 | Continuous monitoring of $PM_{10}$ in ambient air using the Wedding and Associates Beta Gauge Automated Particle Sampler |
| IO-1.3 | Determination of $PM_{10}$ in ambient air using a continuous TEOM Paticular Sampler |
| IO-2 | Integrated sampling of suspended particulate matter (SPM) |
| IO-2.1 | Sampling of ambient air for SPM using high volume sampler |
| IO-2.2 | Sampling for SPM in ambient air using a dichotomous sampler |
| IO-2.3 | Sampling of ambient air for SPM <10um ($PM_{10}$) using a low volume Partisol sampler |
| IO-2.4 | Calculations, standard volume |
| IO-3 | Chemical species analysis of filter collected SPM |
| IO-3.1 | Selection, preparation and extraction of filter material |
| IO-3.2 | Determination of toxic metals in ambient particulate matter using AA |
| IO-3.3 | Determination of elements captured on filter material and analyzed by XRF |
| IO-3.4 | Determination of metals captured on glass fiber filter and analyzed by ICP |
| IO-3.5 | Determination of metals captured on glass fiber filter and analyzed by ICP-MS |
| IO-3.6 | Analysis of ambient air particles for metals using PIXE spectroscopy |
| IO-3.7 | Determination of elements captured on glass fiber filters and analyzed by neutron activation spectroscopy |
| IO-4 | Determination of reactive acidic and basic gases and strong acidity of atmospheric fine particles in ambient air using annular denuder technology |
| IO-4.1 | Determination of strong acidity of atmospheric fine particles <2.5 um using annular denuder technology |
| IO-4.2 | Determination of reactive acidic and basic gases and strong acidity of atmospheric fine particles in ambient air using annular denuder technology |
| IO-5 | Sampling and analysis for atmospheric mercury |
| IO-5.1 | Sampling and analysis of vapor and particle phase mercury in ambient air utilizing cold vapor atomic fluorescence spectrometry |

**Table 5-9.  Quality Assurance Handbook for Air Pollution Measurement Systems**

| Volume | Description |
|--------|-------------|
| I | Field Guide to Environmental Quality Assurance EPA/600/R-94/038A |
| II | Ambient Air Methods EPA/600/R-94/038b |
| III | Stationary Source-Specific Methods EPA/600/R-94/038c, September, 1994 |
| IV | Meteorological Measurements EPA/6--/R-94/038d, March, 1995 |
| Va | QA Manual for Precipitation Measurement Systems |
| Vb | Operations and Maintenance for Precipitation Measurement Systems |

[18] Available from the EPA publications office in Cincinnati.

### Table 5-10. Compendium of Methods for the determination of Air Pollutants in indoor air

| Method | Description |
|---|---|
| IP-1A | Determination of volatile organic compounds (VOCs) in indoor air using stainless steel canisters |
| IP-1B | Determination of volatile organic compounds (VOCs) in indoor air using solid absorbent tubes |
| IP-2A[19] | Determination of nicotine in indoor air using XAD-4 sorbent tubes |
| IP-2B | Determination of nicotine in indoor air using treated filter cassettes |
| IP-3A | Determination of carbon monoxide (CO) or carbon dioxide ($CO_2$) in indoor air using nondispersive infrared (NDIR) |
| IP-3B | Determination of carbon monoxide (CO) or carbon dioxide ($CO_2$) in indoor air using gas filter correlation |
| IP-3C | Determination of carbon monoxide in indoor air using electrochemical oxidation |
| IP-4A | Determination of air exchange rate in indoor air using perfluorocarbon tracer (PFT) |
| IP-4B | Determination of air exchange rate in indoor air using tracer gas |
| IP-5A | Determination of nitrogen dioxide ($NO_2$) in indoor air using a continuous luminox monitor |
| IP-5B | Determination of nitrogen dioxide ($NO_2$) in indoor air using Palmes diffusion tubes |
| IP-5C | Determination of nitrogen dioxide ($NO_2$) in indoor air using passive sampling device |
| IP-6A | Determination of formaldehyde and other aldehydes in indoor air using a solid adsorbent cartridge |
| IP-6B | Determination of formaldehyde and other aldehydes in indoor air using a continuous colorimetric analyzer |
| IP-6C | Determination of formaldehyde and other aldehydes in indoor air using a passive sampling device |
| IP-7 | Determination of benzo(a)pyrene [B(a)P] and other polynuclear aromatic hydrocarbons (PAHs) in indoor air |
| IP-8 | Determination of organochlorine pesticides in indoor air |
| IP-9 | Determination of reactive acidic and basic gases and particulate matter in indoor air (annular denuder technique) |
| IP-10A | Determination of respirable particulate matter in indoor air using size specific impaction |
| IP-10B | Determination of respirable particulate matter in indoor air using a continuous particulate monitor |

### Table 5-11. CLP Draft Statement of Work for Air Analysis at CERCLA Sites

| Section | Description |
|---|---|
| 1 | Analytical method for the determination of volatile organic compounds (VOCs) in air collected in SUMMA canisters and analyzed by GC/MS |
| 2 | Analytical method for the determination of volatile organic compounds (VOCs) in air collected on tenax and analyzed by GC/MS |
| 3 | Analytical method for the determination of semivolatiles collected by PUF/XAD-2 and analyzed by GC/MS |
| 4 | Analytical methods for the determination of inorganic compounds collected on Hi-Vol filters and analyzed by inductively coupled plasma (ICP) atomic emission spectrometry or graphite furnace atomic absorption (GFAA) spectrometry |

---

[19] A recent article by Nelson, P.R., D.L. Heavner, B.B. Collie, K.C. Maliolo and M.W. Ogden. "Effect of Ventilation and Sampling Time on Environmental Tobacco Smoke Component Ratios." *Environ. Sci. Technol.* 1992. 26(10) pp. 1909-1915, suggests that 3-ethenylpyridine may be a more appropriate indicator of tobacco smoke than nicotine. The analysis is similar.

# List of Analytes

**Table A-1. Halogenated Volatile Organic Target Analytes**

| Target Analyte | CAS No. | Structure |
|---|---|---|
| Bromodichloromethane | 75-27-4 | $BrCl_2CH$ |
| Bromochloromethane | 74-97-5 | $BrCH_2Cl$ |
| Bromoform | 75-25-2 | $Br_3CH$ |
| Bromomethane | 74-83-9 | $BrCH_3$ |
| Carbon tetrachloride | 56-23-5 | $CCl_4$ |
| Chlorobenzene | 108-90-7 | |
| Chloroethane | 75-00-3 | $ClCH_2CH_3$ |
| 2-Chloroethylvinyl ether | 100-75-8 | |
| Chloroform | 67-66-3 | $CHCl_3$ |
| Chloromethane | 74-87-3 | $CH_3Cl$ |
| Dibromomethane | 74-95-3 | $Br_2CH_2$ |
| Dibromochloromethane | 124-48-1 | $Br_2ClCH$ |
| 1,2-Dichlorobenzene | 95-50-1 | |
| 1,3-Dichlorobenzene | 541-73-1 | |
| 1,4-Dichlorobenzene | 106-46-7 | |
| Dichlorodifluoromethane | 75-71-8 | $CCl_2F_2$ |

Continued on next page.

### Table A-1.  Halogenated Volatile Organic Target Analytes, *continued*

| Target Analyte | CAS No. | Structure |
|---|---|---|
| 1,1-Dichloroethane | 75-34-3 | $Cl_2CHCH_3$ |
| 1,2-Dichloroethane | 107-06-2 | $ClCH_2CH_2Cl$ |
| 1,1-Dichloroethene | 75-35-4 | $Cl_2C=CH_2$ |
| *cis*-1,2-Dichloroethene | 156-59-4 | |
| *trans*-1,2-Dichloroethene | 156-60-5 | |
| 1,2-Dichloropropane | 78-87-5 | $ClCH_2CHClCH_3$ |
| *cis*-1,3-Dichloropropene | 10061-01-5 | |
| *trans*-1,3-Dichloropropene | 10061-02-6 | |
| DBCP Dibromochloropropane | 96-12-8 | $BrCH_2CH_2BrCH_2Cl$ |
| EDB Ethylenedibromide | 106-93-4 | $BrCH_2CH_2Br$ |
| Hexachlorobutadiene | 87-68-3 | $Cl_2C=CCl-CCl=CCl_2$ |
| Methylene chloride | 75-09-2 | $CH_2Cl_2$ |
| 1,1,2,2-Tetrachloroethane | 79-34-5 | $Cl_2CHCHCl_2$ |
| Tetrachloroethene | 127-18-4 | $Cl_2C=CCl_2$ |
| 1,1,1-Trichloroethane | 71-55-6 | $Cl_3CCH_3$ |
| 1,1,2-Trichloroethane | 79-00-5 | $Cl_2CHCH_2Cl$ |
| Trichloroethene | 79-01-6 | $Cl_2C=CHCl$ |
| Trichlorofluoromethane | 75-69-4 | $CCl_3F$ |
| Vinyl chloride | 75-01-4 | $ClHC=CH_2$ |

## Table A-2.  Aromatic Volatile Organic Target Analytes

| Target Analyte | CAS No. | Structure |
|---|---|---|
| Benzene | 71-43-2 | |
| Toluene | 108-88-3 | |
| Ethylbenzene | 100-41-4 | |
| Chlorobenzene | 108-90-7 | |
| 1,2-Dichlorobenzene | 95-50-1 | |
| 1,3-Dichlorobenzene | 541-73-1 | |
| 1,4-Dichlorobenzene | 106-46-7 | |
| *n*-Butylbenzene | 104-51-8 | |
| *s*-Butylbenzene | 135-98-8 | |
| *tert*-Butylbenzene | 98-06-6 | |
| 4-Isopropyltoluene | 99-87-6 | |
| Styrene | 100-42-5 | |
| *m*-Xylene | 108-38-3 | |
| *o*-Xylene | 95-47-6 | |
| *p*-Xylene | 106-42-3 | |

## Table A-3. Other Common Volatile Analytes

| Target Analyte | CAS No. | Structure |
|---|---|---|
| Acetone | 67-64-1 | $CH_3C(=O)CH_3$ |
| Acetonitrile | 75-05-8 | $CH_3CN$ |
| Acrolein | 107-02-8 | $CH_2=CHCHO$ |
| Acrylonitrile | 107-13-1 | $CH_2=CHCN$ |
| Ethyl ether | 60-29-7 | $CH_3CH_2OCH_2CH_3$ |
| p-Dioxane | 123-91-1 | |
| Methyl ethyl ketone (MEK) | 78-93-3 | $CH_3CH_2C(=O)CH_3$ |
| Methyl isobutyl ketone (MIBK) | 108-10-1 | $(CH_3)_2CHCH_2C(=O)CH_3$ |
| 2-Hexanone | 591-78-6 | $CH_3CH_2CH_2CH_2C(=O)CH_3$ |
| Allyl alcohol | 107-18-6 | $CH_2=CHCH_2OH$ |
| Carbon disulfide | 75-15-0 | $S=C=S$ |
| Ethanol | 64-10-5 | $CH_3CH_2OH$ |
| Ethylene oxide | 75-21-8 | |
| Ethylmethacrylate | 97-63-2 | $CH_3CH=CHCO_2CH_2CH_3$ |
| Methylmethacrylate | 80-62-6 | $CH_3CH=CHCO_2CH_3$ |
| Propargyl alcohol | 107-19-7 | $HCCCH_2OH$ |
| Vinyl acetate | 108-05-4 | $CH_2=CHO_2CCH_3$ |

## Table A-4. Basic Semivolatile Organic Target Analytes

| Target Analyte | CAS No. | Structure |
|---|---|---|
| 4-Aminobiphenyl | 92-67-1 | |
| Aniline | 62-53-3 | |
| Benzidine | 92-87-5 | |
| 4-Chloroaniline | 106-47-8 | |
| 3,3'-Dichlorobenzidine | 91-94-1 | |
| Dimethylaminoazobenzene | 60-11-7 | |
| a,a-Dimethylphenethylamine | 122-09-8 | |

Continued on next page.

## Table A-4. Basic Semivolatile Organic Target Analytes, *continued*

| Target Analyte | CAS No. | Structure |
|---|---|---|
| Diphenylamine | 122-39-4 | |
| 1,2-Diphenylhydrazine | 122-66-7 | |
| 1-Naphthylamine | 134-32-7 | |
| 2-Naphthylamine | 91-59-8 | |
| 2-Nitroaniline | 88-77-4 | |
| 3-Nitroaniline | 99-09-2 | |
| 4-Nitroaniline | 100-01-6 | |
| 2-Picoline | 109-06-89 | |
| Pyridine | 129-00-0 | |

## Table A-5. Neutral Semivolatile Organic Target Analytes

| Target Analyte | CAS No. | Structure |
|---|---|---|
| Acenaphthene | 83-32-9 | |
| Acenaphthylene | 208-96-8 | |
| Acetophenone | 98-86-2 | |

Continued on next page.

**Table A-5. Neutral Semivolatile Organic Target Analytes,** *continued*

| Target Analyte | CAS No. | Structure |
|---|---|---|
| Alachlor | 15972-60-8 | |
| Aldrin | 309-00-2 | |
| Anthracene | 120-12-7 | |
| Aroclor (PCBs)[*] | | $Cl_{1-10}$ |
| 1016 | 12674-11-2 | $Cl_2-Cl_3$ |
| 1221 | 11104-28-2 | $Cl-Cl_2$ |
| 1232 | 11141-16-5 | $Cl-Cl_3$ |
| 1242 | 53469-21-9 | $Cl_2-Cl_4$ |
| 1248 | 12672-29-6 | $Cl_3-Cl_5$ |
| 1254 | 11097-69-1 | $Cl_4-Cl_6$ |
| 1260 | 11096-82-5 | $Cl_5-Cl_8$ |
| 1262 | 37324-23-5 | $Cl_5-Cl_8$ |
| Atrazine | 1912-24-9 | |
| Benz(a)anthracene | 56-55-3 | |
| Benzo(a)pyrene | 50-32-8 | |

Continued on next page.

[*] Aroclor is the tradename for polychlorinated biphenyls (PCBs). They are a mixture of compounds. The trade number gives the percentage by mass of chlorine in the mixture. For instance Aroclor 1242 contains 42% by weight chlorine. PCBs from the former Soviet Union have been correlated to the Aroclors as Sovol = Aroclor 1254 and trichlorodiphenyl = Aroclor 1242. Ivanov and Sandell, *Environ. Sci. Technol.* 26(10) pp. 2012-2017.

## Table A-5. Neutral Semivolatile Organic Target Analytes, *continued*

| Target Analyte | CAS No. | Structure |
|---|---|---|
| Benzo(b)fluoranthene | 205-99-2 | |
| Benzo(ghi)perylene | 191-24-2 | |
| Benzo(k)fluoranthene | 207-08-9 | |
| Benzyl alcohol | 100-51-6 | $CH_2OH$ |
| BHC ** <br> g-BHC (Lindane) | 58-89-8 | (Cl, Cl, Cl, Cl, Cl, Cl substituted cyclohexane) |
| Bis(2-chloroethoxy)methane | 111-91-1 | $ClCH_2CH_2OCH_2OCH_2CH_2Cl$ |
| Bis(2-chloroethyl) ether | 111-44-4 | $ClCH_2CH_2OCH_2CH_2Cl$ |
| Bis(2-chloroisopropyl) ether | 108-60-1 | $ClCH_2(CH_3)CHOCH(CH_3)CH_2Cl$ |
| Bis(2-ethylhexyl) phthalate | 117-81-7 | $CO_2CH_2CH(CH_2CH_3)CH_2CH_2CH_2CH_3$ <br> $CO_2CH_2CH(CH_2CH_3)CH_2CH_2CH_2CH_3$ |
| Bis(2-ethylhexyl)adipate | 103-23-1 | $C_4H_9(C_2H_5)CHCH_2O_2C(C_4H_8)CO_2CH_2CH(C_2H_5)C_4H_9$ |
| Butyl benzyl phthalate | 85-68-7 | $CO_2CH_2$ <br> $CO_2(CH_2)_3CH_3$ |

Continued on next page.

----

** BHC are the initials from the incorrect name benzene hexachloride; the correct name is 1,2,3,4,5,6-Hexachlorocyclohexane. Eight well-described isomers are known, which are indicated by greek letters. γ-BHC is the insecticide Lindane, specifically 1α,2α,3β,4α,5α,6β–Hexachlorocyclohexane.

Genium Publishing Corporation

**Table A-5. Neutral Semivolatile Organic Target Analytes,** *continued*

| Target Analyte | CAS No. | Structure |
|---|---|---|
| Chlordane [***] | 57-74-9 | |
| Chrysene | 218-01-9 | |
| Di-*n*-butyl phthalate | 84-74-2 | $CO_2(CH_2)_3CH_3$ $CO_2(CH_2)_3CH_3$ |
| Di-*n*-octyl phthalate | 117-84-0 | $CO_2(CH_2)_7CH_3$ $CO_2(CH_2)_7CH_3$ |
| Dibenz(a,h)anthracene | 53-70-3 | |
| Dibenzofuran | 132-64-9 | |
| Dibutylchlorendate | 1770-80-5 | COO-n-Bu COO-n-Bu |
| Dieldrin | 60-57-1 | |
| Diethyl phthalate | 84-66-2 | $CO_2CH_2CH_3$ $CO_2CH_2CH_3$ |
| Dimethyl phthalate | 131-11-3 | $CO_2CH_3$ $CO_2CH_3$ |

Continued on next page.

[***] Chlordane is a mixture of positionally chlorinated insecticide compounds derived from cyclopentadiene dimer. Heptachlor is one of the components.

**Table A-5.  Neutral Semivolatile Organic Target Analytes,** *continued*

| Target Analyte | CAS No. | Structure |
|---|---|---|
| Endosulfan I | 959-98-8 | |
| Endosulfan II | 33212-65-9 | |
| Endosulfan sulfate | 1031-07-8 | |
| Endrin | 72-20-8 | |
| Endrin aldehyde | 7421-93-4 | |
| Endrin ketone | 53494-70-5 | |
| Ethyl methanesulfonate | 62-50-0 | $CH_3SO_2OCH_2CH_3$ |
| Fluoranthene | 206-44-0 | |
| Fluorene | 86-73-7 | |
| Halowax (Polychlorinated naphthalenes) | | $Cl\text{-}Cl_8$ |
| 1000 | 58718-66-4 | 26% Cl  $Cl\text{-}Cl_4$ |
| 1001 | 58718-67-5 | 50% Cl  $Cl\text{-}Cl_4$ |

Continued on next page.

**Table A-5. Neutral Semivolatile Organic Target Analytes,** *continued*

| Target Analyte | CAS No. | Structure |
|---|---|---|
| 1013 | 12616-35-2 | 56% Cl $Cl_3$-$Cl_6$ |
| 1014 | 12616-36-3 | 62% Cl $Cl_3$-$Cl_7$ |
| 1051 | 2234-13-1 | 70% Cl $Cl_7$-$Cl_8$ |
| 1099 | 39450-05-0 | 52% Cl $Cl$-$Cl_4$ |
| Heptachlor | 76-44-8 | |
| Heptachlor epoxide | 1024-57-3 | |
| Hexachlorobenzene | 118-74-1 | |
| Hexachlorobutadiene | 87-68-3 | $Cl_2C=CClCCl=CCL_2$ |
| Hexachlorocyclo-pentadiene | 77-47-4 | |
| Hexachloroethane | 67-72-1 | $Cl_3CCCl_3$ |
| Indeno(1,2,3-cd)pyrene | 193-39-5 | |
| Isophorone | 78-59-1 | |
| Methoxychlor | 72-43-5 | |
| Methyl methanesulfonate | 66-27-3 | $CH_3SO_2OCH_3$ |

Continued on next page.

**Table A-5.  Neutral Semivolatile Organic Target Analytes,** *continued*

| Target Analyte | CAS No. | Structure |
|---|---|---|
| N-Nitrosodi-n-propylamine | 621-64-7 | $(n\text{-}C_3H_7)_2N\text{-}NO$ |
| N-Nitrosodibutylamine | 924-16-3 | $(C_4H_9)_2N\text{-}NO$ |
| N-Nitrosodimethylamine | 62-75-9 | $(CH_3)_2N\text{-}NO$ |
| N-Nitrosodiphenylamine | 86-30-6 | $(C_6H_5)_2N\text{-}NO$ |
| N-Nitrosopiperidine | 100-75-4 | |
| Naphthalene | 91-20-3 | |
| Nitrobenzene | 98-95-3 | |
| Pentachlorobenzene | 608-93-5 | |
| Pentachloronitrobenzene | 82-68-8 | |
| Phenacetin | 62-44-2 | $CH_3CH_2O$—⬡—$NHCOCH_3$ |
| Phenanthrene | 85-01-8 | |
| Pronamide | 23950-58-5 | |
| Pyrene | 129-00-0 | |
| Simazene | 122-34-9 | |

Continued on next page.

**Table A-5. Neutral Semivolatile Organic Target Analytes,** *continued*

| Target Analyte | CAS No. | Structure |
|---|---|---|
| Toxaphene **** | 8001-35-2 | |
| 1-Chloronaphthalene | 90-13-1 | |
| 2-Chloronaphthalene | 91-58-7 | |
| 2-Methylnaphthalene | 91-57-6 | |
| 3-Methylcholanthrene | 56-49-5 | |
| 4-Bromophenyl phenyl ether | 101-55-3 | |
| 4-Chlorophenyl phenyl ether | 7005-72-3 | |
| 4,4'-DDD | 72-54-8 | |
| 4,4'-DDE | 72-55-9 | |
| 4,4'-DDT | 50-29-3 | |
| 2,4-Dinitrotoluene | 121-14-2 | |

Continued on next page.

---

**** Toxaphene is a mixture of compounds derived from the chlorination of camphene. It contains 67-69% chlorine by weight.

**Table A-5.  Neutral Semivolatile Organic Target Analytes,** *continued*

| Target Analyte | CAS No. | Structure |
|---|---|---|
| 2,6-Dinitrotoluene | 606-20-2 | |
| 1,2,4-Trichlorobenzene | 120-82-1 | |
| 7,12-Dimethyl-benz(a)anthracene | 57-97-6 | |
| 1,2,4,5-Tetrachlorobenzene | 95-94-3 | |
| 2,3,7,8-Tetrachlorobenzodioxin (2,3,7,8-TCDD) | 1746-01-6 | |

**Table A-6.  Acidic Semivolatile Organic Target Analytes**

| Target Analyte | CAS No. | Structure |
|---|---|---|
| Benzoic acid | 65-85-0 | |
| 4-Chloro-3-methylphenol | 59-50-7 | |
| 2-Chlorophenol | 95-57-8 | |
| 2,4-Dichlorophenol | 120-83-2 | |
| 2,6-Dichlorophenol | 87-65-0 | |

Continued on next page.

**Table A-6. Acidic Semivolatile Organic Target Analytes,** *continued*

| Target Analyte | CAS No. | Structure |
|---|---|---|
| 2,4-Dimethylphenol | 105-67-9 | |
| 2,4-Dinitrophenol | 51-28-5 | |
| 2-Methyl-4,6-dinitrophenol | 534-52-1 | |
| 2-Methylphenol | 95-48-7 | |
| 4-Methylphenol | 106-44-5 | |
| 2-Nitrophenol | 88-75-5 | |
| 4-Nitrophenol | 100-02-7 | |
| Pentachlorophenol | 87-86-5 | |
| Phenol | 108-95-2 | |
| 2,3,4,6-Tetrachlorophenol | 58-90-2 | |
| 2,4,5-Trichlorophenol | 95-95-4 | |
| 2,4,6-Trichlorophenol | 88-06-2 | |

**Table A-7. Herbicide Analytes**

| Target Analyte | CAS No. | Structure |
|---|---|---|
| Dalapon | 75-99-0 | $CH_3CCl_2COOH$ |
| 2,4-D | 133-90-4 | |
| Dinoseb | 88-85-7 | |
| Picloram | 1918-02-1 | |
| 2,4,5-T | 93-76-5 | |
| 2,4,5-TP (Silvex) | 93-72-1 | |
| Dicamba | 1918-00-9 | |
| Dichlorprop | 120-36-5 | |
| MCPA | 94-74-6 | |
| MCPP | 7085-19-0 | |

## Table A-8. Organic Disinfection Byproducts

| Target Analyte | CAS No. | Structure |
|---|---|---|
| Bromochloroacetonitrile | 83463-62-1 | $BrClCHCN$ |
| Chloral hydrate | 75-87-6 | $Cl_3CC(OH)_2$ |
| Chloropicrin | 76-06-2 | $Cl_3CNO_2$ |
| Dibromoacetonitrile | 3252-43-5 | $Br_2CHCN$ |
| Dichloroacetonitrile | 3018-12-0 | $Cl_2CHCN$ |
| Trichloroacetonitrile | 545-06-2 | $Cl_3CCN$ |
| 1,1,1-Trichloropropanone | 918-00-3 | $Cl_3CC(=O)CH_3$ |
| 1,1-Dichloropropanone | 513-88-2 | $Cl_2CHC(=O)CH_3$ |
| Monobromoacetic acid | 79-08-3 | $BrCH_2COOH$ |
| Monochloroacetic acid | 79-11-8 | $ClCH_2COOH$ |
| Dibromoacetic acid | 631-64-1 | $Br_2CHCOOH$ |
| Dichloroacetic acid | 79-43-6 | $Cl_2CHCOOH$ |
| Bromochloroacetic acid | 5589-96-3 | $BrClCHCOOH$ |
| Trichloroacetic acid | 76-03-9 | $Cl_3CCOOH$ |
| Dalapon | 75-99-0 | $CH_3CCl_2COOH$ |

## Table A-9. Nitrogen-Phosphorous Pesticides Determined by NPD-GC

| Target Analyte | CAS No. | Structure |
|---|---|---|
| Famphur | 52-85-7 | $(CH_3O)_2PO-\bigcirc-SO_2N(CH_3)_2$ |
| Asulam | 3337-71-1 | $NH_2-\bigcirc-SO_2NHCO_2CH_3$ |
| Dichlorvos | 62-73-7 | $(CH_3O)_2P(=O)OCH=CCl_2$ |
| Dimethoate | 60-51-5 | $(CH_3O)_2P(=S)SCH_2C(=O)NHCH_3$ |
| Disulfoton | 298-04-4 | $(CH_3CH_2O)_2P(=S)SCH_2CH_2SCH_2CH_3$ |
| Fensulfothion | 115-90-2 | $(CH_3CH_2O)_2PO-\bigcirc-SCH_3$ (with P=O and S=O) |
| Merphos | 150-50-5 | $(n\text{-}CH_3CH_2CH_2CH_2)_3P$ |
| Methyl parathion | 298-00-0 | $(CH_3O)_2PO-\bigcirc-NO_2$ (with P=O) |
| Monocrotophos | 919-44-8 | $(CH_3O)_2P(=O)O(CH_3)C=CHC(=O)NHCH_3$ |
| Naled | 300-76-5 | $(CH_3O)_2P(=O)OCHBrCBrCl_2$ |
| Phorate | 298-02-2 | $(CH_3CH_2O)_2P(=S)SCH_2SCH_2CH_3$ |
| Trichlorfon | 52-68-6 | $(CH_3O)_2P(=O)OCHOHCCl_3$ |
| Thiofanox | 39196-18-4 | $(CH_3)_3C(CH_3SCH_2)C=NOC(=O)NHCH_3$ |
| tris-(2,3-Dibromopropyl) phosphate | 126-72-7 | $(CH_2BrCHBrCH_2O)_3P=O$ |

## Table A-10. Target Analytes Assayed by HPLC

| Target Analyte | CAS No. | Structure |
|---|---|---|
| Aldicarb (Temik) | 116-06-3 | $CH_3SC(CH_3)_2CH=NOC(O)NHCH_3$ |
| Aldicarb sulfone | 1646-88-4 | $CH_3S(O)_2C(CH_3)_2CH=NOC(O)NHCH_3$ |
| Aldicarb sulfoxide | 1646-87-3 | $CH_3S(O)C(CH_3)_2CH=NOC(O)NHCH_3$ |
| Baygon (Propoxur) | 114-26-1 | |
| Carbaryl (Sevin) | 63-25-2 | |
| Carbofuran (Furadan) | 1563-66-2 | |
| Dioxacarb | 6988-21-2 | |
| 3-Hydroxycarbofuran | 16655-82-6 | |
| Methiocarb (Mesurol) | 2032-65-7 | |
| Methomyl (Lannate) | 16752-77-5 | $CH_3(CH_3S)C=NOC(O)NHCH_3$ |
| Oxamyl (Vydate) | 23135-22-0 | $(CH_3)_2NCO(CH_3S)C=NOC(O)NHCH_3$ |
| Promecarb | 2631-37-0 | |

Continued on next page.

## Table A-10. Target Analytes Assayed by HPLC, *continued*

| Target Analyte | CAS No. | Structure |
|---|---|---|
| Formaldehyde | 50-00-0 | $H_2CO$ |
| Acetaldehyde | 75-07-0 | $H_3CCHO$ |
| Acrylamide | 79-06-1 | $H_2C=CHCONH_2$ |
| Acrylonitrile | 107-13-1 | $H_2C=CHCN$ |
| Acrolein | 107-02-8 | $H_2C=CHCHO$ |
| **Miscellaneous** | | |
| Caffeine | 58-08-2 | |
| Nicotine | 54-11-5 | |

# Common Acronyms

**AA.** atomic absorption

**ATP.** adenosine triphosphate

**BAT.** best available technology

**BDL.** below detection limit

**BDMC.** 4-bromo-3,5-dimethylphenyl -N-methylcarbamate

**BFB.** 4-bromofluorobenzene

**BHC.** 1,2,3,4,5,6-hexachlorocyclo-hexane

**BN.** base neutral

**BNA.** base neutral and acid

**BOD.** biochemical oxygen demand

**BTEX.** benzene, toluene, ethyl benzene and xylene

**CBOD.** carbonaceous biochemical oxygen demand

**CCC.** calibration check compounds

**CCV.** continuing calibration verification

**CERCLA.** Comprehensive Environmental Response, Compensation & Liability Act

**CFR.** Code of Federal Regulations

**CLP.** contract laboratory program

**CNCl.** cyanogen chloride

**CND.** 1-chloro-2,4-dinitrobenzene

**CNS.** central nervous system

**COD.** chemical oxygen demand

**CTAS.** cobalt thiocyanate active substances

**CWA.** Clean Water Act

**DAD.** diode array detector

**DBC.** dibutylchlorendate

**DBUB.** 4,4-dibromooctafluoro-biphenyl

**DCPA.** 3,5-dichlorophenylacetic acid

**DDD.** 2,2-bis(4-chlorophenyl)-1,1-dichloroethane

**DDE.** 2,2-bis(4-chlorophenyl)-1,1-dichloroethene

**DDT.** 2,2-bis(4-chlorophenyl)-1,1,1-trichloroethane

**DER.** Department of Environmental Regulation

**DFTPP.** decafluorotriphenylphosphine

**DI.** deionized

**DMR.** discharge monitoring report

**DNA.** deoxyribonucleic acid

**DNPH.** 2,4-dinitrophenylhydrazine

**DO.** dissolved oxygen

**DOC.** dissolved organic carbon

**DOE.** Department of Energy

**DPD.** N,N-diethylphenylene diamine

**DQO.** data quality objective

**DRO.** diesel range organics

**EC.** effective concentration

**ECD.** electron capture detector

**EDTA.** disodium ethylenediaminetetra-acetic acid

**ELCD.** electrolytic conductivity detector

**EPP.** electronic pressure programming

**EPA.** Environmental Protection Agency

**EQL.** estimated quantitation limit

**FACTS.** free available chlorine test, syringaldazine

**FAS.** ferrous ammonium sulfate

**FC.** fecal coliform

**FDA.** Food and Drug Administration

**FDCA.** Food, Drug and Cosmetic Act

**FFAP.** free fatty acids polyester

**FID.** flame ionization detector

**FIFRA.** Federal Insecticide, Fungicide and Rodenticide Act

**FPD.** flame photometric detector

**FTIR.** fourier transform infrared

**GC.** gas chromatography

**GC/FTIR.** gas chromatograph/fourier transform infrared

**GC/MS.** gas chromatograph/mass spectrometer

**GFAA.** graphite furnace atomic absorption

**GPC.** gel permeation chromatography

**GRO.** gasoline range organics

**H-P.** Hewlett-Packard

**HBr.** hydrogen bromide

**HCN.** hydrogen cyanide

**HDPE.** high density polyethylene

**HEPES.** 4-[2-hydroxyethyl]-1-piperazine ethanesulfonic acid

**HPLC.** high pressure liquid chromatography

**HPLC-DAD.** high pressure liquid chromatography-diode array detector

**HPLC/MS.** high pressure liquid chromatography/mass spectroscopy

**HSL.** Hazardous Substance List

**IC.** inorganic carbon

**ICAP.** inductively coupled argon plasma

**ICP.** inductively coupled plasma

**ICV.** initial calibration verification

**ID.** inside diameter

**IDL.** instrument detection limit

**IR.** infrared

**IR-TPH.** infrared - total petroleum hydrocarbons

**IS.** internal standard

**JTU.** Jackson turbidity unit

**K-D.** Kuderna-Danish concentrator

**KBr.** potassium bromide

**KF.** Karl Fisher

**KHP.** potassium hydrogen phthalate

**KOH.** potassium hydroxide

**LAS.** linear alkylbenzene sulfonate

**LC.** lethal concentration

**LCV.** leuco crystal violet

**LD.** lethal dose

**LIMS.** laboratory information management system

**LUST.** leaking underground storage tank

**M-FC.** membrane - fecal coliform

**M/Z.** mass/charge

**MBAS.** methylene blue active substance

**MBTH.** N-methylbenzothiazolinon hydrazine

**MC.** method code

**MCE.** mixed cellulose ester

**MCL.** maximum contaminant levels

**MDL.** method detection limits

**MMO-MUG.** minimal media o-nitrophenyl-ß-D-galactopyranoside/4-methylumbelliferyl-ß-D-glucuronide

**MTB.** methyl thymol blue

**MUG.** 4-methylumbelliferyl-ß-D-glucuronide

**NDIR.** non-dispersive infrared

**NDOC.** non-dissolved organic carbon

**NED.** N-napthyl ethylenediamine dichloride

**NIST.** National Institute for Standards and Technology

**NMHC.** non-methane hydrocarbons

**NMOC.** non-methane organic compounds

**NMR.** nuclear magnetic resonance

**NORM.** naturally occuring radioactive materials

**NPDES.** National Pollutant Discharge Elimination System

**NPL.** National Priority List

**ONP.** o-nitrophenol

**ONPG.** o-nitrophenyl-ß-D-galactopyranoside

**OPA.** o-phthalaldehyde

**OV.** Ohio Valley

**P-A.** presence-absence

**PAH.** polycyclic aromatic hydrocarbons

**PAO.** phenyl arsineoxide

**PCB.** polychlorinated biphenyl

**PCDD.** polychlorinated dibenzo-p-dioxins

**PCE.** perchloroethene

**PDS.** post digestion spikes

**PE.** performance evaluation

**PEG.** polyethylene glycol

**PES.** post extraction spikes

**PFTBA.** perfluorotributylamine

**PID.** photo ionization detector

**POC.** purgeable organic carbon

**POTW.** publicly owned treatment works

**PQL.** practical quantitation levels

**PUF.** polyurethane foam

**PVC.** polyvinyl chloride

**QA.** quality assurance

**QC.** quality control

**RCRA.** Resource Conservation and Recovery Act

**RF.** response factors

**RNA.** ribonucleic acid

**RPD.** relative percent difference

**RSD.** relative standard deviation

**RSH.** mercaptans

**RT.** retention time

**SARA.** Superfund Amendments and Reauthorization Act

**SD.** standard deviation

**SDWA.** Safe Drinking Water Act

**SFE.** supercritical fluid extraction

**SM.** Standard Methods for the Examination of Water and Wastewater

**SOW.** statement of work

**SPADNS.** sodium 2-(parasulfophenyl-azo)-1,8-dihydroxy-3,6-naphthalene disulfonate

**SPCC.** system performance check compounds

**SPE.** solid phase extraction

**STP.** standard temperature and pressure

**SVI.** sludge volume index

**TAL.** target analyte list

**TC.** total carbon

**TCDD.** tetrachlorodibenzodioxin

**TCE.** trichloroethene

**TCL.** target compound list

**TCLP.** toxic characteristic leaching procedure

**TCMP.** 2-chloro-6-trichloromethyl pyridine

**TDS.** total dissolved solids

**THC.** total hydrocarbons content

**THM.** trihalomethane

**TIC.** tentatively identified compounds

**TJA.** Thermal Jerrol Ash

**TOC.** total organic carbon

**TPH.** total petroleum hydrocarbons

**TRS.** total reduced sulfur

**TS.** total solids

**TSCA.** Toxic Substances Control Act

**TSD.** treatment, storage, and disposal

**TSS.** total suspended solids

**TTHM.** total trihalomethanes

**TV.** true value

**TVDS.** total volatile dissolved solids

**TVS.** total volatile solids

**TVSS.** total volatile suspended solids

**USACE.** U.S. Army Corps of Engineers

**UST.** underground storage tanks

**UVDAD.** ultra violet diode array detector

**VOA.** volatile organic analysis

**VOC.** volatile organic compounds

**WP.** water pollution

**WS.** water supply

**ZHE.** zero headspace extraction

# Specialized Laboratory Glassware

In the environmental laboratory there are a number of very specialized pieces of glassware not found in other laboratories. They are for the most part used in the organics sample preparation area. The thick lines on the diagrams represent assembly points, which may be Teflon® lined threaded joints or ground glass joints (linear or ball design).

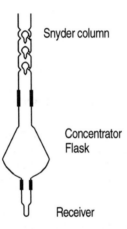

Snyder column

Concentrator Flask

Receiver

**Figure C-1. Kuderna-Danish concentrator.**

The Kuderna-Danish (K-D) concentrator is used to reduce the volume of organic solvent sample extracts. Boiling chips (Teflon® is prefered, but a variety of materials is used.) are placed in the tip of the receiver, the extract is added, and the apparatus is heated on a steam table. Clean solvent is added to the top of the Snyder column to wet the balls. The sample is concentrated until 3-4 mL remain in the receiver, then removed from the heat source and allowed to cool. The extract is transferred to a volumetric flask[1] for final concentration to an appropriate volume under a gentle stream of nitrogen gas. The volume graduations on the receiver are only approximate

---

[1]  A very useful procedure is to obtain 2 mL Class A volumetric tubes with ground glass stoppers and calibrate them at the 1.000 mL level with an etch mark on the glass. The tubes hold about 4 mL of extract and are very easy to monitor as the solvent level drops to the 1 mL level during nitrogen blowdown. Internal standards can then be added and the contents of the tube shaken with the stopper in place before final transfer to an autosampler vial.

and should never be used as the final volume determination prior to analysis. Care must be taken to avoid reducing the volume of the extract below 1 mL to avoid target analyte and surrogate loss.

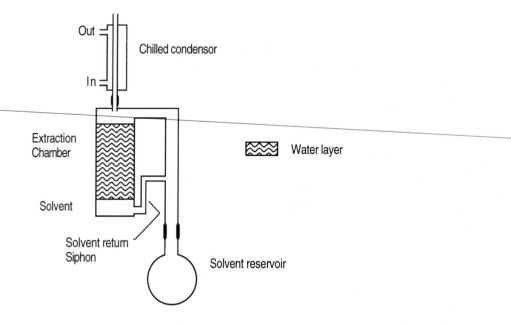

**Figure C-2. Continuous liquid-liquid extractor for heavier than water solvents.**

The continuous liquid-liquid extractor is used when intractable emulsions form on shaking the sample with organic solvents during the separatory funnel liquid-liquid extraction procedure. The sample is placed in the extraction chamber, which already contains about 100 mL of solvent. Extraction solvent is placed in the reservoir and heated to boiling. Solvent condenses in the chilled condensor and drips down through the aqueous sample. The analytes are partitioned into the solvent layer and slowly siphoned into the solvent reservoir. After 18-24 hours operation the unit is allowed to cool, and the solvent is dried with anhydrous sodium sulfate and concentrated in a K-D concentrator. If a BNA extraction is being performed the sample is first acidified and extracted for 18-24 hours, then basified and extraction continued for another 18-24 hours, a lengthy process. A one-piece extraction chamber is illustrated, however commercially available modular units are easier to clean and less prone to breakage. A shut-off valve in the solvent return siphon is very useful. Continuous liquid-liquid extractors are available that incorporate a K-D concentrator in the design as illustrated in Figure C-3. Other modifications include a water-jacketed receiver/concentrator flask for use with heated water circulators.

The use of the siphon tube allows water to become entrained in the extracting solvent, and, on solvent removal, the major part of the resulting concentrate can be water. A recent technology advance adds a hydrophobic membrane to the bottom of the sample chamber. This allows rapid and efficient separation of the extraction solvent from the water sample and immediate return of the solvent to the concentrator reservoir[2]. The elimination of the solvent pool at the bottom of the extraction chamber shortens the extraction time to 4-6 hours, reduces solvent usage to less than 100 mL, and makes the technique more time efficient and competitive with separatory funnel methods. A further advantage is elimination of water from the sample concentrate without further sample manipulation.

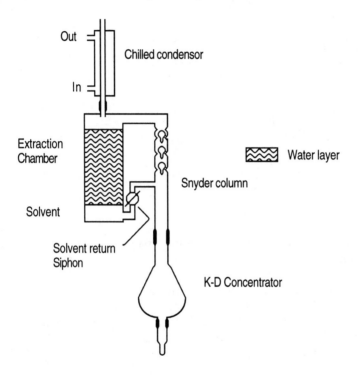

**Figure C-3. Continuous liquid-liquid extractor with built-in K-D concentrator.**

---

[2] Accelerated One-Step™ Extractor-Concentrator, Corning Glassworks, Corning, NY. One-Step is a registered trademark of Corning Glassworks.

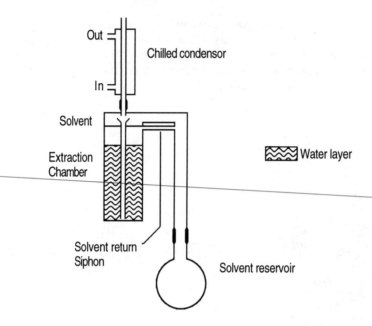

**Figure C-4. Continuous liquid-liquid extractor for use with lighter-than-water solvents.**

    A continuous liquid-liquid extractor for use with lighter-than-water solvents is illustrated in Figure C-4. The drops of solvent from the condensor fall into a tube that opens at the bottom of the extraction chamber. Solvent exiting from the tube percolates upward through the aqueous sample and collects at the top of the chamber. It then drains through an upper siphon into the solvent reservoir.

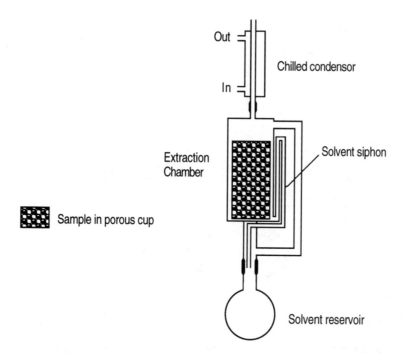

Out

Chilled condensor

In

Extraction
Chamber

Solvent siphon

Sample in porous cup

Solvent reservoir

**Figure C-5. Soxhlet extractor.**

The soxhlet extractor is designed for removal of extractable materials from solid matrices. It can be operated with any solvent, even water, due to the batchwise extraction mechanism. The sample is placed in a porous container, either glass with a fritted bottom or a totally porous cup made of cellulose or cotton. For organic extractions the sample is commonly mixed with a drying agent (anhydrous sodium sulfate or magnesium sulfate monohydrate, depending on the method) prior to placement in the cup. A glasswool plug is commonly placed on top of the solid in the cup when the sample has a lower density than the solvent. This prevents the solid from floating out of the cup and being siphoned into the solvent reservoir. Boiling solvent drips from the condensor into the extraction chamber containing the sample until the chamber fills to the top of the siphon, at which time the solvent drains almost completely back into the solvent reservoir. The fill and drain cycle is allowed to continue for 4 to 24 hours, depending on the method.

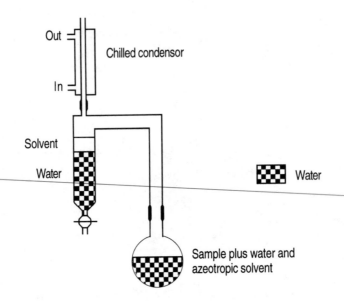

**Figure C-6.  Dean-Starke trap.**

The Dean-Starke trap is used to separate water from a sample by distillation as the azeotrope with an appropriate lighter-than-water solvent, commonly toluene.  The layers separate in the trap, and the upper toluene layer returns to the heated flask.  The toluene-water azeotrope is approximately 12% water, while toluene is only soluble to the extent of 0.067% in water.

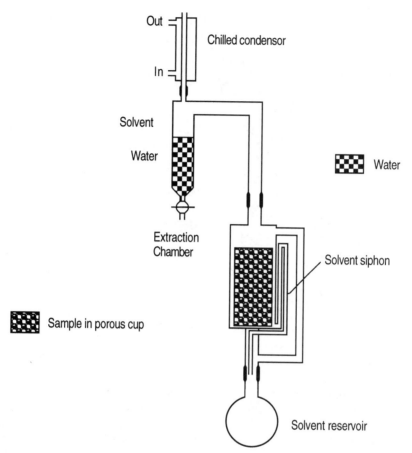

**Figure C-7. Soxhlet/Dean-Starke extractor.**

A soxhlet extractor has been combined with a Dean-Starke trap, as illustrated in Figure C-7, which eliminates the need to mix the sample with a drying agent prior to extraction.

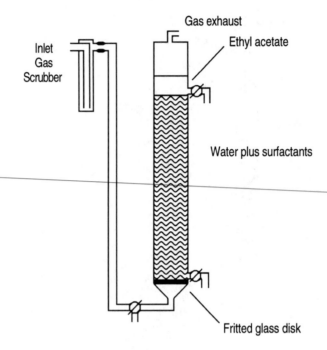

**Figure C-8. Sublation apparatus.**

The sublation apparatus (Figure C-8) is used to separate surfactants from aqueous samples. A stream of nitrogen is bubbled up through the water sample, forming surfactant micelles. On contact of the micelles with the upper layer of ethyl acetate, the surfactants dissolve into the organic solvent. After operation for 5 minutes at 1 L/min flow rate, the ethyl acetate layer is drained, fresh ethyl acetate added, and the extraction continued. The combined ethyl acetate layers are concentrated to dryness, leaving the surfactants as a solid residue for further analysis.

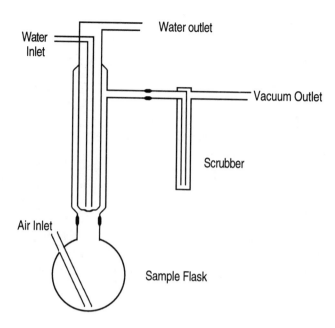

**Figure C-9. Distillation apparatus for cyanide or sulfide.**

Cyanide and sulfide analyses are subject to many interferences. To remove interferences, the samples are strongly acidified in the sample flask of Figure C-9, generating HCN or $H_2S$. Vigorous boiling of the sample transfers the cyanide or sulfide acids to the gas phase, and they are swept out of the sample flask by the air stream generated by application of a vacuum at the outlet. Water is removed from the air stream by the condensor and the target analytes trapped in the scrubber by an appropriate absorbing solution; sodium hydroxide for cyanide, and zinc acetate for sulfide.

# APPENDIX **D**

# References

## I. QUALITY CONTROL/QUALITY ASSURANCE

1.  *Handbook for Analytical Quality Control in Water and Wastewater.* EPA 600/4-79-019. March 1979. NTIS number PB-297 451.

2.  *Manual for Analytical Quality Control for Pesticides and Related Compounds in Human and Environmental Samples.* EPA 600/1-79-009. 1979.

3.  *Manual for the Certification of Laboratories Analyzing Drinking Water. Criteria and Procedures Quality Assurance.* EPA 570/9-90/008 April 1990. Change 1 EPA 570/9-90/008A. Oct., 1991. Change 2 EPA 814B-92-002. Sept., 1992.

4.  *Manual for the Evaluation of Laboratories Performing Aquatic Toxicity Tests.* EPA/600/4-90/031. NTIS number PB91-148353.

5.  Garfield, F.M., *Quality Assurance Principles for Analytical Laboratories.* AOAC, Arlington, VA, 1984.

6.  Gautier, M.A. and E.S. Gladney, "A quality assurance program for health and environmental chemistry." *American Laboratory* July, 1987.

7.  Keith, L.H., *Principles of Environmental Sampling.* American Chemical Society, 1987.

8.  Taylor, J.K., *Principles of Quality Assurance of Chemical Measurements,* U.S. Department of Commerce, February, 1985.

9.  Taylor, J.K., *Quality Assurance of Chemical Measurements.* Orlando Fla.: Lewis Publishers. 1987.

## II. TECHNICAL

10. *Air Sampling Instruments for Evaluation of Atmospheric Contaminants.* American Conference of Governmental Industrial Hygienists, 7th Edition, S.V. Hering Editor, Cincinnati, Ohio, 1989.

11. *Annual Book of ASTM Standards.* Vol 11.01 and 11.02 (Water I and II). American Society for Testing and Materials. Latest Edition.

12. *Compendium of Methods for the Determination of Air Pollutants in Indoor Air.* EPA, April 1990. (NTIS PB90-200288).

13. *Compendium of Methods for the Determination of Toxic Organic Compounds in Ambient Air.* EPA, June 1988. (NTIS PB90-127374).

14. *Environmental Compliance Branch Standard Operating Procedures and Quality Assurance Manual.* U.S. EPA Region IV Environmental Services Division. February, 1991.

15. *Georgia Modified Standard Method: Hazardous Waste Management Program Groundwater Testing Appendix IX.* Environmental Protection Division, Georgia Department of Natural Resources, February 1991.

16. Kostecki, P.T. and E.J. Calabrese. *Hydrocarbon Contaminated Soils* Volumes 1 and 2. Chelsea, MI. Lewis Publishers, 1991.

17. Leichnitz, K. *Detector Tube Handbook.* National Draeger, Inc. 412-787-8383, Drägerwerk, AG PO Box 1339 D-24 Lübeck FDR, 6th Edition, 1985.

18. Lodge, J.P., Jr. *Methods for Air Sampling and Analysis.* 3rd Edition, Intersociety Committee APCA, ACS, AIChE, APWA, ASME, AOAC, HPS & ISA, Chelsea, MI; Lewis Publishers, 1989.

19. *Microbiological Methods for Monitoring the Environment.* EPA 600/8-78-017. 1978.

20. *Methods for Chemical Analysis of Water and Wastes.* EPA 600/4-79-020, Revised March, 1983. NTIS number PB84-128677.

21. *Methods for Collection and Analysis of Aquatic Biological and Microbiological Samples,* Book 5, Chapter A4. U.S. Geological Survey, 1977.

22. *Methods for Determination of Inorganic Substances in Water and Fluvial Sediments,* Book 5, Chapter A1. U.S. Geological Survey, 1979.

23. *Methods for Measuring the Acute Toxicity of Effluents to Freshwater and Marine Organisms,* 3rd Edition. EPA 600/4-85/019, 1985. NTIS number PB85-205383.

24. *Methods for Measuring the Acute Toxicity of Effluents and Receiving Water Freshwater and Marine Organisms.* 4th Edition. EPA/60/4-90/027. NTIS number PB91-167650.

25. *Methods for the Determination of Metals in Environmental Samples.* EPA 600/4-91/010. June, 1991.

26. *Methods for the Determination of Nonconventional Pesticides in Municipal and Industrial Wastewater.* EPA 821RR-92-002. April, 1992.

27. *Methods for the Determination of Organic Compounds in Drinking Water.* EPA 600/4-88/039, December, 1988. NTIS number PB89-220461, Supplement 1, EPA 600/4-90/020, July, 1990, Supplement 2 EPA 600/R-92/129, NTIS PB92-207703, August, 1992.

28. *Methods for the Determination of Organic Substances in Water and Fluvial Sediments,* Book 5, Chapter A3. U.S. Geological Survey, 1983.

29. *Methods of Soil Analysis.* Part 2, Chemical and Microbiological Properties. A.L. Page, ed., 2nd edition, 1982.

30. *NIOSH Manual of Analytical Methods* U.S. Department of Health and Human Services, 3rd Edition, 15 February, 1984. 2nd Supplement, 15 August, 1987.

31. *Official Methods of Analysis of the Association of Official Analytical Chemists.* 15th Edition, AOAC 1986.

32. *POTW Sludge Sampling and Analysis Guidance Document* , USEPA August 1989.

33. *Precision Gas Detector System Manual.* Sensidyne, Inc. 12345 Starkey Rd., Largo FL 33453. 1985. Tel 800-451-9444.

34. *Procedures for Handling and Chemical Analysis of Sediments and Water Samples.* EPA/Corps of Engineers CE-81-1. March, 1981.

35. *RCRA Groundwater Monitoring Technical Enforcement Guidance Document,* (TEGD). EPA OSWER-9950.1. September, 1986.

36. *Short-term Methods for Estimating the Chronic Toxicity of Effluents and Receiving Waters to Freshwater Organisms,* 2nd edition. EPA 600/4-89/001. 1989. NTIS number PB89-207013.

37. *Short-term Methods for Estimating the Chronic Toxicity of Effluents and Receiving Waters to Marine and Estuarine Organisms.* EPA 600/4-87/028. 1988. NTIS number PB89-220503.

38. *Standard Methods for the Examination of Water and Wastewater,* 16th Edition. AWWA 1985.

39. *Standard Methods for the Examination of Water and Wastewater,* 17th Edition. AWWA 1989.

40. *Standard Methods for the Examination of Water and Wastewater,* 18th Edition. AWWA 1992, 6666 West Quincy Avenue, Denver, CO 80235.

41. Sulcek, Z and P. Povondra 1989 *Methods for Decomposition in Inorganic Analysis* CRC Press, Boca Raton FL, ISBN 0-8493-4963-X

42. *Test Methods for Evaluating Solid Waste - Physical/Chemical Methods,* EPA/SW-846, 3rd Edition, 1986, Revision 1, July, 1992.

43. 40 CFR, Part 136., Analytical Methods for Examining Water and Wastewater.

44. *US EPA Contract Laboratory Program Statement of Work for Inorganic Analysis,* EPA SOW ILM03.0, 1993.

45. *US EPA Contract Laboratory Program Statement of Work for Organic Analysis,* EPA SOW OLMO2.1, 1994.

46. *US EPA Contract Laboratory Program Statement of Work for Analysis of Air Toxics from Superfund Sites*

## III. GENERAL

47. Benefield, L.D., J.F. Judkins and B.L. Weand. *Process Chemistry for Water and Wastewater Treatment.* Englewood Cliffs, NJ: Prentice-Hall, 1982.

48. Bunce, N. *Environmental Chemistry.* Winnipeg, Canada: Wuerz Publishing, 1990.

49. Cotton, F.A., and G. Wilkinson *Advanced Inorganic Chemistry,* 5th Edition, New York, NY Wiley & Sons. 1988.

50. Hunt, D.T.E. and A.L. Wilson. *The Chemical Analysis of Water.* 2nd Edition, Royal Society of Chemistry, London, 1986.

51. Kaufman, J.A. *Waste Disposal in Academic Institutions.* Chelsea, MI: Lewis Publishers, 1990.

52. Manahan, S.E. *Environmental Chemistry,* 5th Edition, Chelsea, MI: Lewis Publishers, 1991.

53. March, J. *Advanced Organic Chemistry,* 4th Edition, New York, NY: Wiley & Sons, 1992.

54. Snoeyink, V.L. and D. Jenkins. *Water Chemistry.* New York, NY: John Wiley & Sons, 1980.

55. Wagner, R.E. *Guide to Environmental Analytical Methods*, 3rd Edition, Schenectady, NY: Genium Publishing Corporation, 1996. 1-800-243-6486.

56. Water Pollution Control Federation. *The Clean Water Act of 1987.* WPCF 601 Wythe St, Alexandria, Va. 22314, 1987, WPCF No. P0070JR.

57. Wentz, C.A. *Hazardous Waste Management.* New York, NY: McGraw-Hill Book Company, 1989.

# Vendors

## I. ANALYTICAL STANDARDS

NSI Environmental Solutions, P.O. Box 12313, Research Triangle Park, NC 27709. 800-234-7837

AccuStandard, Inc., 25 Science Park, Box 1, New Haven, CT 06511. 203-786-5290

Analytical Products Group, Inc., 2730 Washington Blvd., Belpre, OH 45714. 800-272-4442 (PET Program)

Ultra Scientific, 250 Smith Street, North Kingston RI 02852. 401-294-9400

SPEX CertiPrep, 203 Norcross Avenue, Metchen NJ 08840. 800-522-7739 or 908-549-7144.

Environmental Resource Associates, 5540 Marshall Street, Arvada, Colorado 80002. 800-372-0122 (PET Program)

Chem Service, 660 Tower Lane, P.O. Box 599, West Chester, PA 19381-0599. 610-692-3026

Plasma-Chem Corporation, 5142 West Hurley Pond Rd., Farmingdale, NJ 07727. 800-343-0437

American Type Culture Collection, 12301 Parklawn Dr., Rockville, MD 20852. 800-638-6597

Fisher Scientific, 2775 Pacific Drive, Norcross, GA 30091. 770-449-5050

VWR Scientific Products, P.O. Box 626, Bridgeport, NJ 08014. 800-234-5227

Protocol Analytical Supplies, Inc., 472 Lincoln Blvd., Middlesex, NJ 08846. 800-862-0080

Standard Reference Materials, National Institute of Standards and Technology, Building 202, Room 204, Gaithersburg, MD 20899. 301-975-6776

Radian International LLC, P.O. Box 201088, Austin TX 78720-1088, 1-800-848-7837

Restek Corporation, 110 Benner Cir. Bellefonte PA 16823-8812, 1-800-356-1688

Analytical Standards, Inc., P.O. Box 183, 6331 Emerson Avenue, Parkersburg, WV 26102-0183, (304) 442-4274

## II. PRE-CLEANED SAMPLE CONTAINERS

Eagle Picher Environmental Services, 36 B.J. Tunnell Blvd. East, Miami, OK 74354-3300. 800-331-7425

Industrial Glassware, 130 Bogden Blvd., Millville, NJ 08332. 609-327-2688

I-Chem, 2 Bolden Circle, New Castle, DE 19720. 800-443-1689

Qorpak, 1195 Washington Pike, Bridgeville, PA 15017. 412-257-3100

**Cleaning Protocols**

Organic and metals glass sample containers
- Wash with laboratory grade non-phosphate detergent
- Rinse 3 times with distilled water
- Rinse with 1:1 nitric acid
- Rinse 3 times with ASTM Type 1 organic free water
- Oven dry for 1 hour
- Rinse with hexane, methylene chloride, acetone or methanol
- Oven dry for 1 hour

Volatile organic glass sample containers
- Wash with laboratory grade non-phosphate detergent
- Rinse 3 times with distilled water
- Rinse 3 times with ASTM Type 1 organic free water
- (optional methanol rinse)
- Oven dry 1 hour

Metals plastic sample containers
- Wash with laboratory grade non-phosphate detergent
- Rinse 3 times with distilled water
- Rinse with 1:1 nitric acid
- Rinse 3 times with ASTM Type 1 organic free water
- Air dry

Plastic sample containers for other nutrients and demands
- Rinse three times with deionized water
- Fill with deionized water and let sit 48 hours
- Empty and air dry

Suitable non-phosphate detergents include Liquinox or Alconox for organics, Liquinox for inorganic anions, and Liquinox, Acationox or Micro for inorganic cations

# Regulatory Contact Directory

## NATIONAL AND REGIONAL CONTACTS

### ENVIRONMENTAL HOTLINES

**Asbestos & Small Business Ombudsman Office**
All except VA ...............................(800) 368-5888
VA only ...........................................(703) 557-1938
TDD machine ................................(703) 557-2824
Provides information to the public sector, including individual citizens and community services on the handling and abatement of asbestos in schools, the workplace and the home.

**Chemical Manufacturers Association Hotlines**
National.............................................(703) 741-5000
Non-emergency information on chemicals
Chemical Referral Center (CRC)
Chemtree Non-emergency.........(800) 262-8200
Provides Chemical Emergency Information.

**CHEMTREC**
National.............................................(800) 424-9300
Dist. of Columbia...........................(202) 887-4620

**Consumer Product Safety Commission Hotline**
National.............................................(800) 638-2772

**Emergency Planning and Community Right-to-Know (Title III SARA) Hotline**
National .........................................(800) 535-0202
Virginia ..........................................(703) 920-9877
Provides regulatory, policy and technical assistance to federal agencies, local and state governments, the public and regulated community in response to questions related to the Emergency Planning and Community Right-to-Know Act (Title III of SARA). Information on reporting of hazardous substances for community planning purposes.

**EPA Hotline** ...................................(800) 438-2474

**EPA Superfund (Region II Investigative Hotline)**
Restricted area codes as follows: 809, 201, 609, 908, 906, 212, 315, 516, 518, 607, 716, 718, 914.............................................(800) 245-2738
Enables the Superfund Civil Investigators to receive information relevant to specific Superfund Site Enforcement Investigations.

**TSCA Assistance Information Services**
............................................................(202) 554-1404
Provides technical assistance and information about the Toxic Substances Control Act (TSCA), the Asbestos School Hazard Abatement Act (ASHAA), the Asbestos Hazard Emergency Response Act (AHERA), the Asbestos School Hazard Abatement Reauthorization Act (ASHARA), the Residential Lead-based Pain Hazard Reduction Act, and the Pollution Prevention Act (PPA), and 33/50 Program.

**Mercury Hotline**
National.............................................(800) 833-3505
Provides answers to questions. No emergency Service

**National Pesticides Telecommunications Network**
National, incl. US, PR, and Virgin Island
............................................................(800) 858-7378
Fax: ..................................................(541) 737-0761
Provides the medical, veterinary, professional communities and general public with information on: pesticides and herbicides product information, recognition and management of pesticide poisonings, toxicology and symptomatic reviews, safety information, health and environmental effects, clean-up and disposal procedures.

**National Radon Hotline**

National...................................(800) 767-7236
Radon testing information. A message records
names and addresses of callers and a brochure
on radon is sent via 1st class mail.

**National Response Center - U.S. Coast
Guard Oil and Hazardous Material Spills**

National except DC ...................(800) 424-8802
DC and outside U.S. ....................(202) 267-2675
For reporting of oil and hazardous material
spills. NOTE: Please have ready as much
relevant data as possible when calling.

**Occupational Safety and Health
Administration Referral Service**

National...................................(800) 321-6742
24-hour access line to report unsafe and hazardous work practices.

**Office of the Inspector General - Public
Information**

Washington, DC.............................(202) 619-1142
Office of Special Council for Whistle
    Blower.........................................(800) 872-9855

**RCRA/Superfund/Community Right-to-
Know (Title III) Hotline**

International ...................................(800) 424-9346
TDD machine.................................(800) 553-7672
Answers factual questions from the regulated
community, other interested parties and the
public about EPA's RCRA regulations and
policies; referrals for obtaining related documents. RCRA, Underground Storage Tanks
(USTs), Superfund/CERCLA and Pollution
Prevention/Waste Minimization.

**Risk Communication Hotline**

.................................................(202) 260-5606
Responds to questions from EPA program
offices and regions, and external inquiries as
time permits, regarding the EPA's Risk
Communication Program and risk
communication issues.

**Safe Drinking Water Hotline**

National...................................(800) 426-4791
Provides assistance and regulatory knowledge
to the regulated community (public water systems) and the public on the regulations and
programs developed in response to the Safe
Drinking Water Act Amendments of 1986.

**Substance Identification Hotline**

National...................................(800) 848-6538
Identifies chemical by CAS number or Name

**US Department of Transportation (U.S.
DOT)**

National...................................(202) 366-4488
Information of DOT CFR-49 regulations.

## OTHER REGIONAL AND NATIONAL CONTACTS

**Centers for Disease Control (CDC)**

National...................................(404) 639-3535
Answers technical and public questions.

**Environmental Export Council (EEC)**

National...................................(202) 466-6933

**EPA Assistant Administrator for
Enforcement and Compliance Monitoring**

National...................................(202) 564-2440
Provides direction for the review and enforcement of compliance activities.

**EPA Assistant Administrator for Research
and Development**

National...................................(202) 260-7676
Provides technical information for the EPA
administrator on scientific and technical
issues.

**EPA General Information**

National...................................(617) 565-3420
Referral service to appropriate program office.

**EPA General Information - Environmental
Issues**

.................................................(303) 312-6312
General information - environmental issues.

**EPA Public Center**

National...................................(202) 260-7751
Provides guidance about general
environmental information for the public.

**Ctr. for Hazardous Materials (CHMR)**

.................................................(412) 826-5320
Regulatory, toxic waste minimization, pollu-
tion prevention, publications and referrals.

**Ctr. for International Env. Law**

National...................................(202) 332-4840

**Food and Drug Administration (FDA)
Hazardous Waste Ombudsman**

National ...................................(800) 262-7937
The hazardous waste management program
established under RCRA is a highly complex

regulatory program developed by EPA. It assists the public and regulated community in resolving problems concerning any program or requirement under the Hazardous Waste Program. The ombudsman handles complaints from citizens and the regulated community, obtains facts, sorts information, and substantiates policy.

**Mobile Sources**
National.............................................(313) 668-4200
Complaints regarding auto emission tampering, emission, auto warranty, recall notices, fuel issues, CSC recycling, auto air conditioning.

**National Institute for Occupational Safety and Health (NIOSH)**
National.............................................(800) 356-4674

**National Institute of Standards and Technology (NIST)**
National.............................................(301) 975-2000
Previously the National Bureau of Standards (NBS).

**National Technical Information Service (NTIS)**
National.............................................(703) 487-4600
.......................................................(800) 553-6847
Source of information services (technical documents and databases) and documents from federal agencies, industries, and universities.

**Nuclear Regulatory Commission**
.......................................................(800) 368-5642
NRC provides information about technical questions and documents regarding hazardous materials and wastes.

**Public Health Service**
National.............................................(301) 443-2403

**Water and Waste Water Information (600-series methods)**
National.............................................(202) 260-7120
Provides information on testing methods for water and waste water (600-series methods) contained in CFR-40 part 136.

**Wetlands Protection**
National, VI and Guam..............(800) 832-7828
Responsive to public interest, questions and requests for information about the values and functions of wetlands and options for their protection. Provides referrals to callers when necessary.

# ENVIRONMENTAL DATABASE AND COMPUTER CONTACTS

**CERCLIS - Helpline**
National.............................................(703) 908-2066
Answering machine for all off-hour callers. Technical Support and referrals to the users of CERCLIS database, Waste LAN and Clean LAN.

**EPA Office of Research and Development Electronic Bulletin Board (ORD BBS)**
National (1200 and 2400 baud)
.......................................................(513) 569-7610
(9600 baud).....................................(513) 569-7700

**STORET**
National.............................................(800) 424-9067
.......................................................(202) 260-8161
Technical support for STORET users.

**Solid Waste Information Clearinghouse Hotline (SWICH)**
National.............................................(800) 424-9346
Online service, modem. SWICH computer system. All aspects of solid waste management, including: source reduction, recycling, composting, planning education and training, public participation, legislation and regulation, waste combustion, collection, transfer, disposal, landfill gas and special waster.

**Facility Index System (FINDS)**
National.............................................(800) 908-2493
Technical user support; FINDS users only.

**Customer Technical Support National Computer Center (NCC)**
National.............................................(800) 334-2405
NC only ...........................................(919) 541-7862
Provides NCC customers with technical assistance, problem diagnosis, solution and tracking. Supports mainframe IBM.

# US EPA Contacts

**USEPA Analytical Operations Branch (OS-230)**
401 M Street, SW
Room M-2624
Washington, DC 20460
(202) 260-2090

**USEPA Contracts Mgmt. Div. (MD-33)**
79 Alexander Drive
Research Triangle Park, NC 27711
(919) 541-3699

**USEPA Environmental Monitoring Systems Laboratory (EMSL/LV)**
944 East Harmon Avenue
Las Vegas, NV 89108

*Mailing Address:*
P.O. Box 93478
Las Vegas, NV 89193-3478

*Data To:*
**EMSL/LV Executive Center**
944 East Harmon Ave.
Las Vegas, NV 89119
Attn: Data Audit Staff

**USEPA National Enforcement Investigations Center (NEIC)**
Denver Federal Center
Building 53
W1 Entrance, 2nd Floor
Denver, CO 80225
(303) 236-5073

**USEPA Environmental Monitoring Systems Laboratory (EMSL/Cincinnati)**
26 W. M. L. King Dr.
Cincinnati, OH 45268
(513) 569-7325
(513) 569-7931 for General Info Directory

**USEPA PE Studies Coordinator**
National Water Quality Assurance Programs Branch
USEPA, EERD
26 W. M.L. King Drive, Room 525
Cincinnati, OH 45268
(513) 569-7196
FAX (513) 569-7115

## USEPA REGION I

**USEPA Region I**
J.F. Kennedy Federal Bldg.
One Congress Street
Boston, MA 02203-0001
(617) 565-3420
FAX: (617) 565-3660

**USEPA Region I, QA Coordinator**
Mrs. Denise DePierro
Environmental Services Division
US EPA, Region 1
60 Westview Street
Lexington, MA 02173
(617) 860-4365
FAX: (617) 860-4397

## USEPA REGION II

**USEPA Region II**
290 Broadway
New York, NY 10007-1866
(212) 637-5000
FAX: (212) 637-3526

**USEPA Region II, QA Coordinator**
Mr. John Bourbon
Monitoring Management Branch, ESD
US EPA, Region 2
2890 Woodbridge Ave., M.S. 103
Edison, NJ 08837
(908) 321-6729
FAX: (908) 906-6824

DMR QA Coordinator (Linda Manuel) for NY, NJ, Puerto Rico and US Virgin Islands
..............................................................(908) 321-6766

## USEPA REGION III

**USEPA Region III**
841 Chestnut Buidling
Philadelphia, PA 19107
(215) 566-5000
FAX: (215) 566-5103

**USEPA Region III, QA Coordinator**
Mr. Charles Jones, Jr.
Env. Assessment & Protection Div.
US EPA, Region 3
841 Chestnut Buidling (3EP10)
Philadelphia, PA 19107
(215) 566-2710
FAX: (215) 566-2782

## USEPA REGION IV

**USEPA Region IV**
100 Alabama St. SW
Atlanta, GA 30303
(404) 562-9900
FAX: (404) 562-8174

**USEPA Region IV, QA Coordinator**
Mr. Ralph Gentry, Office of Qual Assurance
Science & Eccosystem Support Div.
US EPA, Region 4
980 College Station Road
Athens, GA 30605-2720
(706) 355-8553
FAX: (706) 355-8803

## USEPA REGION V

**USEPA Region V**
77 West Jackson Blvd.
Chicago, IL 60604-3507
(312) 353-2000
FAX: (312) 353-4135

**USEPA Region V, QA Coordinator**
Mr. Robert Gnaedinger
Standards & Applied Science Branch
US EPA, Water Division, Region 5
77 West Jackson Blvd.
Chicago, IL 60604
(312) 353-2975
FAX: (312) 353-4342

## USEPA REGION VI

**USEPA Region VI**
US EPA, Region 6
Fountain Place 12th Floor, Suite 1200
1445 Ross Avenue
Dallas, TX 75202-2733
(214) 665-6444
FAX: (214) 665-7113

**USEPA Region VI Laboratory**
10625 Fallstone Road
Houston, TX 77099-4303
(713) 983-2100
FAX: (713) 983-2248

**USEPA Region VI, QA Coordinator**
Mr. Don Johnson
Enforcement and Compliance Div.
US EPA, Region 6
1445 Ross Avenue
Dallas, TX 75202-2733
(214) 665-8343
FAX: (214) 665-2168
Recorded Info: (214) 665-8397

## USEPA REGION VII

**USEPA Region VII**
726 Minnesota Avenue
Kansas City, KS 66101
(913) 551-7000
FAX: (913) 551-7467

**USEPA Region VII, QA Coordinator**
Mr. Douglas Brune
Environmental Services Division
US EPA, Region 7
25 Funston Road
Kansas City, KS 66115
(913) 551-5180
FAX (913) 551-5218

## USEPA REGION VIII

**USEPA Region VIII**
999 18th Street, Suite 500
Denver, Co 80202-2466
(303) 312-6312
FAX (303) 312-6339

**USEPA Region VIII, QA Coordinator**
Mr. John Manhart (8ES-LB)
US EPA, Region 8, ESD, Lab. Br.
P.O. Box 25366
Denver Federal Center, Bldg. 56, W-1
Denver , CO 80225
(303) 236-7366
FAX: (303) 236-8235

## USEPA REGION IX

**USEPA Region IX**
75 Hawthorne Street
San Franscisco, CA  94105
(415) 744-1305
FAX: (415) 744-2499

**USEPA Region IX, QA Coordinator**
Ms. Carolyn Tambwekar
US EPA, Region 9 Lab, Bldg 201
1337 S. 46th St., P-3-1
Richmond, CA 94804
(510) 412-2383
FAX; (510) 412-2304

## USEPA REGION X

**USEPA Region X**
US EPA, Region 10
1200 Sixth Avenue
Seattle, WA 98101
(206) 553-1200
FAX: (206) 553-0149

## USEPA REGION X, continued

**USEPA Region X, QA Coordinator**
Mr. Arthur Dan Baker
Office of Environmental Assessment
US EPA, Region 10
1200 Sixth Avenue (OEA-095)
Seattle, WA 98101
(206) 553-1692
FAX: (206) 553-8210

**Manchester Environmental Lab**
7411 Beach Drive East
Port Orchard, WA 98366
(360) 871-0748
FAX: (360) 871-8747

## MISCELLANEOUS

Ms. Natalie Murff
US EPA, NERL, EERD, NWQAPB
26 West M. L. King Drive, Room 525
Cincinnati, OH 45268
(513) 569-7196
FAX: (513) 569-7115

## MISCELLANEOUS INFORMATION

**Federal Information Center**
Can provide you with a federal phone number
for any federal agency located in the US.
(800) 688-9889

**Cooler Returns**
T. Head and Company
950 Herndon Parkway
Suite 230
Herndon, VA 22070
(703) 473-3886

**ERT Edison**
USEPA Environmental Response Branch
GSA Raritan Depot
Woodbridge Avenue
Edison, NJ 08837
FTS 340-6649, 6689, 6743

**EPA Libraries**
Research Triangle, North Carolina
1-919-541-2777
Cincinnati, Ohio
1-513-569-7562

**OSW Methods Section**
1-202-260-4761

**ASTM**
100 Barr Harbor Drive
West Conshohocken, PA 19428-2959
1-610-832-9585

**Government Printing Office**
1-202-572-2303

**National Center for Environmental Publications and Information (NCEPI)**
1-513-489-8190

**USGS Books and Open File Publications**
Denver Federal Center
Box 25425
Denver, CO 80225
1-303-202-4700
FAX 1-303-202-4693

## STATE CONTACTS

### Alabama

Alabama Dept. of Environmental Management
Chief, Land Division
1751 W. L. Dickinson Drive
Montgomery, AL 36130
Phone: (205) 271-7730
Fax: (205) 271-7950

### Alaska

Alaska Dept. of Environmental Conservation
Solid and Hazardous Waste Mgt.
Pouch 0
Juneau, AK 99811
Phone: (907) 465-5150
Fax: (907) 456-5362

Alaska Dept. of Environmental Conservation
Chief, Spill Planning and Prevention
Pouch 0
Juneau, AK 99811
Phone: (907) 465-5250

Alaska Dept. of Environmental Conservation
Contaminated Sites Section
Pouch 0
Juneau, AK 99811
Phone: (907) 465-2630
UST Information
...............................................................(907) 465-5200

### Arizona

Arizona Dept. of Environmental Quality
Assistant Director, Office of Waste Programs
3033 N. Central Avenue
7th Floor
Phoenix, AZ 85002
Phone: (602) 207-2300
Fax: (602) 257-6874

Arizona Dept. of Environmental Quality
Hazardous Waste Section
3033 N. Central
Room 403C
Phoenix, AZ 85002
Phone: (602) 257-6995
Fax: (602) 257-6948

Environmental Lab Licensure
AZ Dept of Health Services
Phoenix, AZ 85012
DMR QA Coordinator (Steven Baker)
...............................................................(602) 255-3454
UST Information
...............................................................(602) 207-4288

### Arkansas

Arkansas Dept. of Poll. Control and Ecology
Chief, Hazardous Waste Division
P.O. Box 8913
Little Rock, AR 72219-8913
Phone: (501) 562-0831 or
         (501) 682-0580
Fax: (501) 682-0880 or
         (501) 682-0707
PE Studies Coordinator (Jeff Ruhr)
...............................................................(501) 682-0955
DMR QA Coordinator (Dick Cassat)
...............................................................(501) 562-7444
UST Information
...............................................................(501) 562-6533

State Quality Assurance Coordinator
Jeff Ruehr, QA Officer
AR Dept. of Poll. Control & Ecology
Technical Services Division
8001 National Drive
Little Rock, AR 72209
Phone: (501) 682-0955
Fax: (501) 682-0798

### California

California Dept. of Toxic Substances Control
Haz. Waste Management Program
P.O. Box 806
Sacramento, CA 95812-0806
Phone: (916) 323-6042
Fax: (916) 372-4495

CA State Water Resources Control Board
Chief, Div. of Clean Water Programs
2014 T Street
Suite 130
Sacramento, CA 95814
Phone: (916) 227-4400
Fax: (916) 227-4349
DMR QA Coordinator (Bill Ray)
...............................................................(916) 657-1123

State Quality Assurance Coordinator
Dr. Theodore Belsky
Environmental Lab Accreditation Program
California. Dept. of Health Services
2151 Berkeley Way
Annex #2
Berkeley CA 94704-1011
Phone: (510) 540-2800
Fax: (510) 849-5106
PE Studies Coordinator (Dr. T. Belsky)
...............................................................(510) 540-2800
UST Information
...............................................................(916) 227-4337

## Colorado

Colorado Dept. of Health
Hazardous Materials and Waste Mgt. Div.
4300 Cherry Creek Dr. South
Denver, CO 80222-1530
Phone: (303) 692-3300
Fax: (303) 759-4355
UST Information
...............................................(303) 692-3330
DMR QA Coordinator (Derald Lang)
...............................................(303) 692-3562

Public Utilities Commission
Hazardous Materials Transportation Permits
1580 Logan Street, Off. Level 1
Denver, CO 80203
Phone: (303) 894-2000
Fax: (303) 894-2065

State Quality Assurance Coordinator
Judy Donaldson
Supervisor of Certification Unit
Lab CLIA
CO Dept. of Public Health & Environ.
8100 Lowry Blvd.
Denver, CO 80220-6928
Phone: (303) 692-3290
Fax: (303) 344-9989

## Connecticut

Connecticut Waste Management Bureau
Bureau Chief
79 Elm Street
Hartford, CT 06106
Phone: (860) 424-3023
Fax: (860) 424-4059
UST Information
...............................................(203) 566-5599

Connecticut Resource Recovery Authority
President
179 Allyn St., Suite 603
Hartford, CT 06103
Phone: (860) 549-6390
Fax: (860) 522-2390

State Quality Assurance Coordinator
Nick Mascelletti, Super. Env. Lab Consultant
State of Connecticut Dept of Public Health
Division of Env. Health, Lab Certification
450 Capitol Ave
MS #51 LAB
PO Box 340308
Hartford, CT 03134
Phone: (860) 509-7367
Fax: (860) 509-7295
DMR QA Coordinator (Donald Gonyea)
...............................................(860) 424-3827

## Delaware

Delaware Dept. of Natural Resources and
    Environmental Control
Haz. Waste Management Branch Manager
P.O. Box 1401
89 Kings Highway
Dover, DE 19903
Phone: (302) 739-3689
Fax: (302) 739-5060
DMR QA Coordinator (Joe Mulrooney)
...............................................(302) 739-5731
UST Information
...............................................(302) 323-4588

## District of Columbia

Dept. of Consumer and Regulatory Affairs
Pesticides, Haz. Waste, and Underground
    Storgage Tank Division
2100 M. Luther King, Jr. Ave., SE, Suite #203
Washington, DC 20020
Phone: (202) 645-6080
DMR QA Coordinator (William Ruby)
...............................................(202) 645-6601

## Florida

Florida Dept. of Environmental Regulation
Administrator, Solid and Haz. Waste
Twin Towers Office Bldg
2600 Blair Stone Road
Tallahassee, FL 32399-2400
Phone: (904) 488-0300
Fax: (904) 921-8061
DMR QA Coordinator (Carlos Boueres)
...............................................(904) 488-2796
UST Information
...............................................(904) 488-0190

State Quality Assurance Coordinator
Dr. Carl Kircher
FL DHRS, Lab Services
Water Certification Program
1217 Pearl Street
Jacksonville, FL 32202
Phone: (904) 791-1574
Fax: (904) 791-1591
PE Studies Coordinator (Dr. C. Kircher)
...............................................(904) 791-1574

## Georgia

Hazardous Waste Management Branch
Floyd Towers East
205 Butler Street, SE
Atlanta, GA 30334
Phone: (404) 656-2833
Fax: (404) 651-9425
UST Information
...............................................(404) 362-2687

EPD, DNR
Water Protection Branch
Atlanta Tradeport
4244 International Pkwy Suite 110
Atlanta, GA 30354
DMR QA Coordinator (Jeff Larsen)
..............................................................(404) 362-2680

Drinking Water Program, EPD
GA Dept. of Nat. Rescources
Floyd Towers East, Rm 1362
205 Butler St. SE
Atlanta, GA 30334
PE Studies Coordinator (Loretta Lambert)
..............................................................(404) 651-5164

State Quality Assurance Coordinator
Kerry Wilkes
EPD Lab
Ga Dept. of Natural Resources
Technology Park
455 14th Street
Atlanta, GA 30318-7900
Phone: (404) 206-5246
Fax: (404) 206-5268

## Hawaii

Hawaii Dept. of Health
Mgr, Solid and Hazardous Waste Branch
919 Ala Moana Blvd.
Room 212
Honolulu, HI 96814
Phone: (808) 586-4226
Fax: (808) 586-7509
UST Information
..............................................................(808) 586-4225

Hawaii Dept. of Health
Hazard Evaluation and Emerg. Response
Manager
919 Ala Moana Blvd.
Room 206
Honolulu, HI 96814
Phone: (808) 586-4249
Fax: (808) 586-7537

State Quality Assurance Coordinator
Jodi Nakamura
HI Dept Health
State Labs, Env. Microbio.
2725 Waimano Home Rd
Pearl City HI 96782
Phone: (808) 453-6678
Fax: (808) 453-6685
PE Studies Coordinator (Jodi Nakamura)
..............................................................(808) 453-6678
DMR QA Coordinator (Randy Chow)
..............................................................(808) 453-6684

## Idaho

Division of Environmental Quality
RCRA Programs
1410 North Hilton Street
Boise, ID 83706
Phone: (208) 373-0502
Fax: (208) 373-0417
UST Information
..............................................................(208) 334-5860

## Illinois

Illinois Environmental Protection Agency, Dir.
2200 Churchill Road
Springfield, IL 62706
Phone: (217) 782-3397
Fax: (217) 782-9039
PE Studies Coordinator (Mary Beth Lawhorn)
..............................................................(217) 785-8508
DMR QA Coordinator (Erin Rednour)
..............................................................(217) 782-9720
UST Information
..............................................................(217) 782-6761

Illinois Environmental Protection Agency
Public Information Officer
Division of Land Pollution Control
2200 Churchill Road
Springfield, IL 62706
Phone: (217) 782-3397; Fax: (217) 785-7725

Haz. Waste Research and Information Center
Illinois Energy and Natural Resources
David Thomas - Director
1 E. Hazelwood Drive
Champaign, IL 61820
Phone: (217) 333-8941
Fax: (217) 333-8944

## Indiana

Indiana Dept. of Environmental Management
Branch Chief, Office of Hazardous Waste Mgt.
Indiana Government Center North
100 N. Senate Ave.
P.O. Box 6015
Indianapolis, IN 46206-6015
Phone: (317) 232-3292
Fax: (317) 232-3403

Laboratory Improvement Branch
Indiana State Dept. of Health
1330 W. Michigan St
Indianapolis, IN 46202-1964
PE Studies Coordinator (Phillip Zillinger)
..............................................................(317) 633-0201
DMR QA Coordinator (Steve Kim)
..............................................................(317) 232-8793
UST Information
..............................................................(317) 232-8603

## Iowa

State Quality Assurance Coordinator
Stacy Freburg
University Hygenic Laboratory
102 Oakdale Campus
Iowa City, IA 52242
Phone: (319) 355-4500
Fax: (319) 355-4555

Iowa Dept of Natural Resources
Henry A. Wallace Building
900 E. Grand
Des Moines, IA 50319
DMR QA Coordinator (Charles Furrey)
...............................................................(515) 281-4067

UST Information
...............................................................(515) 281-8957

## Kansas

Bureau of Air and Radiation
Dir., Kansas Dept. of Health and Environment
Forbes Field, Building 283
Topeka, KS 66620
Phone: (913) 296-1593
Fax: (913) 296-1545

Bureau of Waste Management
Dir., Kansas Dept. of Health and Environment
Forbes Field, Building 740
Topeka, KS 66620
Phone: (913) 296-1600
Fax: (913) 296-1592
PE Studies Coordinator (Jack McKenzie)
...............................................................(913) 296-1639
UST Information
...............................................................(913) 296-1684

State Quality Assurance Coordinator
Jack McKenzie
Kansas Health and Environment Lab
Laboratory Improvement Office
Forbes Field, Building 740
Topeka, KS 66620-0001
Phone: (913) 296-1639
Fax: (913) 296-1641

## Kentucky

Kentucky Dept. of Environmental Protection
Director, Div. of Waste Mgt.
Omega Bldg., Ft. Boone Plaza
Frankfort, KY 40601
Phone: (502) 564-6716 ext 214;
Fax: (502) 564-4049
DMR QA Coordinator (Donna Drury)
...............................................................(502) 564-3410
UST Information
...............................................................(502) 564-6716

Division of Enviromental Services
100 Sower Blvd. Rm 104
Frankfort, KY 40601
PE Studies Coordinator (Scott Bryan)
...............................................................(502) 564-6120

State Quality Assurance Coordinator
Gary Levy
Division of Water
Kentucky Dept. of Environmental Protection
14 Reilly Road
Frankfort, KY 40601
Phone: (502) 564-3410
Fax: (502) 564-4245

State Quality Assurance Coordinator
John Knafl
Reclamation & Enforcement - Soap Br.
KY Dept. for Surface Mining
#2 Hudson Hollow Complex
Frankfort, KY 40601
Phone: (502) 564-2356 Ext. 712
Fax: (502) 564-5848

## Louisiana

Louisiana Dept. of Environmental Quality
Office of Solid and Hazardous Waste
P.O. Box 82178
Baton Rouge, LA 70884-2178
Phone: (504) 765-0355
Fax: (504) 765-0617
UST Information
...............................................................(504) 765-0741

Louisiana Dept. of Environmental Quality
Administrator, Ground Water Protection Div.
P.O. Box 82215
Baton Rouge, LA 70884-2215
Phone: (504) 765-0585
Fax: (504) 765-0602

State Quality Assurance Coordinator
Jeanne Mixon
LA Dept. of Health and Hospitals
325 Loyola Ave
New Orleans, LA 70112
Phone: (504) 568-3455
Fax: (504) 568-5393
PE Studies Coordinator (Jeanne Mixon)
...............................................................(504) 568-3455

LA Dept of Environmental Quality
Water Pollution Control Division
3501 Shateau Blvd
West Wing Suit 1
Kennere, LA 70065
DMR QA Coordinator (Tom Bradley)
...............................................................(504) 471-2800

## Maine

Bureau of Hazardous Materials and Solid
  Waste Control
Director
Maine Dept of Environmental Protection
State House Station #17
Augusta, ME 04333
Phone: (207) 287-2651
Fax: (207) 287-7826
DMR QA Coordinator (David Dodge)
.................................................(207) 287-7659
UST Information
.................................................(207) 289-2651

State Quality Assurance Coordinator
Michael Soldano
Maine Dept of Human Services
State House Station #12
Augusta, ME 04333
Phone: (207) 287-2727
Fax: (207) 287-6832
PE Studies Coordinator (Michael Soldano)
.................................................(207) 287-2727

## Maryland

Haz. and Solid Waste Management Admin.
Director
Maryland Dept. of the Environment
2500 Broening Highway
Baltimore, MD 21224
Phone: (301) 631-3304; Fax: (301) 631-3321
UST Information
.................................................(410) 631-3442

Water Quality Lab
MD Dept. of Health and Mental Hygiene
201 West Preston St
Baltimore MD 21202
PE Studies Coordinator (Mary Stancavage)
.................................................(410) 767-6150
DMR QA Coordinator (Marlene Patillo)
.................................................(410) 631-3634

## Massachusetts

Massachusetts Dept. of Environmental Affairs
Director, Executive Office
100 Cambridge Street
20th Floor
Boston, MA 02202
Phone: (617) 727-9800
Fax: (617) 727-2754
PE Studies Coordinator (Anne Marie Allen)
.................................................(508) 682-5237 x 333
UST Information
.................................................(617) 935-2160

State Quality Assurance Coordinator
Anne Marie Allen
MA Dept of Environ. Protection
Lawrence Experiment Station
37 Shattuck Street
Lawrence, MA 01843
Phone: (508) 682-5237, ext. 333
Fax: (508)688-0352

MA Dept of Env. Protection
Div. of Water Pollution Control
Training Center, Route 20
Millbury, MA 01527
DMR QA Coordinator (Ping Lee)
.................................................(508) 756-7281

## Michigan

Waste Management Division
Michigan Dept. of Natural Resources
Chief, Hazardous Waste Permits Section
P.O. Box 30241
Lansing, MI 48909
Phone: (517) 373-2730
Fax: (517) 373-4797
UST Information
.................................................(517) 373-8168

State Quality Assurance Coordinator
Dr.. George Su
MI Dept. of Natural Resources
Environ. Response Division Lab
3500 N. Logan Street
Lansing, MI 48909
Phone: (517) 335-9800
Fax: (517) 335-9600
PE Studies Coordinator (George Su)
.................................................(517) 335-9800

## Minnesota

Minnesota Pollution Control Agency
Director, Hazardous Waste Div.
520 Lafayette Rd. North
St. Paul, MN 55155
Phone: (612) 297-8502
Fax: (612) 297-8676
DMR QA Coordinator (Kim Sandrock)
.................................................(612) 296-7387
UST Information
.................................................(612) 297-8594

Hazardous Waste Division
Minnesota Pollution Control Agency
Chief, Program Development
520 Lafayette Rd. North
St. Paul, MN 55155
Phone: (612) 297-8355
Fax: (612) 297-8676

Minnesota Tech. Assistance Prog. (MnTAP)
1313 5th Street, SE, Suite 207
Director
Minneapolis, MN 55414
Phone: (612) 627-4646 or(800) 247-0015
Fax: (612) 627-4769

State Quality Assurance Coordinator
Al Tupy
Lab Services Section
MN Dept. of Health
717 Deleware St, SE
Minneapolis MN 55440
Phone: (612) 623-5680
Fax: (612) 623-5514

## Mississippi

Mississippi Dept. of Environmental Quality
Chief, Hazardous Waste Division
P.O. Box 10385
Jackson, MS 39289-0385
Phone: (601) 961-5062
Fax: (601) 961-5741
DMR QA Coordinator (Phillip Bass)
...................................................(601) 961-5143

UST Information
...................................................(601) 939-8460

State Quality Assurance Coordinator
Earskin Phillips
Mississippi Dept. of Environmental Quality
P.O. Box 10385
Jackson, MS 39289-0385
Phone: (601) 939-8460
Fax: (601) 939-8479

Bureau of Public Health Labs
MS State Dept of Health
2423 North State St., PO Box 1700
Jackson MS 39215-1700
PE Studies Coordinator (Sammie Malone)
...................................................(601) 960-7592

## Missouri

Missouri Dept. of Natural Resources
Dir., Hazardous Waste Program
205 Jefferson St.
P.O. Box 176
Jefferson City, MO 65102
Phone: (573) 751-3176
Fax: (573) 751-7869
Solid Waste Program - (573) 751-5401
DMR QA Coordinator (Jack Pate)
...................................................(314) 751-1399

UST Information
...................................................(816) 795-8655

## Montana

Montana Dept. of Health and Env. Quality
Solid and Hazardous Waste Div.
2209 Phoenix Ave/P.O. Box 200901
Helena, MT 59620-0901
Phone: (406) 444-2821
Fax: (406) 444-1499
UST Information
...................................................(406) 444-5970

State Quality Assurance Coordinator
Dennis Braun
MT Dept. of Public Health and Human Serv.
Chemistry Laboratory
Cogswell Bldg
Helena MT 59620
Phone: (406) 444-2643
Fax: (406) 444-1802

MT. Dept of Environmental Quality
P.O. Box 200901
1520 E. 6th St.
Helena, MT 59620-0901
DMR QA Coordinator (Mike Pasichnyk)
...................................................(406) 444-2406

## Nebraska

Nebraska Dept. of Environmental Quality
Haz. Waste Section
CERCLA Unit Supervisor
P.O. Box 98922
Lincoln, NE 68509
Phone: (402) 471-2186
Fax: (402) 471-2909
UST Information
...................................................(402) 471-4230

Nebraska Dept. of Environmental Quality
Hazardous Waste Sec., RCRA Unit Supervisor
P.O. Box 98922
Lincoln, NE 68509
Phone: (402) 471-2186
Fax: (402) 471-2909
DMR QA Coordinator (Brian Gorman)
...................................................(402) 471-4253

## Nevada

Division of Environmental Protection
Nevada Dept. of Conserv. and Natural Res.
Chief, Waste Mgt. Bureau
Capitol Complex
123 W. Nye Lane
Carson City, NV 89710
Phone: (702) 687-5872
Fax: (702) 885-0868
DMR QA Coordinator (Wendall McCurry)
...................................................(702) 687-4670

UST Information
...............................................................(702) 687-5872

NV State Bureau of License & Certification
1475 Terminal Way, Suite D
Reno, NV 89502
PE Studies Coordinator (Jack Ruckman)
...............................................................(702) 688-2888

State Quality Assurance Coordinator
Robert Vicks
NV State Health Lab
1660 N. Virginia
Peno, NV 89503
Phone: (702) 688-1335
Fax: (702) 688-1460

## New Hampshire

New Hampshire Dept. of Environmental Serv.
Dir., Waste Management. Division
6 Haven Drive
Concord, NH 03301-6509
Phone: (603) 271-2906
Fax: (603) 271-2456
DMR QA Coordinator (Stephanie Larson)
...............................................................(603) 271-2457
UST Information
...............................................................(603) 271-3503

State Quality Assurance Coordinator
NH Dept. of Environ. Services
Lab Services Unit
P.O. Box 95, Hazen Drive
Concord, NH 03301
Phone: (603) 271-2991
PE Studies Coordinator (Charles Dyer)
...............................................................(603) 271-2991

## New Jersey

New Jersey Dept. of Environmental Protection
Assistant Commissioner
Site Remediation Program
401 E. State Street
CN 028-6th Floor East
Trenton, NJ 08625
Phone: (609) 292-1250
Fax: (609) 633-2360
UST Information
...............................................................(609) 984-3156

NJ Dept. of Env. Protection and Energy
Director
Div. of Responsible Party Site Remediation
401 E. State Street
CN 028-5th Floor East
Trenton, NJ 08625
Phone: (609) 633-1408
Fax: (609) 633-1454

State Quality Assurance Coordinator
Michale DiBalsi
NJ Dept. of Environmental Protection
Office of Quality Assurance
9 Ewing St., CN-424
Trenton NJ 08625
Phone: (609) 292-3950
Fax: (609) 777-1774
PE Studies Coordinator (Michale DiBalsi)
...............................................................(609) 292-3950

## New Mexico

New Mexico Environment Dept.
Groundwater Quality Bureau
P.O. Box 26110
Santa Fe, NM 87502
Phone: (505) 827-2922
Fax: (505) 827-2965
DMR QA Coordinator (Patrick Hanson)
...............................................................(505) 827-2799
UST Information
...............................................................(505) 827-0079

State Quality Assurance Coordinator
Pat Hanson
NM Environment Department
Surface Water Quality Bureau
P.O. Box 26110
Santa Fe, NM 87502
Phone: (505) 827-2799
Fax: (505) 827-0160

New Mexico Environment Dept.
Chief
Hazardous and Radioactive Mat'ls Bureau
*Physical Location:*
2044A Galisteo St
Santa Fe, NM 87505
Phone: (505) 827-1564

Drinking Water Bureau
2052 Gallisto
PO Box 26110
Santa Fe NM 87505
PE Studies Coordinator (Barbara Geisler)
...............................................................(505) 827-7536

## New York

NYS Dept. of Environmental Conserv.
Div. of Solid and Hazardous Materials
50 Wolf Rd.
Room 488
Albany, NY 12233-7250
Phone: (518) 457-6934
Fax: (518) 457-0629
UST Information
...............................................................(518) 457-7363

New York State Dept. of Health
Wadsworth Center for Laboratories & Reseach
Environmental Laboratory Approval Program
P.O. Box 509
Albany, NY 12201-0509

## North Carolina

N. Carolina Dept. of Env., Health, and Natural
    Resources
Director
Division of Solid Waste Management
P.O. Box 27687
Raleigh, NC 27611-7687
Phone: (919) 733-4996
Fax: (919) 733-4810
UST Information
.................................................(919) 733-1320

State Quality Assurance Coordinator
William Edwards
DEM/Lab Section
NCDEHNR
4405 Reedy Creek Road
Raleigh, NC 27601
Phone: (919) 733-3908
Fax: (919) 733-6241
DMR QA Coordinator (William Edwards)
.................................................(919) 733-3908

Div. of Health Services
306 N. Wilmington St.
Raleigh NC 27611-8047
PE Studies Coordinator (Don Beesley)
.................................................(919) 733-7308

## North Dakota

N. Dakota Dept. of Health and Waste Mgt.
P.O. Box 5520
Bismarck, ND 58506-5520
Phone: (701) 328-5166
Fax: (701) 328-5200
DMR QA Coordinator (Jean Pfiefer)
.................................................(701) 221-5228
UST Information
.................................................(701) 221-5166

State Quality Assurance Coordinator
Errol Erickson
ND Dept. of Health
Chemistry Division
2635 East Main St.
PO Box 937
Bismarck ND 58501
Phone: (701) 328-6172
Fax: (701) 328-6145
PE Studies Coordinator (Errol Erickson)
.................................................(701) 328-6172

## Ohio

Ohio Environmental Protection Agency
Chief, Div. of Solid and Hazardous Waste Mgt.
1800 Watermark Drive
P.O. Box 1049
Columbus, OH 43266-0149
Phone: (614) 644-2917
Fax: (614) 644-2329
UST Information
.................................................(614) 752-7941

Ohio Dept. of Health Labs
1571 Perry St. PO Box 2568
Columbus, OH 43266-0068
PE Studies Coordinator (James Dolfi)
.................................................(614) 466-2278

Ohio EPA
1571 Perry St
Columbus, OH 43201
DMR QA Coordinator (Amy Minichillo)
.................................................(614) 644-4240

Ohio Environmental Protection Agency
Div. of Solid & Infectous Waste Mgt.
2305 Westbrooke Drive
Building C
Columbus, OH 43228-9644
Phone: (614) 644-2621
Fax: (614) 728-5315

## Oklahoma

Dept. of Environmental Quality
Waste Mgt. Div. (Hazardous Waste)
1000 Northeast Tenth Street
Oklahoma City, OK 73117-1299
Phone: (405) 271-5338
Fax: (405) 271-8425
DMR QA Coordinator (Aaron Milligan)
.................................................(405) 271-5240
UST Information
.................................................(405) 521-3107

State Quality Assurance Coordinator
Anthony Bright
OK Dept. of Environ. Quality
State Environ. Lab
1000 NE Tenth St.
Oklahoma City, OK 73117-1212
Phone: (405) 271-5240  ext. 121
Fax: (405) 271-1836
PE Studies Coordinator (Anthony Bright)
.................................................(405) 271-5240 x121

## Oregon

Oregon Dept. of Environmental Quality
Waste Mgt/Environmental Cleanup Div.
811 SW 6th Ave.

Portland, OR 97204
Phone: (503) 229-5913
Fax: (503) 229-6977
UST Information
..............................................................(503) 229-6764

Oregon Dept. of Environmental Quality
Administrator, Environmental Cleanup Div.
811 SW 6th Ave.
Portland, OR 97204
Phone: (503) 229-5254
Fax: (503) 229-6124
DMR QA Coordinator (Renato Dulay)
..............................................................(503) 229-5374

## Pennsylvania

Pennsylvania Dept. of Environmental
Resources
Dir., Bureau of Land Recycling & Waste Mgt.
P.O. Box 2063
Harrisburg, PA 17105-2063
Phone: (717) 783-2388
Fax: (717) 787-1904
UST Information
..............................................................(717) 772-5835

Pennsylvania Dept. of Environmental
Protection
Municipal & Residual Waste
P.O. Box 8472
Harrisburg, PA 17105-8472
Phone: (717) 787-7381
Fax: (717) 787-1904
DMR QA Coordinator (LaRue Wyrick)
..............................................................(717) 787-8184

State Quality Assurance Coordinator
Ted Lyter
PA DER, Bureau of Labs
Labs Certification Program
3rd & Reilly Sts., PO Box 1467
Harrisburg, PA 17105-1467
Phone: (717) 783-7150
Fax: (717) 783-1502
PE Studies Coordinator (Ted Lyter)
..............................................................(717) 783-7150

## Rhode Island

Rhode Island Dept. of Environmental Waste
Dept. of Environment
Waste Management Division.
291 Promenade Street
Providence, RI 02908
Phone: (401) 277-2797
DMR QA Coordinator (Ben Lovesky)
..............................................................(401) 277-3961
UST Information
..............................................................(401) 277-2234

State Quality Assurance Coordinator
Deborah Dehmel
Div. of Facilities Regulation
Cannon Building, 33 Capitol Hill
Providence, RI 02908
Phone: (401) 277-4526
Fax: (401) 277-3999
PE Studies Coordinator (Deborah Dehmel)
..............................................................(401) 277-4526

## South Carolina

S. Carolina Dept. of Health and Env. Control
Chief., Bureau of Solid and Haz. Waste Mgt.

*Physical Location:*
8901 Farrow Road
Columbia, SC 29203
Phone: (803) 896-4000
Fax: (803) 896-4001
UST Information
..............................................................(803) 734-5331

*Mailing Address:*
2600 Bull St.
Columbia, SC 29400

State Quality Assurance Coordinator
R. Wayne Davis
Lab Certification
SC Dept. of Health & Env. Control
P.O. Box 72
State Park, SC 29147
Phone: (803) 935-6856
Fax: (803) 935-6859
PE Studies Coordinator (R. Wayne Davis)
..............................................................(803) 935-6856

## South Dakota

S. Dakota Dept. of Env. and Natural Res.
Office of Waste Mgt.
Joe Foss Building
523 E. Capital Avenue
Pierre, SD 57501-3181
Phone: (605) 773-3153
Fax: (605) 773-6035
DMR QA Coordinator (Andrea Griese)
..............................................................(605) 773-6045
UST Information
..............................................................(605) 773-3296

State Quality Assurance Coordinator
Mike Smith
SD Dept. of Health, Lab Services
500 E. Capitol Ave.
Pierre, SD 57501-5093
Phone: (605) 773-3368
Fax: (605) 773-6129

S. Dakota Highway Patrol, Commerce and
Regulation
320 N. Nicollet
Pierre, SD 57501
Phone: (605) 773-3105; Fax: (605) 773-6046

## Tennessee

Tennessee Dept. of Environment and
Conservation
Director, Div. of Solid Waste Mgt.
401 Church St.
L&C Tower, 5th Floor
Nashville, TN 37243-1535
Phone: (615) 532-0780
UST Information
.................................................(615) 532-0945

TN Dept. of Environment and Conservation
Director, Div. of Superfund
401 Church St.
L&C Tower, 4th Floor
Nashville, TN 37243-1535
Phone: (615) 532-0900
DMR QA Coordinator (Pamela Townsend)
.................................................(615) 532-0677

Tennessee Dept. of Env. and Conservation
Director, Div. of Superfund
Doctors Bldg, 706 Church Street
Nashville, TN 37243-1538
Phone: (615) 741-6287

State Quality Assurance Coordinator
Charles Mickle
Lab Services
TN Department of Health
630 Ben Allen Rd
Nashville, TN 37247-0801
Phone: (615) 262-6354
Fax: (615) 262-6393
PE Studies Coordinator (Charles Mickle)
.................................................(615) 262-6354

## Texas

Texas Water Commission
Dir., Hazardous and Solid Waste Division
P.O. Box 13087, Capitol Station
Austin, TX 78711-3087
Phone: (512) 239-1000
Fax: (512) 463-8408

Texas Dept. of Health
Occupational Safety and Health Division
1100 West 49th Street
Austin, TX 78756-3199
Phone: (512) 834-6600
PE Studies Coordinator (Sharon Duboise)
.................................................(512) 458-7587

Texas NRCC
P.O. Box 13087
Capitol Station
Austin, TX 78711
DMR QA Coordinator (Sheila Meyers)
.................................................(512) 239-0425
UST Information
.................................................(512) 908-2247

State Quality Assurance Coordinator
Burt Harrison
HQ AFCEE/ERC
3207 North Road E.
Brooks AFB, TX 78235-5357
Phone: (210) 536-5226
Fax: (210) 536-5989

## Utah

Utah Dept. of Environmental Quality
Dir., Div. of Solid and Hazardous Waste
288 North 1460 West St.
Salt Lake City, UT 84114-4880
Phone: (801) 538-6170
Fax: (801) 538-6715
DMR QA Coordinator (Mike Herkimer)
.................................................(801) 538-6146
UST Information
.................................................(801) 536-4100

State Quality Assurance Coordinator
Craig Odekirk
Bureau of Lab Improvement
Utah State Health Laboratory
46 North Medical Drive
Salt Lake City, UT 84113-1105
Phone: (801) 584-8468
PE Studies Coordinator (Craig Odekirk)
.................................................(801) 584-8468

## Vermont

Vermont Agency of Natural Resources
Director
Hazardous Mat'ls Mgt. Div.
103 South Main St.
Waterbury, VT 05676
Phone: (802) 241-3888
Fax: (802) 241-3296
UST Information
.................................................(802) 241-3888

Vermont Dept. of Health
Occupations and Radiological Health Div.
Director
108 Cherry Street
Burlington, VT 05402
Phone: (802) 865-7730
Fax: (802) 865-7745

State Quality Assurance Coordinator
Andrew Fish
VT Dept. of Environ. Conservation
WW Management Division
103 South Main St.
Waterbury, VT 05676
Phone: (802) 241-3822
Fax: (802) 241-2596

## Virginia

Virginia Dept. of Waste Management
Div. of Regulation
629 East Main Street
Richmond, VA 23219
Phone: (804) 225-2667; Fax: (804) 762-4500
UST Information
...............................................................(804) 527-5188

State Quality Assurance Coordinator
Alicia Ordona
Div. of Consolidated Labs
Commonwealth of Virginia
1 North 14th Street
Richmond, VA 23219
Phone: (804) 786-3411
Fax: (804) 371-7973
DMR QA Coordinator (Lisa McMillan)
...............................................................(804) 762-4032

## Washington

Washington Dept. of Ecology
Mgr., Solid and Hazardous Waste Program
P.O. Box 47600
Olympia, WA 98504
Phone: (360) 407-6000
Fax: (360) 407-6102
UST Information
...............................................................(206) 459-6000

State Quality Assurance Coordinator
Stewart Lombard
WA State Dept of Ecology
P.O. Box 488
2350 Colchester
Manchester, WA 98353
Phone: (360) 895-4649
Fax: (360) 895-4648
DMR QA Coordinator (Stewart Lombard)
...............................................................(360) 895-4649

## West Virginia

Bureau of Environment
Div. of EP, Office of Waste Management
1356 Hansford St.
Charleston, WV 25301
Phone: (304) 558-5929
Fax: (304) 558-0256

UST Information
...............................................................(304) 558-6371
Air Pollution Control Commission
1558 Washington Street, East
Charleston, WV 25311
Phone: (304) 558-4022
Public Information Line: (304) 558-3381

West Virginia Division of Highways
Secretary/Commissioner of Highways
Building 5, Room A-109
Charleston, WV 25305
Phone: (304) 558-3505

WV EPD
Water Resources Office
1201 Greenbriar St.
Charleston, WV 25305
DMR QA Coordinator (Don Caldwell)
...............................................................(304) 558-0321

## Wisconsin

Wisconsin Dept. of Natural Resources
Director
Bureau of Solid and Haz. Waste Mgt.
P.O. Box 7921
Madison, WI 53707
Phone: (608) 266-1327
Fax: (608) 267-2768

State Quality Assurance Coordinator
Mike Kvitrud
WI Dept. of Nat. Resources
101 South Webster
Madison, WI 53707
Phone: (608) 261-8459
Fax: (608) 267-5231
PE Studies Coordinator (Carol Lochner)
...............................................................(608) 267-7633
UST Information
...............................................................(608) 267-7560

## Wyoming

Wyoming Dept. of Environmental Quality
Solid and Hazardous Waste Div.
122 West 25th St.
Herschler Building
Cheyenne, WY 82002
Phone: (307) 777-7752
Fax: (307) 777-5973
UST Information
...............................................................(307) 777-7096

WY DEQ
Water Quality Division
122 W. 25th St.
Cheyenne, WY 82002

DMR QA Coordinator (John Wagner)
.................................................................(307) 777-7781

## American Somoa

Environmental Quality Commission
American Somoa Government
Pago Pago, AS 96799
DMR QA Coordinator (Pati Faiai)
.................................................................(684) 633-2304

## Guam

Guam EPA
D-107 Harmon Plaza
130 Rojas St
Harmon, Guam 96911
DMR QA Coordinator (Kenneth Morphew)
.................................................................(671) 646-8863

## Nothern Islands

NI Div. of Environmental Quality
Mariana Island
P.O. Box 1304
Saipan, CM 96984
DMR QA Coordinator (Russell Mecham)
.................................................................(670) 234-6984

## Puerto Rico

State Quality Assurance Coordinator
Luis Quintero Ocasio, QAO
Puerto Rico Dept. of Health
Institute for Health Labs
Call Box 70184
San Juan, PR 00936-0184
Phone: (809) 274-7711
Fax: (809) 759-6210

## Internet Addresses of Interest

EPA Federal Register "listserv"
    listserver@unixmail.rtpnc.epa.gov
to sign on, in the body of the message put
"subscribe [ ] *your name*"
where [ ] can be:

EPA-AIR

EPA-GENERAL

EPA-MEETINGS

EPA-PEST

EPA-PRESS

EPA-SAB

EPA-SPECIES

EPA-TOX

EPA-TRI

EPA-WASTE

EPA-WATER

EPAFR-CONTENTS

EPA Homepage
    http://www.epa.gov.

Government Printing Office Pathway Services
    http://www.access.gpo.gov./su_docs/aces/
aces140.html. (access to the archives of
Federal Register copies from 1995 on) Water
Environment Federation
    http://www.wef.org

ASTM
    http://www.astm.org

CFR
    http://www.law.house.gov/cfr.htm (out of
date versions and very slow to update)

    http://www.access.gpo.gov/nara/cfr/cfr-
retrive.html#page1 (40 CFR in its most up-to-
date form, but not a lot else. Appendices are
pulled up by requesting the last Section prior
to the Appendix. For example to get 40 CFR
136, App A-C, request 40 CFR 136.5)

*For a more complete listing see:*

Schupp, J.F., 1995.
*Environmental Guide to the Internet*,
Government Institutes, Inc.
4 Research Place, Suite 200
Rockville, MD 20850

# Alphabetical Elements List

| Element | Symbol | Mass |
|---|---|---|
| Actinium | Ac | 227 |
| Aluminum | Al | 26.98 |
| Americium | Am | 243 |
| Antimony | Sb | 121.8 |
| Argon | Ar | 39.95 |
| Arsenic | As | 74.92 |
| Astatine | At | 210 |
| Barium | Ba | 137.3 |
| Berkelium | Bk | 247 |
| Beryllium | Be | 9.012 |
| Bismuth | Bi | 209.0 |
| Boron | B | 10.81 |
| Bromine | Br | 79.90 |
| Cadmium | Cd | 112.4 |
| Calcium | Ca | 40.08 |
| Californium | Cf | 249 |
| Carbon | C | 12.01 |
| Cerium | Ce | 140.1 |
| Cesium | Cs | 132.9 |
| Chlorine | Cl | 35.45 |
| Chromium | Cr | 52.00 |
| Cobalt | Co | 58.93 |
| Copper | Cu | 63.55 |
| Curium | Cm | 247 |
| Dysprosium | Dy | 162.5 |
| Einsteinium | Es | 254 |
| Erbium | Er | 167.3 |

Continued on next page.

## Alphabetical Elements List, *continued*

| Element | Symbol | Mass |
|---|---|---|
| Europium | Eu | 152.0 |
| Fermium | Fm | 253 |
| Fluorine | F | 19.00 |
| Francium | Fr | 223 |
| Gadolinium | Gd | 157.3 |
| Gallium | Ga | 69.72 |
| Germanium | Ge | 72.59 |
| Gold | Au | 197.0 |
| Hafnium | Hf | 178.5 |
| Helium | He | 4.003 |
| Holmium | Ho | 164.9 |
| Hydrogen | H | 1.008 |
| Indium | In | 114.8 |
| Iodine | I | 126.9 |
| Iridium | Ir | 192.2 |
| Iron | Fe | 55.85 |
| Krypton | Kr | 83.80 |
| Lanthanum | La | 138.9 |
| Lawrencium | Lr | 257 |
| Lead | Pb | 207.2 |
| Lithium | Li | 6.941 |
| Lutetium | Lu | 175.0 |
| Magnesium | Mg | 24.31 |
| Manganese | Mn | 54.94 |
| Mendelevium | Md | 256 |
| Mercury | Hg | 200.6 |
| Molybdenum | Mo | 95.94 |
| Neodymium | Nd | 144.2 |
| Neon | Ne | 20.18 |
| Neptunium | Np | 237 |
| Nickel | Ni | 58.69 |
| Niobium | Nb | 92.91 |
| Nitrogen | N | 14.01 |
| Nobelium | No | 253 |

Continued on next page.

**Alphabetical Elements List,** *continued*

| Element | Symbol | Mass |
|---|---|---|
| Osmium | Os | 190.2 |
| Oxygen | O | 16.00 |
| Palladium | Pd | 106.4 |
| Phosphorus | P | 30.97 |
| Platinum | Pt | 195.1 |
| Plutonium | Pu | 242 |
| Polonium | Po | 210 |
| Potassium | K | 39.10 |
| Praseodymium | Pr | 140.9 |
| Promethium | Pm | 147 |
| Protactinium | Pa | 231 |
| Radium | Ra | 226 |
| Radon | Rn | 222 |
| Rhenium | Re | 186.2 |
| Rhodium | Rh | 102.9 |
| Rubidium | Rb | 85.47 |
| Ruthenium | Ru | 101.1 |
| Samarium | Sm | 150.4 |
| Scandium | Sc | 44.96 |
| Selenium | Se | 78.96 |
| Silicon | Si | 28.09 |
| Silver | Ag | 107.9 |
| Sodium | Na | 22.99 |
| Strontium | Sr | 87.62 |
| Sulfur | S | 32.07 |
| Tantalum | Ta | 180.9 |
| Technetium | Tc | 99 |
| Tellurium | Te | 127.6 |
| Terbium | Tb | 158.9 |
| Thallium | Tl | 204.4 |
| Thorium | Th | 232.0 |
| Thulium | Tm | 168.9 |
| Tin | Sn | 118.7 |

Continued on next page.

## Alphabetical Elements List, *continued*

| Element | Symbol | Mass |
|---|---|---|
| Titanium | Ti | 47.88 |
| Tungsten | W | 183.9 |
| Unnilennium[1] | Une | 266 |
| Unnihexium | Unh | 263 |
| Unnioctium | Uno | 265 |
| Unnipentium | Unp | 260 |
| Unniquadium | Unq | 257 |
| Unniseptium | Uns | 262 |
| Uranium | U | 238.0 |
| Vanadium | V | 50.94 |
| Xenon | Xe | 131.3 |
| Ytterbium | Yb | 173.0 |
| Yttrium | Y | 88.91 |
| Zinc | Zn | 65.39 |
| Zirconium | Zr | 91.22 |

[1] IUPAC proposed (1997) the following names for the un-named transuranics: 104 Rutherfordium (Rf), 105 Dubnium (Db), 106 Seaborgium (Sg), 107 Bohrium (Bh), 108 Hassium (Hs), and 109 Meitnerium (Mt). The ACS has been using the same names except 105 Hahnium and 107 Nielsbohrium.

# Periodic Chart

| | | | | | | | | | | | | | | | | | |
|---|---|---|---|---|---|---|---|---|---|---|---|---|---|---|---|---|---|
| 1<br>H<br>1.008 | | | | | | | | | | | | | | | | | 2<br>He<br>4.003 |
| 3<br>Li<br>6.941 | 4<br>Be<br>9.01 | | | | | | | | | | | 5<br>B<br>10.81 | 6<br>C<br>12.01 | 7<br>N<br>14.01 | 8<br>O<br>16.00 | 9<br>F<br>19.00 | 10<br>Ne<br>20.18 |
| 11<br>Na<br>22.99 | 12<br>Mg<br>24.31 | | | | | | | | | | | 13<br>Al<br>26.98 | 14<br>Si<br>28.09 | 15<br>P<br>30.97 | 16<br>S<br>32.06 | 17<br>Cl<br>35.45 | 18<br>Ar<br>39.95 |
| 19<br>K<br>39.10 | 20<br>Ca<br>40.08 | 21<br>Sc<br>44.96 | 22<br>Ti<br>47.88 | 23<br>V<br>50.94 | 24<br>Cr<br>52.00 | 25<br>Mn<br>54.94 | 26<br>Fe<br>55.85 | 27<br>Co<br>58.93 | 28<br>Ni<br>58.69 | 29<br>Cu<br>63.55 | 30<br>Zn<br>65.38 | 31<br>Ga<br>69.72 | 32<br>Ge<br>72.59 | 33<br>As<br>74.92 | 34<br>Se<br>78.96 | 35<br>Br<br>79.90 | 36<br>Kr<br>83.80 |
| 37<br>Rb<br>85.47 | 38<br>Sr<br>87.62 | 39<br>Y<br>88.91 | 40<br>Zr<br>91.22 | 41<br>Nb<br>92.91 | 42<br>Mo<br>95.94 | 43<br>Tc<br>98 | 44<br>Ru<br>101.1 | 45<br>Rh<br>102.9 | 46<br>Pd<br>106.4 | 47<br>Ag<br>107.9 | 48<br>Cd<br>112.4 | 49<br>In<br>114.8 | 50<br>Sn<br>118.7 | 51<br>Sb<br>121.7 | 52<br>Te<br>127.6 | 53<br>I<br>126.9 | 54<br>Xe<br>131.3 |
| 55<br>Cs<br>132.9 | 56<br>Ba<br>137.3 | 57<br>La<br>138.9 | 72<br>Hf<br>178.5 | 73<br>Ta<br>180.9 | 74<br>W<br>183.8 | 75<br>Re<br>186.2 | 76<br>Os<br>190.2 | 77<br>Ir<br>192.2 | 78<br>Pt<br>195.1 | 79<br>Au<br>197.0 | 80<br>Hg<br>200.6 | 81<br>Tl<br>204.4 | 82<br>Pb<br>207.2 | 83<br>Bi<br>209.0 | 84<br>Po<br>209 | 85<br>At<br>210 | 86<br>Rn<br>222 |
| 87<br>Fr<br>223 | 88<br>Ra<br>226.0 | 89<br>Ac<br>227.0 | 104<br>Unq<br>257 | 105<br>Unp<br>260 | 106<br>Unh<br>263 | 107<br>Uns<br>262 | 108<br>Uno<br>265 | 109<br>Une<br>266 | | | | | | | | | |

| | | | | | | | | | | | | | |
|---|---|---|---|---|---|---|---|---|---|---|---|---|---|
| 58<br>Ce<br>140.1 | 59<br>Pr<br>140.9 | 60<br>Nd<br>144.2 | 61<br>Pm<br>145 | 62<br>Sm<br>150.4 | 63<br>Eu<br>152.0 | 64<br>Gd<br>157.3 | 65<br>Tb<br>158.9 | 66<br>Dy<br>162.5 | 67<br>Ho<br>164.9 | 68<br>Er<br>167.3 | 69<br>Tm<br>168.9 | 70<br>Yb<br>173.0 | 71<br>Lu<br>175.0 |
| 90<br>Th<br>232.0 | 91<br>Pa<br>231.0 | 92<br>U<br>238.0 | 93<br>Np<br>237.0 | 94<br>Pu<br>244 | 95<br>Am<br>243 | 96<br>Cm<br>247 | 97<br>Bk<br>247 | 98<br>Cf<br>251 | 99<br>Es<br>252 | 100<br>Fm<br>257 | 101<br>Md<br>258 | 102<br>No<br>259 | 103<br>Lr<br>260 |

# APPENDIX ▌I

From the U.S. Government Printing Office via GPO Access [40CFR136.3]

## TITLE 40--PROTECTION OF ENVIRONMENT

### CHAPTER I--ENVIRONMENTAL PROTECTION AGENCY (CONTINUED)

### PART 136--GUIDELINES ESTABLISHING TEST PROCEDURES FOR THE ANALYSIS OF POLLUTANTS--Sec. 136.3  Identification of test procedures.

(a) Parameters or pollutants, for which methods are approved, are listed together with test procedure descriptions and references in Tables IA, IB, IC, ID, and IE. The full text of the referenced test procedures are incorporated by reference into Tables IA, IB, IC, ID, and IE. The references and the sources from which they are available are given in paragraph (b) of this section. These test procedures are incorporated as they exist on the day of approval and a notice of any change in these test procedures will be published in the Federal Register. The discharge parameter values for which reports are required must be determined by one of the standard analytical test procedures incorporated by reference and described in Tables IA, IB, IC, ID, and IE, or by any alternate test procedure which has been approved by the Administrator under the provisions of paragraph (d) of this section and Secs. 136.4 and136.5 of this part 136. Under certain circumstances (Sec. 136.3 (b) or (c) or 40 CFR 401.13) other test procedures may be used that may be more advantageous when such other test procedures have been previously approved by the Regional Administrator of the Region in which the discharge will occur, and providing the Director of the State in which such discharge will occur does not object to the use of such alternate test procedure.

## Table IA.  List of Approved Biological Methods

| Parameter and units | Method [1] | EPA | Standard Methods, 18th Ed. | ASTM | USGS |
|---|---|---|---|---|---|
| **Bacteria:** | | | | | |
| 1. Coliform (fecal), number per 100 mL. | Most Probable Number (MPN), 5 tube, 3 dilution, or | p. 132 [3] | 9221C E [4] | | |
| | Membrane filter (MF), single step.[2] | p. 124 [3] | 9222D [4] | B-0050-85 [5] | |
| 2. Coliform (fecal) in presence of chlorine, number per 100 mL. | MPN, 5 tube, 3 dilution, or | p. 132 [3] | 9221C E [4] | | |
| | MF, single step [6]. | p. 124 [3] | 9222D [4] | | |
| 3. Coliform (total), number per 100 mL. | MPN, 5 tube, 3 dilution, or | p. 114 [3] | 9221B [4] | | |
| | MF [2] single step or two step. | p. 108 [3] | 9222B [4] | B-0025-85 [5] | |

Continued on next page.

## Table IA. List of Approved Biological Methods, *continued*

| Parameter and units | Method [1] | EPA | Standard Methods, 18th Ed. | ASTM | USGS |
|---|---|---|---|---|---|
| **Bacteria, *continued*** | | | | | |
| 4. Coliform (total), in presence of chlorine, number per 100 mL. | MPN, 5 tube, 3 dilution, or | p. 114 [3] | 9221B [4] | | |
| | MF [2] with enrichment | p. 111 [3] | 9222(B+B.5c)[4] | | |
| 5. Fecal streptococci, number per 100 mL. | MPN, 5 tube, 3 dilution | p. 139 [3] | 9230B [4] | | |
| | MF [2], or | p. 136 [3] | 9230C [4] | B-0055-85 [5] | |
| | Plate count | p. 143 [3] | | | |
| **Aquatic Toxicity** | | | | | |
| 6. Toxicity, acute, fresh water organisms, $LC_{50}$, percent effluent | Daphnia, Ceriodaphnia, | Sec. 9 [7] | | | |
| | Fathead Minnow, Rainbow Trout, Brook Trout, or Bannerfish Shiner mortality | | | | |
| 7. Toxicity, acute, estuarine and marine organisms, $LC_{50}$, percent effluent | Mysid, Sheepshead Minnow, or Menidia spp. mortality | Sec. 9 [7] | | | |
| 8. Toxicity, chronic, fresh water organisms, NOEC or $IC_{25}$, percent effluent | Fathead minnow larval survival and growth | 1000.0 [8] | | | |
| | Fathead minnow embryo-larval survival and teratogenicity | 1001.0 [8] | | | |
| | Ceriodaphnia survival and reproduction | 1002.0 [8] | | | |
| | Selenastrum growth | 1003.0 [8] | | | |
| 9. Toxicity, chronic, estuarine and marine organisms, NOEC or $IC_{25}$, percent effluent | Sheepshead minnow larval survival and growth | 1004.0 [9] | | | |
| | Sheepshead minnow embryo-larval survival and teratogenicity | 1005.0 [9] | | | |
| | Menidia beryllina larval survival and growth | 1006.0 [9] | | | |
| | Mysidopsis bahia survival, growth, and fecundity | 1007.0 [9] | | | |
| | Arbacia punctulata fertilization | 1008.0 [9] | | | |
| | Champia parvula reproduction | 1009.0 [9] | | | |

**Notes to Table IA:**

[1] The method must be specified when results are reported.

[2] A 0.45 um membrane filter (MF) or other pore size certified by the manufacturer to fully retain organisms to be cultivated and to be free of extractables which could interfere with their growth.

[3] USEPA. 1978. Microbiological Methods for Monitoring the Environment, Water, and Wastes. Environmental Monitoring and Support Laboratory, U.S. Environmental Protection Agency, Cincinnati, Ohio. EPA/600/8-78/017.

[4] APHA. 1992. Standard Methods for the Examination of Water and Wastewater. American Public Health Association. 18th Edition. Amer. Publ. Hlth. Assoc., Washington, DC.

**Notes to Table IA:** *continued*

[5] USGS. 1989. U.S. Geological Survey Techniques of Water-Resources Investigations, Book 5, Laboratory Analysis, Chapter A4, Methods for Collection and Analysis of Aquatic Biological and Microbiological Samples, U.S. Geological Survey, U.S. Department of Interior, Reston, Virginia.

[6] Because the MF technique usually yields low and variable recovery from chlorinated wastewaters, the Most Probable Number method will be required to resolve any controversies.

[7] USEPA. 1993. Methods for Measuring the Acute Toxicity of Effluents to Freshwater and Marine Organisms. Fourth Edition. Environmental Monitoring Systems Laboratory, U.S. Environmental Protection Agency, Cincinnati, Ohio. August 1993, EPA/600/4-90/027F.

[8] USEPA. 1994. Short-term Methods for Estimating the Chronic Toxicity of Effluents and Receiving Waters to Freshwater Organisms. Third Edition. Environmental Monitoring Systems Laboratory, U.S. Environmental Protection Agency USEPA. 1994, Cincinnati, Ohio (July 1994, EPA/600/4-91/002).

[9] Short-term Methods for Estimating the Chronic Toxicity of Effluents and Receiving Waters to Marine and Estuarine Organisms. Second Edition. Environmental Monitoring Systems Laboratory, U.S. Environmental Protection Agency, Cincinnati, Ohio (July 1994, EPA/600/4-91/003). These methods do not apply to marine waters of the Pacific Ocean.

## Table IB. List of Approved Inorganic Test Procedures

| Parameter, units and method | Reference (method number or page) | | | | |
| --- | --- | --- | --- | --- | --- |
| | EPA [1] | Standard Methods 18th ed. | ASTM | USGS [2] | Other |
| **1. Acidity, as CaCO₃/, mg/L:** | | | | | |
| Electrometric endpoint or | 305.1 | 2310 B(4a) | D1067-92 | | |
| phenolphthalein endpoint | | | | | |
| **2. Alkalinity, as CaCO₃/, mg/L:** | | | | | |
| Electrometric or | 310.1 | 2320 B | D1067-92 | I-1030-85 | 973.43.[3] |
| Colorimetric titration to pH 4.5, manual or automated | 310.2 | | | I-2030-85 | |
| **3. Aluminum--Total,[4] mg/L; Digestion [4] followed by:** | | | | | |
| AA direct aspiration [36] | 202.1 | 3111 D | | I-3051-85 | |
| AA furnace | 202.2 | 3113 B | | | |
| Inductively Coupled Plasma [5] Atomic Emission Spectrometry (ICP/AES) [36] | 200.7 | 3120 B | | | |
| Direct Current Plasma (DCP) [36] | | | D4190-82(88) | | Note 34 |
| Colorimetric (Eriochrome cyanine R) | | 3500-Al D | | | |
| **4. Ammonia (as N), mg/L:** | | | | | |
| Manual, distillation (at pH 9.5),[6] followed by: | 350.2 | 4500-NH3/ B | | | 973.49.[3] |
| Nesslerization | 350.2 | 4500-NH3/ C | D1426-93(A) | I-3520-85 | 973.49.[3] |
| Titration | 350.2 | 4500-NH3/ E | | | |
| Electrode | 350.3 | 4500-NH3/ F or G | D1426-93(B) | | |
| Automated phenate, or | 350.1 | 4500-NH3/ H | | I-4523-85 | |
| Automated electrode | | | | | Note 7 |
| **5. Antimony-Total,[4] mg/L; Digestion [4] followed by:** | | | | | |
| AA direct aspiration [36] | 204.1 | 3111 B | | | |
| AA furnace | 204.2 | 3113 B | | | |
| ICP/AES [36,5] | 200.7 | 3120 B | | | |
| **6. Arsenic-Total,[4] mg/L: Digestion [4] followed by.** | 206.5 | | | | |
| AA gaseous hydride | 206.3 | 3114 B 4.d | D2972-93(B) | I-3062-85 | |
| AA furnace | 206.2 | 3113 B | D2972-93(C) | | |
| ICP/AES,[36] or | 200.7 | 3120 B | | | |

Continued on next page.

## Table IB. List of Approved Inorganic Test Procedures, *continued*

| Parameter, units and method | EPA [1] | Standard Methods 18th ed. | ASTM | USGS [2] | Other |
|---|---|---|---|---|---|
| **6. Arsenic-Total,[4] mg/L: Digestion [4] followed by:** *Continued* | | | | | |
| Colorimetric (SDDC) | 206.4 | 3500-As C | D2972-93(A) | I-3060-85 | |
| **7. Barium--Total,[4] mg/L; Digestion [4] followed by:** | | | | | |
| AA direct aspiration [36] | 208.1 | 3111 D | | I-3084-85 | |
| AA furnace | 208.2 | 3113 B | D4382-91 | | |
| ICP/AES [36] | 200.7 | 3120 B | | | |
| DCP [36] | | | | | Note 34 |
| **8. Beryllium--Total,[4] mg/L; Digestion [4] followed by:** | | | | | |
| AA direct aspiration | 210.1 | 3111 D | D3645-93(88)(A) | I-3095-85 | |
| AA furnace | 210.2 | 3113 B | D3645-93(88)(B) | | |
| ICP/AES | 200.7 | 3120 B | | | |
| DCP, or | | | D4190-82(88) | | Note 34 |
| Colorimetric (aluminon) | | 3500-Be D | | | |
| **9. Biochemical oxygen demand (BOD5), mg/L:** | | | | | |
| Dissolved Oxygen Depletion | 405.1 | 5210 B | | I-1578-78 8 | 973.44,[3] p. 17[9] |
| **10. Boron [37]--Total, mg/L:** | | | | | |
| Colorimetric (curcumin) | 212.3 | 4500-B B | | I-3112-85 | |
| ICP/AES, or | 200.7 | 3120 B | | | |
| DCP | | | D4190-82(88) | | Note 34 |
| **11. Bromide, mg/L:** | | | | | |
| Titrimetric | 320.1 | | D1246-82(88)(C) | I-1125-85 | p. S44[10] |
| **12. Cadmium--Total,[4] mg/L; Digestion [4] followed by:** | | | | | |
| AA direct aspiration [36] | 213.1 | 3111 B or C | D3557-90(A or B) | I-3135-85 or I-3136-85 | 974.27,[3] p. 37[9] |
| AA furnace | 213.2 | 3113 B | D3557-90(D) | | |
| ICP/AES [36] | 200.7 | 3120 B | | I-1472-85 | |
| DCP [36] | | | D4190-82(88) | | Note 34 |
| Voltametry,[11] or | | | D3557-90(C) | | |
| Colorimetric (Dithizone) | | 3500-Cd D | | | |
| **13. Calcium--Total,[4] mg/L; Digestion [4] followed by:** | | | | | |
| AA direct aspiration | 215.1 | 3111 B | D511-93(B) | I-3152-85 | |
| ICP/AES | 200.7 | 3120 B | | | |
| DCP, or | | | | | Note 34 |
| Titrimetric (EDTA) | 215.2 | 3500-Ca D | D511-93(A) | | |
| **14. Carbonaceous biochemical oxygen demand (CBOD5), mg/L [12]:** | | | | | |
| Dissolved Oxygen Depletion with nitrification inhibitor | | 5210 B | | | |

Continued on next page.

## Table IB.  List of Approved Inorganic Test Procedures, *continued*

| Parameter, units and method | EPA [1] | Standard Methods 18th ed. | ASTM | USGS [2] | Other |
|---|---|---|---|---|---|
| **15. Chemical oxygen demand (COD), mg/L;** | | | | | |
| Titrimetric, or | 410.1 410.2 410.3 | 5220 C | D1252-88(A) | I-3560-85 I-3562-85 | 973.46,[3] p. 17[9] |
| Spectrophotometric, manual or automated | 410.4 | 5220 D | D1252-88(B) | I-3561-85 | Notes 13 or 14 |
| **16. Chloride, mg/L:** | | | | | |
| Titrimetric (silver nitrate) or | | 4500-Cl- B | D512-89(B) | I-1183-85 | |
| (Mercuric nitrate) | 325.3 | 4500-Cl- C | D512-89(A) | I-1184-85 | 973.51[3] |
| Colorimetric, manual or | | | | I-1187-85 | |
| Automated (Ferricyanide) | 325.1 325.2 | 4500-Cl;- E | | I-2187-85 | |
| **17. Chlorine--Total residual, mg/L; Titrimetric:** | | | | | |
| Amperometric direct | 330.1 | 4500-Cl D | D1253-86(92) | | |
| Iodometric direct | 330.3 | 4500-Cl B | | | |
| Back titration ether end-point [15] or | 330.2 | 4500-Cl C | | | |
| DPD-FAS | 330.4 | 4500-Cl F | | | |
| Spectrophotometric, DPD | 330.5 | 4500-Cl G | | | |
| Or Electrode | | | | | Note 16 |
| **18. Chromium VI dissolved, mg/L; 0.45 micron filtration** | | | | | |
| AA chelation-extraction or | 218.4 | 3111 C | | I-1232-85 | |
| Colorimetric (Diphenylcarbazide) | | 3500-Cr D | D1687-92(A) | I-1230-85 | |
| **19. Chromium--Total,[4] mg/L; Digestion [4] followed by:** | | | | | |
| AA direct aspiration [36] | 218.1 | 3111 B | D1687-92(B) | I-3236-85 | 974.27[3] |
| AA chelation-extraction | 218.3 | 3111 C | | | |
| AA furnace | 218.2 | 3113 B | D1687-92(C) | | |
| ICP/AES [36] | 200.7 | 3120 B | | | |
| DCP,[36] or | | | D4190-82(88) | | Note 34 |
| Colorimetric (Diphenylcarbazide) | | 3500-Cr D | | | |
| **20. Cobalt--Total,[4] mg/L; Digestion [4] followed by:** | | | | | |
| AA direct aspiration | 219.1 | 3111 B or C | D3558-90(A or B) | I-3239-85 | p. 37[9] |
| AA furnace | 219.2 | 3113B | D3558-90(C) | | |
| ICP/AES [5] | 200.7 | 3120 B | | | |
| DCP | | | D4190-82(88) | | Note 34 |
| **21. Color platinum cobalt units or dominant wavelength, hue, luminance purity:** | | | | | |
| Colorimetric (ADMI), or | 110.1 | 2120 E | | | Note 18 |
| (Platinum cobalt), or | 110.2 | 2120 B | | I-1250-85 | |
| Spectrophotometric | 110.3 | 2120 C | | | |
| **22. Copper--Total,[4] mg/L; Digestion ;[4] followed by:** | | | | | |
| AA direct aspiration [36] | 220.1 | 3111 B or C | D1688-90(A or B) | I-3270-85 or I3271-85 | 974.27 [3], p. 37[9] |

Continued on next page.

## Table IB. List of Approved Inorganic Test Procedures, *continued*

| Parameter, units and method | EPA [1] | Standard Methods 18th ed. | ASTM | USGS [2] | Other |
|---|---|---|---|---|---|
| **22. Copper--Total,[4] mg/L; Digestion ;[4] followed by:** | | | | | |
| AA furnace | 220.2 | 3113 B | D1688-90(C) | | |
| ICP/AES [36] | 200.7 | 3120 B | | | |
| DCP [36] or | | | D4190-82(88) | | Note 34 |
| Colorimetric (Neocuproine) or | | 3500-Cu D | | | |
| (Bicinchoninate) | | 3500-Cu E | | | Note 19 |
| **23. Cyanide--Total, mg/L: Manual distillation with MgCl$_2$ followed by:** | | 4500-CN C | D2036-91(A) | | |
| Titrimetric, or | 335.2 | 4500-CN D | | | p. 22[9] |
| Spectrophotometric, manual [31] | | 4500-CN E | D2036-91(A) | I-3300-85 | |
| Automated [20, 31] | 335.3 | | | | |
| **24. Cyanide amenable to chlorination,mg/L Manual distillation with MgCl$_2$ followed by:** | 335.1 | 4500-CN G | D2036-91(B) | | |
| Titrimetric or | 335.2 | 4500-CN D | | | |
| Spectrophotometric | | 4500-CN E | | | |
| **25. Fluoride--Total, mg/L: Manual distillation [6] followed by:** | | 4500-F B | | | |
| Electrode, manual or | 340.2 | 4500-F C | D1179-93(B) | | |
| Automated | | | | I-4327-85 | |
| Colorimetric (SPADNS) | 340.1 | 4500-F D | D1179-93(A) | | |
| or Automated complexone | 340.3 | 4500-F E | | | |
| **26. Gold--Total,[4] mg/L; Digestion [4] followed by:** | | | | | |
| AA direct aspiration | 231.1 | 3111 B | | | |
| AA furnace, or | 231.2 | | | | |
| DCP | | | | | Note 34 |
| **27. Hardness--Total, as CaCO3/, mg/L** | | | | | |
| Automated colorimetric, | 130.1 | | | | |
| Titrimetric (EDTA), or Ca plus Mg as their carbonates, by ICP or AA direct aspiration (See Parameters 13 and 33) | 130.2 | 2340 B or C | D1126-86(92) | I-1338-85 | 973.52B[3] |
| **28. Hydrogen ion (pH), pH units** | | | | | |
| Electrometric measurement, | 150.1 | 4500-H+ B | D1293-84(90)(A or B) | I-1586-85 | 973.41[3] |
| Automated electrode | | | | | Note 21 |
| **29. Iridium--Total,[4] mg/L; Digestion [4] followed by:** | | | | | |
| AA direct aspiration or | 235.1 | 3111 B | | | |
| AA furnace | 235.2 | | | | |
| **30. Iron--Total,[4] mg/L; Digestion [4] followed by:** | | | | | |
| AA direct aspiration [36] | 236.1 | 3111 B or C | D1068-90(A or B) | I-3381-85 | 974.27[3] |
| AA furnace | 236.2 | 3113 B | D1068-90(C) | | |
| ICP/AES [36] | 200.7 | 3120 B | | | |
| DCP [36] or | | | D4190-82(88) | | Note 34 |
| Colorimetric (Phenanthroline) | | 3500-Fe D | D1068-90(D) | | Note 22 |

Continued on next page.

## Table IB. List of Approved Inorganic Test Procedures, *continued*

| Parameter, units and method | EPA [1] | Standard Methods 18th ed. | ASTM | USGS [2] | Other |
|---|---|---|---|---|---|
| **31. Kjeldahl Nitrogen--Total, (as N), mg/L:** | | | | | |
| Digestion and distillation followed by: | 351.3 | 4500-NH3 B or C. | D3590-89(A) | | |
| Titration | 351.3 | 4500-NH3 E | D3590-89(A) | | 973.48 [3] |
| Nesslerization | 351.3 | 4500-NH3 C | D3590-89(A) | | |
| Electrode | 351.3 | 4500-NH3 F or G | | | |
| Automated phenate colorimetric | 351.1 | | | I-4551-88 | |
| Semi-automated block digester colorimetric | 351.2 | | D3590-89(B) | | |
| Manual or block digester potentiometric | 351.4 | | D3590-89(A) | | |
| Block Digester, followed by: Auto distillation and Titration, or | | | | | Note 39 |
| Nesslerization | | | | | Note 40 |
| Flow injection gas diffusion | | | | | Note 41 |
| **32. Lead--Total,[4] mg/L; Digestion [4] followed by:** | | | | | |
| AA direct aspiration [36] | 239.1 | 3111 B or C | D3559-90(A or B) | I-3399-85. | 974.27[3] |
| AA furnace | 239.2 | 3113 B | D3559-90(D) | | |
| ICP/AES [36] | 200.7 | 3120 B | | | |
| DCP [36] | | | D4190-82(88) | | Note 34 |
| Voltametry [11] or | | | D3559-90(C) | | |
| Colorimetric (Dithizone) | | 3500-Pb D | | | |
| **33. Magnesium--Total,[4] mg/L; Digestion [4] followed by:** | | | | | |
| AA direct aspiration | 242.1 | 3111 B | D511-93(B) | I-3447-85 | 974.27[3] |
| ICP/AES [5] | 200.7 | 3120 B | | | |
| DCP, or | | | | | Note 34 |
| Gravimetric | | 3500-Mg D | | | |
| **34. Manganese--Total,[4] mg/L; Digestion [4] followed by:** | | | | | |
| AA direct aspiration [36] | 243.1 | 3111 B. | D858-90(A or B) | I-3454-85 | 974.27[3] |
| AA furnace | 243.2 | 3113 B | D858-90(C) | | |
| ICP/AES [36, 5] | 200.7 | 3120 B | | | |
| DCP [36] or | | | D4190-82(88) | | Note 34 |
| Colorimetric (Persulfate), or | | 3500-Mn D | | | 920.203[3] |
| (Periodate) | | | | | Note 23 |
| **35. Mercury--Total,[4] mg/L:** | | | | | |
| Cold vapor, manual or | 245.1 | 3112 B | D3223-91 | I-3462-85 | 977.22[3] |
| Automated | 245.2 | | | | |
| **36. Molybdenum--Total,[4] mg/L; Digestion [4] followed by:** | | | | | |
| AA direct aspiration | 246.1 | 3111 D | | I-3490-85 | |
| AA furnace | 246.2 | 3113 B | | | |

Continued on next page.

## Table IB.  List of Approved Inorganic Test Procedures, *continued*

| Parameter, units and method | EPA [1] | Standard Methods 18th ed. | ASTM | USGS [2] | Other |
|---|---|---|---|---|---|
| **36. Molybdenum--Total,[4] mg/L; Digestion [4] followed by:** *continued* | | | | | |
| ICP/AES[5] | 200.7 | 3120 B | | | |
| DCP | | | | | Note 34 |
| **37. Nickel--Total,[4] mg/L;  Digestion [4] followed by:** | | | | | |
| AA direct aspiration [36] | 249.1 | 3111 B or C | D1886-90(A or B) | I-3499-85 | |
| AA furnace | 249.2 | 3113 B | D1886-90(C) | | |
| ICP/AES [36, 5] | 200.7 | 3120 B | | | |
| DCP [36], or | | | D4190-82(88) | | Note 34 |
| Colorimetric (heptoxime) | | 3500-Ni D | | | |
| **38. Nitrate (as N), mg/L:** | | | | | |
| Colorimetric (Brucine sulfate), or | 352.1 | | | | 973.50,[3] 419 D,[17] |
| Nitrate-nitrite N minus Nitrite N (See parameters 39 and 40) | | | | | p. 28[9] |
| **39. Nitrate-nitrite (as N), mg/L:** | | | | | |
| Cadmium reduction, Manual | 353.3 | 4500-NO3- E | D3867-90(B) | | |
| Automated, or | 353.2 | 4500-NO3- F | D3867-90(A) | I-4545-85 | |
| Automated hydrazine | 353.1 | 4500-NO3-H | | | |
| **40. Nitrite (as N), mg/L; Spectrophotometric:** | | | | | |
| Manual or | 354.1 | 4500-NO2- B | | | Note 25 |
| Automated (Diazotization) | | | I-4540-85 | | |
| **41. Oil and grease--Total recoverable, mg/L:** | | | | | |
| Gravimetric (extraction) | 413.1 | 5520 B [38] | | | |
| **42. Organic carbon--Total (TOC), mg/L:** | | | | | |
| Combustion or oxidation | 415.1 | 5310 B, C, or D | D2579-93 (A or B) | | 973.47,[3] p. 14[24] |
| **43. Organic nitrogen (as N), mg/L:** | | | | | |
| Total Kjeldahl N (Parameter 31) minus ammonia N (Parameter 4) | | | | | |
| **44. Orthophosphate (as P), mg/L; Ascorbic acid method:** | | | | | |
| Automated, or | 365.1 | 4500-P F | | I-4601-85 | 973.56[3] |
| Manual single reagent | 365.2 | 4500-P E | D515-88(A) | | 973.55[3] |
| Manual two reagent | 365.3 | | | | |
| **45. Osmium--Total,[4] mg/L; Digestion [4] followed by:** | | | | | |
| AA direct aspiration | 252.1 | 3111 D | | | |
| AA furnace | 252.2 | | | | |
| **46. Oxygen, dissolved, mg/L:** | | | | | |
| Winkler (Azide modification), or | 360.2 | 4500-O C | D888-92(A) | I-1575-78 [8] | 973.45B[3] |
| Electrode | 360.1 | 4500-O G | D888-92(B) | I-1576-78 [8] | |
| **47. Palladium--Total,[4] mg/L; Digestion [4] followed by:** | | | | | |
| AA direct aspiration, or | 253.1 | 3111 B | | | p. S27[10] |
| AA furnace | 253.2 | | | | p. S28[10] |
| DCP | | | | | Note 34 |

Continued on next page.

## Table IB. List of Approved Inorganic Test Procedures, *continued*

| Parameter, units and method | EPA [1] | Standard Methods 18th ed. | ASTM | USGS [2] | Other |
|---|---|---|---|---|---|
| **48. Phenols, mg/L:** | | | | | |
| Manual distillation [26] followed by: | 420.1 | | | | Note 27 |
| Colorimetric (4AAP) manual, or | 420.1 | | | | Note 27 |
| Automated [19] | 420.2 | | | | |
| **49. Phosphorus (elemental), mg/L:** | | | | | |
| Gas-liquid chromatography | | | | | Note 28 |
| **50. Phosphorus--Total, mg/L:** | | | | | |
| Persulfate digestion followed by: | 365.2 | 4500-P B,5 | | | 973.55[3] |
| Manual or | 365.2, 365.3 | 4500-P E | D515-88(A) | | |
| Automated ascorbic acid reduction | 365.1 | 4500-P F | | I-4600-85 | 973.56[3] |
| Semi-automated block digestor | 365.4 | | D515-88(B) | | |
| **51. Platinum--Total,[4] mg/L; Digestion [4] followed by:** | | | | | |
| AA direct aspiration | 255.1 | 3111 B | | | |
| AA furnace | 255.2 | | | | |
| DCP | | | | | Note 34 |
| **52. Potassium--Total,[4] mg/L; Digestion [4] followed by:** | | | | | |
| AA direct aspiration | 258.1 | 3111 B | | I-3630-85 | 973.53[3] |
| ICP/AES [5] | 200.7 | 3120 B | | | |
| Flame photometric, or | | 3500-K D | | | |
| Colorimetric | | | | | 317 B[17] |
| **53. Residue--Total, mg/L:** | | | | | |
| Gravimetric, 103-105 deg | 160.3 | 2540 B | | I-3750-85 | |
| **54. Residue--filterable, mg/L:** | | | | | |
| Gravimetric, 180 deg | 160.1 | 2540 C | | I-1750-85 | |
| **55. Residue--nonfilterable (TSS), mg/L:** | | | | | |
| Gravimetric, 103-105 deg. post washing of residue | 160.2 | 2540 D | | I-3765-85 | |
| **56. Residue--settleable, mg/L:** | | | | | |
| Volumetric, (Imhoff cone), or gravimetric | 160.5 | 2540 F | | | |
| **57. Residue--Volatile, mg/L:** | | | | | |
| Gravimetric, 550 deg | 160.4 | | | I-3753-85 | |
| **58. Rhodium--Total,[4] mg/L; Digestion [4] followed by:** | | | | | |
| AA direct aspiration, or | 265.1 | 3111 B | | | |
| AA furnace | 265.2 | | | | |
| **59. Ruthenium--Total,[4] mg/L; Digestion [4] followed by:** | | | | | |
| AA direct aspiration, or | 267.1 | 3111 B | | | |
| AA furnace | 267.2 | | | | |
| **60. Selenium--Total,[4] mg/L; Digestion [4] followed by:** | | | | | |
| AA furnace | 270.2 | 3113 B | D3859-93(B) | | |
| ICP/AES[36, 5] | 200.7 | 3120 B | | | |
| AA gaseous hydride | | 3114 B | D3859-93(A) | I-3667-85 | |
| **61. Silica [37]--Dissolved, mg/L; 0.45 micron filtration followed by:** | | | | | |
| Colorimetric, Manual or | 370.1 | 4500-Si D | D859-88 | I-1700-85 | |
| Automated (Molybdosilicate), or | | | | I-2700-85 | |

Continued on next page.

## Table IB.  List of Approved Inorganic Test Procedures, *continued*

| Parameter, units and method | EPA [1] | Standard Methods 18th ed. | ASTM | USGS [2] | Other |
|---|---|---|---|---|---|
| 61. Silica[37]--Dissolved, mg/L; 0.45 micron filtration followed by: *Continued* | | | | | |
| ICP[5] | 200.7 | 3120 B | | | |
| 62. Silver--Total,[4] mg/L; Digestion[4, 29] followed by: | | | | | |
| AA direct aspiration | 272.1 | 3111 B or C | | I-3720-85 | 974.27,[3] p. 37[9] |
| AA furnace | 272.2 | 3113 B | | | |
| ICP/AES [5] | 200.7 | 3120 B | | | |
| DCP | | | | | Note 34 |
| 63. Sodium--Total,[4] mg/L; Digestion [4] followed by: | | | | | |
| AA direct aspiration | 273.1 | 3111 B | | I-3735-85 | 973.54[3] |
| ICP/AES[5] | 200.7 | 3120 B | | | |
| DCP, or | | | | | Note 34 |
| Flame photometric | | 3500 Na D | | | |
| 64. Specific conductance, micromhos/cm at 25°C: | | | | | |
| Wheatstone bridge | 120.1 | 2510 B | D1125-91(A) | I-1780-85 | 973.40[3] |
| 65. Sulfate (as $SO_4$), mg/L: | | | | | |
| Automated colorimetric (barium chloranilate) | 375.1 | | | | |
| Gravimetric | 375.3 | 4500-$SO_4$-2 C or D | | | 925.54[3] |
| Turbidimetric | 375.4 | | D516-90 | | 426C[30] |
| 66. Sulfide (as S), mg/L: | | | | | |
| Titrimetric (iodine), or | 376.1 | 4500-S-2 E | | I-3840-85 | |
| Colorimetric (methylene blue) | 376.2 | 4500-S-2 D | | | |
| 67. Sulfite (as $SO_3$), mg/L: | | | | | |
| Titrimetric (iodine-iodate) | 377.1 | 4500-SO3-2 B | | | |
| 68. Surfactants, mg/L: | | | | | |
| Colorimetric (methylene blue) | 425.1 | 5540 C | D2330-88 | | |
| 69. Temperature,  deg.C: | | | | | |
| Thermometric | 170.1 | 2550 B | | | Note 32 |
| 70. Thallium--Total,[4] mg/L; Digestion[4] followed by: | | | | | |
| AA direct aspiration | 279.1 | 3111 B | | | |
| AA furnace | 279.2 | | | | |
| ICP/AES[5] | 200.7 | 3120 B | | | |
| 71. Tin--Total,[4] mg/L; Digestion[4] followed by: | | | | | |
| AA direct aspiration | 282.1 | 3111 B. | | I-3850-78 [8] | |
| AA furnace, or | 282.2 | 3113 B | | | |
| ICP/AES [5] | 200.7 | | | | |
| 72. Titanium--Total,[4] mg/L; Digestion[4] followed by: | | | | | |
| AA direct aspiration | 283.1 | 3111 D | | | |
| AA furnace | 283.2 | | | | |
| DCP | | | | | Note 34 |
| 73. Turbidity, NTU: | | | | | |
| Nephelometric | 180.1 | 2130 B | D1889-88(A) | I-3860-85 | |
| 74. Vanadium--Total,[4] mg/L; Digestion[4] followed by: | | | | | |
| AA direct aspiration | 286.1 | 3111 D | | | |

Continued on next page.

## Table IB.  List of Approved Inorganic Test Procedures, *continued*

| Parameter, units and method | Reference (method number or page) | | | | |
|---|---|---|---|---|---|
| | EPA [1] | Standard Methods 18th ed. | ASTM | USGS [2] | Other |
| **74. Vanadium--Total,[4] mg/L; Digestion [4] followed by:** *Continued* | | | | | |
| AA furnace | 286.2 | | D3373-93 | | |
| ICP/AES[5] | 200.7 | 3120 B | | | |
| DCP or | | | D4190-82(88) | | Note 34 |
| Colorimetric (Gallic acid) | | 3500-V D | | | |
| **75. Zinc--Total,[4] mg/L; Digestion [4] followed by:** | | | | I-3900-85 | |
| AA direct aspiration [36] | 289.1 | 3111 B or C | D1691-90 (A or B) | | 974.27,[3] p. 37[9] |
| AA furnace. | 289.2 | | | | |
| ICP/AES [36, 5] | 200.7 | 3120 B | | | |
| DCP[36] or | | | D4190-82(88) | | Note 34 |
| Colorimetric (Dithizone) | | 3500-Zn E | | | |
| (Zincon) | | 3500-Zn F | | | Note 33 |

### Table IB Notes:

[1] "Methods for Chemical Analysis of Water and Wastes," Environmental Protection Agency, Environmental Monitoring Systems Laboratory-Cincinnati (EMSLCI), EPA-600/4-79-020, Revised March 1983 and 1979 where applicable.

[2] Fishman, M.J., et al, "Methods for Analysis of Inorganic Substances in Water and Fluvial Sediments," U.S. Department of the Interior, Techniques of Water--Resource Investigations of the U.S. Geological Survey, Denver, CO, Revised 1989, unless otherwise stated.

[3] "Official Methods of Analysis of the Association of Official Analytical Chemists," methods manual, 15th ed. (1990).

[4] For the determination of total metals the sample is not filtered before processing. A digestion procedure is required to solubilize suspended material and to destroy possible organic-metal complexes. Two digestion procedures are given in "Methods for Chemical Analysis of Water and Wastes, 1979 and 1983". One (section 4.1.3), is a vigorous digestion using nitric acid. A less vigorous digestion using nitric and hydrochloric acids (section 4.1.4) is preferred; however, the analyst should be cautioned that this mild digestion may not suffice for all samples types. Particularly, if a colorimetric procedure is to be employed, it is necessary to ensure that all organo-metallic bonds be broken so that the metal is in a reactive state. In those situations, the vigorous digestion is to be preferred making certain that at no time does the sample go to dryness. Samples containing large amounts of organic materials may also benefit by this vigorous digestion, however, vigorous digestion with concentrated nitric acid will convert antimony and tin to insoluble oxides and render them unavailable for analysis. Use of ICP/AES as well as determinations for certain elements such as antimony, arsenic, the noble metals, mercury, selenium, silver, tin, and titanium require a modified sample digestion procedure and in all cases the method write-up should be consulted for specific instructions and/or cautions.

*Note to Table IB Note 4:* If the digestion procedure for direct aspiration AA included in one of the other approved references is different than the above, the EPA procedure must be used. Dissolved metals are defined as those constituents which will pass through a 0.45 micron membrane filter. Following filtration of the sample, the referenced procedure for total metals must be followed. Sample digestion of the filtrate for dissolved metals (or digestion of the original sample solution for total metals) may be omitted for AA (direct aspiration or graphite furnace) and ICP analyses, provided the sample solution to be analyzed meets the following criteria: **a.** has a low COD (20) **b.** is visibly transparent with a turbidity measurement of 1 NTU or less, **c.** is colorless with no perceptible odor, and. is of one liquid phase and free of particulate or suspended matter following acidification.

[5] The full text of Method 200.7, "Inductively Coupled Plasma Atomic Emission Spectrometric Method for Trace Element Analysis of Water and Wastes," is given at Appendix C of this Part 136.

[6] Manual distillation is not required if comparability data on representative effluent samples are on company file to show that this preliminary distillation step is not necessary: however, manual distillation will be required to resolve any controversies.

[7] Ammonia, Automated Electrode Method, Industrial Method Number 379-75 WE, dated February 19, 1976, (Bran & Luebbe (Technicon) Auto Analyzer II, Bran & Luebbe Analyzing Technologies, Inc., Elmsford, NY 10523. *Notes continued on next page.*

**Table IB Notes:** *continued*

8 The approved method is that cited in "Methods for Determination of Inorganic Substances in Water and Fluvial Sediments", USGS TWRI, Book 5, Chapter A1 (1979).

9 American National Standard on Photographic Processing Effluents, Apr. 2, 1975. Available from ANSI, 1430 Broadway, New York, NY 10018.

10 "Selected Analytical Methods Approved and Cited by the United States Environmental Protection Agency", Supplement to the Fifteenth Edition of Standard Methods for the Examination of Water and Wastewater (1981).

11 The use of normal and differential pulse voltage ramps to increase sensitivity and resolution is acceptable.

12 Carbonaceous biochemical oxygen demand ($CBOD_5$) must not be confused with the traditional $BOD_5$ test which measures "total BOD". The addition of the nitrification inhibitor is not a procedural option, but must be included to report the $CBOD_5$ parameter. A discharger whose permit requires reporting the traditional $BOD_5$ may not use a nitrification inhibitor in the procedure for reporting the results. Only when a discharger's permit specifically states $CBOD_5$ is required can the permittee report data using the nitrification inhibitor.

13 OIC Chemical Oxygen Demand Method, Oceanography International Corporation, 1978, 512 West Loop, P.O. Box 2980, College Station, TX 77840.

14 Chemical Oxygen Demand, Method 8000, Hach Handbook of Water Analysis, 1979, Hach Chemical Company, P.O. Box 389, Loveland, CO 80537.

15 The back titration method will be used to resolve controversy.

16 Orion Research Instruction Manual, Residual Chlorine Electrode Model 97-70, 1977, Orion Research Incorporated, 840 Memorial Drive, Cambridge, MA 02138. The calibration graph for the Orion residual chlorine method must be derived using a reagent blank and three standard solutions, containing 0.2, 1.0, and 5.0 ml 0.00281 N potassium iodate/100 ml solution, respectively.

17 The approved method is that cited in Standard Methods for the Examination of Water and Wastewater, 14th Edition, 1976.

18 National Council of the Paper Industry for Air and Stream Improvement, (Inc.) Technical Bulletin 253, December 1971.

19 Copper, Biocinchoinate Method, Method 8506, Hach Handbook of Water Analysis, 1979, Hach Chemical Company, P.O. Box 389, Loveland, CO 80537.

20 After the manual distillation is completed, the autoanalyzer manifolds in EPA Methods 335.3 (cyanide) or 420.2 (phenols) are simplified by connecting the re-sample line directly to the sampler. When using the mainfold setup shown in Method 335.3, the buffer 6.2 should be replaced with the buffer 7.6 found in Method 335.2.

21 Hydrogen ion (pH) Automated Electrode Method, Industrial Method Number 378-75WA, October 1976, Bran & Luebbe (Technicon) Autoanalyzer II. Bran & Luebbe Analyzing Technologies, Inc., Elmsford, NY 10523.

22 Iron, 1,10-Phenanthroline Method, Method 8008, 1980, Hach Chemical Company, P.O. Box 389, Loveland, CO 80537.

23 Manganese, Periodate Oxidation Method, Method 8034, Hach Handbook of Wastewater Analysis, 1979, pages 2-113 and 2-117, Hach Chemical Company, Loveland, CO 80537.

24 Wershaw, R.L., et al, "Methods for Analysis of Organic Substances in Water," Techniques of Water-Resources Investigation of the U.S. Geological Survey, Book 5, Chapter A3, (1972 Revised 1987) p. 14.

25 Nitrogen, Nitrite, Method 8507, Hach Chemical Company, P.O. Box 389, Loveland, CO 80537.

26 Just prior to distillation, adjust the sulfuric-acid-preserved sample to pH 4 with 1 + 9 NaOH.

27 The approved method is cited in Standard Methods for the Examination of Water and Wastewater, 14th Edition. The colorimetric reaction is conducted at a pH of $10.0 \pm 0.2$. The approved methods are given on pp 576-81 of the 14th Edition: Method 510A for distillation, Method 510B for the manual colorimetric procedure, or Method 510C for the manual spectophotometric procedure.

28 R. F. Addison and R.G. Ackman, "Direct Determination of Elemental Phosphorus by Gas-Liquid Chromatography," Journal of Chromatography, vol. 47, No. 3. pp. 421-426, 1970.

29 Approved methods for the analysis of silver in industrial wastewaters at concentrations of 1 mg/L and above are inadequate where silver exists as an inorganic halide. Silver halides such as the bromide and chloride are relatively insoluble in reagents such as nitric acid but are readily soluble in an aqueous buffer of sodium thiosulfate and sodium hydroxide to pH of 12. Therefore, for levels of silver above 1 mg/L, 20 mL of sample should be diluted to 100 mL by adding 40 mL each of 2 M $Na_2S_2O_3$ and NaOH. Standards should be prepared in the same manner. For levels of silver below 1 mg/L the approved method is satisfactory.

30 The approved method is that cited in Standard Methods for the Examination of Water and Wastewater, 15th Edition.

31 EPA Methods 335.2 and 335.3 require the NaOH absorber solution final concentration to be adjusted to 0.25 N before colorimetric determination of total cyanide. *Notes continued on next page.*

**Table IB Notes:** *continued*

[32] Stevens, H.H., Ficke, J.F., and Smoot, G.F., "Water Temperature--Influential Factors, Field Measurement and Data Presentation", Techniques of Water-Resources Investigations of the U.S. Geological Survey, Book 1, Chapter D1, 1975.

[33] Zinc, Zincon Method, Method 8009, Hach Handbook of Water Analysis, 1979, pages 2-231 and 2-333, Hach Chemical Company, Loveland, CO 80537.

[34] "Direct Current Plasma (DCP) Optical Emission Spectrometric Method for Trace Elemental Analysis of Water and Wastes, Method AES0029," 1986-- Revised 1991, Fison Instruments, Inc., 32 Commerce Center, Cherry Hill Drive, Danvers, MA 01923.

[35] Precision and recovery statements for the atomic absorption direct aspiration and graphite furnace methods, and for the spectrophotometric SDDC method for arsenic are provided in Appendix D of this part titled, "Precision and Recovery Statements for Methods for Measuring Metals".

[36] "Closed Vessel Microwave Digestion of Wastewater Samples for Determination of Metals", CEM Corporation, P.O. Box 200, Matthews, NC 28106-0200, April 16, 1992. Available from the CEM Corporation.

[37] When determining boron and silica, only plastic, PTFE, or quartz laboratory ware may be used from start until completion of analysis.

[38] Only the trichlorofluoromethane extraction solvent is approved.

[39] Nitrogen, Total Kjeldahl, Method PAI-DK01 (Block Digestion, Steam Distillation, Titrimetric Detection), revised 12/22/94, Perstop Analytical Corporation.

[40] Nitrogen, Total Kjeldahl, Method PAI-DK02 (Block Digestion, Steam Distillation, Colorimetric Detection), revised 12/22/94, Perstop Analytical Corporation.

[41] Nitrogen, Total Kjeldahl, Method PAI-DK03 (Block Digestion, Automated FIA Gas Diffusion), revised 12/22/94, Perstop Analytical Corporation.

## Table IC. List of Approved Test Procedures for Non-Pesticide Organic Compounds

| Parameter [1] | EPA Method No. [27] | | | | | |
|---|---|---|---|---|---|---|
| | GC | GC/MS | HPLC | Standard Methods 18th Ed. | ASTM | Other |
| 1. Acenaphthene | 610 | 625, 1625 | 610 | 6410 B, 6440 B | D4657-92 | |
| 2. Acenaphthylene | 610 | 625, 1625 | 610 | 6410 B, 6440 B | D4657-92 | |
| 3. Acrolein | 603[4] | 624, 1624 | | | | |
| 4. Acrylonitrile | 603[4] | 624, 1624 | 610 | | | |
| 5. Anthracene | 610 | 625, 1625 | 610 | 6410 B, 6440 B | D4657-92 | |
| 6. Benzene | 602 | 624, 1624 | | 6210 B, 6220 B | | |
| 7. Benzidine | | 625, 1625[5] | 605 | | | Note[3], p.1 |
| 8. Benzo(a)anthracene | 610 | 625, 1625 | 610 | 6410 B, 6440 B | D4657-92 | |
| 9. Benzo(a)pyrene | 610 | 625, 1625 | 610 | 6410 B, 6440 B | D4657-92 | |
| 10. Benzo(b)fluoranthene | 610 | 625, 1625 | 610 | 6410 B, 6440 B | D4657-92 | |
| 11. Benzo(g, h, i)perylene | 610 | 625, 1625 | 610 | 6410 B, 6440 B | D4657-92 | |
| 12. Benzo(k)fluoranthene | 610 | 625, 1625 | 610 | 6410 B, 6440 B | D4657-92 | |
| 13. Benzyl chloride | | | | | | Note[3], p. 130: Note[6], p. S102 |
| 14. Benzyl butyl phthalate | 606 | 625, 1625 | | 6410 B | | |
| 15. Bis(2-chloroethoxy)methane | 611 | 625, 1625 | | 6410 B | | |
| 16. Bis(2-chloroethyl) ether | 611 | 625, 1625 | | 6410 B | | |
| 17. Bis (2-ethylhexyl)phthalate | 606 | 625, 1625 | | 6410 B, 6230 B | | |
| 18. Bromodichloromethane | 601 | 624, 1624 | | 6210 B, 6230 B | | |
| 19. Bromoform | 601 | 624, 1624 | | 6210 B, 6230 B | | |
| 20. Bromomethane | 601 | 624, 1624 | | 6210 B, 6230 B | | |
| 21. 4-Bromophenylphenylether | 611 | 625, 1625 | | 6410 B | | |
| 22. Carbon tetrachloride | 601 | 624, 1624 | | 6230 B, 6410 B | | Note[3] p.130 |
| 23. 4-Chloro-3-methylphenol | 604 | 625, 1625 | | 6410 B, 6420 B | | |

Continued on next page.

## Table IC. List of Approved Test Procedures for Non-Pesticide Organic Compounds, *continued*

| Parameter [1] | GC | GC/MS | HPLC | Standard Methods 18th Ed. | ASTM | Other |
|---|---|---|---|---|---|---|
| 24. Chlorobenzene | 601, 602 | 624, 1624 | | 6210 B, 6220 B, 6230 B | | Note[3] p.130 |
| 25. Chloroethane | 601 | 624, 1624 | | 6210 B, 6230 B | | |
| 26. 2-Chloroethylvinyl ether | 601 | 624, 1624 | | 6210 B, 6230 B | | |
| 27. Chloroform | 601 | 624, 1624 | | 6210 B, 6230 B | | Note[3] p.130 |
| 28. Chloromethane | 601 | 624, 1624 | | 6210 B. 6230 B | | |
| 29. 2-Chloronaphthalene | 612 | 625, 1625 | | 6410 B | | |
| 30. 2-Chlorophenol | 604 | 625, 1625 | | 6410 B, 6420 B | | |
| 31. 4-Chlorophenylphenylether | 611 | 625, 1625 | | 6410 B | | |
| 32. Chrysene | 610 | 625, 1625 | 610 | 6410 B, 6440 B | D4657-92 | |
| 33. Dibenzo(a,h)anthracene | 610 | 625, 1625 | 610 | 6410 B, 6440 B | D4657-92 | |
| 34. Dibromochloromethane | 601 | 624, 1624 | | 6210 B, 6230 B | | |
| 35. 1, 2-Dichlorobenzene | 601,602, 612 | 624,625,1625 | | 6410 B, 6230 B, 6220 B | | |
| 36. 1, 3-Dichlorobenzene | 601,602, 612 | 624,625,1625 | | 6410 B, 6230 B, 6220 B | | |
| 37. 1,4-Dichlorobenzene | 601,602, 612 | 624,625,1625 | | 6410 B, 6230 B, 6220 B | | |
| 38. 3, 3'-Dichlorobenzidine | | 625, 1625 | 605 | 6410 B | | |
| 39. Dichlorodifluoromethane | 601 | | | 6230 B | | |
| 40. 1, 1-Dichloroethane | 601 | 624, 1624 | | 6230 B, 6210 B | | |
| 41. 1, 2-Dichloroethane | 601 | 624, 1624 | | 6230 B, 6210 B | | |
| 42. 1, 1-Dichloroethene | 601 | 624, 1624 | | 6230 B, 6210 B | | |
| 43. *trans*-1, 2-Dichloroethene | 601 | 624, 1624 | | 6230 B, 6210 B | | |
| 44. 2, 4-Dichlorophenol | 604 | 625/1625 | | 6420 B, 6410 B | | |
| 45. 1, 2-Dichloropropane | 601 | 624, 1624 | | 6230 B, 6210 B | | |
| 46. *cis*-1, 3-Dichloropropene | 601 | 624, 1624 | | 6230 B, 6210 B | | |
| 47. *trans*-1, 3-Dichloropropene | 601 | 624, 1624 | | 6230 B, 6210 B | | |
| 48. Diethyl phthalate | 606 | 625, 1625 | | 6410 B | | |
| 49. 2, 4-Dimethylphenol | 604 | 625, 1625 | | 6420 B, 6410 B | | |
| 50. Dimethyl phthalate | 606 | 625, 1625 | | 6410 B | | |
| 51. Di-n-butyl phthalate | 606 | 625, 1625 | | 6410 B | | |
| 52. Di-n-octyl phthalate | 606 | 625, 1625 | | 6410 B | | |
| 53. 2, 3-Dinitrophenol | 604 | 625, 1625 | | 6420 B, 6410 B | | |
| 54. 2,4-Dinitrotoluene | 609 | 625, 1625 | | 6410 B | | |
| 55. 2, 6-Dinitrotoluene | 609 | 625, 1625 | | 6410 B | | |
| 56. Epichlorohydrin | | | | | | Note [3], p. 130, Note [6], p. S102 |
| 57. Ethylbenzene | 602 | 624, 1624 | | 6220 B, 6210 B | | |
| 58. Fluoranthene | 610 | 625, 1625 | 610 | 6410 B, 6440 B | D4657-92 | |
| 59. Fluorene | 610 | 625, 1625 | 610 | 6410 B, 6440 B | D4657-92 | |
| 60. Hexachlorobenzene | 612 | 625, 1625 | | 6410 B | | |
| 61. Hexachlorobutadiene | 612 | 625, 1625 | | 6410 B | | |
| 62. Hexachlorocyclopentadiene | 612 | [5] 625, 1625 | | 6410 B | | |
| 63. Hexachloroethane | 616 | 625, 1625 | | 6410 B | | |
| 64. Ideno(1,2,3-cd) pyrene | 610 | 625, 1625 | 610 | 6410 B, 6440 B | D4657-92 | |

The header spanning "EPA Method No. [27]" covers the columns GC, GC/MS, HPLC, Standard Methods 18th Ed., ASTM, Other.

Continued on next page.

## Table IC. List of Approved Test Procedures for Non-Pesticide Organic Compounds, *continued*

| Parameter [1] | EPA Method No. [2] [7] | | | | | |
|---|---|---|---|---|---|---|
| | GC | GC/MS | HPLC | Standard Methods 18th Ed. | ASTM | Other |
| 65. Isophorone | 609 | 625, 1625 | | 6410 B | | |
| 66. Methylene chloride | 601 | 624, 1624 | | 6230 B | | Note[3], p. 130 |
| 67. 2-Methyl-4,6-dinitrophenol | 604 | 625, 1625 | | 6420 B, 6410 B | | |
| 68. Naphthalene | 610 | 625, 1625 | 610 | 6410 B, 6440 B | | |
| 69. Nitrobenzene | 609 | 625, 1625 | | 6410 B | | |
| 70. 2-Nitrophenol | 604 | 625, 1625 | | 6410 B, 6420 B | | |
| 71. 4-Nitrophenol | 604 | 625, 1625 | | 6410 B, 6420 B | | |
| 72. N-Nitrosodimethylamine | 607 | 625, 1625 | | 6410 B | | |
| 73. N-Nitrosodi-n-propylamine | 607 | 625, 1625[5] | | 6410 B | | |
| 74. N-Nitrosodiphenylamine | 607 | 625, 1625[5] | | 6410 B | | |
| 75. 2,2-Oxybis(1-chloropropane) | 611 | 625, 1625 | | 6410 B | | |
| 76. PCB-1016 | 608 | 625 | | 6410 B | | Note[3], p. 43, Note [8] |
| 77. PCB-1221 | 608 | 625 | | 6410 B | | Note[3], p. 43, Note [8] |
| 78. PCB-1232 | 608 | 625 | | 6410 B | | Note[3], p. 43, Note [8] |
| 79. PCB-1242 | 608 | 625 | | 6410 B | | Note[3], p. 43, Note [8] |
| 80. PCB-1248 | 608 | 625 | | 6410 B | | Note[3], p. 43, Note [8] |
| 81. PCB-1254 | 608 | 625 | | 6410 B | | Note[3], p. 43, Note [8] |
| 82. PCB-1260 | 608 | 625 | | 6410 B | | Note[3], p. 43, Note [8] |
| 83. Pentachlorophenol | 604 | 625, 1625 | | 6410 B, 6630 B | | Note[3], p.140 |
| 84. Phenanthrene | 610 | 625, 1625 | 610 | 6410 B, 6440 B | D4657-92 | |
| 85. Phenol | 604 | 625, 1625 | | 6420 B, 6410 B | | |
| 86. Pyrene | 610 | 625, 1625 | 610 | 6410 B, 6440 B | D4675-92 | |
| 87. 2,3,7,8- Tetrachlorodibenzo-p-dioxin | | Note [5a], 613 | | | | |
| 88. 1,1,2,2-Tetrachloroethane | 601 | 624, 1624 | | 6230 B, 6210 B | | Note[3], p. 130 |
| 89. Tetrachloroethene | 601 | 624, 1624 | | 6230 B, 6210 B | | Note[3], p. 130 |
| 90. Toluene | 602 | 624, 1624 | | 6210 B, 6220 B | | |
| 91. 1,2,4-Trichlorobenzene | 612 | 625, 1625 | | 6410 B | | Note[3], p. 130 |
| 92. 1,1,1-Trichloroethane | 601 | 624, 1624 | | 6210 B, 6230 B | | |
| 93. 1,1,2-Trichloroethane | 601 | 624, 1624 | | 6230 B, 6210 B | | Note[3], p. 130 |
| 94. Trichloroethene | 601 | 624, 1624 | | 6230 B, 6210 B | | |
| 95. Trichlorofluoromethane | 601 | 624, 1624 | | 6230 B, 6210 B | | |
| 96. 2,4,6-Trichlorophenol | 604 | 625, 1625 | | 6410 B, 6240 B | | |
| 97. Vinyl chloride | 601 | 624, 1624 | | 6230 B, 6210 B | | |

**Table IC notes:**

[1] All parameters are expressed in micrograms per liter ($\mu$g/L).

[2] The full text of Methods 601-613, 624, 625, 1624, and 1625, are given at appendix A, "Test Procedures for Analysis of Organic Pollutants," of this part 136. The standardized test procedure to be used to determine the method detection limit (MDL) "Definition and Procedure for the Determination of the Method Detection Limit" of this part 136.

*Notes continued on the next page.*

**Table IC notes:** *continued*

3 "Methods for Benzidine: Chlorinated Organic Compounds, Pentachlorophenol and Pesticides in Water and Wastewater," U.S. Environmental Protection Agency, September, 1978.

4 Method 624 may be extended to screen samples for Acrolein and Acrylonitrile. However, when they are known to be present, the preferred method for these two compounds is Method 603 or Method 1624.

5 Method 625 may be extended to include benzidine, hexachlorocyclopentadiene, N-nitrosodimethylamine, and N-nitrosodiphenylamine. However, when they are known to be present, Methods 605, 607, and 612, or Method 1625, are preferred methods for these compounds.

5a 625, Screening only.

6 "Selected Analytical Methods Approved and Cited by the United States Environmental Protection Agency", Supplement to the Fifteenth Edition of Standard Methods for the Examination of Water and Wastewater (1981).

7 Each Analyst must make an initial, one-time demonstration of their ability to generate acceptable precision and accuracy with Methods 601-603, 624, 625, 1624, and 1625 (See Appendix A of this Part 136) in accordance with procedures each in section 8.2 of each of these Methods. Additionally, each laboratory, on an on-going basis must spike and analyze 10% (5% for Methods 624 and 625 and 100% for methods 1624 and 1625) of all samples to monitor and evaluate laboratory data quality in accordance with sections 8.3 and 8.4 of these Methods. When the recovery of any parameter falls outside the warning limits, the analytical results for that parameter in the unspiked sample are suspect and cannot be reported to demonstrate regulatory compliance. *Note:* These warning limits are promulgated as an "interim final action with a request for comments."

8 "Organochlorine Pesticides and PCBs in Wastewater Using Empore TM Disk", 3M Corp. Revised 10/28/94.

## Table ID. List of Approved Test Procedures for Pesticides [1]

| Parameter | Method | EPA[2][7] | Standard Methods 18th Ed | ASTM | Other |
|---|---|---|---|---|---|
| 1. Aldrin | GC | 608 | 6630 B & C | D3086-90 | Note[3], p. 7; note[4], p. 30; note[8] |
| | GC/MS | 625 | 6410 B | | |
| 2. Ametryn | GC | | | | Note[3], p. 83; Note[6], p. S68 |
| 3. Aminocarb | TLC | | | | Note[3], p. 94; Note[6], p. S16 |
| 4. Atraton | GC | | | | Note[3], p. 83; Note[6], p. S68 |
| 5. Atrazine | GC | | | | Note[3], p. 83; Note[6], p. S68 |
| 6. Azinphos methyl | GC | | | | Note[3], p. 25; Note[6], p. S51 |
| 7. Barban | TLC | | | | Note[3], p. 104; Note[6], p. S64 |
| 8. a-BHC | GC | 608 | 6630 B & C | D3086-90 | Note[3], p. 7; Note[8] |
| | GC/MS | 625[5] | 6410 B | | |
| 9. b-BHC | GC | 608 | 6630 C | D3086-90 | Note[8] |
| | GC/MS | 625[5] | 6410 B | | |
| 10. d-BHC | GC | 608 | 6630 C | D3086-90 | Note[8] |
| | GC/MS | 625[5] | 6410 B | | |
| 11. g-BHC (Lindane) | GC | 608 | 6630 B & C | D3086-90 | Note[3], p. 7; note[4], p. 30; note[8] |
| | GC/MS | 625 | 6410 B | | |
| 12. Captan | GC | | 6630 B | D3086-90 | Note[3], p. 7 |
| 13. Carbaryl | TLC | | | | Note[3], p. 94: Note[6], p. S60 |
| 14. Carbophenothion | GC | | | | Note[4], p. 30; Note[6], p. S73 |
| 15. Chlordane | GC | 608 | 6630 B & C | D3086-90 | Note[3], p. 7; Note[8] |
| | GC/MS | 625 | 6410 B | | |
| 16. Chloropropham | TLC | | | | Note[3], p. 104; Note[6], p. S64 |
| 17. 2,4-D | GC | | 6640 B | | Note[3], p. 115; Note[4], p. 35 |
| 18. 4,4'-DDD | GC | 608 | 6630 B & C | D3086-90 | Note[3], p. 7; Note[4], p. 30; Note[8] |
| | GC/MS | 625 | 6410 B | | |
| 19. 4,4'-DDE | GC | 608 | 6630 B & C | D3086-90 | Note[3], p. 7; Note[4], p. 30; Note[8] |
| | GC/MS | 625 | 6410 B | | |

Continued on next page.

## Table ID. List of Approved Test Procedures for Pesticides [1], *continued*

| Parameter | Method | EPA[27] | Standard Methods 18th Ed | ASTM | Other |
|---|---|---|---|---|---|
| 20. 4,4'-DDT | GC | 608 | 6630 B & C | D3086-90 | Note[3], p. 7; Note[4], p. 30; Note[8] |
| | GC/MS | 625 | 6410 B | | |
| 21. Demeton-O | GC | | | | Note[3], p. 25; Note[6], p. S51 |
| 22. Demeton-S | GC | | | | Note[3], p. 25: Note[6], p. S51 |
| 23. Diazinon | GC | | | | Note[3], p. 25; Note[4], p. 30; Note[6], p. S51 |
| 24. Dicamba | GC | | | | Note[3], p. 115 |
| 25. Dichlofenthion | GC | | | | Note[4], p. 30; Note[6], p. S73 |
| 26. Dichloran | GC | | 6630 B & C | | Note[3], p. 7 |
| 27. Dicofol | GC | | | D3086-90 | |
| 28. Dieldrin | GC | 608 | 6630 B & C | | Note[3], p. 7; Note[4], p. 30; Note[8] |
| | GC/MS | 625 | 6410 B | | |
| 29. Dioxathion | GC | | | | Note[4], p. 30; Note[6], p. S73 |
| 30. Disulfoton | GC | | | | Note[3], p. 25; Note[6], p. S51 |
| 31. Diuron | TLC | | | | Note[3], p. 104; Note[6], p. S64 |
| 32. Endosulfan I | GC | 608 | 6630 B & C | D3086-90 | Note[3], p. 7; Note[8] |
| | GC/MS | 625[5] | 6410 B | | |
| 33. Endosulfan II | GC | 608 | 6630 B & C | D3086-90 | Note[3], p. 7; Note[8] |
| | GC/MS | 625[5] | 6410 B | | |
| 34. Endosulfan Sulfate | GC | 608 | 6630 C | | Note[8] |
| | GC/MS | 625 | 6410 B | | |
| 35. Endrin | GC | 608 | 6630 B & C | D3086-90 | Note[3], p. 7; Note[4], p. 30; Note[8] |
| | GC/MS | 625[5] | 6410 B | | |
| 36. Endrin aldehyde | GC | 608 | | | Note[8] |
| | GC/MS | 625 | | | |
| 37. Ethion | GC | | | | Note[4], p. 30; Note[6], p. S73 |
| 38. Fenuron | TLC | | | | Note[3], p. 104; Note[6], p. S64 |
| 39. Fenuron-TCA | TLC | | | | Note[3], p. 104; Note[6], p. S64 |
| 40. Heptachlor | GC | 608 | 6630 B & C | D3086-90 | Note[3], p. 7; Note[4], p. 30; Note[8] |
| | GC/MS | 625 | 6410 B | | |
| 41. Heptachlor epoxide | GC | 608 | 6630 B & C | D3086-90 | Note[3], p. 7; Note[4], p.30; Note[6], p. S73; Note[8] |
| | GC/MS | 625 | 6410 B | | |
| 42. Isodrin | GC | | | | Note[4], p. 30; Note[6], p. S73 |
| 43. Linuron | GC | | | | Note[3], p. 104; Note[6], p. S64 |
| 44. Malathion | GC | | 6630 C | | Note[3], p. 25; Note[4], p. 30; Note[6], p. S51 |
| 45. Methiocarb | TLC | | | | Note[3], p. 94; Note[6], p. S60 |
| 46. Methoxychlor | GC | | 6630 B & C | D3086-90 | Note[3], p. 7; Note[4], p. 30; Note[8] |
| 47. Mexacarbate | TLC | | | | Note[3], p. 94; Note[6], p. S60 |
| 48. Mirex | GC | | 6630 B & C | | Note[3], p. 7 |
| 49. Monuron | TLC | | | | Note[3], p. 104; Note[6], p. S64 |
| 50. Monuron | TLC | | | | Note[3], p. 104; Note[6], p. S64 |
| 51. Nuburon | TLC | | | | Note[3], p. 104; Note[6], p. S64 |
| 52. Parathion methyl | GC | | 6630 C | | Note[3], p. 25; Note[4], p. 30 |
| 53. Parathion ethyl | GC | | 6630 C | | Note[3], p. 25 |

Continued on next page.

## Table ID.  List of Approved Test Procedures for Pesticides [1], *continued*

| Parameter | Method | EPA[2][7] | Standard Methods 18th Ed | ASTM | Other |
|---|---|---|---|---|---|
| 54. PCNB | GC | | 6630 B & C | | Note[3], p. 7 |
| 55. Perthane | GC | | | D3086-90 | |
| 56. Prometron | GC | | | | Note[3], p. 83; Note[6], p. S68 |
| 57. Prometryn | GC | | | | Note[3], p. 83; Note[6], p. S68 |
| 58. Propazine | GC | | | | Note[3], p. 83; Note[6], p. S68 |
| 59. Propham | TLC | | | | Note[3], p. 104; Note[6], p. S64 |
| 60. Propoxur | TLC | | | | Note[3], p. 94; Note[6], p. S60 |
| 61. Secbumeton | TLC | | | | Note[3], p. 83; Note[6], p. S68 |
| 62. Siduron | TLC | | | | Note[3], p. 104; Note[6], p. S64 |
| 63. Simazine | GC | | | | Note[3], p. 83; Note[6], p. S68 |
| 64. Strobane | GC | | 6630 B & C | | Note[3], p. 7 |
| 65. Swep | TLC | | | | Note[3], p. 104; Note[6], p. S64 |
| 66. 2,4,5-T | GC | | 6640 B | | Note[3], p. 115; Note[4], p. 35 |
| 67. 2,4,5-TP (Silvex) | GC | | 6640 B | | Note[3], p. 115 |
| 68. Terbuthylazine | GC | | | | Note[3], p. 83; Note[6], p. S68 |
| 69. Toxaphene | GC | 608 | 6630 B & C | D3086-90 | Note[3], p. 7; Note[4], p. 30; Note [8] |
| | GC/MS | 625 | 6410 B | | |
| 70. Trifluralin | GC | | 6630 B | | Note[3], p. 7 |

**Table ID notes:**

[1] Pesticides are listed in this table by common name for the convenience of the reader. Additional pesticides may be found under Table 1C, where entries are listed by chemical name.

[2] The full text of Methods 608 and 625 are given at Appendix A. "Test Procedures for Analysis of Organic Pollutants," of this Part 136.  The standardized test procedure to be used to determine the method detection limit (MDL) for these test procedures is given at Appendix B. "Definition and Procedure for the Determination of the Method Detection Limit", of this Part 136.

[3] "Methods for Benzidine, Chlorinated Organic Compounds, Pentachlorophenol and Pesticides in Water and Wastewater," U.S. Environmental Protection Agency, September, 1978. This EPA publication includes thin-layer chromatography (TLC) methods.

[4] "Methods for Analysis of Organic Substances in Water and Fluvial Sediments," Techniques of Water-Resources Investigations of the U.S. Geological Survey, Book 5, Chapter A3 (1987).

[5] The method may be extended to include $\alpha$-BHC, $\gamma$-BHC, endosulfan I, endosulfan II, and endrin. However, when they are known to exist, Method 608 is the preferred method.

[6] "Selected Analytical Methods Approved and Cited by the United States Environmental Protection Agency." Supplement to the Fifteenth Edition of Standard Methods for the Examination of Water and Wastewater (1981).

[7] Each analyst must make an initial, one-time, demonstration of their ability to generate acceptable precision and accuracy with Methods 608 and 625  (See Appendix A of this Part 136) in accordance with procedures given in section 8.2 of each of these methods. Additionally, each laboratory, on an on-going basis, must spike and analyze 10% of all samples analyzed with Method 608 or 5% of all samples analyzed with Method 625 to monitor and evaluate laboratory data quality in accordance with Sections 8.3 and 8.4 of these methods. When the recovery of any parameter falls outside the warning limits, the analytical results for that parameter in the unspiked sample are suspect and cannot be reported to demonstrate regulatory compliance. These quality control requirements also apply to the Standard Methods, ASTM Methods, and other Methods cited. *Note:* These warning limits are promulgated as an "Interim final action with a request for comments."

[8] "Organochlorine Pesticides and PCBs in Wastewater Using Empore; TM Disk", 3M Corporation, Revised 10/28/94.

## Table IE. List of Approved Radiologic Test Procedures

| Parameter | Method | EPA[2][7] | Standard Methods 18th Ed | ASTM | Other |
|---|---|---|---|---|---|
| 1. Alpha-Total, pCi per liter | Proportional or scintillation counter | 900 | 7110 B | D1943-90 | pp. 75 and 78[3] |
| 2. Alpha-Counting error, pCi per liter | Proportional or scintillation counter | Appendix B | 7110 B | D1943-90 | P. 79 |
| 3. Beta-Total, pCi per liter | Proportional counter | 900.0 | 7110 B | D1890-90 | pp. 75 and 78[3] |
| 4. Beta-Counting error, pCi | Proportional counter | Appendix B | 7110 B | D1890-90 | p. 79 |
| 5. (a) Radium Total pCi per liter | Proportional counter | 903.0 | 7500Ra B | D2460-90 | |
| 5. (b)Ra, pCi per liter | Scintillation counter | 903.1 | 7500Ra C | D3454-91 | p. 81 |

**Table IE notes:**

[1] "Prescribed Procedures for Measurement of Radioactivity in Drinking Water," EPA-600/4-80-032 (1980), U.S. Environmental Protection Agency, August 1980.

[2] Fishman, M.J. and Brown, Eugene, "Selected Methods of the U.S. Geological Survey of Analysis of Wastewaters," U.S. Geological Survey, Open-File Report 76-177 (1976).

[3] The method found on p. 75 measures only the dissolved portion while the method on p. 78 measures only the suspended portion. Therefore, the two results must be added to obtain the "total".

(b) The full texts of the methods from the following references which are cited in Tables IA, IB, IC, ID, and IE are incorporated by reference into this regulation and may be obtained from the sources identified. All costs cited are subject to change and must be verified from the indicated sources. The full texts of all the test procedures cited are available for inspection at the Environmental Monitoring Systems Laboratory, Office of Research and Development, U.S. Environmental Protection Agency, 26 West Martin Luther King Dr., Cincinnati, OH 45268 and the Office of the Federal Register, Room 8301, 1110 L Street, NW., Washington, DC 20408.

### References, Sources, Costs, and Table Citations Used to Develop These Tables:

(1) The full text of Methods 601-613, 624, 625, 1624, and 1625 are printed in appendix A of this part 136. The full text for determining the method detection limit when using the test procedures is given in appendix B of this part 136. The full text of Method 200.7 is printed in appendix C of this part 136. Cited in: Table IB, Note 5; Table IC, Note 2; and Table ID, Note 2.

(2) USEPA. 1978. Microbiological Methods for Monitoring the Environment, Water, and Wastes. Environmental Monitoring and Support Laboratory, U.S. Environmental Protection Agency, Cincinnati, Ohio. EPA/600/8-78/017. Available from: National Technical Information Service, 5285 Port Royal Road, Springfield, Virginia 22161, Publ. No. PB-290329/AS. Cost: $36.95. Table IA, Note 3

(3) "Methods for Chemical Analysis of Water and Wastes," U.S. Environmental Protection Agency, EPA-600/4-79-020, March 1979, or "Methods for Chemical Analysis of Water and Wastes," U.S. Environmental Protection Agency, EPA-600/4-79-020, Revised March 1983. Available from: ORD Publications, CERI, U.S. Environmental Protection Agency, Cincinnati, Ohio 45268, Table IB, Note 1.

(4) "Methods for Benzidine, Chlorinated Organic Compounds, Pentachlorophenol and Pesticides in Water and Wastewater," U.S. Environmental Protection Agency, 1978. Available from: ORD Publications, CERI, U.S. Environmental Protection Agency, Cincinnati, Ohio 45268, Table IC, Note 3; Table D, Note 3.

(5) "Prescribed Procedures for Measurement of Radioactivity in Drinking Water," U.S. Environmental Protection Agency, EPA-600/4-80032, 1980. Available from: ORD Publications, CERI, U.S. Environmental Protection Agency, Cincinnati, Ohio 45268, Table IE, Note 1.

(6) American Public Health Association. 1992. Standard Methods for the Examination of Water and Wastewater. 18th Edition. Amer. Publ. Hlth. Assoc., 1015 15th Street NW, Washington, DC 20005. Cost: $160.00. Table IA, Note 4.

(7) Ibid, 15th Edition, 1980. Table IB, Note 30; Table ID.

(8) Ibid, 14th Edition, 1975. Table IB, Notes 17 and 27.

(9) "Selected Analytical Methods Approved and Cited by the United States Environmental Protection Agency," Supplement to the 15th Edition of Standard Methods for the Examination of Water and Wastewater, 1981. Available from: American Public Health Association, 1015 Fifteenth Street NW., Washington, DC 20036. Cost available from publisher. Table IB, Note 10; Table IC, Note 6; Table ID, Note 6.

(10) Annual Book of ASTM Standards, Water and Environmental Technology, Section 11, Volumes 11.01 and 11.02, 1994 in 40 CFR 136.3, Tables IB, IC, ID and IE.

**References, Sources, Costs, and Table Citations Used to Develop These Tables:** *continued*

(11) USGS. 1989. U.S. Geological Survey Techniques of Water-Resources Investigations, Book 5, Laboratory Analysis, Chapter A4, Methods for Collection and Analysis of Aquatic Biological and Microbiological Samples, U.S. Geological Survey, U.S. Department of the Interior, Reston, Virginia. Available from: USGS Books and Open-File Reports Section, Federal Center, Box 25425, Denver, CO 80225. Cost: $18.00. Table IA, Note 5.

(12) "Methods for Determination of Inorganic Substances in Water and Fluvial Sediments," by M.J. Fishman and Linda C. Friedman, Techniques of Water-Resources Investigations of the U.S. Geological Survey, Book 5 Chapter A1 (1989). Available from: U.S. Geological Survey, Denver Federal Center, Box 25425, Denver, CO 80225. Cost: $108.75 (subject to change). Table IB, Note 2.

(13) "Methods for Determination of Inorganic Substances in Water and Fluvial Sediments," N.W. Skougstad and others, editors. Techniques of Water-Resources Investigations of the U.S. Geological Survey, Book 5, Chapter A1 (1979). Available from: U.S. Geological Survey, Denver Federal Center, Box 25425, Denver, CO 80225. Cost: $10.00 (subject to change), Table IB, Note 8.

(14) "Methods for the Determination of Organic Substances in Water and Fluvial Sediments," Wershaw, R.L., et al, Techniques of Water Resources Investigations of the U.S. Geological Survey, Book 5, Chapter A3 (1987). Available from: U.S. Geological Survey, Denver Federal Center, Box 25425, Denver, CO 80225. Cost: $0.90 (subject to change). Table IB, Note 24; Table ID, Note 4.

(15) "Water Temperature--Influential Factors, Field Measurement and Data Presentation," by H.H. Stevens, Jr., J. Ficke, and G.F. Smoot, Techniques of Water-Resources Investigations of the U.S. Geological Survey, Book 1, Chapter D1, 1975. Available from: U.S. Geological Survey, Denver Federal Center, Box 25425, Denver, CO 80225. Cost: $1.60 (subject to change). Table IB, Note 32.

(16) "Selected Methods of the U.S. Geological Survey of Analysis of Wastewaters," by M.J. Fishman and Eugene Brown; U.S. Geological Survey Open File Report 76-77 (1976). Available from: U.S. Geological Survey, Branch of Distribution, 1200 South Eads Street, Arlington, VA 22202. Cost: $13.50 (subject to change). Table IE, Note 2.

(17) "Official Methods of Analysis of the Association of Official Analytical Chemicals", Methods manual, 15th Edition (1990). Price: $240.00. Available from: The Association of Official Analytical Chemists, 2200 Wilson Boulevard, Suite 400, Arlington, VA 22201. Table IB, Note 3.

(18) "American National Standard on Photographic Processing Effluents," April 2, 1975. Available from: American National Standards Institute, 1430 Broadway, New York, New York 10018. Table IB, Note 9.

(19) "An Investigation of Improved Procedures for Measurement of Mill Effluent and Receiving Water Color," NCASI Technical Bulletin No. 253, December 1971. Available from: National Council of the Paper Industry for Air and Stream Improvements, Inc., 260 Madison Avenue, New York, NY 10016. Cost available from publisher. Table IB, Note 18.

(20) Ammonia, Automated Electrode Method, Industrial Method Number 379-75WE, dated February 19, 1976. Technicon Auto Analyzer II. Method and price available from Technicon Industrial Systems, Tarrytown, New York 10591. Table IB, Note 7.

(21) Chemical Oxygen Demand, Method 8000, Hach Handbook of Water Analysis, 1979. Method price available from Hach Chemical Company, P.O. Box 389, Loveland, Colorado 80537. Table IB, Note 14.

(22) OIC Chemical Oxygen Demand Method, 1978. Method and price available from Oceanography International Corporation, 512 West Loop, P.O. Box 2980, College Station, TX 77840. Table IB, Note 13.

(23) ORION Research Instruction Manual, Residual Chlorine Electrode Model 97-70, 1977. Method and price available from ORION Research Inc., 840 Memorial Dr, Cambridge, MA 02138. Table IB, Note 16.

(24) Bicinchoninate Method for Copper. Method 8506, Hach Handbook of Water Analysis, 1979, Method and price available from Hach Chemical Company, P.O. Box 300, Loveland, CO 80537. Table IB, Note 19.

(25) Hydrogen Ion (pH) Automated Electrode Method, Industrial Method Number 378-75WA. October 1976. Bran & Luebbe (Technicon) Auto Analyzer II. Method and price available from Bran & Luebbe Analyzing Technologies, Inc. Elmsford, N.Y. 10523. Table IB, Note 21.

(26) 1,10-Phenanthroline Method using FerroVer Iron Reagent for Water, Hach Method 8008, 1980. Method and price available from Hach Chemical Company, P.O. Box 389 Loveland, CO 80537. Table IB, Note 22.

(27) Periodate Oxidation Method for Manganese, Method 8034, Hach Handbook for Water Analysis, 1979. Method and price available from Hach Chemical Company, P.O. Box 389, Loveland, CO 80537. Table IB, Note 23.

(28) Nitrogen, Nitrite--Low Range, Diazotization Method for Water and Wastewater, Hach Method 8507, 1979. Method and price available from Hach Chemical Company, P.O. Box 389, Loveland, CO 80537. Table IB, Note 25.

(29) Zincon Method for Zinc, Method 8009. Hach Handbook for Water Analysis, 1979. Method and price available from Hach Chemical Company, P.O. Box 389, Loveland, Colorado 80537. Table IB, Note 33.

**References, Sources, Costs, and Table Citations Used to Develop These Tables:** *continued*

(30) "Direct Determination of Elemental Phosphorus by Gas-Liquid Chromatography," by R.F. Addison and R.G. Ackman, Journal of Chromatography, Volume 47, No. 3, pp. 421-426, 1970. Available in most public libraries. Back volumes of the Journal of Chromatography are available from Elsevier/North-Holland, Inc., Journal Information Center, 52 Vanderbilt Avenue, New York, NY 10164. Cost available from publisher. Table IB, Note 28.

(31) "Direct Current Plasma (DCP) Optical Emission Spectrometric Method for Trace Elemental Analysis of Water and Wastes", Method AES 0029, 1986-Revised 1991, Fison Instruments, Inc., 32 Commerce Center, Cherry Hill Drive, Danvers, MA 01923. Table B, Note 34.

(32) "Closed Vessel Microwave Digestion of Wastewater Samples for Determination of Metals", CEM Corporation, P.O. Box 200, Matthews, North Carolina 28106-0200, April 16, 1992. Available from the CEM Corporation. Table IB, Note 36.

(33) "Organochlorine Pesticides and PCBs in Wastewater Using Empore TM Disk" Test Method 3M 0222, Revised 10/28/94. 3M Corporation, 3M Center Building 220-9E-10, St. Paul, MN 55144-1000. Method available from 3M Corporation. Table IC, Note 8 and Table ID, Note 8.

(34) USEPA. 1993. Methods for Measuring the Acute Toxicity of Effluents to Freshwater and Marine Organisms. Fourth Edition, December 1993. Environmental Monitoring Systems Laboratory, U.S. Environmental Protection Agency, Cincinnati, Ohio (EPA/600/4-90/027F). Available from: National Technical Information Service, 5285 Port Royal Road, Springfield, Virginia 22161, Publ. No. PB-91-167650. Cost: $31.00. Table IA, Note 17. See changes in the manual, listed in Part V of this rule.

(35) "Nitrogen, Total Kjeldahl, Method PAI-DK01 (Block Digestion, Steam Distillation, Titrimetric Detection)", revised 12/22/94. Available from Perstorp Analytical Corporation, 9445 SW Ridder Rd., Suite 310, P.O. Box 648, Wilsonville, OK 97070. Table IB, Note 39.

(36) "Nitrogen, Total Kjeldahl, Method PAI-DK02 (Block Digestion, Steam Distillation, Colorimetric Detection)", revised 12/22/94. Available from Perstorp Analytical Corporation, 9445 SW Ridder Rd., Suite 310, P.O. Box 648, Wilsonville, OK 97070. Table IB, Note 40.

(37) "Nitrogen, Total Kjeldahl, Method PAI-DK03 (Block Digestion, Automated FIA Gas Diffusion)", revised 12/22/94 Available from Perstorp Analytical Corporation, 9445 SW Ridder Rd., Suite 310, P.O. Box 648, Wilsonville, OK 97070. Table IB, Note 41.

(38) USEPA. 1994. Short-term Methods for Estimating the Chronic Toxicity of Effluents and Receiving Waters to Freshwater Organisms. Third Edition. July 1994. Environmental Monitoring Systems Laboratory, U.S. Environmental Protection Agency, Cincinnati, Ohio. (EPA/600/4-91/002). Available from: National Technical Information Service, 5285 Port Royal Road, Springfield, Virginia 22161, Publ. No. PB-92-139492. Cost: $31.00. Table IA, Note 8.

(39) USEPA. 1994. Short-term Methods for Estimating the Chronic Toxicity of Effluents and Receiving Waters to Marine and Estuarine Organisms. Second Edition, July 1994. Environmental Monitoring Systems Laboratory, U.S. Environmental Protection Agency, Cincinnati, Ohio. EPA/600/4-91/003. Available from: National Technical Information Service, 5285 Port Royal Road, Springfield, Virginia 22161, Publ. No. PB-92139484. Cost: $45.00. Table IA, Note 9.

(c) Under certain circumstances the Regional Administrator or the Director in the Region or State where the discharge will occur may determine for a particular discharge that additional parameters or pollutants must be reported. Under such circumstances, additional test procedures for analysis of pollutants may be specified by the Regional Administrator, or the Director upon the recommendation of the Director of the Environmental Monitoring Systems Laboratory--Cincinnati.

(d) Under certain circumstances, the Administrator may approve, upon recommendation by the Director, Environmental Monitoring Systems Laboratory--Cincinnati, additional alternate test procedures for nationwide use.

(e) Sample preservation procedures, container materials, and maximum allowable holding times for parameters cited in Tables IA, IB, IC, ID, and IE are prescribed in Table II. Any person may apply for a variance from the prescribed preservation techniques, container materials, and maximum holding times applicable to samples taken from a specific discharge. Applications for variances may be made by letters to the Regional Administrator in the Region in which the discharge will occur. Sufficient data should be provided to assure such variance does not adversely affect the integrity of the sample. Such data will be forwarded, by the Regional Administrator, to the Director of the Environmental Monitoring Systems Laboratory--Cincinnati, Ohio for technical review and recommendations for action on the variance application. Upon receipt of the recommendations from the Director of the Environmental Monitoring Systems Laboratory, the Regional Administrator may grant a variance applicable to the specific charge to the applicant. A decision to approve or deny a variance will be made within 90 days of receipt of the application by the Regional Administrator.

## Table II. Required Containers, Preservation Techniques, and Holding Times

| Parameter Number/name | Container [1] | Preservation [2,3] | Maximum holding time [4] |
|---|---|---|---|
| **Table IA--Bacteria Tests:** | | | |
| 1-4 Coliform, fecal and total | P,G | Cool, 4˚C, 0.008% $Na_2S_2O_3$ | 6 hours |
| 5 Fecal streptococci | P,G | Cool, 4˚C, 0.008% $Na_2S_2O_3$ | 6 hours |
| **Table IA--Aquatic Toxicity Tests:** | | | |
| 6-10 Toxicity, acute and chronic | P,G | Cool, 4˚C [16] | 6 hours |
| **Table IB--Inorganic Tests:** | | | |
| 1. Acidity | P, G | Cool, 4˚C | 14 days |
| 2. Alkalinity | P, G | Cool, 4˚C | 14 days |
| 4. Ammonia | P, G | Cool, 4˚C, $H_2SO_4$ to pH<2 | 28 days |
| 9. Biochemical oxygen demand | P, G | Cool, 4˚C | 48 hours |
| 10. Boron | P, PFTE, or Quartz | $HNO_3$ to pH<2 | 6 months |
| 11. Bromide | P, G | None required | 28 days |
| 14. Biochemical oxygen demand, carbonaceous | P, G | Cool, 4˚C | 48 hours |
| 15. Chemical oxygen demand | P, G | Cool, 4˚C, $H_2SO_4$ to pH<2 | 28 days |
| 16. Chloride | P, G | None required | 28 days |
| 17. Chlorine, total residual | P, G | None required | Analyze immediately |
| 21. Color | P, G | Cool, 4˚C | 48 hours |
| 23-24. Cyanide, total and amenable to chlorination | P, G | Cool, 4˚C, NaOH to pH>12, 0.6g ascorbic acid [5] | 14 days[6] |
| 25. Fluoride | P | None required. | 28 days |
| 27. Hardness | P, G | $HNO_3$ to pH2, $H_2SO_4$ to pH<2 | 6 months |
| 28. Hydrogen ion (pH) | P, G | None required | Analyze immediately |
| 31, 43. Kjeldahl and organic nitrogen | P, G | Cool, 4˚C, $H_2SO_4$ to pH<2 | 28 days |
| **Metals:[7]** | | | |
| 18. Chromium VI | P, G | Cool, 4˚C | 24 hours |
| 35. Mercury | P, G | $HNO_3$ to pH<2 | 28 days |
| 3, 5-8, 12, 13, 19, 20, 22, 26, 29, 30, 32-34, 36, 37, 45, 47, 51, 52, 58-60, 62, 63, 70-72, 74, 75. Metals,except boron, chromium VI and mercury | P, G | $HNO_3$ to pH<2 | 6 months |
| 38. Nitrate | P, G | Cool, 4˚C | 48 hours |
| 39. Nitrate-nitrite | P, G | Cool, 4˚C, $H_2SO_4$ to pH<2 | 28 days |
| 40. Nitrite | P, G | Cool, 4˚C | 48 hours |
| 41. Oil and grease | G | Cool to 4˚C, HCl or $H_2SO_4$ to pH<2 | 28 days |
| 42. Organic Carbon | P, G | Cool to 4 C HC1 or $H_2SO_4$ or $H_3PO_4$, to pH<2 | 28 days |
| 44. Orthophosphate | P, G | Filter immediately, Cool, 4˚C | 48 hours |
| 46. Oxygen, Dissolved Probe | G Bottle and top | None required | Analyze immediately |
| 47. Winkler | G Bottle and top | Fix on site and store in dark | 8 hours |
| 48. Phenols | G only | Cool, 4˚C, H2SO4 to pH<2 | 28 days |
| 49. Phosphorus (elemental) | G | Cool, 4˚C | 48 hours |
| 50. Phosphorus, total | P, G | Cool, 4˚C, H2SO4 to pH<2 | 28 days |
| 53. Residue, total | P, G | Cool, 4˚C | 7 days |
| 54. Residue, Filterable | P, G | Cool, 4˚C | 7 days |
| 55. Residue, Nonfilterable (TSS) | P, G | Cool, 4˚C | 7 days |

Continued on next page.

## Table II.  Required Containers, Preservation Techniques, and Holding Times, *continued*

| Parameter Number/name | Container [1] | Preservation [2,3] | Maximum holding time [4] |
|---|---|---|---|
| 56. Residue, Settleable | P, G | Cool, 4°C | 48 hours |
| 57. Residue, volatile | P, G | Cool, 4°C | 7 days |
| 61. Silica | P, PFTE, or Quartz | Cool, 4°C | 28 days |
| 64. Specific conductance | P, G | Cool, 4°C | 28 days |
| 65. Sulfate | P, G | Cool, 4°C | 28 days |
| 66. Sulfide | P, G | Cool, 4°C add zinc acetate plus sodium hydroxide to pH>9 | 7 days |
| 67. Sulfite | P, G | None required | Analyze immediately |
| 68. Surfactants | P ,G | Cool, 4°C | 48 hours |
| 69. Temperature | P, G | None required | Analyze immediately |
| 73. Turbidity | P, G | Cool, 4°C | 48 hours |
| **Table IC.  Organic Tests[8]** | | | |
| 13, 18-20, 22, 24-28, 34-37, 39-43, 45-47, 56, 66, 88, 89, 92-95, 97. Purgeable Halocarbons | G, Telflon-lined septum | Cool, 4°C, 0.008% $Na_2S_2O_3$[5] | 14 days |
| 6, 57, 90. Purgeable aromatic hydrocarbons | G, Telflon-lined septum | Cool, 4°C, 0.008% $Na_2S_2O_3$[5], HCl to pH<2 [9] | 14 days |
| 3, 4, Acrolein and acrylonitrile | G, Telflon-lined septum | Cool, 4°C, 0.008% $Na_2S_2O_3$[5] Adjust pH to 4-5 [10] | 14 days |
| 23, 30, 44, 49, 53, 67, 70, 71, 83, 85, 96. Phenols [11] | G, Teflon-lined cap | Cool, 4°C, 0.008% $Na_2S_2O_3$[5] | 7 days until extraction, 40 days after extraction |
| 7, 38. Benzidines[11] | G, Teflon-lined cap | Cool, 4°C, 0.008% $Na_2S_2O_3$[5] | 7 days until extraction |
| 13, 14, 17, 48, 50-52. Phthalate esters [11] | G, Teflon-lined cap | Cool, 4°C | 7 days until extraction, 40 days after extraction |
| 72-74. Nitrosamines [11,14] | G, Teflon-lined cap | Cool, 4°C, store in dark, 0.008% $Na_2S_2O_3$ [5] | 7 days until extraction, 40 days after extraction |
| 76-82. PCBs [11] | G, Teflon-lined cap | Cool, 4°C | 7 days until extraction, 40 days after extraction |
| 54, 55, 65, 69. Nitroaromatics and isophorone [11] | G, Teflon-lined cap | Cool, 4°C, store in dark, 0.008% $Na_2S_2O_3$[5] | 7 days until extraction, 40 days after extraction |
| 1, 2, 5, 8-12, 32, 33, 58, 59, 64, 68, 84, 86. Polynuclear aromatic hydrocarbons[11] | G, Teflon-lined cap | Cool, 4°C, store in dark, 0.008% $Na_2S_2O_3$[5] | 7 days until extraction, 40 days after extraction |
| 15, 16, 21, 31, 75 Haloethers[11] | G, Teflon-lined cap | Cool, 4°C, 0.008% $Na_2S_2O_3$[5] | 7 days until extraction, 40 days after extraction |
| 29, 35-37, 60-63, 91. Chlorinated hydrocarbons [11] | G, Teflon-lined cap | Cool, 4°C | 7 days until extraction, 40 days after extraction |
| 87. TCDD[11] | G, Teflon-lined cap | Cool, 4°C, 0.008% $Na_2S_2O_3$[5] | 7 days until extraction, 40 days after extraction |
| **Table ID.  Pesticides Tests:** | | | |
| 1-70. Pesticides[11] | G, Teflon-lined cap | Cool, 4°C, pH 5-9[15] | 7 days until extraction, 40 days after extraction |

Continued on next page.

## Table II.  Required Containers, Preservation Techniques, and Holding Times, *continued*

| Parameter Number/name | Container [1] | Preservation [2,3] | Maximum holding time [4] |
|---|---|---|---|
| **Table IE--Radiological Tests:** | | | |
| 1-5. Alpha, beta and radium | P, G | HNO$_3$ to pH<2 | 6 months |

**Table II Notes**

1  Polyethylene (P) or glass (G). For microbiology, plastic sample containers must be made of sterilizable materials (polypropylene or other autoclavable plastic).

2  Sample preservation should be performed immediately upon sample collection. For composite chemical samples each aliquot should be preserved at the time of collection. When use of an automated sampler makes it impossible to preserve each aliquot, then chemical samples may be preserved by maintaining at 4°C until compositing and sample splitting is completed.

3  When any sample is to be shipped by common carrier or sent through the United States Mails, it must comply with the Department of Transportation Hazardous Materials Regulations (49 CFR part 172). The person offering such material for transportation is responsible for ensuring such compliance. For the preservation requirements of Table II, the Office of Hazardous Materials, Materials Transportation Bureau, Department of Transportation has determined that the Hazardous Materials Regulations do not apply to the following materials: Hydrochloric acid (HCl) in water solutions at concentrations of 0.04% by weight or less (pH about 1.96 or greater); Nitric acid (HNO3) in water solutions at concentrations of 0.15% by weight or less (pH about 1.62 or greater); Sulfuric acid (H2SO4) in water solutions at concentrations of 0.35% by weight or less (pH about 1.15 or greater); and Sodium hydroxide (NaOH) in water solutions at concentrations of 0.080% by weight or less (pH about 12.30 or less).

4  Samples should be analyzed as soon as possible after collection. The times listed are the maximum times that samples may be held before analysis and still be considered valid. Samples may be held for longer periods only if the permittee, or monitoring laboratory, has data on file to show that for the specific types of samples under study, the analytes are stable for the longer time, and has received a variance from the Regional Administrator under Sec. 136.3/(e). Some samples may not be stable for the maximum time period given in the table. A permittee, or monitoring laboratory, is obligated to hold the sample for a shorter time if knowledge exists to show that this is necessary to maintain sample stability. See Sec. 136.3/(e) for details. The term "analyze immediately" usually means within 15 minutes or less of sample collection.

5  Should only be used in the presence of residual chlorine.

6  Maximum holding time is 24 hours when sulfide is present. Optionally all samples may be tested with lead acetate paper before pH adjustments in order to determine if sulfide is present. If sulfide is present, it can be removed by the addition of cadmium nitrate powder until a negative spot test is obtained. The sample is filtered and then NaOH is added to pH 12.

7  Samples should be filtered immediately on-site before adding preservative for dissolved metals.

8  Guidance applies to samples to be analyzed by GC, LC, or GC/MS for specific compounds.

9  Sample receiving no pH adjustment must be analyzed within seven days of sampling.

10  The pH adjustment is not required if acrolein will not be measured. Samples for acrolein receiving no pH adjustment must be analyzed within 3 days of sampling.

11  When the extractable analytes of concern fall within a single chemical category, the specified preservative and maximum holding times should be observed for optimum safeguard of sample integrity. When the analytes of concern fall within two or more chemical categories, the sample may be preserved by cooling to 4°C, reducing residual chlorine with 0.008% sodium thiosulfate, storing in the dark, and adjusting the pH to 6-9; samples preserved in this manner may be held for seven days before extraction and for forty days after extraction. Exceptions to this optional preservation and holding time procedure are noted in footnote 5 (re: the requirement for thiosulfate reduction of residual chlorine), and footnotes 12, 13 (re: the analysis of benzidine).

12  If 1,2-diphenylhydrazine is likely to be present, adjust the pH of the sample to 4.0 ± 0.2 to prevent rearrangement to benzidine.

13  Extracts may be stored up to 7 days before analysis if storage is conducted under an inert (oxidant-free) atmosphere.

14  For the analysis of diphenylnitrosamine, add 0.008% Na$_2$S$_2$O$_3$ and adjust pH to 7-10 with NaOH within 24 hours of sampling.

15  The pH adjustment may be performed upon receipt at the laboratory and may be omitted if the samples are extracted within 72 hours of collection. For the analysis of aldrin, add 0.008% Na$_2$S$_2$O$_3$.

16  Sufficient ice should be placed with the samples in the shipping container to ensure that ice is still present when the samples arrive at the laboratory. However, even if ice is present when the samples arrive, it is necessary to immediately measure the temperature of the samples and confirm that the 4°C temperature maximum has not

**Table II Notes,** *continued*

been exceeded. In the isolated cases where it can be documented that this holding temperature can not be met, the permittee can be given the option of on-site testing or can request a variance. The request for a variance should include supportive data which show that the toxicity of the effluent samples is not reduced because of the increased holding temperature.

# GLOSSARY

**601-602.** EPA GC methods for determination of volatile organic compounds by PID Hall detectors in series.

**AA.** Atomic absorption spectrometric method for metals.

**Accuracy.** The ability of a test to give the true amount of target analyte.

**Acetonitrile partition.** A technique for removing fat and oil interference from organic extracts.

**Acid digestion.** Method for obtaining metal analytes in solution for analysis.

**Acid extractables.** Organic analytes that are removed from acidified water with methylene chloride.

**Acid-base partition.** Clean-up technique for organic analysis.

**Activated carbon.** Carbon heated to 900 °C in the absence of oxygen.

**Activated charcoal.** Charcoal heated to 900 °C in the absence of oxygen.

**Acute.** Immediate effects.

**Alkalinity.** A measure of the acid-neutralizing ability of the sample.

**Ames Test.** A common screening test for mutagenic properties.

**Analyte-free water.** Water that has been treated to remove impurities of interest.

**Analytical balance.** Electronic balance capable of accurate weighings to 0.1 mg.

**Analytically valid.** Term used to indicate a procedure has been performed with sufficient controls to assure a high degree of confidence in the result.

**Appendix I.** Municipal landfill leachate monitoring list for detection, 40 CFR 258

**Appendix II.** Municipal landfill leachate monitoring list for assessment, 40 CFR 258

**Areal composite sample.** Samples taken over an area then mixed to give an overall analysis of the site.

**Areal domain.** Samples taken at a variety of points within a larger sampling site.

**Ascarite.** A sodium hydroxide treated asbestos.

**Ash.** Residue left from a sample after heating to 555 °C.

**Atomic absorption.** Method of analysis based on atomizing a metal sample in a flame and monitoring the absorption of specific wavelengths of light passed through the flame.

**ATP.** Adenosine triphosphate, a polyphosphate biochemical.

**Audits.** Examination of test procedures or other laboratory processes and comparison of the findings to a written standard, may be performed by an internal or external person to the laboratory.

**Autotune.** A software program that adjusts voltages and currents in a MS analyzer to achieve standard results.

**Baghouse filters.** Large cloth bags used to filter particulates from industrial air emissions.

**Bar code.** Optical pattern of narrow and wide bars used for sample tracking.

**Base-neutral extractables.** Compounds extractable from basic or neutral water solutions with organic solvents.

**Bench worksheets.** Papers used to record sample preparation and analysis work and notes by the technician as the work is being performed.

**BFB.** 4-bromofluorobenzene.

**BFB tuning requirements.** Abundance and mass detection requirements that must be met before analysis of compounds begins.

**Biochemical oxygen demand (BOD).** Oxygen requirement for bacteria to consume organic matter in a waste stream.

**Blank analysis.** QC measure that checks for contamination of analyte in reagents used for a test.

**Blank preservatives.** Analysis of preservatives used for samples to check for contamination.

**Blank samples.** Reagent water-filled containers prepared in the field and analyzed in the lab.

**BN.** Base/neutral organic target analytes.

**BNA analysis.** Base/neutral/acid extractable organics analyzed by GC/MS.

**BOD.** See biochemical oxygen demand.

**BOD bottles.** 300 mL bottles with ground glass stopper that is tapered at the bottom so as not to trap air bubbles in the bottle.

**BOD5.** Biochemical oxygen demand for a 5-day test.

**Breakpoint chlorination.** Addition of chlorine to water until all the chlorine demand has been satisfied and a residual remains.

**Brown Ring Test.** Qualitative test for nitrite.

**BTEX.** Benzene, toluene, ethylbenzene and xylene test.

**Buffers.** Solutions of a weak acid and a salt of the acid or a weak base and a salt of the base that are capable of maintaining pH on addition of acid or base.

**C, H, O pesticides.** Carbon-, hydrogen-, and oxygen-containing pesticides.

**Calculation Worksheets.** Forms filled out by the technician that record the mathematical transformation of raw analytical data into final results.

**Calibration Check Compounds.** A small group of representative compounds used to check the validity of instrument calibrations for a larger number of analyte compounds.

**Calibration Checks.** Procedures used to check instrument calibration.

**Calibration Curve.** Graphical plot of instrument response against amount of analyte in standards. Most often gives a straight line result.

**Calibration Factor.** Also called a response factor, it is a number used to multiply the instrument response and arrive at the amount of analyte.

**California Method.** Slang term for the GC-FID determination of diesel fuel.

**Carbamates.** Polar pesticides characterized by the presence of a urethane function.

**Carcinogenesis.** Uncontrolled replication of cells in the body resulting in tumors.

**Cascade impactor.** Device used for the speciation of particulates in air.

**CBOD.** Carbonaceous biochemical oxygen demand.

**CCC.** Calibration check compounds.

**CCV.** Continuing calibration verification.

**CERCLA.** Comprehensive Environmental Response, Compensation and Liability Act.

**Chain of custody.** Legal document recording who had the sample and over what period of time as it moves from the sampling point to the laboratory.

**Chemiluminescence.** Production of light from a chemical process.

**Chlorinated acid herbicides.** Herbicides structurally related to 2,4-dichloro phenoxyacetic acid.

**Chlorinated hydrocarbons.** Non-polar poly chlorinated hydrocarbon materials used mainly as pesticides.

**Chlorinated pesticides.** Non-polar poly chlorinated hydrocarbons.

**Chlorination.** Addition of chlorine to water for disinfection purposes.

**Chlorination disinfection by-products.** Chemicals resulting from addition of chlorine to water that contains organic materials.

**Chronic.** Effects seen over the long-term.

**Clean-up methods.** Procedures used to reduce interferences in organic sample extracts prior to analysis.

**CLP.** Contract Laboratory Program.

**CLP Deliverables.** Required quality control results and analytical documentation that must accompany each sample report on submission to EPA under the CLP.

**CLP SOW.** Contract Laboratory Program Statement of Work.

**Cobalt thiocyanate Active Substances.** non-ionic surfactants.

**COD.** Chemical oxygen demand.

**Cold vapor.** An AA method used with an optical cell replacing the flame.

**Coliform bacteria.** Any anaerobic and aerobic, gram negative, non-spore forming, rod-shaped bacteria that ferment lactose within 48 hours at 35 °C to produce carbon dioxide and acid.

**Colorimetric indicator tubes.** Scaled glass tubes packed with reagents that produce a color on passage of target analyte containing metered amounts of air through the tube.

**Composite Samples.** Individual samples are mixed together to make a single sample.

**Confirmed Test.** Second phase test of total or fecal coliform that confirms identification.

**Container Blanks.** Empty containers that are rinsed with reagent water and tested to insure freedom from target analytes. Generally performed by the lot number of the containers.

**Continuing Calibration Verification.** Standards are reanalyzed on a daily basis to reconfirm the validity of the instrument calibration.

**Continuous liquid-liquid extraction.** Device for extraction of organic analytes from water by dripping extraction solvent through the sample.

**Control charts.** Day-by-day or batch-by-batch plots of accuracy or precision as a process monitor.

**Control level.** ±3 standard deviations from the mean on a control chart.

**Conventional pollutants.** $BOD_5$, TSS, pH, and fecal coliform tests standard on most NPDES permits

**Correlation coefficient.** A mathematical measure of the goodness of fit, ranges from 0 to 1 with 1 being a perfect fit.

**CTAS.** Cobalt thiocyanate active substances.

**DAD.** Diode array detector.

**Data quality objectives.** Statements of the expected performance of the laboratory with respect to accuracy, precision, and MDL of each test procedure for each analyte.

**DBCP.** 1,2-Dibromo-3-chloropropane.

**DBOB.** 4,4'-Dibromooctafluorobiphenyl.

**DCAA.** 2,4-Dichlorophenylacetic acid.

**De-tuning.** After an MS passes autotune requirements for PFTBA, the voltage and current settings for the MS are changed in a set fashion so that the MS can meet the tune criteria for BFB or DFTPP.

**Dean-Starke trap.** A glassware device for separation of water from an organic material by azeotropic distillation.

**Denuders.** Devices for removing target analytes from air.

**DFTPP.** Decafluorotriphenylphospine.

**Diesel range organics.** Organic compounds determined by GC-FID that have retention times between decane and pentacosane, often assumed as diesel fuel.

**Digestion.** Solubilizing of metal analytes through heating with a variety of acids or oxidizers.

**Digestion logs.** Bound notebooks kept by technicians that record the details of the preparation of metals samples for analysis.

**Discharge Monitoring Report.** Periodic summaries of analytical results of wastewater effluents required of NPDES permit holders.

**DMR.** Discharge monitoring report.

**DNPH.** 2,4-dinitrophenyl hydrazine.

**Dose.** Dose/response.

**DPD.** N,N-diethyl phenylenediamine.

**DQO.** Data quality objectives.

**DRO method.** Diesel range organics referring to diesel fuel.

**EDB.** Ethylene dibromide.

**ELCD.** Electrolytic conductivity detector or Hall detector.

**Electrostatic precipitators.** Large scale devices that short circuit the static charges on particulates in air streams and result in removal of particulates.

**EQL.** Estimated quantitation limit.

**Equipment blanks.** Sampling equipment is rinsed with reagent water that is tested to determine contamination levels on the equipment.

**Estimated quantitation limit.** A term used to replace MDL when the MDL cannot be determined or is unavailable for the matrix, often 10 to 12 times a determined MDL.

**Extraction logs.** Logs maintained by the semivolatiles organic extraction technicians that detail everything that was performed on the sample.

**F- series.** Hazardous wastes from generic industrial sources.

**FAS.** Ferrous ammonium sulfate.

**FDA.** Food and Drug Administration.

**FDCA.** Food, Drug, and Cosmetic Act.

**Fecal coliform.** Coliform bacteria found in mammalian intestinal tracts.

**Field duplicate samples.** Duplicate samples obtained in the field and analyzed in the lab to assess field precision in sampling.

**Field log book.** A bound notebook maintained by the field operators that details every aspect of the sampling event.

**FIFRA.** Federal Insecticide, Fungicide, and Rodenticide Act.

**Filter cassette.** Device for holding membrane or glass fiber filters for removal of target analytes from air.

**Final analytical report.** Summary of the analytical results obtained by the laboratory and sent to the client.

**Fixed solids.** Another term for ash.

**Flash point.** Temperature at which a sample creates sufficient vapor to support combustion in air.

**Flow domain.** Set volumes of sample removed from a stationary sampling location after every set amount of flow.

**FPD.** Flame photometric detector.

**Freon 113.** 1,1,2-trichlorotrifluoroethane.

**FTIR.** Fourier transform infrared spectrophotometer.

**Gas chromatography.** Separatory technique that uses a solid or liquid absorbent and an inert gas stream as mobile phase - separation mechanisms are vapor pressure and chemical affinity.

**Gasoline range organic.** All organic materials that elute from a GC with retention times between 2-methyl pentane and trimethylbenzene - assumed to be gasoline fuel.

**GC.** Gas chromatography.

**GC/FTIR.** Gas chromatography - fourier transform infrared spectro-photometer interfaced together.

**GC/MS.** Gas chromatography - mass spectrometer interfaced together.

**Gel permeation Column.** A clean-up technique that separates compounds based on molecular size.

**GFAA.** Graphite furnace atomic absorption.

**GPC.** Gel permeation chromatography.

**Grab Sample.** A sample obtained in a single instant of time at a single location.

**Graphite furnace.** A carbon tube that is electrically heated in an AA to replace the flame as the atomization source.

**GRO method.** Gasoline range organics, used in reference to gasoline analysis.

**Groundwater.** Subsurface water.

**Halowaxes.** Polychlorinated derivatives of naphthalene.

**Hardness.** Dissolved metal content of water, expressed as calcium carbonate.

**High performance liquid chromatography.** Separation technique that uses a solid absorbent and liquid mobile phase - separation mechanism is chemical partitioning.

**Holding times.** Elapsed time between moment of sampling and initiation of analysis.

**Hotplate Digestion.** Open beaker method of acid digestion of metals.

**HPLC.** High pressure liquid chromatography.

**HPLC-DAD.** High pressure liquid chromatography with a diode array detector.

**HPLC/MS.** High pressure liquid chromatography interfaced to a mass spectrometer.

**ICAP.** Inductively coupled argon plasma emission spectrometer.

**ICP.** Inductively coupled argon plasma emission spectrometer.

**ICV.** Initial calibration verification.

**IDL.** Instrument detection limit.

**Immunity.** Ability of an organism to develop protecting antibodies to a foreign agent after an initial exposure.

**Impingers.** Glassware device for passing air through a liquid solution.

**Indicators.** Chemicals added to a sample that signal an end to a process by a color change.

**Inductively Coupled Argon Plasma.** 6,000 to 10,000 °C thermal source for excitation of metal atoms in emission spectrometry.

**Initial Calibration Verification.** Immediate analysis of standards from a different manufacturer than that of the calibration standards to check suitability of a calibration curve.

**Instrument Detection Limit**. Minimum signal level that can be differentiated from instrument background noise with 99% confidence.

**Instrument Maintenance.** Regular and nonscheduled procedures required to keep an instrument in top operational condition.

**Integrated sample.** A variety of different sampling methods used to form an overall picture of the sampling site.

**Internal chain of custody.** A record of who had the sample over what period of time within the laboratory.

**Internal standards.** Compounds added to the sample after sample preparation for qualitative and quantitative instrument analysis - the compounds serve to give a standard of retention time and response, which is invariant from run-to-run with the instruments.

**Ion chromatography.** Instrument very similar to an HPLC used for analysis of anions or cations.

**IR.** Infrared spectrophotometric.

**IR-TPH.** Infrared determination of total petroleum hydrocarbons.

**IRIS.** Plasma emission spectrometer that uses a photodetector to simultaneously record all the emission lines of a sample.

**Isotope dilution.** Addition of isotopically labeled analytes to a sample to assess sample preparation and serve as internal standard for analysis.

**K-D concentrator.** Kuderna-Danish concentrator - glassware device for removal of solvents from an organic extract.

**K-series.** Listed hazardous wastes from specific industrial processes.

**KHP.** Potassium hydrogen phthalate.

**Kuderna-Danish concentrator.** Glassware device for removal of solvents from an organic extract.

**Laboratory control sample.** Known amounts of target analytes are added to reagent water and analyzed. Serves as a quality control on the sample preparation process.

**Landfill leachate.** Liquid that drains from the bottom of the site into the ground.

**Langelier's Index.** An analytical measure of the corrosivity of water.

**LAS.** Linear alkylbenzene sulfonate.

**Lauric acid value.** Standardization procedure for Florosil.

**LC.** Lethal concentration.

**LD5.** Lethal dose for 5% of the test subjects.

**LD50.** Lethal dose for 50% of the test subjects.

**Legally defensible.** Analytical results supported by the necessary documentation to withstand challenge in a US court of law.

**Lethal concentration.** Amount of substance in water solution that the test organism was exposed to that resulted in the death.

**LIMS.** Laboratory information management system.

**LUST.** Leaking underground storage tanks remediation program.

**MASA Methods.** Methods of Air Sampling and Analysis, Lodge, 3rd Edition.

**Matrix spikes.** Target analyte added to a sample in known amount to determine recovery for the specific matrix..

**Maximum Contaminant Levels.** Regulatory action levels for primary drinking water analytes.

**MBAS.** Methylene blue active substances.

**MBTH.** N-Methyl benzothiazolinon hydrazone.

**MCE.** Mixed cellulose ester membrane for metals analysis of air samples.

**MDL.** Method detection limits.

**Method Detection Limits.** Minimum level of a target analyte that can be determined with 99% confidence.

**Methylene Blue Active Substances.** Anionic surfactants that can be extracted into chloroform solution by a ion-pairing mechanism with methylene blue.

**MSDS.** Material safety data sheets.

**MTB.** Methyl thymol blue.

**MUG.** 4-Methylumbelliferyl-ß-D-glucuronide.

**Multiple Sampling.** More than one sample taken from a site to assess pollution.

**Mutagenesis.** Inheritable damage to DNA of an organism caused by a foreign chemical or agent.

**N & P Pesticides.** Nitrogen and/or phosphorous-containing pesticides.

**NDIR.** Non-dispersive infrared analyzer.

**NED.** N-Napthyl-ethylenediamine dichloride.

**Nipples.** Permanent sampling ports in the sides of smoke stacks.

**Nitrogen Inhibition.** Chemicals added to BOD test to eliminate nitrogen oxidation demand on the results.

**NMHC.** Non-methane hydrocarbons.

**NMOC.** Non-methane organic compounds.

**Non-conventional pollutants.** Nitrogen forms, phosphorous, chloride, sulfate and other substances that may endanger water quality while not necessarily being toxic.

**NPDES.** National Pollutant Discharge Elimination System.

**NTU.** Nephelometric turbidity unit.

**ONPG.** $o$-Nitrophenyl-ß-D-galactopyranoside.

**OPA.** Ortho phthalaldehyde.

**P-A.** Presence-absence of total or fecal coliforms.

**P-series.** Acutely hazardous wastes from commercial chemical products, intermediates and residues.

**PAH.** Polynuclear aromatic hydrocarbons.

**PAO.** Phenylarsine oxide.

**Pathogenic bacteria.** Disease causing bacteria.

**PCBs.** Polychlorinated biphenyls.

**PDS.** Post digestion spike - independently checks the calibration of the AA, GFAA, or ICP instrument.

**PE Samples.** Performance evaluation samples.

**Performance evaluation.** Blind samples sent to the laboratory by outside parties for evaluation of qualitative and quantitative accuracy.

**PES.** Post extraction spike - a solution of extraction solvent containing surrogates, matrix spikes and internal standards for evaluating instrument calibration.

**PFTBA.** Perfluorotributylamine

**pH.** The negative log of the activity of the hydrogen ion.

**Phenoxy-acid herbicides.** See chlorinated acid herbicides.

**Phthalate esters.** As a group they are the most common form of laboratory contamination.

**Pitot.** Sampling tube for stack gas analysis.

**Post column derivatization.** Chemical procedure for derivatization of compounds after they elute from the separation column and before they enter the detector.

**POTW.** Publicly owned treatment works.

**ppm.** Parts per million.

**ppt.** Parts per trillion.

**PQL.** Practical quantitation levels.

**Practical Quantitation Levels.** Some randomly selected multiple, often 10 or 12, of the same sample.

**Precision.** The closeness of agreement between two or more analyses of the same sample.

**Presence-absence.** Qualitative test for total or fecal coliforms.

**Preservatives.** Chemical or physical treatment of the sample to assure continued presence of the target analytes at the same level as when the sample was first taken.

**Primary standard.** Analytical standard compounds that are stable solids, easy to purify to a known and reproducible level.

**PUF.** Polyurethane foam used as a trapping material for sampling of semivolatile organic compounds from air.

**QC check standards.** Analytical standards obtained from a different source than the manufacturer of the calibration standards, used as an independent check on the calibration.

**Qualified data.** Data derived from a sample analysis where something about the sample, the sampling procedure, or the analysis is not in accordance with specifications.

**Qualitative analysis.** The analytical process to determine what is in the sample.

**Quality assurance program.** The written overall program in the laboratory that details all the steps and procedures used to produce data of a known and stated quality.

**Quality control.** An individual procedure used in the quality assurance program. A matrix spike performed on a metals sample is a quality control, the use of matrix spikes in all procedures in the laboratory is quality assurance.

**Quantitative analysis.** After an analyte is identified in the sample, quantitiative analysis is used to determine how much is there.

**r.** Regression coefficient with values between 0 to 1 - a value of 1.00 is perfect correlation of the points to the equation.

**Raw data.** Unprocessed data from the analysis.

**Reagent blanks.** An analyte-free sample of water, air or solid is processed with all the reagents in the procedure, then analyzed to discover any interference from the reagents used in the batch.

**Relative percent difference.** The difference between two values divided by the average of the values, expressed as a percent.

**Representative sample.** The degree to which a single sample of the whole can give results identical to analysis of the whole.

**Residues.** Remainder after removal of water or other liquids, see solids and total solids.

**Resistance.** Ability of a single organism, due to a genetic difference, to survive challenge by a toxic material that would be fatal to most of the rest of the population of the organism.

**Respirable.** Particles that pass the nasal membranes and hairs to lodge deep in the lungs.

**Response factors.** Multiplication factors for converting instrument response to mass of analyte.

**Retention time.** Elapsed time between injection of sample to elution on the chromatogram.

**RF.** Response factor.

**RPD.** Relative percent difference.

**RT.** Retention time.

**Run logs.** A bound logbook for each instrument listing consecutively what was run, when, by whom, how much was analyzed, and what file name the raw data is filed under.

**Sample container logs.** A written account of either the in-house cleaning of sample containers and results of blank analyses, or a record of receipt of pre-cleaned containers along with manu-facturers' certificates and results of blank analyses by lot.

**Sample disposition logs.** A written record of how samples were disposed after the required post-analysis holding times.

**Sample duplicate.** Analysis of two aliquots of sample in the same analytical batch to assess precision.

**Sample preparation logs.** Written record of the preparation of standards including weights, dilutions, and person performing the work.

**Sample receipt logbooks.** Written records of when samples were received, description of the samples, client name, date sampled, requested analyses, and person performing the log-in.

**Sample result worksheets.** Also described as work orders, these are sheets that give the analyst basic information about what tests are requested for the samples and may also provide space for entry of sample analysis results.

**Sample splits.** A single sample is divided into two containers that are sent to different labs for analysis.

**Secondary Drinking Water Standards.** Includes materials which affect the taste, odor, color and other non-health related qualities of water and collectively serve as a suggested list for states to act upon.

**Sequential samples.** A series of identical samples obtained under time or flow domain that are analyzed as a separate samples.

**SFE.** Supercritical fluid extraction, normally of solids.

**SOW.** Contract Laboratory Program Statement of Work, in essence a request for bid for services to EPA.

**SPCC.** System performance check compounds.

**Stacks.** Points of discharge of air from industrial processes to the atmosphere.

**Standard receipt logs.** Written record of the receipt of standards, including date, manufacturer's certificate of analysis, person logging standards, etc.

**Surrogates.** Compounds added to the sample prior to preparation, then monitored after analysis to detect problems in the sample preparation procedure.

**SVI.** Sludge volume index.

**TAL.** Target analyte list.

**TCDD.** 2,3,7,8-Tetrachloro-dibenzodioxin.

**TCL.** Target compound list.

**TCLP.** Toxic characteristic leaching procedure.

**TCMP.** 2-Chloro-6-trichloromethylpyridine.

**TDS.** Total dissolved solids.

**Temperature monitoring logs.** Written logs that record the twice daily checking of temperature on refrigerators, ovens and incubators, along with repair notes.

**Teratogenesis.** Birth defects caused by chemical exposure.

**THC.** Total hydrocarbon content.

**THM.** Trihalomethanes.

**TIC.** Tentatively identified compounds.

**Time domain.** Identical samples obtained at the same location at set intervals of time.

**TOC.** Total organic carbon.

**TOX.** Total organic halide.

**TPH.** Total petroleum hydrocarbon.

**Trip blanks.** VOC sample containers assembled with reagent water at the laboratory, then taken to the field and back to the lab, analyzed to reveal contamination that occurs by passage of volatile compounds through the septum into the container.

**TRS.** Total reduced sulfur.

**TS.** Total solids.

**TSCA.** Toxic Substances Control Act.

**TSD.** Treatment, storage and disposal facility for hazardous waste.

**TSS.** Total suspended solids.

**TTHM.** Total trihalomethanes.

**TVDS.** Total volatile dissolved solids.

**TVS.** Total volatile solids.

**TVSS.** Total volatile suspended solids.

**U-series.** Hazardous waste of a general nature from commercial chemical products, intermediates, or residues.

**UST.** Underground storage tanks.

**Vertical composite sample.** Grab samples at a variety of depths at one sampling location that are mixed together to form a single sample representing the water column.

**VOA.** Volatile organic analysis.

**VOC.** Volatile organic compounds.

**Warning Level.** ±2 standard deviations from the mean on a control chart.

**Work assignments.** Printouts of samples that require the same test by a worker for processing as a batch.

**WP.** Biannual performance evaluation samples sent out by EPA in support of the water pollution programs under the Clean Water Act.

**WP analytes.** A list of the analytes in the WP studies.

**WS.** Biannual performance evaluation samples sent out by EPA in support of the water supply programs under the Safe Drinking Water Act.

**XAD-2.** Insoluble, porous, non-polar polystyrene Amberlite resin used for isolation of organic materials from air streams.

**ZHE.** Zero headspace extractor.

# INDEX

601-602. **266, 279, 284**
AA. **211**
Accuracy. **111, 130, 131**
Acetaldehyde. **341**
Acetonitrile partition. **302**, **303**
Acid digestion. **207**
Acid extractables. **267, 305**
Acid-base partition. **323**
Acrolein. **342, 447**
Acrylamide. **324, 342**
Acrylonitrile. **342**
Activated carbon. **268**
Activated charcoal. **439**
Activated florisil. **308**
Acute. **192**
Adipate esters. **286**
Adsorbent traps. **439**
Air sampling. **437**
Alkalinity. **199**
Allylthiourea. **203**
Alumina column. **321**
Alumina microcolumn. **302**
Ames Test. **193**
Amide pesticides. **310**
Amine pesticides. **312**
Ammonia. **224, 241**
Amperometric detection. **181**
Amperometric titration. **227**
Analyte-free water. **269**
Analytical balance. **147**
Analytical methodologies. **34**
Analytically valid. **110**
Annular denuders. **438**
Appendix I. **389**
Appendix II. **390**

Areal composite sample. **84**
Areal domain. **83**
Arsenic. **453**
Asbestos. **453**
Ascarite. **453**
Ash. **177**
Atomic absorption. **211**
ATP. **246**
Audits. **160**
Automated soxhlet extraction. **319**
Autotune. **343**
Azeotropic distillation. **283**

### B

Baghouse filters. **440**
Bar code. **83**
Barium methylthymol blue. **451**
Base-neutral extractables. **267, 305**
Bench worksheets. **145**
Benomyl. **309**
Bensulide. **312**
Benzidines. **297**
Beryllium. **453**
BFB. **343**
BFB tuning requirements. **273, 279, 343**
Biochemical oxygen demand (BOD). **203**
Blank analysis. **81**
Blank preservatives. **153**
Blank samples. **153**
BN. **267**
BNA analysis. **267, 305**
BOD. **203**
BOD bottles. **203**
$BOD_5$. **203**

Breakpoint chlorination. **224**
Bromoxynil. **318**
Brown ring test. **243**
BTEX. **365, 394**
Buffers. **197**

**C**

C, H, O pesticides. **303**
C.I. 348
Calculating standard deviation. **132**
Calculation worksheets. **147**
Calibration check compounds. **279, 280, 281**
Calibration checks. **160**
Calibration curve. **134, 147**
Calibration factor. **302**
California Method. **278**
Capillary electrophoresis. **284**
Carbamates. **293, 310, 342**
Carbendazim. **309**
Carbon dioxide. **444**
Carbon monoxide. **443**
Carbon oxides. **443**
Carcinogenesis. **193**
Cascade impactor. **440**
Catalytic reduction. **444**
CBOD. **203**
CCC. **279, 280, 281**
CCV. **160**
CERCLA.. **3, 397**
CFR. **1**
Chain of custody. **81, 144**
Chelation agents. **234**
Chemical hazards. **383**
Chemical oxygen demand. **205**
Chemiluminescence. **449, 452, 453**
Chemiluminescent reaction. **453**
Chlorinated acid herbicides. **289**
Chlorinated herbicides. **302**
Chlorinated hydrocarbons. **301, 331**
Chlorinated pesticides. **287**
Chlorinated phenols. **222**
Chlorination. **222**
Chlorination disinfection by-products. **295**

Chlorine. **448**
2-Chloro-6-trichloromethylpyridine. **203**
Chromogenic Substrate Coliform Test. **190**
Chromotropic acid. **243, 445**
Chronic. **192**
Clean Water Act. **8**
Clean-up methods. **321**
CLP. **397, 445**
CLP deliverables. **397**
CLP SOW. **267**
Coating materials. **439**
Cobalt thiocyanate active substances. **232**
COD. **205**
Code of Federal Regulations **1**
Cold traps. **439**
Cold vapor. **221**
Coliform bacteria. **186**
Colorimetric indicator tubes. **441**
Colour Index. **348**
Complexometric titration. **200**
Composite samples. **84**
Comprehensive Environmental Response, Compensation and Liability Act (Superfund). **3, 397**
Conductivity. **185**
Confirmed test. **186**
Container blanks. **153**
Continuing calibration verification. **160**
Continuous liquid-liquid extraction. **318**
Contract Laboratory Program. **397, 445**
Contract Laboratory Program Statement of Work. **267, 398**
Control charts. **161**
Control level. **161, 163**
Correlation coefficient. **115, 147**
Corrosivity characteristic (D002). **384**
CTAS. **232**
Cyanazine. **308**
Cyanide. **237, 385**
Cyanogen chloride. **238**
Cyclones. **440**
Cyprinodon variegatus. **193**

**D**

DAD. **294**
Dafnia. **193**
Dansylhydrazine. **446**
Data quality objectives. **130, 133, 134**
Dazomet. **317**
DBCP. **272**
DCAA. **289**
De-tuning. **344**
Deactivated silica gel. **303**
Dean-Starke trap. **181**
Decafluorotriphenylphospine. **291, 305, 313, 314, 343**
Denuders. **438**
DFTPP. **291, 305, 313, 314, 343**
Diazald. **289**
Diazomethane. **289, 290**
Diazonium salts. **242**
2,3,7,8-Dibenzodioxin. **288, 302**
Dichlorophen. **297**
Diesel range organics. **278, 394**
Diethylenetriamine pentaacetic acid. **234**
Digestion. **206**
Digital thermometers. **182**
Dinitro aromatic pesticides. **313**
Dinitroaniline pesticides. **308**
Diode array detector. **294**
Diquat. **294**
Discharge Monitoring Report. **8, 9, 167**
Dissolved oxygen. **202**
Dithiocarbamate pesticides. **309**
DMR. **8, 9, 167, 172**
DMR chemical analytes. **172**
DNP. **341**
DNPH. **446**
Dose/Response curves. **192**
DPD. **227**
DQO. **130, 133, 134**
Drinking water. **3, 267**
Drinking water monitoring requirements. **4, 5, 6, 7**
DRO method. **278, 322, 394**
DTPA. **234**
Dust-fall buckets. **440**

**E**

ECD. **265**
EDB - ethylene dibromide., **272**
EDTA. **234**
ELCD. **265, 270, 271, 275, 279, 284**
Electrochemical oxidation. **444**
Electrolytic conductivity detector. **265, 270, 271, 275, 279, 284**
Electron capture detector. **265**
Electrostatic precipitators. **440**
Endothall. **294**
Environmental Protection Agency. **2**
EPA Methods:

| | |
|---|---|
| 1 | **441** |
| 10 | **444** |
| 101 | **453** |
| 102 | **453** |
| 104 | **453** |
| 10A | **444** |
| 10B | **444** |
| 11 | **449** |
| 12 | **453** |
| 120.1 | **185** |
| 130 | **200** |
| 1311 | **386** |
| 1312 | **389** |
| 15 | **449** |
| 150.1 | **194** |
| 15A | **449** |
| 16 | **449** |
| 160 | **177** |
| 160.1 | **178** |
| 160.2 | **178** |
| 160.3 | **177** |
| 160.4 | **178** |
| 160.5 | **178** |
| 1624 | **278** |
| 1625 | **313** |
| 1656 | **314** |
| 1657 | **315** |
| 1658 | **316** |
| 1659 | **317** |
| 1660 | **317** |
| 1661 | **318** |
| 16A | **449** |

EPA Methods: *continued*

| | | | | |
|---|---|---|---|---|
| 16B | **450** | | 502.2 | **271** |
| 180.1 | **184** | | 5030 | **283** |
| 2 | **441** | | 5031 | **283** |
| 245.1 | **221** | | 504 | **272** |
| 25 | **445** | | 5040 | **283** |
| 25A | **445** | | 5041 | **283** |
| 25B | **445** | | 505 | **285** |
| 3005 | **207** | | 506 | **286** |
| 3010 | **207** | | 507 | **286** |
| 3015 | **208** | | 508A | **288** |
| 3050 | **207** | | 510.1 | **222** |
| 3051 | **208, 209** | | 5100 | **283** |
| 310.1 | **199** | | 513 | **288** |
| 330 | **222** | | 515.1 | **289** |
| 335 | **237** | | 515.2 | **291** |
| 3510 | **318** | | 524.1 | **272** |
| 3520 | **318** | | 524.2 | **273** |
| 3540 | **319** | | 525 | **291** |
| 3541 | **319** | | 531.1 | **294** |
| 3550 | **319** | | 547 | **293** |
| 3560 | **319** | | 548 | **294** |
| 3580 | **320** | | 549 | **294** |
| 3600 | **321** | | 549.1 | **295** |
| 3610 | **321** | | 550 | **295** |
| 3611 | **321** | | 551 | **295** |
| 3620 | **322** | | 552 | **296** |
| 3630 | **322** | | 6 | **450, 451** |
| 3640 | **322** | | 601 | **275** |
| 365 | **244** | | 602 | **275** |
| 3650 | **323** | | 604 | **296** |
| 3660 | **323** | | 604.1 | **297** |
| 3665 | **323** | | 605 | **297** |
| 376 | **240** | | 606 | **298** |
| 3810 | **283** | | 607 | **298** |
| 3820 | **283** | | 608 | **298** |
| 405.1 | **203** | | 608.1 | **299** |
| 410.1 | **205** | | 608.2 | **299** |
| 410.4 | **205** | | 609 | **300** |
| 413 | **234** | | 610 | **300** |
| 415.1 | **230** | | 611 | **301** |
| 418.1 | **364** | | 612 | **301** |
| 420 | **235** | | 613 | **302** |
| 425 | **232** | | 614 | **302** |
| 501 | **269** | | 614.1 | **302** |
| 502.1 | **270** | | 615 | **302** |
| | | | 616 | **303** |

EPA Methods: *continued*

| | |
|---|---|
| 617 | **303** |
| 618 | **304** |
| 619 | **304** |
| 622 | **304** |
| 624 | **276** |
| 627 | **308** |
| 629 | **308** |
| 630.1 | **309** |
| 631 | **309** |
| 632 | **310** |
| 632.1 | **310** |
| 633 | **311** |
| 633.1 | **311** |
| 634 | **311, 312** |
| 635 | **311** |
| 636 | **312** |
| 641 | **312** |
| 645 | **312** |
| 646 | **313** |
| 6A | **444, 451** |
| 6B | **451** |
| 6C | **450** |
| 7 | **452** |
| 7A | **452** |
| 7B | **452** |
| 7C | **452** |
| 7D | **452** |
| 8 | **451** |
| 8011 | **283** |
| 8015 | **278** |
| 8020 | **283** |
| 8021 | **279** |
| 8030 | **283** |
| 8031 | **283** |
| 8032 | **324** |
| 8040 | **324** |
| 8080 | **325** |
| 8081 | **325** |
| 8121 | **331** |
| 8240 | **279** |
| 8250 | **332** |
| 8260 | **281** |
| 8270 | **335** |
| 8275 | **338** |
| 8315 | **341** |
| 8316 | **342** |
| 8318 | **342** |
| 8321 | **342** |
| 9010 | **237** |
| 9030 | **240** |
| 9073 | **364** |

Air analysis   **454**

| | |
|---|---|
| IP-3A | **444** |
| IP-5A | **452** |
| IP-5B | **452** |
| IP-5C | **452** |
| IP-6A | **446** |
| IP-6B | **446** |
| IP-6C | **446** |
| TO-11 | **446** |
| TO-12 | **445** |
| TO-5 | **446** |

EQL. **279**
Equipment blanks. **153**
Eriochrome Black T. **200**
Escherichia coli. **186**
Estimated quantitation limit. **279**
Ethylene diamine tetraacetic acid. **234**
Ethylene dibromide. **272**
Evaporation rate. **442**
Extraction fluids. **386**

**F**

F- series. **383**
FAS. **205**
Fat and oil removal. **302**
Fathead minnows. **193**
Fats and oils. **303**
FDA. **20**
FDCA. **20**
Fecal coliform. **186**
Federal Insecticide, Fungicide, and Rodenticide Act. **19**
Ferroin indicator. **205**
Ferrous ammonium sulfate. **205**
FID. **265**
Field duplicate samples. **153**
Field log book. **80**
FIFRA. **19**
Filter cassette. **437**

Final analytical report. **82, 150**
Fixed solids. **177**
Flame ionization detector. **265**
Flame photometric detector. **265**
Flash point. **383**
Florisil column. **322**
Florisil standardization. **322**
Flow domain. **83**
Food and Drug Administration. **20**
Food, Drug, and Cosmetic Act. **20**
Formaldehyde. **445**
Formazin. **184**
Formic acid. **447**
Fourier transform infrared
    spectrophotometer. **443**
FPD. **265**
Free atmospheric chlorine. **448**
Freon. **113, 234**
FTIR. **443**

**G**

Gas chromatography. **394**
Gas chromatography - fourier transform
    infrared spectrophotometer
    interfaced. **266**
Gas chromatography - mass spectrometer
    interfaced. **266, 445**
Gasoline range organic. **278, 365, 394**
GC. **394**
GC/FTIR. **266**
GC/MS. **266, 445**
GC/MS purgeable organics. **272, 273,
    276**
Gel permeation column. **322**
Gentistic acid. **243**
GFAA. **212**
Glyphosate. **293**
Good Laboratory Practice Standards. **20**
GPC. **323**
Grab sample. **83, 440**
Graphite furnace. **212**
Graphite furnace atomic absorption. **212**
GRO method. **278, 365, 394**
Groundwater. **267, 389**
Groundwater monitoring. **389**

**H**

Hall detector. **265**
Haloacetic acids. **296**
Haloethers. **301**
Halogenated and aromatic volatiles. **279**
Halowaxes. **323**
Hardness. **200**
Hazardous waste characterization. **267,
    383**
Hazardous Waste Management. **2**
Henderson-Hasselbalch equation. **197**
Heteropoly blue. **246**
Hexachlorophene. **297**
Hexavalent chromium. **217**
High performance liquid
    chromatography. **267, 446**
High pressure liquid chromatography
    interfaced to a mass spectrometer.
    **266, 284**
High pressure liquid chromatography
    with a diode array detector. **266**
Holding times. **85, 407**
Hotplate digestion. **206**
HPLC. **267, 446**
HPLC-DAD. **266**
HPLC/MS. **266, 284**
Hydrocarbons. **444**
Hydrogen sulfide. **240, 449**

**I**

ICAP. **213**
ICP. **213**
ICV. **160**
IDL. **134**
Ignitability characteristic (D001). **383**
Immunity. **192**
Impingers. **439**
Indicators. **197**
Inductively coupled argon plasma
    emission spectrometer. **213**
Infrared detector. **265**
Infrared determination of total petroleum
    hydrocarbons. **322**
Infrared spectrophotometric. **394, 450,
    452**

Infrared spectroscopy. **443**
Initial calibration verification. **160**
Inorganic phosphates. **245, 246**
Instrument detection limit. **134**
Instrument maintenance. **147**
Integrated sample. **84**
Internal chain of custody. **83, 148**
Internal standards. **269, 281**
Iodometric direct. **225**
Iodometric indirect. **226**
Iodometric titration. **449**
Ion chromatography. **284**
Ion trap MS. **284**
Ion-pairing reagent. **294**
IR. **396, 452, 454**
IR-TPH. **322**
IRD. **265**
IRIS. **213**
Isotope dilution. **313**

**K**

K-D concentrator. **318**
K-series. **383**
Karl Fisher titration. **181**
KHP. **204, 205**
Kjeldahl method. **244**
Kuderna-Danish concentrator. **318**

**L**

Laboratory control sample. **159**
Laboratory information management
    system. **81**
Landfill leachate. **267**
Langelier's Index. **201**
LAS - linear alkylbenzene sulfonate. **232**
Laughing gas. **452**
Lauric acid value. **322**
LC. **192**
LD$_5$. **192**
LD$_{50}$. **192**
Lead. **453**
Leaking underground storage tanks. **66,
    393**
Legally defensible. **110, 398**

Lethal concentration. **192**
Lethal dose. **192**
Lethane. **312**
Leuco Crystal Violet. **229**
LIMS. **81**
Linear alkylbenzene sulfonate. **232**
Linear regression. **115**
Liquid-membrane-liquid extraction. **320**
List of specific wastes. **383**
Luminol. **452**
LUST. **66, 393**

**M**

M-Endo. **189**
M-FC. **189**
MASA. **445**
MASA Methods:
    114    **447**
    116    **445**
    202    **448**
    407    **452**
    720C   **451**
    720F   **451**
MASA Methods - Methods of Air
    Sampling and Analysis, Lodge, 3rd
    Edition. **445**
Mass selective detector. **265**
Mass spectrometer tuning. **343**
Material Safety Data Sheets. **442**
Matrix spikes. **153, 318**
Maximum Contaminant Levels. **4**
MBAS. **232**
MBTH. **446**
MCE. **453**
MDL. **4, 36**
Membrane filter test. **189**
Mercaptans. **449**
Mercury. **221, 453**
Mercury removal of sulfur. **303**
Mercury-filled thermometers. **182**
Metals. **206, 453**
Method detection limits. **4, 136**
N-methyl benzothiazolinon hydrazone.
    **446**
Methyl isothiocyanate. **317**

Methyl orange. **198, 229, 448**
Methyl thymol blue. **451**
Methylene blue. **203, 449**
Methylene blue active substances. **232**
Microcrustaceans. **193**
Microextraction. **304**
Microwave. **208, 209**
Midget impingers. **439**
Mixed cellulose ester membrane. **453**
Moisture. **180**
Molecular sieves. **268**
Mono-phosphates. **245**
MPN. **186**
MS. **265**
MSDS. **442**
MTB. **451**
MUG. **190**
Multiple sampling. **83**
Municipal landfill. **386**
Mutagenesis. **193**

**N**

N & P pesticides. **286**
N-napthyl-ethylenediamine dichloride.
    **243**
National Pollutant Discharge Elimination
    System. **8**
NDIR. **443, 445**
NED. **243**
Nephelometer. **184**
Nephelometric turbidity unit. **184**
Nessler tubes. **242**
Nessler's reagent. **242**
Nipples. **441**
Nitrate. **243**
Nitric oxide. **452**
Nitrite. **242**
Nitroaromatics. **300**
Nitrogen. **241**
Nitrogen dioxide. **452**
Nitrogen inhibition. **203**
Nitrogen oxides. **452**
Nitrogen-phosphorous detector. **265**
o-Nitrophenyl-b-D-galactopyranoside.
    **190**

Nitrosamines. **298**
Nitrous oxide. **452**
NMHC. **445**
NMOC. **445**
Non-conventional pollutants. **8**
Non-dispersive IR. **443**
Non-dispersive infrared analyzer. **443,
    445**
Non-methane hydrocarbons. **445**
Non-methane organic compounds. **445**
Non-volatile solvent extractable
    compounds. **342**
Nonhalogenated volatile organics. **278**
NPD. **265**
NPDES. **8**
NTU. **184**

**O**

Oil & grease. **234, 394**
ONPG. **190**
OPA. **293**
Operator certification. **160**
Organic analytes. **444**
Organochlorine pesticides. **298, 299, 303,
    325**
Organohalide pesticides. **285, 314**
Organonitrogen pesticides. **311**
Organophosphorous pesticides. **302, 304,
    315**
Orthophosphate. **244**
Ortho phthalaldehyde. **293**
Orthotolidine. **229**
Oxidizer. **384**
Ozone. **453**

**P**

P-A. **190**
P-series. **383**
PAH. **295, 300, 322, 341**
PAO. **449**
Paraquat. **294**
Particulates. **440**
Pathogenic bacteria. **186**
PCBs. **285, 288, 298, 303, 319, 322, 325**

PDS. **160**
PE samples. **160, 167**
Percent recovery. **132**
Perfluorotributylamine. **343**
Performance evaluation. **160**
PES. **160**
PFTBA. **343**
pH. **194**
pH electrode. **195**
pH paper. **197**
pH standards. **198**
Phenate method. **242**
Phenolphthalein. **198**
Phenols. **296, 322, 324**
Phenoxy-acid herbicides (see also
    chlorinated acid herbicides). **316**
Phenylarsine oxide. **449**
Phosphomolybdate. **246**
Phosphorous. **244**
Photo-ionization detector. **265**
Phthalate esters. **286, 325**
Phthalates. **298**
PID. **265**
Pimephales promelas. **193**
Pitot. **441**
Polychlorinated biphenyls. **285, 288, 298,**
    **303, 319, 322, 325**
Polynomial regression. **117**
Polynuclear aromatic hydrocarbons. **295,**
    **300, 322, 341**
Polyphosphates. **245**
Polyurethane foam. **439**
Post column derivatization. **293**
Post digestion spikes. **160**
Post extraction spikes. **160**
Potassium biiodate. **226**
Potassium hydrogen phthalate. **205**
Potentiometric detection. **181**
POTW. **8**
ppm. **442**
ppt. **222**
PQL. **136, 138**
Practical Quantitation Levels. **136, 138**
Precision. **111, 130, 131**
Presence-absence. **190**
Preservatives. **84**

Presumptive test. **186**
Primary Drinking Water Standards. **3**
Primary standard. **205**
Publicly owned treatment works. **8**
PUF. **439, 445**
Pulsed fluorescence. **450**
Purge and trap. **266, 268**
Purgeable aromatics. **275**
Purgeable halocarbons. **275**
Pyrethrins. **317**

**Q**

QC check standards. **159**
Quadrupole GC/MS. **284**
Qualified data. **81**
Qualitative analysis. **261**
Quality assurance program. **110**
Quality control. **153**
Quantitative analysis. **261**

**R**

r. **115, 147**
Rainbow trout. **193**
Raw data. **147**
Reactivity characteristic. **385**
Reagent blanks. **156**
Record keeping. **80**
Relative percent difference. **132**
Representative sample. **83**
Residues. **177**
Resistance. **192**
Resolution of PAH pairs. **305**
Resource Conservation and Recovery
    Act. **2**
Respirable. **440**
Response factors. **119**
Restricted storage. **83**
Retention time. **269, 305**
Reversed phase media. **439**
RF. **119**
Rotenone. **311**
RPD. **132**
RT. **269, 305**
Run logs. **147**

**S**

Safe Drinking Water Act. **3**
Safety. **80**
Salmo gairdneri. **193**
Salmonella. **193**
Sample container logs. **150**
Sample containers. **81**, **84**
Sample disposition logs. **150**
Sample duplicate. **155**
Sample labeling. **81**
Sample preparation logs. **150**
Sample receipt. **81**
Sample receipt logbooks. **144**
Sample result worksheets. **148**
Sample seal. **83**
Sample security. **83**
Sample splits. **161**
Sampling procedures. **80**
Secondary Drinking Water Standards. **4**
Semivolatile organic compounds. **291**,
   **313, 332, 335, 338**
Semivolatiles. **267, 283, 445**
Separatory funnel liquid-liquid
   extraction. **318**
Sequential samples. **84**
Settleable solids. **177**
SFE. **319**
Sheepshead minnows. **193**
Silica gel. **268, 302, 439**
Silica gel column. **302**
Sludge volume index. **177**
Snyder column. **318**
Sodium thiosulfate. **240, 449**
Solid phase extraction. **320**
Solid Waste Management. **2**
Solids. **177, 267**
Sonication. **319**
Sonication extraction. **319**
SOW. **398**
Soxhlet extraction. **319**
SPCC. **279, 281**
SPE. **321**
Stacks. **437, 441**
Standard Methods:

2130 **184**
2320 **199**
2340 **200**
2510 **185**
2540 **177**
2540 B **177**
2540 C **178**
2540 D **178**
2540 E **178**
2540 F **178**
2550 **182**
2710 D **178**
3030 F **206**
3030 G **206**
3030 H **206**
3030 I **206**
3500-Hg B **221**
4500-Cl **222**
4500-CN **237**
4500-H+ **194**
4500-NH3 **241**
4500-O **202**
4500-P **244**
4500-S **240**
5210 **203**
5220 **205**
5220 D **205**
5310 **230**
5320 **231**
5520 **234**
5530 **235**
5540 **232**
8010 **191**
9221 **186**
9221 D **190**
9222 **189**
9223 **190**
Standard receipt logs. **150**
Statement of Work. **398**
Static charges. **437**
Stormwater. **17**
Sublation. **232**
Substitute wastewater. **159**
Sulfide. **240, 385**
Sulfur clean-up. **323**
Sulfur compounds. **448**

Sulfur dioxide. **450**
Sulfur removal. **302**
Sulfuric acid/permanganate. **323**
SUMMA® canister. **440**
Supercritical fluid extraction. **319**
Superfund. **397**
Surfactants. **232**
Surrogates. **155, 269, 318**
SVI. **177**
Synthetic freshwater. **159**
Synthetic precipitation leaching
    procedure. **389**
Synthetic seawater. **159**
Syringaldazine. **228**
System performance check compounds.
    **279, 281**

**T**

t-statistic. **137**
TAL. **398**
Target analyte list. **398**
Target compound list. **398**
TCDD. **288, 302**
TCL. **398**
TCLP. **341, 386**
TCMP. **203**
TDS. **177**
Tedlar. **440**
Temperature. **182**
Temperature monitoring logs. **182**
Tenax. **268, 439**
Tentatively identified compounds. **266,
    398**
Teratogenesis. **193**
THC. **445**
Thermometer. **182**
Thiabendazole. **312**
Thiocarbamate pesticides. **311**
Thiophosphate pesticides. **305**
Thiosulfate. **226**
THM. **222, 269**
Thorin. **451**
TIC. **266, 398**
Time domain. **83**
TOC. **231**

Total dissolved solids. **177**
Total hydrocarbon content. **445**
Total organic carbon. **231**
Total organic halide. **231**
Total petroleum hydrocarbons. **234, 235,
    364, 394**
Total phenols. **235**
Total reduced sulfur. **449**
Total solids. **177**
Total suspended solids. **177**
Total trihalomethanes. **269**
Total volatile dissolved solids. **177**
Total volatile solids. **177**
Total volatile suspended solids. **177**
TOX. **231**
Toxic characteristic leaching procedure.
    **341, 386**
Toxic pollutants. **8**
Toxic Substances Control Act. **20**
Toxicant. **192**
Toxicity characteristic. **386**
Toxicity testing. **171, 191**
Toxicology. **192**
TPH. **234, 235, 364, 394**
Trapping solutions. **439**
Treatment, storage and disposal facility
    for hazardous waste. **2**
Triazine pesticides. **304**
Trihalomethane. **222, 269**
Triiodide. **226**
Trip blanks. **153**
TRS. **449**
TS. **177**
TSCA. **20**
TSD. **2**
TSS. **177**
TTHM. **269**
Turbidity. **184**
TVDS. **177**
TVS. **177**
TVSS. **177**

**U**

U-series. **383**
Ultrasonic. **319**

Underground storage tanks. **3, 393**
Urea pesticides. **310**
UST. **3, 393**

### V

Vapor pressure. **442**
Venturi scrubbers. **440**
Vertical composite sample. **84**
VOA. **268**
VOC. **266, 278, 279, 281, 444**
Volatile aromatic/unsaturated organics. **272**
Volatile halogenated organics. **270**
Volatile organic acids. **200**
Volatile organic analysis. **268**
Volatile organic compounds. **266, 278, 279, 281, 444**
Volatile organic sampling train. **283**
Volatile organics. **271**
Volatile pesticides. **304**
Volatiles. **268**
VOST. **283**

### W

Warning Level. **161, 163**
Waste dilution. **320**
Wastewater. **3, 267**
Water fleas.**193**
Winkler Method. **202**
Work assignments. **144**
WP. **167**
WP analytes. **167, 168**
WS. **167**
WS Analytes in WS038. **170**

### X

XAD-2. **439, 445**

### Z

Zero Headspace Extractor. **386**
ZHE. **386**
Ziram. **309**